A HISTORY OF HORTICULTURE

IN AMERICA

By ULYSSES PRENTISS HEDRICK

Grapes of New York
Plums of New York
Cherries of New York
Peaches of New York
Manual of American Grape Growing
Sturtevant's Notes on Edible Plants
Cyclopedia of Hardy Fruits
The Pears of New York
Systematic Pomology
Small Fruits of New York
The Vegetables of New York
A History of Agriculture in the State of New York
Fruits for the Home Garden
Grapes and Wines from Home Vineyards
The Land of the Crooked Tree

A HISTORY OF
Horticulture in America
TO 1860

By U. P. Hedrick

NEW YORK
OXFORD UNIVERSITY PRESS
1950

Copyright 1950 by Oxford University Press, Inc.

PRINTED IN THE UNITED STATES OF AMERICA

TO

MY FORMER COLLEAGUES

IN THE HORTICULTURAL DEPARTMENT

OF THE

NEW YORK STATE AGRICULTURAL EXPERIMENT STATION

GENEVA, NEW YORK

CONTENTS

Preface, xi

PART I

PART II

PART III

LIST OF ILLUSTRATIONS

PREFACE

AS the title states, this history ends with 1860. The years under survey cover but a small part of the history of horticulture in America, if progress be measured in accomplishments rather than in years. In fact, this book is scarcely more than an introduction, even though the 450 years since Columbus brought the first European plants to the New World cover a period several times the length of that from 1860 to the present.

In none of the regions mentioned in chapter headings in this book, and in no state in the Union, is there a complete history of horticulture, although there are many brief ones, usually found in the annual reports of horticultural societies. Of these *The History of the Massachusetts Horticultural Society,* published in 1880, written by the secretary of the society, Robert Manning, Jr., is an account of what had taken place in the United States up to the organization of the Society in 1829, and from then until 1880 in Massachusetts. If this book stimulates the writing of similar books for individual states, it will help to justify the author's work in writing it.

This history is primarily concerned with gardening, fruit growing, and viticulture; not with gardens, orchards, and vineyards. It would be a delightful task to give descriptions of early gardens, orchards, and vineyards, of which there are many records; but such a history would require more than one volume. The places described in this text are only those that are significant examples of progress.

Horticulture in America is so dependent upon plants from the wilds of this country, as well as those from foreign countries, that a chapter on plant explorers and botanic gardens is included. So, too, many fruits, vegetables, and flowers were domesticated, and many new varieties of species long cultivated were introduced in the last half-century of the period under consideration, making it necessary to write a chapter on plant breeding.

Perhaps it will be a surprise to some readers to see the rather large number of citations from books of travel. But in these is found much good material that does not appear in official documents, botanies, agricultural books, and papers. Many of the early travelers in America were farmers, interested in everything pertaining to agricultural plants and farm practices. To be sure, this material must be taken with a grain of salt, as travelers are notoriously prejudiced—especially Englishmen on a first visit to America, Northerners traveling in the South, Southerners in the North.

Advertisements are almost the only sources of information about the fruits, vegetables, and flowers grown in the colonies in the eighteenth century. During these hundred years there were but two or three books on agriculture, and they hardly mentioned horticultural matters; there were no agricultural papers. Advertisements, then, are history unrecorded elsewhere.

Agriculture and, even more particularly, horticulture are unique in their origins. Both were developed under seven different national groups. The Indians, the original inhabitants, made a fairly good start in growing vegetables at least; the Spaniards introduced most of the cultivated plants of Europe; French, Dutch, and Swedes early brought over their favorite esculents and ornamentals, each group growing them in its own way; a little later the Germans brought their plants and arts to modify horticulture in several widely separated regions such as New York, Pennsylvania, Wisconsin, Missouri, and Texas. Superimposed on the materials and arts of these six minor nations were British agriculture and horticulture. To the English, Scotch, and Irish the whole country is much indebted for introducing Old-World plants and the methods of growing them.

Most of the research for this volume was carried on in the library of the New York State Agricultural Experiment Station, rich in horticultural books, and in the library of Hobart College, which has most of the standard works on general history. The author is grateful to the staffs of the libraries for helpful cooperation.

Acknowledgments are due to horticulturists in nearly every agricultural college and experiment station in the United States and Canada for material supplied and facts verified. Particular mention must be made of Mr. George Graves, for his painstaking care in checking the finished manuscript. In justice to these colleagues, it must be said that the author alone is responsible for the interpretations of the facts given him by fellow workers.

U. P. HEDRICK

Geneva, New York
15 *January* 1950

PART I

1

INDIAN GARDENS

A LL the tribes of North American Indians supplemented their common fare of fish and game with fruits and vegetables. Corn, beans, pumpkins, and squashes grew so well that their culture, in some tribes, such as the Cherokees and Iroquois, furnished the chief means of sustenance. These four vegetables, along with tobacco, gourds, and the sunflower, came to our northern Indians from Peru by way of Mexico.

When Pizarro overthrew the Incas in Peru, and a little later when Cortez conquered Mexico, the gardens of the two regions were those of an advanced civilization. The Spaniards were surprised and delighted with the strange plants and their many uses. In one country or the other—often the plants were common to both as well as to the regions between—they found the agave, guava, banana, cactus, avocado, cassava, cotton, capsicum or pepper, beans of several species, maize or American corn, tobacco, physalis or husk tomato, prickly pear, potato, sweet potato, pumpkin, and squash. All these are described in the accounts of the plants and animals in the New World published by the Spaniards Oveido and Acosta in the sixteenth century. For three centuries Oveido and Acosta were authorities on the plants of tropical America, so accurately were their books written.

These early Spanish writers said that the New World gardens surpassed any similar ones in the Old World. Besides plants for food, medicine, and the arts, there were flowers in abundance. Acosta says the Peruvians offered them so many nosegays as they traveled about, that they were not able to carry them all. Some of these plants have been cultivated so long that botanists are unable to identify their wild ancestors. Before Columbus came to

3

the New World, South American food plants had been carried north and east as far as Canada and New England.

As Asa Gray wrote long ago, had civilization begun in the Western Hemisphere rather than in the Eastern, the number of cultivated plants in the two hemispheres would have been approximately equal. In particular, this would have been true of fruits. North America is a natural orchard. More than two hundred species of tree, bush, vine, and small fruits were in common use by the Indians when the Whites came. Besides these, there were at least fifty varieties of nuts, and an even greater number of herbaceous plants. Although but few bulbs were cultivated, wild bulbs were eaten by the Indians in times of famine.

Unfortunately, the agriculture of the Indians of North America was but an inferior form of that practiced by the Peruvians and Mexicans. One reason for this was probably that our northern Indians had no beast of burden—horse, ass, mule, elephant, camel, or even the South American llama or alpaca. Their only domesticated animal was the dog, useful in the chase and in getting food, but of little value for agricultural work. Farming and gardening were carried on by the squaw, 'the Indian's mule,' as Champlain called her.

Another handicap to Indian horticulture was that the Indians had such an abundance of game. Buffalo, deer, bear, rabbits, squirrels, passenger pigeons, ducks, geese of several species, wild turkeys, and a score of other fowls abounded, so that food could easily be had in the hunt. Near the oceans, the Great Lakes, and a thousand rivers, fish were plentiful and easy to catch.

Yet the botanical knowledge of early North American Indians was not inconsiderable. They knew a half hundred or more plants that were good for food or drink; they used as many more for their physical ailments; perhaps quite as many were collected for dyes, deodorants, hair tonics, and clothing. Out of wood particularly selected for the purpose were made wigwams, bows, arrows, and canoes. Their domestic economy required grasses, roots, and barks for baskets, and gum and resins for watertight canoes and household utensils. Few Whites now know anywhere near so many wild plants as every North American Indian had to know in order to live.

All the early visitors to America mentioned the vegetables grown by the Indians. Some, it would seem, also grew flowers, or at least cultivated the wild flowers of the region. When laying out their villages, they preserved trees to shelter crops from the sun. Captain John Smith says that the Indians along the James River planted mulberry and locust trees, grapes, wild roses, and sunflowers. Probably the Cherokees in the South and the Iroquois in New York were as good gardeners as the white settlers who became their neighbors. Certainly the crops of corn, beans, and squash grown by the Indians were lifesavers to the first settlers from Europe.

Most of the fruits that supplied the Indians grew wild. In the prolific wilderness were many sunlit openings made by wind or fire, in which grew black or red raspberries, blackberries, dewberries, and strawberries. Wild grapes of one species or another grew in every part of eastern America; blueberries throve in the plains; cranberries in the swamps; mulberries and persimmons in the thickets south of the Potomac; while plums, crab apples, or cherries grew in every part of the country from Canada to the Gulf. Grapes and small fruits grew in such profusion that the Indian seldom had to plant them. It was different with tree fruits. Indians were fond of mulberries, persimmons, cherries, and plums, all of which they cooked, ate out of hand, and used in making pemmican. New York Indians planted plums around their villages, and copses of them are to be found to this day near the sites of old towns. Sometimes it is certain that species must have been brought far from their original habitats. The Canadian plum, *Prunus nigra,* is found near camp sites of the Iroquois in New York, brought without question from the St. Lawrence region. Cartier, in 1534, discovered that the Indians on the banks of the St. Lawrence made prunes from this plum, as the Iroquois later did in western New York.

In July 1528, Cabeza de Vaca found in Florida 'maize, beans, and pumpkins in great plenty and beginning to be fit for gathering.' In 1535-6, when he was passing through Texas, the Indians supplied him with prickly pears and occasionally maize: but after crossing 'a great river,' probably the Rio Grande, he and his companions came to a region having 'fine dwellings of civilization, whose inhabitants lived on beans and pumpkins; and, when the season was not too dry for raising it, maize.' [1]

When De Soto landed in Florida, not far from Tampa Bay, in 1539, there were 'fields of maize, beans, and pumpkins,' and, still further westward, at Coligoa, 'beans and pumpkins were in great plenty; both were larger and better than those of Spain; the pumpkins when roasted had nearly the taste of chestnuts.' [2]

By all odds, the best of the many records of Indian gardening written in the seventeenth century was one by Captain John Smith, in his *Description of Virginia,* printed in Oxford in 1612. He gives in detail the Indian methods of clearing land, and planting the several crops, and tells how the produce was used. From a hundred less well-told accounts of Indian gardening in America east of the Mississippi, one may generalize and say that the gardening and cooking methods of all the Indian tribes were much the same, though some tribes were much more skilled in tilling the land than others.

Early travelers gave the Cherokees of the Carolinas and Georgia credit for being the best husbandmen. They grew corn, beans of several kinds, squashes in variety, gourds, and sunflowers. They also grew the marsh mallow, *Althæa officinalis,* for its thick mucilaginous roots. Vegetables, fruits, and nuts were so abundant and so commonly used that the Cherokees were probably on the whole vegetarian.

Just as the Cherokees were the best gardeners in the southeastern part of the United States, so the Iroquois surpassed all other Indian tribes in the Northeast. For generations they carried on a primitive agriculture in New York, so that when the Europeans came, the early reporters, whether English, French, Dutch, or Swedes, made much in their accounts of the curious food plants the Indians grew. To people who had never before seen a cornstalk, a climbing bean, a pumpkin, a squash, or a gourd, an Indian garden must have seemed strange indeed.

Wherever the Jesuit fathers went, they taught the Indians to grow apples, peaches, and many vegetables. They found the Indians growing tobacco—'Iroquois' is said to be a corruption of

[1] Gray and Hammond, p. 374.   [2] Ibid.

Ireokwa, the Indian word for tobacco. In Sullivan's raid in western New York during the Revolutionary War, 60,000 bushels of corn, 3000 bushels of beans, and 40 orchards of apples and peaches, one of which contained 1500 peach trees, are said to have been destroyed. As with the Cherokees, the principal crops of the Iroquois were corn, beans, squash, melon, tobacco, and sunflowers, and after the first Whites came, apples and peaches.

Indian gardens and orchards were community property, cared for by women under the leadership of the Amazons of the tribe. Parker, the best authority on the northern Indians and one of whose ancestors was a Seneca, gives a pleasant picture of the gardens of the Senecas, chief of the several tribes of the Iroquois. He tells us that the field matron 'regulated the work and supervised the singing and rest periods, when games were played or stories told.' The men, according to him, 'did the clearing and burning, the women did the hoeing.' The products of the communal fields 'were stored in clan granaries and pits, but any individual might have his own garden and reserve the fruits for himself.' The Seneca had more than a dozen varieties of corn, and cultivated them with studious care, even understanding that varieties planted too closely together would 'visit and establish colonies' on the cobs of their neighbors. They had several varieties of squashes and melons, and ten or more varieties of beans. They grew sunflowers for the oil to be pressed from the seeds. There were many wild foods that needed no cultivation, but which could be gathered in great quantities: pond-lily roots, cattail roots, artichoke tubers, wild leeks, mushrooms, lichens, and many varieties of nuts and berries.

The Seneca cooks seem to have had many recipes for preparing vegetable dishes; corn was prepared in a score of ways, among them soup, gruel, hominy, samp, hulled corn, bread, pudding, and parched meal. These corn foods were mixed with beans and berries, nuts, and sunflower oil. Iroquois corn culture was well developed, and exercised a powerful influence on social and economic life. It compelled industry and thrift, and was largely responsible for a sedentary village existence.[3]

[3] Parker, pp. 71-2.

Some of the tribes of western Indians were nearly as good farmers as the Cherokees and Iroquois. The Whites who visited the Great Plains and the Rocky Mountains from Coronado, in 1541, down to the hundreds of visitors in the nineteenth century, say so much about the crops grown by the aborigines of these regions that one has to believe much of their food came from the soil, despite the abundance of buffalo. Their crops, in order of importance, were corn, beans, squashes, pumpkins, tobacco, and sunflowers. Trappers, traders, buffalo hunters, and explorers bartered fur for the products of Indian agriculture. These western Indians soon learned from the Spaniards how to grow European vegetables.

The best farmers on the Great Plains were the Mandans in what is now the Dakotas. When the Whites came to Mandan villages, the Indians were growing some dozen or more varieties of corn; at least six kinds of beans, one of which, the Great Northern, is still grown by the Whites as a valuable field bean; and an amazing number of pumpkins, squashes, and gourds. To these they quickly added cucumbers and watermelons, obtained from the Spaniards, besides which they grew a species of tobacco and several varieties of sunflowers. Through long growing and selection, these crops had been adapted to the heat, drought, and short season of this northern land. Seeds and remains of plants in Indian burial places, as well as present cultural practices, show that this tribe, at least, cultivated several plants now considered weeds, such as lambs-quarter and pigweed, and used several wild fruits, if they did not actually plant them: the native plums, cherries, Juneberries, buffalo berries, thornapples, wild grapes, and even rose haws, among others.

When in the sixteenth century the Spaniards came to the region that is now western Texas, New Mexico, and Arizona, they found corn and beans commonly grown. The southwestern Indians also grew pumpkins, squashes, and gourds, and ate some wild fruits and nuts, especially nuts of the piñon pine.

Corn, the most important of the Indian crops, was grown in every part of the United States where it is now planted. The French made a punitive expedition into the wilds of western New York in 1697 and 'destroyed 120,000,000 bushels of corn.'

Although probably a military exaggeration, there must have been much corn, for western New York was ever after known by the French as 'the granary of the Iroquois.' Both dent and flint corns were grown in many varieties, the two distinct types, no doubt, being distributed according to climate.

Corn was prepared for use much as it is today. It first came to the table in the roasted-ear stage, at which time most Indian tribes held a Green Corn Festival, in which the grain was celebrated as 'Our Life' and 'Our Supporter.' Later in the season, hominy and a coarse corn meal were made. The meal was cooked into a mush or baked as unleavened bread, 'the yellow cakes of Mondamin,' as Hiawatha called it. Probably the commonest way in which most Indian tribes prepared corn was to char it by setting up unshelled cobs before a fire to roast until all the moisture was dried out of the kernels, after which it could be kept indefinitely to be used in several nutritious dishes. A common Indian artifact found near old village sites of the aborigines is the crude stone mortar and pestle, with which corn meal was made. Often the mortar was a hollowed stump. This method of making corn meal was also used by many early white settlers.

Thomas Ashe, an early writer of the settlements in South Carolina, tells of the several uses to which early settlers put corn, mostly learned from the Indians. Speaking first of the Whites at Charles Town, eleven years after it was settled in 1671, he says:

Their Provision which grows in the Field is chiefly Indian Corn, which produces a vast Increase, yearly, yielding Two plentiful Harvests, of which they make a wholesome Bread, and good Biskit, which give a strong, sound, and nourishing Diet; with Milk I have eaten it dress'd in various ways: Of the Juice of the Corn, when green, the Spaniards with chocolet, aromatis'd with Spices, made a rare Drink of an excellent Delicacy. I have seen the English among the Caribbes roast the green Ear on the Coals, and eat it with a great deal of Pleasure. The Indians in Carolina parch the ripe Corn, then pound it to a Powder, putting it in a Leathern Bag: When they use it they take a little quantity of the Powder in the Palm of their Hands, mixing it with Water, and sup it off: with this they will travel for several days. . . The American Physicians observe that it breeds good Blood, removes and opens Oppellation and Obstructions. At Carolina they lately invented a way of making with it a good sound Beer; but it's

strong and heady; By Maceration, when duly fermented, a strong
Spirit like Brandy may be drawn off from it, by the help of an Alem-
bic.[4]

Sweet corn does not seem to have been widely grown by the
Indians. Will and Hyde, in *Corn among the Indians of the Upper
Mississippi Valley*, list 104 varieties of corn of which only 4 are
sweet corns. In gardens of the Whites, sweet corn was hardly
known until 1850, although the story is that it had been introduced from Indian corn fields on the banks of the Susquehanna
in 1779. In that year, Lieutenant Richard Bagnal, an officer in
General Sullivan's army in the expedition against the Iroquois in
western New York, found sweet corn and carried seed to his
home in Plymouth, Massachusetts. For nearly a century after,
however, gardeners continued to grow field corn for table use,
which, the country over, came to table as 'roasting ears.'

The Incas in Peru and the Aztecs in Mexico had red, white,
and blue popcorns when the Spaniards conquered these countries. It seems probable that all the Indian tribes who grew field
corn also grew popcorn. Some field corns also 'pop'; that is, the
kernels turn inside out through the explosion of moisture in the
grain when sufficient heat is applied. It is an easy matter to de-
velop a popping corn from field corn, and this the aborigines did
centuries ago. Popcorn is not mentioned by the first colonial
writers, but the Whites must have had seed from the Indians in
all of the early settlements, and later, long before the Revolution,
it was a common fireside luxury, with apples and cider, to be
found at every social gathering on winter evenings.

Corn is one of the few cultivated plants of which the wild
ancestor is not known. Nor does it ever run wild, as almost all
other cultivated plants do in one part of the world or another.
The high state of its development when the Europeans came to
the New World bespeaks many centuries of cultivation.

The Indians grew corn without the aid of animals, and had,
therefore, to keep it free from the competition of weeds by hard
labor. They must have had crude hoes, the blades of which were
probably the shoulder bones of large animals; near the shores of
seas, lakes, or rivers, they used large shells. Wooden spades, no

4 Ashe, *Carolina*, etc., pp. 145-6.

doubt, were also used. All grains but corn are cultivated in close fellowship from seed broadcast; plants of corn must be tilled as individuals. It seems the Indians, at least some of them, kept pure cultures of corn. Will says the Mandans kept no less than thirteen varieties pure by means of isolated culture. To grow grains *en masse* it is necessary to have horses or oxen, of which the early settlers in Virginia and Massachusetts had neither at first. Without corn, grown as the Indians grew it, the first white settlers would hardly have lived.

Peas were an early introduction to the American continent, but in early records, the word *peason* refers sometimes also to beans. In 1493, according to Peter Martyr, peason were grown by Columbus at Isabella Island; in 1535, they are mentioned by Cartier as grown by the Indians of Hochelaga, now Montreal; and in 1613, peas obtained from the French traders were grown by the Indians of the Ottawa River; in 1540, they are mentioned in New Mexico by Alarcón, and 'small, white peas' by Coronado; in 1562 peason were cultivated by the Florida Indians, as related by Ribault. In 1602 peas were sown by Gosnold on the Elizabeth Islands off the coast of Massachusetts, according to Smith; in 1629, in Massachusetts, there was 'a store of green peas . . . as good as ever I eat in England,' growing in the governor's garden, according to the Reverend Francis Higginson. In 1614 peas were mentioned by Smith as being grown by the New England Indians. In 1690, Bancroft says Spanish peas were grown by the Indians of Mexico; and in 1775, Romans says green peas were obtained the year round at Mobile, Alabama. In 1779 General Sullivan's expedition against the Indians of western New York destroyed the growing peas of the Indians who occupied the territory near Geneva.[5]

From the first Spanish explorers in the early part of the sixteenth century onward, every writer who mentioned the plants used for food by the Indians named beans with corn and pumpkins. Cabeza de Vaca found beans cultivated by the Indians of Florida in 1528 and later in New Mexico in 1535; De Soto found beans in Indian fields with corn and pumpkins when he landed

5 Sturtevant, p. 442.

at Tampa Bay in 1539; Smith found beans in Virginia; Josselyn and Wood in New England; Cartier and Father Segard in Canada. Beans are mentioned as grown in Indian gardens west to the Rockies and south to Mexico. Beans, corn, pumpkins, and squash were 'the four sisters' of Indian agriculture. Where one was grown, the others were almost always found in the same field.

In thinking of Indian gardens in North America, one must visualize four species of beans, each with many varieties, belonging to the genus *Phaseolus*. Most common of these are the varieties of *Phaseolus vulgaris*, of which we now have about 500 listed in current publications, many types of which the Indians grew. Here belong the common pole and the bush beans. The next most common type, in Indian as well as modern gardens, is the lima, *Phaseolus lunatus*, of which there are three outstanding groups, Big Limas, Small Limas, and Potato Limas, each with varieties that early came into Indian gardens from South America. The third species is *Phaseolus acutifolius*, the tepary, a chief food of the arid regions of Arizona and New Mexico. The fourth bean the Indians grew is the beautiful scarlet runner, *Phaseolus coccineus*, now grown in many varieties both for food and as an ornamental plant.

French influence on American agriculture had its beginnings in the visit of Giovanni da Verrazano, the first European to set foot on our Atlantic seaboard. Upon his return from his voyage of discovery in 1524, he published so glowing a description of what he had seen that Frenchmen for the next two centuries sought to establish settlements in this country. From him came the first account of Indian beans. He wrote: 'Their ordinaire food is of pulse, whereof they have great store, differing in color and taste from ours, of good and pleasant taste.' [6]

Another French account of Indian beans comes from Champlain, who, in 1605, writing of the Indians of the Kennebec region of what is now Maine, says: 'With this corn they put in each hill three or four Brazilian beans which are of different colors. When they grow up, they interlace with the corn, which reaches to the height of five or six feet; and they keep the ground very free

[6] Hakluyt, p. 61.

from weeds.'[7] Still another Frenchman, Lascarbot, writing in 1608, likens the beans of this northern region to those of the South: 'between the kernals of corn,' he tells us, 'they plant beans marked with various colors.'[8] A dozen or more French Jesuit writers might be quoted to show how commonly corn and beans were used as Indian foods.

Josselyn, in his *New-Englands Rarities,* discovered two kinds of beans 'proper to New England.'[9] Almost without question, these are the common garden bean, *Phaseolus vulgaris,* and the scarlet runner, or multiflora bean, *P. coccineus.*

John Lawson gives a very good description of the beans grown by the Indians in the Carolinas. He says: 'The Kidney-Beans were here before the English came, being very plentiful in Indian Corn fields.' The Bushel bean he describes as very flat, white, and mottled with a purple figure, and says it was trained on 'poles.' To quote further: 'Indian Rounceval, or Miraculous Pulse, so called from their long pods and great increase; they are very good, and so are the Bonivis, Calavances, Nanticokes, and abundance of other pulse.'[10]

So much is said about corn in the early accounts of the domestic economy of American Indians that the bean in pre-European agriculture seems to have been overlooked. If the crops of the whole continent are considered, the several kinds of beans were grown in about as large quantities as the several corns. Perhaps early visitors from the Old World magnified the importance of corn because it was a strange plant to them, while beans had been known in Europe. Beans furnished the Indians with indispensable albumins, which could be had in no other vegetable, or so satisfactorily in any animal food.

The Indians planted pumpkin and squashes between the hills of corn and beans, just as some farmers do now. From descriptions and from the pumpkins and squashes now grown on Indian reservations, we can determine the kinds they had when the Whites first came to America. The northeastern tribes grew the

[7] Champlain, II: 64.
[8] Lascarbot, p. 835.
[9] Josselyn, p. 59.
[10] Lawson, pp. 76-7.

Pie Pumpkin, the Summer Crook-necks, and the Bush-scallop
squashes; the southern Indians planted the Winter Crook-necks,
the golden and striped Cushaws, and the Sweet Potato squashes.
The New England Indians, at least, grew the Boston Marrow and
Autumn Turban. The Summer Crook-necks were grown by
many tribes, but the Hubbard type was not known.

Here, as with beans and corn, one might cite reference after
reference to show how widespread was the culture of these vegetables in Indian gardens in every part of the country in which
they now are grown. The Indians boiled them as soon as they
were edible, or dried them for winter use. The seeds were considered a prime delicacy. The northern Indians gave preference to
pumpkins and the autumn squashes; the southern tribes to patty-
pan squashes; while the Indians of the Great Plains were fond of
an oblate green and white squash, represented by the Mandan of
today.

Captain John Smith says the Indians of Virginia 'plant amongst
their corn pumpions, and a fruit like unto our muskmelon, but
less and worse, which they call macocks.' Strachey describes these
'macock gourds' in similar words, and also says the 'macocks is of
the form of our pumpions—I must confess nothing so good—of a
more waterish taste.' He also mentions 'a kind of million,' which
they 'put into their walnut-milk, and so make a kind of toothsome
meat.' [11]

La Hontan describes the squashes (citrouilles) of Canada as
sweet and of a different kind from those of Europe, where, 'as
several persons assured him, they would not grow.' 'They are
the size of our melons; the flesh yellow as saffron. They usually
bake them in an oven, but they are better roasted under embers,
Indian fashion.' La Hontan believed them to be 'of the
country.' [12]

Adrien Van der Donck, who put on record so much about life
in New Netherland, tells us a good deal about squashes. The
Netherlanders, he says, called this vegetable *quaasiens,* a name
derived from the aborigines. To Van der Donck it was 'a delightful fruit,' both to the eye because of its fine variety of colors,
and to the mouth for its agreeable taste. Evidently he was writing

[11] Strachey, p. 72.   [12] La Hontan, II: 61.

of summer squash, for he says, 'When it is planted in the middle of April, the fruit is fit to eat by the first of July.' The Indians ate the squashes before they were ripe, 'when they had attained a certain size, they immediately placed them on the fire without any further trouble.'

Sagard, in his *Histoire du Canada du pays des Hurons,* several times mentions the squashes the Hurons grew, seemingly in great abundance, which he found 'very good baked or boiled.' He describes a novel method by which the Indians hastened the germination of the seeds of these *citrouilles du pays* and 'raise them with great ease.' This ability to force plants, it would seem, is the outstanding accomplishment of Indian gardeners.

The Huron women would gather a great quantity of rotted wood from around old stumps in the forest. This they powdered and placed in a large box made out of bark; in it were planted the seeds of the pumpkins, several times as many as were needed. The box was suspended over the smoke of a fire, which warmed the wood powder little by little. The seeds germinated in a few days. When the plants were of proper size, they were separated and placed in selected places in the fields, where, afterward, their fruits were gathered in season.[13]

Gourds of many kinds were indispensable to Indian domestic economy, and were grown by all Indians who tilled the soil. They were used for dishes, dippers, jugs, bottles, and bowls, were worn as ornaments, as rattles, and from them were made masks for ceremonial rites. When properly ripened and dried, and so hard-shelled that mice could not gnaw through, they were used as containers for seeds. There was a belief among white settlers that seeds kept in calabashes retained their power of germination longer. Later, when pottery replaced gourds, the designs for the clay vessels were often suggested by the shapes of the disused gourds.

The watermelon is a native of tropical Africa, but the first Spaniards who came to the New World must have brought its seeds, for when the English came, watermelons were grown by the Indians from Canada to the Gulf, and from the Atlantic to the Rockies. Captain John Smith does not mention the water-

[13] Sagard, pp. 266-8.

melon in Virginia, but Josselyn speaks of it as a fruit 'proper to the countrie' in Massachusetts. Hilton, before 1664, found it cultivated by the Indians in Florida. Father Marquette, in descending the Wisconsin and Mississippi Rivers in 1673, speaks of watermelons 'which,' he says, 'are excellent, especially those with red seed.' [14] Woods in 1822 mentions them in Indian gardens in Illinois as being 'in great plenty and vast size.' [15] All the explorers in the Great Plains found most tribes of Indians growing watermelons.

The Spaniards brought cucumbers to Haiti in 1494. In 1535 Cartier found 'very great cucumbers' grown on the site of what is now Montreal. De Soto, in 1509, saw cucumbers in Florida 'better than in Spain.' Captains Amidas and Barlow found cucumbers in Indian gardens in Virginia in 1584. They were also being grown by the Iroquois when the first Europeans visited them.

Tobacco was grown by all American Indians who tilled the soil. Pipes are found in the remains of most Indian villages. When wars came to an end, the tomahawk was buried, the war paint removed, and the peace pipe lighted as a symbol of good will; to smoke it was not only a right but a duty. Indians did not use tobacco for the pleasure it gave them. It was, to them, a sacred plant, ceremoniously used in religious rites, to bring good fortune, to ward off or to cure diseases, and to allay fear. It was passed to establish or seal friendships; and it was in universal use at the peace table. The quid, snuff, cigar, cigarette, cheroot, stogie, hookah, and hubble-bubble were unknown to North American aborigines.

Tobacco is one of the most cosmopolitan of all domesticated plants, but it attains perfection only in few soils and climates. Therefore, while tobacco was grown in nearly all Indian gardens, tribes that could grow it especially well used the cured product as a medium of barter. Such were the Iroquois of New York and the Hurons of Ontario. *Nicotiana Tabacum* is now the commonly cultivated tobacco the world over, but several other species are

14 *Ill. Hort. Soc.*, p. 125.   15 Woods, John, pp. 226-7.

found as escaped plants around the sites of old Indian villages; probably more than one species was grown by the aborigines.

No doubt the Indians of New England raised tobacco and used it as freely as their fellow aborigines did to the south and west. The Puritans, however, opposed its culture and laws were passed restricting its use. When it became known that Virginians were getting rich exporting tobacco, however, the thrifty Yankees began raising and using it. The crop grew so well, and the quality of the leaf was so high in the valley of the Connecticut River that tobacco began to be the main product of this fertile region. In 1753, in order to secure well-ripened, well-cured tobacco, an official inspector was appointed.

The sunflower was grown by many Indian tribes for its large seeds, which were either eaten as they grew or pounded into a cake. An oil was pressed from the seeds and used by both sexes for greasing their hair and for other purposes. In 1615 the sunflower was seen by Champlain among the Hurons. Kalm in 1749 saw it under cultivation by the Indians at Loretto, Canada, in fields of maize, and says the seeds were used with those of maize to make soup. When tobacco could not be obtained, the dried leaves of the sunflower were often used for smoking.

The origin of this plant is one of the puzzles of botany, but it is generally agreed that the wild original came from the Southwest, possibly Mexico. Judging from the large size of the flowers when the Europeans first saw it—many early explorers describe it— it had long been under cultivation by the aborigines. There is no wild original with flowers nearly so large.

The Jerusalem artichoke, a close relative of the sunflower, almost certainly originated west of the Mississippi. It is now a 'run-wild' in all of the northeastern states, indicating that it was once grown in Indian gardens and from these escaped to river banks and marshes, where it is now commonly found. This vegetable was taken to Europe early in the seventeenth century, where it was known as the 'potato of Canada.' All its common names are sad misnomers. It is not an artichoke or even similar to one, as the tuber and not the flower bud is eaten. 'Jerusalem' in the

name is a corruption of the Italian *girasole,* the sunflower, while
'artichoke' comes from a fancied resemblance in taste of the
boiled root to that of the true artichoke. Neither top nor tuber
suggests the potato to give it the name 'potato of Canada.'

The tubers of the Jerusalem artichoke are very nutritious, and
can be produced more cheaply, ton for ton, than potatoes. Yet
the potato has very nearly driven the Jerusalem artichoke from
cultivation both in America and Europe, because its flavor is
better liked and the tuber is more wholesome.

Potatoes were not widely cultivated by North American Indians, if at all. The plant reputed to have been grown by Indians
in Virginia and southward was not the Irish potato, which European settlers in America scarcely grew until after the Revolution,
but something nearer to our sweet potato. Probably the Indians
did not cultivate them as they did other vegetables from South
America, because the potato is hard to transport long distances,
relatively hard to grow, and difficult to store for winter. The
Jerusalem artichoke suited the Indian much better than the
potato.

The Indians had several aromatic beverages with tonic properties, made out of leaves, flowers, bark, and roots. Most notable of
these were sassafras and sarsaparilla. The seeds of the Kentucky
coffee tree were used by several tribes in making a drink, which
was so popular that the tree was planted about villages far to the
north of its natural habitat. A table tea was also made from the
leaves of the hemlock, which Indians and Whites alike used in
winter as a sovereign remedy for scurvy.

Early visitors speak of the use by the Indians of an ilex as a tea.
This was *Ilex Cassine,* cassene, dahoon, or yaupon, and there is
evidence that the Indians cultivated it. It is a native of the southern coasts from the Carolinas to Texas. The leaves were used by
them to make a 'black drink.' Thomas Ashe says of this ilex:

There grows in Carolina the famous Cassiny, whose admirable and
incomparable Vertues are highly applauded by the French and Spanish
Writers: It is the leaves of a certain Tree, which boyl'd in water (as
we do Thea) wonderfully enliven and envigorate the Heart, with
genuine easy Sweats and Transpirations, preserving the Mind free

and serene, keeping the Body brisk, active, and lively, not for an hour, or two, but for as many days, as those Authors report, without any other Nourishment or Subsistence, which, if true, is really admirable; they also add that none amongst the Indians, but their great Men and Captains, who have been famous for their great Exploits and Noble Actions, are admitted to the use of this noble Bevaridge.[16]

Captain John Smith, in 1606, found in Virginia 'many herbs in the spring, commonly dispersed through the woods, good for broths and sallets, as Violets, Pursalain, Sorrell, etc. besides many we use whose names we know not of.' William Wood in his *New Englands Prospect* names 'Purslane' among the plants growing 'in the woods, without either the art or help of man,' and Champlain found plenty of purslane for his salads growing among the corn; on the coast of Maine, 'the savages making no more account of it than if it were a noxious weed.' There is much doubt whether this purslane, *Portulaca oleracea,* the vegetable of the Europeans, the weed of Americans, is the plant seen by early explorers. However, these Europeans ate the plant they saw, as they did many other pot herbs native to the country. It does not appear that American Indians grew any pot herbs.

The Spaniards early brought peaches to Mexico and Florida. The Indians liked them so well that long before Jamestown was settled there were Indian peach orchards from Texas and Arkansas eastward and as far north as peaches will grow. So abundantly were they found as escapes from Indian plantations that early American botanists looked upon the peach as native to America. William Penn, writing from Philadelphia, 16 August 1683, says: 'There are also very good peaches, and in great abundance; not an Indian plantation without them.' [17]

In the South, to this day, here and there from the Gulf to the Ohio and from the Atlantic to the Great Plains, wild peaches may be found. In all parts of this vast region these wild fruits are called 'Indian peaches.' Tree and fruit are quite distinctive. The trees are rather small with wide-spreading branches, purplish bark, and flat persistent leaves. The fruits are small, very pubescent, and streaked with red beneath the skin. The flesh is yellow,

16 Ashe, *Carolina,* etc., pp. 147-8.   17 Watson, I: 46.

or sometimes white or red; the quality is very poor. The fruits
have a touch of wildness, which the best of care does not obliter-
ate. These vigorous Indian peaches are the wild trees from which
nurserymen get pits for stocks upon which to grow named
varieties.

Early white explorers, missionaries, and settlers, of whatever
nationality, brought apple seeds with them, and this fruit was
commonly grown by all Indian tillers of the soil in the eighteenth
century. The apple is not an easy fruit to grow, and the Indians
had no good way of keeping it in winter, so that it was never
so popular as the peach. Seedling apples are not quite so good to
eat out of hand as peaches and plums. About the early French
settlements in Canada and the Illinois Country, as the Middle
West was called in the eighteenth century, some pears and cherries were also grown. There are no records showing that any
Indian tribe grew small fruits of any kind, though they used them
all, including grapes, as found in the wild.

The American mulberry, *Morus rubra,* is a common fruit from
New England to Iowa and southward into the Gulf states. It
grows abundantly in northern Missouri, along the rivers of Kansas, and in Oklahoma. Its large, sweet, black fruit was much liked
by the Indians and no doubt they planted its seeds about their
villages. De Soto, so the accounts of his exploration say, at the
Indian town of Cassasaqua, Georgia, 'was met by twenty men
from the village, each bearing a basket of mulberries'; and
Strachey in the early days of Jamestown saw them planted around
native dwellings.

The may-apple, *Podophyllum peltatum,* having a broad peltate
leaf in the forks of which nods a large creamy-white flower and
later a golden fruit, was grown by the Indians in Virginia and
perhaps occasionally in more northern gardens. It was cultivated
for its sweet pulpy fruits and thick root-stocks, which were much
used in Indian medicine. The Whites should have continued its
cultivation both in the vegetable and flower garden, so much
merit has it for both.

Captain John Smith mentions the passion-flower, Maypop, *Passiflora incarnata,* as a plant cultivated by the Indians in Virginia. He says: 'They plant also Maracocks, a wild fruit like a lemon, which also increase infinitely.' As this plant was mentioned by many other explorers in the south, it was probably grown by the Indians from early times. While no one grows the passion flower now for its fruits, in the South Atlantic States it is still plucked and eaten as it grows wild, under the name 'Maypop.' Strachey says of it, 'of the bigness of a green apple, and hath manie azure or blue kernells, like as a pomegranat, a good summer cooling fruit.' [18]

The Indians of the Far West used a great number of wild plants as foods, some of which, it would seem, might have been domesticated. Among these are the sego lily, and other species of Calochortus. The Mormons, during their first year in Utah, used the cormous roots of these sego lilies in great quantities to ward off starvation, as had hundreds of trappers and pioneers in the Far West before them.

A despicable weed of American gardens, lambs-quarter, or white goosefoot, *Chenopodium album,* was a food highly prized by the Indians, Mexicans, and pioneers in the several southwestern states. The leaves were boiled and eaten as greens, as they are in many parts of Europe today. The seeds of some chenopodiums are reputed to have been gathered, ground into flour, and made into mush or bread, as one of the staples of the vast unirrigated region of the West. Another relative is *C. quinoa,* petty rice or quinoa, the seeds of which were boiled as a rice by the natives of the Pacific slopes of the Andes. Seeds of quinoa were distributed in the United States by the United States Patent Office in 1854, but the plant never came under cultivation in North America.

It could hardly be said that the Indians ever cultivated any of the several opuntias in their gardens, but they used the fruits of some of them as foods; and, no doubt, refrained from destroying plants that furnished a fruit so edible in regions where fruits were scarce. Some opuntia grows from the southern Mississippi Valley west to California, and white pioneers used the fruits even

18 Strachey, VI: 119.

if they did not cultivate them. They have been grown more or less in southern Europe for three centuries. In America these opuntias are occasionally found in the markets as prickly pears, Indian figs, or under the Indian name, *tuna* or Nopal.

The Indians knew and possibly cultivated occasionally several species of *Physalis,* which grow, in one species or another, in nearly every part of warm and temperate North America. White pioneers in all parts of the country have made use of most of the species for pies, sauces, or to eat out of hand. None of our wild plants have more common names. What its Indian names were cannot be said, but it passes among Whites in various parts of North America as strawberry tomato, winter cherry, ground cherry, cherry tomato, husk tomato, purple ground cherry, purple winter cherry, and purple strawberry tomato. Any one of the species of *Physalis* might be improved for garden culture.

Several species of *Camassia,* bulbous herbs of the Lily family, formed the greater part of the vegetable food of the Indians on the northwest coast of America and Vancouver Island. Pioneers in this region also made use of these bulbs under the Indian names camass, kamosh, and quamash.

Indian gardeners in all probability had fewer insect and fungous pests to contend with than their white successors, since most of the very troublesome insects and fungi have been introduced on plants brought from foreign lands. Animals and birds gave a great deal of trouble, against which Indian youths carried on continuous warfare. The Indian had neither preventive nor remedy for smaller pests, except the curious oddments of the medicine man's bag, used with incantations to exorcise insects and diseases.

The mysterious magic of steps of a woman, *sans habillement,* around cultivated crops was an Indian remedy for cutworms. The squaw, who planted and tended the garden, stripped beneath the full moon and dragged her garment of the day, making a magic circle that no worm would cross. Probably this Indian custom, of which Longfellow makes so much in *Hiawatha,* came from early Roman Catholic missionaries, for it seems to have been a part of early Indian gardening only in Canada, in New York, and in the regions near the Great Lakes, parts of the seventeenth-century American domain visited by the Jesuits. These missionaries may have known that a similar custom was practiced in ancient Rome. Pliny says, in Book xvii, Chapter 47, of his *Natural History*: 'Another method, too, of preventing caterpillars, is to make a woman . . . go around each tree, barefoot and ungirth.' He adds in a footnote: 'An absurd notion very similar to some connected with the same subject which have prevailed even in recent times.'

2

COLONIAL NEW ENGLAND

THE PILGRIM Fathers brought from the mother country a love of gardening and full knowledge of its practice. Fruits, vegetables, and flowers are not regarded as necessities in a new country, but the Pilgrims, one judges from the accounts of their domestic economy, were as interested in their flower gardens as they were in the more substantial crops they planted. Early writers mention flowers with evident pride that they were not neglected.

While England was the mother country, many of the Pilgrims came by way of Holland, where they had learned garden practices even better than those of the English. No doubt they brought from Holland crops, varieties, seeds, tools, and, possibly, copies of the wonderful herbals that Dutch botanists were then printing.

We are told that on Wednesday, 7 March 1621, following the first terrible winter in which the Pilgrims landed in the New World, they planted 'garden seeds.' On this day, we may say, gardening by Whites began in New England. That their eyes were open to see what native plants were suitable for gardens may be seen from a report made this same year by Edward Winslow:

Here are Grapes [he wrote] white and red, and very sweete and strong; also Strawberries, Gooseberries, Raspas [raspberries]. Plums of three sorts, white, black, and red, being almost as good as a Damson. Abundance of Roses, white, red, and damask, single but very sweete indeed.[1]

The first entry in the first book of the *Plymouth Colony Records* is a partial list of the 'Meersteads and Garden-Plotes of those who came first, layed out in 1620.' The persons named are, of

[1] Young, A., *Chron. of the First Planters of the Col. of Mass. Bay*, p. 234.

course, members of the famous few who came over in the *May-flower* on her first voyage. They had been grouped in nineteen families, and the houses to which these 'Garden-Plotes' were attached, according to local historians, were built along both sides of what is now Leyden Street in Plymouth.

The settlement at Plymouth was followed by one near Salem in 1628, the Massachusetts Bay Colony, made by the Puritans. The land in the new colony, a virgin soil rich in mold that had been accumulating for ages, was richer than that at Plymouth, and possibly the settlers were better prepared for agriculture. At any rate, the accounts of gardening are fuller, for the Puritans undertook almost at once the cultivation of fruits and vegetables on a large scale; Governors Winthrop and Endicott set examples so remarkable that they have come down to us as America's most notable gardeners in the first half of the seventeenth century. John Winthrop, the first governor of Massachusetts Bay Colony, planted a garden on Conant's Island in Boston Harbor that was long known as 'The Governor's Garden.'

There is a glowing description 'written by a reverend divine now there resident,' published in London in 1630, which gives an idea of the luxuriance of this garden. The author was the Reverend Francis Higginson and the book, *New-England's Plantation*. After writing at some length of 'the aboundant encrease of corne' that 'proves this countrey to bee a wonderment,' the author comes to the garden, of which he says, in part:

The countrie aboundeth naturally with store of good roots of great varietie and good to eat. Our turnips, parsnips, and carrots are here both bigger and sweeter than is ordinary to be found in England. Here are store of pompions, cowcumbers, and other things of that nature which I know not. . . Excellent vines are here, up and down in the woods. Our governor hath already planted a vineyard with great hopes of encrease. Also mulberries, plums, rasberries, carrance, chestnuts, filberds, walnuts, smalnuts, hurtleberries, and hawes of whitethorne, neere as good as our cherries in England; they grow in plentie here.[2]

Although the history of horticulture in New England centers in Massachusetts, the mother colony, Maine had had a colony

---

[2] *Mass. Hist. Soc. Coll.,* First Series, i: 118.

planted in 1603, which persisted nearly a hundred years. Here, too, there were gardens, but, unfortunately, they had not the chroniclers who have ever delighted to write about Massachusetts. Two writers in particular, William Wood and John Josselyn, are quoted by all historians of American agriculture, and from them, together with Higginson's account, we know pretty well what plants were in New England gardens in the seventeenth century.

William Wood came to New England in 1629, and, returning to England in 1633, published the next year *New Englands Prospect,* in which he describes the flora, fauna, and agriculture of the new country. Wood says:

The ground affoards very good kitchin gardens, for Turneps, Parsnips, Carrots, Radishes, and Pompions, Muskmillons, Isquoter-squashes, coucumbers, Onyons, and whatever grows well in *England* grows as well there, many things being better and larger: there is like-wise growing all manner of Hearbes for meate and medicine, and that not only in planted Gardens but in the Woods, without either the art or helpe of man as sweet Marjoran, Purselane, Sorrell, Peneriall, Yar-row, Mirtle, Saxifarilla, Bayes, etc.[3]

Although the English had been in Massachusetts but a few years when Wood visited the colony, he found many gardens in the several settlements. In Dorchester were 'very good arable ground, and hay grounds, faire Corn-fields, and pleasant Gardens with Kitchin-gardens.' Of Roxbury, he wrote, 'The inhabitants have faire houses, store of Cattle, impaled Corne-fields, and fruit-full Gardens.' He found in Boston, 'very good land, affording good Corne-fields, and fruitfull Gardens.' To Lynn he gave high praise, saying, 'There is more *English* tillage than in *New England* and *Virginia* besides.'

The second author to write at length of New England gardens, John Josselyn, paid the New World a visit in 1638-9 and again in 1663-71. Returning to England, he published his observations in two books, *New-Englands Rarities Discovered,* London, 1672; and *An Account of Two Voyages to New England,* London, 1674. The first of these is the earliest work on the natural history of New England, quoted by all writers on the flora and fauna of that region. The second is the longer and more important and

---

[3] Wood, William, *New Englands Prospect,* pp. 11, 12.

contains a full account of the agriculture and horticulture of the new country. Josselyn's accounts are fuller and more ambitious in scope than Wood's, but one feels that they are less trustworthy, especially as the author is hostile to the inhabitants of the Province.

In William Wood's *New Englands Prospect,* little is said about fruits. In Josselyn's *New-Englands Rarities Discovered,* while the space given to fruits is small, the subject is very well covered. Not only are the kinds of fruit set down, but we are told that grafting is not practiced, and that trees are grown from seeds or suckers. Likewise we learn that 'cyder' is plentiful and cheap, and that wine was being made from cherries.

Josselyn also talks of the diseases of fruit trees in the New World, the first account we have of them:

Their fruit Trees are subject to two Diseases, the Meazles, which is when they are burned and scotched by the sun, and Louziness, when the Woodpeckers eat holes in their bark; the way to cure them when they are louzy is to bore a hole in the main root with an Augur, and pour in a quantity of Brandie or Rhum, and then stop it up with a pin made of the same Tree.

The vegetables and fruits Josselyn lists are all commonly found in modern gardens, but few of the herbs and flowers, especially the former, would be found in any modern garden other than that of a collector. The list is:

Spearmint,
Rew, will hardly grow
Fetherfew prospereth exceedingly;
Southernwood, is no plant for this Country, Nor
Rosemary, Nor
Bayes.
White-Salten groweth pretty well, so doth
Lavender-Cotton. But
Lavender is not for the Climate
Penny Royal
Smalledge.
Ground Ivey, or Ale Hoof
Gilly Flowers will continue two years.
Fennell must be taken up, and kept in a Warm Cellar all Winter,
Horseleek prospereth notably

Holly hocks
Enula Canpana, in two years time the Roots rot.
Coriander, and
Dill, and
Annis thrive exceedingly, but Annis Seed, as also the seed of
Fennel seldom comes to maturity; the Seed of Annis is commonly eaten
     by the fly.
Celary never lasts but one Summer, the Roots rot with the Frost.
Sparagus thrives exceedingly, so does
Garden Sorrel, and
Sweet Bryer or Eglantine
Bloodroot but sorrily, but
Patience and
English Roses very pleasantly.
Celandine by the West Country now called Kenning Wort grows but
     slowly.
Muschater, as well as in England.
Dittander or Pepperwort flourisheth notably and so doth
Tansie.

These herbs were prime necessities in cookery and medicine
in the new country. The leaves of the mints, sage, rosemary,
thyme, clary, and tansy were used in medicine; while the seeds of
anise, fennel, caraway, and dill were most frequently used in
cookery. From many of the plants, waters, bitters, liquors, syrups,
and decoctions were made for internal use, and oils, ointments,
salves, and poultices for external use. One gathers not only from
Josselyn but also from other early writers that the herb garden
was larger and better attended by these first New Englanders than
the vegetable garden.

The Pilgrim Fathers, out of touch with the mother country,
of necessity kept up a lively correspondence with physicians and
botanists. All the diseases that arise from exposure, poor housing,
and insanitary conditions swept through the Massachusetts settlements. The remedies known in the old country came mostly from
physic gardens, and the books on medicines recommended nearly
every herb, flower, and fruit as a remedy for this or that disease.
Physicians and botanists in the homeland were besieged for seeds
and plants with medicinal virtues, and were sent in return specimens from American forests supposed to have curative powers.

Ship captains had to keep the seeds and plants from dying during the long trips from continent to continent.

Farms in the colonies of New England were usually small, and nearly all who lived on them held title to the land. Each had its house, barn, outbuildings, orchard, kitchen garden, and flower garden. The fact of holding title, of paying rent neither to over-lord nor king, of being subject to laws he helped to formulate, gave a New Englander a love for his land that few tillers of the soil in other colonies could enjoy in so high a degree—a feeling very conducive to planting gardens and orchards.

Economic conditions were also favorable to gardening in New England. The soil and climate did not restrict cultivation to one or a few crops, as tobacco in Virginia, or indigo, rice, and cotton in the Carolinas and Georgia.

New Englanders sought first to raise food for their own use and then a supply for sale or barter. The constant menace of Indians and of the French from Canada kept the people in com-pact settlements or towns, and about the clustered village dwell-ings gardens were planted. Along the streets and in and about the town pasture or 'common,' trees, chiefly the elm, were planted, so that as years rolled by, beautiful village streets and a shady, grassy common were features of nearly every New England hamlet.

Corn and wheat were the staple crops in New England, and with them the land was planted often to the last square foot. There were few fences, and cattle and hogs grazed freely, even in towns. In newly cleared lands, fields were interspersed with stumps and large roots, between which homemade wooden plows could make no headway, so that the land was prepared for seeds with heavy hoes, which women, who did the gardening, could not wield to advantage. Virgin soil grew the best crops; and, lacking fertilizers, new fields took the place of old when production began to fall.

On no New England farms were there found grapes, rasp-berries, blackberries, dewberries, or strawberries, though wild plants of all these fruits might be seen in natural forest clearings or along waterways. There were few if any named varieties of the several tree fruits; nearly all were seedlings. In vegetable gardens there were about half as many kinds of vegetables growing as there are in modern times—and very few varieties of any. Among the vegetables missing from these early gardens were to-matoes, peppers, eggplant, sweet corn, spinach, rhubarb, and horse-radish. Until the middle of the seventeenth century, pota-toes were not found, and after that they were so sparingly grown for nearly two centuries that they were about the least of the root crops—little esteemed by rich or poor. There may have been in these first gardens a few crops not now commonly grown, such as the Jerusalem artichoke, skirret, chervil, shallots, purslane, in addition to the long list of herbs mentioned by Josselyn. Black mustard was grown in many gardens for its seeds, which were pulverized in mill or mortar to make the condiment used then, as now, the world over.

The first orchard in Massachusetts was planted by William Blaxton (or Blackstone), a clergyman, who owned a small farm on the slope of Beacon Hill at what is now approximately the corner of Beacon and Charles Streets, Boston. Apples in this or-chard continued to bear fruit until as late as 1765. Blaxton was a bookish recluse, fond of flowers as well as of fruits, who came to the colony not later than 1625 and began to plant his garden at once. He is spoken of by several early historians as an eccentric who trained a bull to the saddle and from its back distributed apples and flowers to his friends. In early accounts he appears as the best-known horticulturist in New England.

Blaxton moved from Massachusetts to Study Hill, near Paw-tucket, Rhode Island, in 1635, and became the first white settler and the first gardener in that state. Ninety years after Blaxton's death, Governor Hopkins of Rhode Island wrote of him:

At this new plantation he lived uninterrupted for many years, and there raised an orchard, the first that ever bore apples in the Colony of Rhode Island. He had the first of that sort called yellow sweetings, that were ever in the world; perhaps the richest and most delicious apple of the whole kind.[4]

Blaxton's Yellow Sweeting is an apple now grown as Sweet Rhode Island Greening, and is probably the first named apple to originate in the United States.

[4] *Rhode Island Hist. Soc. Coll.*, VIII: 25.

For the most part the thousands of small orchards planted in the colonies were seedling trees grown in nurseries on the farms. A few rows of seeds were planted, and the seedlings, after having been cultivated for five or six years, were given permanent places about the house, in the pasture, or in an orchard. By the selection thus practiced, weaklings were weeded out and only vigorous trees were planted; and only trees that had stood several cold winters were chosen. All trees were probably pruned high, for the convenience of mowing the grass in which they stood, or to keep sheep from browsing low limbs.

Probably the first nursery in New England was owned by George Fenwick, of Saybrook, Connecticut, who, under date of 6 May 1641, wrote to Governor Winthrop of the Massachusetts Bay Colony:

I am prettie well storred with chirrie & peach & did hope I had a good nurserie of apples, of the apples you sent me last yeare, but the wormes have in a manner destroyed them all as they came up.[5]

An early nurseryman in Connecticut was Henry Wolcott, Jr., whose Account Book is now in the custody of the Connecticut Historical Society.[6] In 1648 Wolcott filled 32 orders for trees for 25 persons; in 1649, trees were sold to 20 persons; a smaller number bought trees in 1650; in 1651, there were but 4 purchases; in 1653, there was only a single entry in the Account Book. The trees were apples, pears, and quinces, of which apple trees for cider were sold in largest numbers, one order being for 500. Prices ranged from two to five pence each, the latter a high price for seedling trees. A few of the apples were named varieties: Summer Pippin, Holland Pippin, London Pippin, Pearmain, and Belly-bond [Belle et Bonne]. It is probable that the Wolcott nursery came to an end in 1653 because the owner wanted to grow apples to make cider, concerning which there are several entries in his diary.

While there are no other records of professional nurserymen in this first half of the seventeenth century, there are several to show that settlers, some of them of prominence, grew trees for exchange. In 1648 Governor Endicott exchanged 500 three-year-

[5] *Mass. Hist. Soc. Coll.*, Fourth Series, VI: 368.
[6] Welles, pp. 16-26.

old apple trees with William Trask for 250 acres of land. Governor Endicott also exchanged trees with Governor Winthrop, as is indicated in a letter written 22 February 1644. Governor Endicott must have been growing trees in a rather large way, for his account ends with the pathetic statement, 'My children burnt mee at least 500 trees by setting the ground on fire neere them.' [7]

Just when New Englanders began to graft and bud fruit trees is impossible to say. Possibly there were some grafted trees in the first plantings, for grafting was common in England and Holland. Early in the eighteenth century varieties began to be carried from place to place, an indication that grafting and budding were being done then.

An early advertisement of grafted fruit trees that appeared in the *Boston News-Letter* of 22 October 1772, reads:

Fruit Trees.—Sarah Dawson, widow of Joseph Dawson, Gardner, in Cambridge Street, at the Cold Bath,—has got, a large Collection of grafted and inoculated English Fruit-Trees of all sorts where Gentlemen may have their Choice among three or four hundred which will be ready to be removed this Fall; also Goose berries and Currant-Bushes; also a large Number of Pares and Plumbs from 7 to 3 Years graft of 9 or 10 different sorts of the best English Fruit; also, Garden Seeds suitable for the West Indies, and all sorts of young Shrubs, dried Sweet Herbs and Celery by the Hundred.

At the end of a hundred years of horticulture in New England, Paul Dudley, F.R.S., in a paper in the *Philosophical Transactions* published in London in 1724, summed up what had been accomplished. He wrote:

Our Apples are, without Doubt, as good as those of *England,* and much fairer to look to, and so are the Pears, but we have not got all the Sorts.

Our Peaches do rather excell those of *England,* and then we have not the Trouble and Expense of Walls for them; for our Peach Trees are all Standards, and I have had in my own Garden seven or eight Hundred fine Peaches of the Rare-ripes, growing at a Time on a Tree.

Our People, of late Years, have run so much on orchards, that in a village near *Boston,* consisting of about forty Families, they made

[7] *Mass. Hist. Soc. Coll.,* Fourth Series, vi: 146, 147.

near three Thousand Barrels of Cyder. This was in the Year 1721. And in another Town of two Hundred Families, in the same year I am credibly inform'd they made near ten Thousand Barrels. Some of our Apple Trees will make six, some have made seven Barrels of Cyder, but this is not common; and the Apples will yield from seven to nine Bushels for a Barrel of Cyder. A good Apple Tree, with us, will measure from six to ten Foot in Girt. I have seen a fine Pearmain, at a foot from the Ground, measure ten Feet, and four Inches round. This Tree, in one Year, has borne thirty-eight Bushels (by measure) of as fine Pearmains, as ever I saw in *England*. . .

An *Orange* Pear Tree grows the largest and yields the fairest Fruit. I know one of them near forty Foot high, that measure six Foot and six Inches in Girt, a Yard from the Ground, and has borne thirty Bushels at a Time; and this year I measured an *Orange* Pear, that grew in my own Orchard, of eleven Inches round the Bulge. I have a *Warden* Pear Tree, that measures five Foot six Inches round. One of my Neighbors has a *Bergamot* Pear Tree that was brought from *England* in a Box, about the year 1643, that now measures six Foot about, and has borne twenty-two Bushels of fine Pears in one Year. About twenty Years since, the Owner took a Cyon, and grafted it upon a common Hedge Pear; but the Fruit does not prove altogether so good, and the Rind or Skin, is thicker than that of the Original.

Our Peach Trees are large and fruitful, and bear commonly in three Years from the Stone. I have one in my Garden of twelve Years Growth, that measures two Foot and an Inch in Girt a Yard from the Ground, which, two Years ago, bare me near a Bushel of fine Peaches. Our common Cherries are not so good as the *Kentish* Cherries of England, and we have no Duke and Heart Cherries, unless in two or three Gardens.[8]

There were orchards from the old trees planted by the Pilgrims still alive until the beginning of this century. We have pictures of an apple tree planted at Marshfield, Massachusetts, in 1648, by Peregrine White, the first English person born in New England. The tree stood as late as 1848, when a lithograph of it was published, at which time it was still bearing fruit. A row of Hunt Russet apple trees stood on the Hunt farm near Concord, Massachusetts, for at least 200 years. Four large, healthy apple trees were growing in 1880 on the Bacon farm, Richmond, Massachusetts, planted more than a century earlier.

[8] Manning, Robert, Jr., pp. 16, 17.

An apple tree of the Orange Sweeting variety stood near the meeting house at Natick; it is said to have been given to the Indians by the Apostle Eliot (d. 1690) with a bit of land. A Pearmain apple tree, imported from England by the Wyllis family, was growing in Hartford, Connecticut, in 1822, which was said to have been planted before 1650. Another Pearmain apple tree, in Weathersfield, Connecticut, imported from England by William Tryan, reported to have been bearing fruit a hundred years before the Revolutionary War, was still giving an annual crop in 1877.

A pear tree long famous in New England was planted by Governor Prince about 1640 at his homestead at Eastham, Cape Cod. It, also, lived until the middle of the nineteenth century, and late in its life produced as many as fifteen bushels of russet pears. It was an early fall fruit, none too good in quality, but was nevertheless largely propagated and distributed throughout eastern Massachusetts under the name 'Fall Pear.' Propagation was either by grafts or suckers, most often the latter. Another of the well-known ancients among pear trees was the Anthony Thatcher tree planted near Yarmouth about 1640. As late as 1872 it was still producing fair crops of fruit, very poor in quality it is true, when compared with the delectable new pears imported from Belgium, France, and England, earlier in the century.

By all accounts the pear was a favorite fruit in colonial New England. A seedling pear is the poorest of all seedling tree fruits, and those planting pear trees usually used suckers, or grafted on seedlings. Aunt Desire and Ewer are two of the New England varieties planted as late as the Revolution. The Sugar pear was a French variety said to have been brought from Acadia as early as 1680.

In *The History of the Massachusetts Horticultural Society,* more complete accounts of these apple trees and several old pear trees in New England are given; [9] as that of the Orange pear tree in the garden of Captain Charles Allen at Salem, Massachusetts, supposed to have been planted about 1670. Two pear trees of named varieties, the Warden—set out on the day the battle of Lexington was fought—and the Messire Jean, stood in the Picker-

[9] *Hist. Mass. Hort. Soc.*, pp. 14-16.

ing garden in Salem until the end of the nineteenth century. Trees of the Black pear in Worcester and the Iron pear in Dorchester are said to be more than two hundred years old. The original tree of the Pinneo, at Columbia, Connecticut, is said to have been 140 years old in 1875.

The chief legacy to horticulture from colonial Rhode Island is the Rhode Island Greening apple. This splendid variety originated near Newport from a seed planted in 1748, at a place now known as Green's End, on land owned by a man named Green who kept a tavern and as a side-business raised trees from seed. It is said that so many cions were taken from this tree that it died from excessive cutting. From Rhode Island the variety was early taken to every northern state.

The Rhode Island Greening was the first really good apple to originate in New England. Previous to its introduction, New Englanders, if they planted grafted trees at all, which few did, grafted seedling trees on Pearmain, Hightop Sweetings, Pig Nose, Foxwell, Bachelor's Button, Yellow Sweeting, Blackston's, Kreton Pippin, Long Red, and Russetin, none of which is now grown.

Black Gilliflower, Roxbury Russet, and Westfield Seek-no-further were three of the most commonly grown apples in the United States in the eighteenth and nineteenth centuries. All were distributed from Connecticut.

For two centuries Black Gilliflower, considered the best of all apples for baking, was grown in all apple regions; and because of its odd shape, striking color, and peculiar aroma was better known than any other apple. Wherever settlers went from Connecticut in this period, this apple was taken with them.

It is not certain where Roxbury Russet originated; probably in Roxbury, Massachusetts. But as early as 1649 it was taken to Connecticut and ever after was more closely identified with that state than any other apple. From Connecticut it was taken by early settlers moving westward to New York, Ohio, Indiana and Michigan, states in which, until the perfection of cold storage, this was the favorite late winter apple. Its history, dating back to 1649, sets the date when fruit growing became an important industry in Connecticut.

Westfield Seek-no-further was, until the beginning of this century, the apple *par excellence* along the Connecticut River in Connecticut and Massachusetts. It originated at Westfield, near Springfield, about the middle of the eighteenth century and soon became a favorite variety in many northern states for cider, and for domestic and market purposes.

The first orchards in Connecticut were planted by the Dutch from New Amsterdam, who, in 1633, built a fortified trading post at what is now Hartford. David Pietersz de Vries, an officer at the fort, wrote in his diary, 12 June 1639: 'I accordingly went to the commander of our little redoubt and invited the minister and mayor and other leading men, with their wives, who were fond of eating cherries, as there were forty or fifty cherry trees standing about the redoubt, full of cherries.' [10] Probably there were apples, pears, and plums, for a little later these fruits are mentioned, and within a hundred years a number of named varieties of tree fruits originated in this state.

The history of gardening in Maine is largely made up of traditions, substantiated, however, by very real fruit trees standing in considerable numbers long after there were well-authenticated local histories. The Frenchman, Sieur de Monts, founded a settlement on St. Croix Island in 1604, and is said to have planted apples and pears, some of which stood for nearly two centuries. At about the same time, Baron St. Castine planted a small orchard at Castine. These orchards antedated any others of hardy fruits in what is now the United States, unless, perhaps, the Spaniards or French had set apples and pears in the deep South. Well along in the nineteenth century there stood, on the east bank of the Sheepscot, below Wiscasset Bay, a pear tree that tradition said was more than 200 hundred years old.[11] It was supposed to have been planted by the French in one of their early attempts to found a colony on the coast of Maine. The town of Old Orchard got its name from a growth of apple trees that stood on its site, planted at an early period, some of which remained as late as 1770. John Josselyn mentions a brother who settled in Scarborough, Maine, about 1643, who was said to have been the owner of sev-

[10] *New York Hist. Soc. Coll.*, p. 82.   [11] *Maine Pom. Soc. Rpt.*, p. 7.

eral farms on which there were trees until the turn of the nineteenth century.

As late as 1870, an old apple tree, nearly dead, stood on the site of ancient Gorgeana in York. The land was the original homestead of Thomas Gorges, an early mayor of Gorgeana, and onetime governor of the Province, who settled there in 1641. There is a tradition that this tree had been brought over from England in a tub more than two hundred years before 1870.

John North came from Ireland in 1730 and settled in Bristol, Maine. He not only set out an orchard and planted a vegetable garden, but grew flowers and shrubs about his house; a hundred years later, when the house was gone, roses, primroses, and barberry bushes grew about the cellar. John North is said to have the distinction, of doubtful credit, of having introduced the oxeye daisy from England. In a very few years it became a pestiferous weed.

Other early orchards in Maine lingered well into the nineteenth century. Among them were orchards at New Harbor, along the Pemaquid River, at Sheepscot Farms, about the ruins of Hammond's Fort in Woolwich, and on Arrowsic Island. These old orchards were of apples and a few pears, but undoubtedly cherries and plums had been grown.

Pioneers in Maine, mostly from Massachusetts and New Hampshire, took fruit-tree seeds with them and planted orchards, despite their fears that the climate was too cold. It was found that the high lands in southern, central, and western Maine were ideal for apples, pears, plums, and cherries. Even peaches were grown in favored spots. Taste for apples and thirst for cider made the apple the favorite fruit, happily the one most suitable for Maine's soil and climate. These first orchards, as in other colonies, were all set with seedling trees grown in farm gardens.

One of the largest of these seedling orchards was planted by Ichabod Howe, who moved from Ipswich, Massachusetts, to Winthrop, Maine, about 1770. The year before he moved, he saved the seeds of all the good apples he ate. From these he raised an orchard in which several trees were good enough to receive varietal names and were largely planted about Winthrop. Howe made the first cider in Winthrop by crushing the apples in a sap trough and pressing out the juice in a cheese press.

In the *American Universal Geography,* the most famous book of its kind at the beginning of the nineteenth century, its author, Jedidiah Morse, writing of orcharding in Maine, says, 'Kennebeck is becoming one of the most remarkable quarters of the United States for apple orchards.' He thinks it is 'problematical whether apple and other fruits will flourish in the northern and eastern parts of this district,' and says, 'on the seacoast they become lousy and die.' There were 'good orchards in Washington County, about the bay of Passamaquoddy.' In the county of York, 'fruit is nearly as plentiful as in New Hampshire.'

As in other parts of New England, most of the tree fruits grown in Maine were seedlings, at least until 1800, when named nursery-grown trees began to be offered. At about this time, Ephriam Goodale, of Bucksport, offered 14 varieties of pears and 10 of apples, together with 'A few Butternut, Plumb & Quince Trees.' As a catalogue, Goodale sent out a broadside, of which his son, the Hon. G. L. Goodale, answering an inquiry in 1873, says: 'I suppose this to be the first catalogue of nursery trees issued in Maine.' [12] Of the varieties of pears mentioned in the catalogue, probably not one could be identified in any part of America today; two of the apples, Maiden's Blush and Pumpkin Sweet, could be found in many old orchards in the northern states and Canada.

Apples were grown in colonial New England almost wholly for cider. About one farmer out of ten had a cider mill. Well-to-do farmers put from 20 to 50 barrels of cider in their cellars every autumn, sufficient to last from harvest to harvest. It was free in every farmhouse to travelers, social and business callers, peddlers, Indians—to all who came.

All the English books on gardening, the only books available to Americans, contained directions for making and keeping cider. So, too, did the books on cookery that came to the colonies. The first American newspapers and almanacs contained directions for making cider, and advertisements from those who had it for sale. To keep well, cider must contain from 12 to 16 per cent of alcohol, to obtain which only apples with a high sugar content were used, so that special varieties were desirable for cider-making

[12] Ibid., p. 18.

when trees began to be grafted. The unfermented juice was sold freely in the autumn as 'apple-juice' to buyers who chose to make cider to suit individual tastes.

Cider could be purchased in every farm market. Colonel John Bellows, a resident of New Hampshire, had an orchard of 30 acres of apples, from which he made, in 1805, 4800 barrels of cider, and every drop of it was drunk in a neighboring town. The price per barrel was seldom more than a few shillings. Farmers used cider to pay the cobbler, tailor, lawyer, doctor, and for board in their children's schools, and donated or turned it in on subscriptions to the preacher. Cider was a chief item of export from colonial New England to the southern colonies and the West Indies.

In *American Husbandry,* the first accurate and comprehensive account of agriculture in the English colonies in America, we are told that there is no farmer or even cottager in New England without a large apple orchard. These apple growers, according to the author, make 'three or four hundreds hogsheads of cyder a man, besides exporting immense quantities of apples from all parts of the province.' The writer further says: 'The orchards in New England are reckoned as profitable as any other part of the plantation.' [13]

Cultivated varieties of currants and gooseberries were early brought to the provinces of New England from Europe. The gooseberries did not thrive, but currants were at home, and a householder in New England might have as good currants as could be grown in any part of the world. Red raspberries, blackberries, and cranberries were not grown until American species were domesticated early in the nineteenth century. All three, together with blueberries, grew so commonly in the wild that there was little need to grow them in gardens. Strawberries were not cultivated until toward the end of the eighteenth century. Nor were grapes planted until there were varieties of native species, introduced in New England early in the nineteenth century.

The European grape cannot be produced successfully in eastern America, a fact that European colonists took three hundred years to discover. Varieties of several native species of grapes are

[13] *American Husbandry,* pp. 41-2.

readily grown, but those of *Vitis vinifera*, the true European grape, are so subject to the attacks of a tiny plant louse, the phylloxera, that they quickly die in America unless grafted on the roots of some native species. Even in grafted vines, fungous diseases play havoc with the foliage, so that between louse and fungi, as one of the early experimenters said, 'a sickness takes hold of the vines and they die.'

In the states to the south of New England, down to the Gulf of Mexico, one or another of a half-dozen wild plums grew wild and were planted for their fruits or as ornamentals, but wild plums are seldom mentioned in New England. The beach plum, *Prunus maritima,* however, grows abundantly near the shore, and somewhat along streams inland. The Canadian plum, *Prunus nigra,* grows sparingly along rivers in New England, and is a splendid fruit to eat out of hand or dried as a prune. No New Englander in the colonial period seems to have tried to domesticate either of these choice wild fruits.

For more than two hundred years after the first settlements, nearly all named varieties of fruits and seeds of vegetables and flowers were imported from Europe. In the seventeenth century there are many accounts of what the settlers brought in the way of seeds and plants and what was sent by the companies founding settlements in the provinces, but one looks in vain for similar accounts of importations in the eighteenth century. Wars and internal and foreign affairs of government and trade were the only subjects discussed by visitors to the colonies when they returned to Europe. For printed statements about agriculture in New England, or any other of the provinces in the eighteenth century, one must rely on the few newspapers published ·between 1700 and the Revolution. Early advertisements give us a good idea of what vegetables and flowers were planted. Merchants made a great point of the fact that seeds came from England or Holland and that they had but recently been imported.

One of the earliest American advertisements of garden seeds and plants is found in an issue of the *Boston Gazette* of February 1719:

Garden Seeds.—Fresh Garden Seeds of all Sorts, lately imported from London, to be sold by Evan Davies, Gardener, at his house over against the Powder House in Boston; As also English Sparrow-grass Roots, Carnation Layers, Dutch Gooseberry and Current bushes.

A Richard Francis seems to have been in the seed business for some years, his first advertisement appearing in the *Boston Gazette* of 19 September 1737, in which he offers 'Garden Roots and all sorts of Sweet Herbs necessary for Masters of Vessels.' On 3 March 1748, he advertises in the *Boston News-Letter* an assortment of garden seeds as follows:

Garden Seeds.—To be Sold, by Richard Francis, Gardner, living at the sign of the black and white Harre at the South end of Boston, fresh and new imported in the last ships from London, all sorts of Garden Seeds, as follows: Windsor, Sandwich, and Hotspur Beans; long Hotspur Ormats, & Hotspur Pease; early Dutch Cabbages; Battersy, Sugar-loaf, large Cabbages; Imperial, Silesia, brown Dutch, & curl'd lettice; orange and yellow Carrots; early Dutch Turnips; green & yellow turnips; smooth & long Parsnips; white, Spanish, Strasburg, & Welsh Onions; London Leek; Short-top London, & Sandwich Reddishes; round-leaf spineges; Colley-flowers; ende (endive) sallet; sweet Marjoram; Thyme; Summer Savory; Hyssop; Sage; Balm; Dubet; Parsley; & Parsley Dubet; Pepper-grass; & single white mustard; Cucumbers; Musmellon; Watermellons; and all sorts of the best flower Seeds.

An advertisement in the *Boston News-Letter* of 5 April 1764 shows an increasing number of varieties of vegetables to be found in Boston:

Garden Seeds.—Imported in the last Ship from London, and to be sold by *Anna Johnson* at her shop at the Head of Black Harre Lane, leading up from Charlestown Ferry:

A fresh assortment of *Garden Seeds,* Peas and Beans, among which are, early charlton, early hotspur, golden hotspur, large and small dwarf, large marrowfat, white rouncevals rose and crown, crooked sugar, and grey Pease; large Windsor, early hotspur, early Lisbon, early yellow, six-weeks long podded, and white Kidney Beans; early Dutch, yorkshire, sugar-loaf, battersea, savoy, and large winter Cabbage; early and late Colliflower, early orange, scarlet and purple carrots; best smelling Parsnips; Endive; Cellery; Asparagus, and Pepper; early prickly, long and short cluster, white and green turkey Cucumber; Thyme and Sweet Marjoram; Balm, Hyssop and Sage; London short and Salmon Raddish; Lavender; green and white goss, green and

white silesia, imperial, cabbage, tennis-ball, marble, and brown dutch
lettice; ripe canary Seeds; red and white Clover; herd's Grass; red top
and tye-grass Seeds; also a Parcel of curious Flower-Seeds.

Seeds were sold in these early years by nurserymen and in general stores where groceries, dry goods, books, and other wares
were for sale. There seem not to have been many dealers in seeds
exclusively, nor were there specialists in garden seeds: those for
field crops were usually offered by the dealer in flower or vegetable seeds.

Coarse seeds, such as those of peas and beans, were probably
home grown, but with the exception of onion seed it is clear from
advertisements that the smaller seeds all came from abroad. It is
hard to fix a date when Connecticut began to have a high reputation for onion seed, the production of which was for a century
after the Revolution almost a monopoly of that state, but as early
as 1764, Gideon Welles, 'on the point,' advertised in the *Newport
Mercury* that he had 'some choice Connecticut onion seed for
sale.' In 1767 6 out of 26 advertisers in the *Boston Gazette* were
from dealers in seeds. The largest dealer in Boston at this time
was William Davidson, who dealt in seeds, wholesale and retail,
for cash. He styles himself 'gardener,' and his place was Seven
Star Lane, where, in 1768, he advertised for sale 56 varieties of
vegetables and herbs, and one flower, the carnation. Most of the
smaller seeds were sold from 2 pence to a shilling an ounce; peas
of several kinds sold from 24 shillings a bushel to 10 pence per
quart.

There were probably many professional gardeners in colonial
New England, emigrants from the Old World, of whom there
are few records. One, however, often mentioned at some length,
was George Heusler, a German, who was said to have been a
gardener to several German princes and eventually to the King
of Holland. He seems to have first lived in America, beginning
about 1780, at Newburyport, Massachusetts, in the employment
of John Tracy. Later he was engaged to lay out the grounds of
wealthy persons in Salem. For some years he advertised fruit trees
for sale on the farm of Mr. Derby. In his nursery he also had a
variety of Old World plants, some of which were advertised as
coming from Asia and Africa.

In the *Proceedings of the Essex Institute* [14] there is a reprint of a bill of sale, in 1799, of trees from Heusler's nursery, which gives some idea of the trees being planted in New England at the close of the eighteenth century. These are: Two each of Semiana, Imperatrice, and Magnum Bonum plums; three each of Brattal'd White, Early Purple, Red Magdalen, and Noblesse peaches; three apricots, twelve Lombardy poplars; and twelve large-leaved poplars. The price per tree for all varieties was two shillings each. The fruits are all European sorts.

In the accounts of gardening in colonial New England, the potato is not mentioned. There were several objections to potatoes, just as there were to its near relative, the tomato, in colonial America. They were thought to be so unwholesome that if eaten daily they would shorten life; also, that they were an aphrodisiac. The latter quality was also attributed to the sweet potato, and it was in that regard that Shakespeare mentioned the sweet potato (not the common potato, according to critics) in *The Merry Wives of Windsor* and *Troilus and Cressida*. They were believed to be harmful for cows, sheep, pigs, or horses. It is rather ironical that the potato and its relatives, the tomato and eggplant, were considered poisonous, while tobacco, a member of the same botanical group and the only one of these garden plants to contain a virulent poison, was not.

In no country but Ireland was the potato regarded as nutritious. As late as 1819, William Cobbett, in his *A Year's Residence in the United States of America,* wrote:

Nor do I say, that it is filthy to eat potatoes. I do not ridicule the using of them as sauce. What I laugh at is, the idea of the use of them being a saving; of their going further than bread; of the cultivation of them in lieu of wheat adding to the human sustenance of a country. . . As food for cattle, sheep or hogs, this is the worst of all the green and root crops; but of this I have said enough before; and therefore, I now dismiss the Potatoe with the hope, that I shall never again have to write the word, or see the thing.[15]

Although Thomas Hariot is said to have taken the potato to England from Virginia in 1585, those cultivated by colonists did

[14] *Pro. Essex Inst.,* II: 174.   [15] Cobbett, William, p. 179.

not come from the Indians of that colony. A colony of Scotch-Irish who settled in Londonderry, New Hampshire, in 1719, is said to have brought the first potatoes to New England. Another lot is said to have been introduced from Peru, probably a little later, under the name 'Bilboas' and 'Spanish potatoes.' These were grown most commonly in Pennsylvania, but were so pungent in taste and odor that they were scarcely edible. The sort brought to New Hampshire by the Scotch-Irish were yellow-fleshed, small, kidney-shaped, and better flavored than the Spanish potatoes, though much inferior to the sorts in cultivation today.

Bermuda potatoes were sold in Boston as early as 1636, for two pence per pound. In 1707, potatoes were served at a Harvard Commencement, but these may have been imported from the South or from Bermuda. The potato did not come into common use in America until about the middle of the nineteenth century, and since then it has more profoundly affected the diet of the whole country than any other food.

While the genesis of the modern potato belongs to a later period, its history may as well be told here. In the 1840's potato blight swept over Ireland, and year after year destroyed the crop, so that in 20 years it is estimated more than a million Irish died of starvation. In these same years the disease spread in America from field to field like a wave of fire. The potato, it seemed, could no longer be grown in American gardens. The blight, we now know, is caused by a fungus, but at that time scientists and gardeners were ignorant of the cause of the epidemic. It was assumed that because the plant was no longer propagated from seed, cuttings of the tubers alone being used, the potato had degenerated and needed sexual reproduction to restore its rigor. The Reverend Chauncy Enoch Goodrich of Utica, New York, acting under this theory, brought seed of the wild potato from Chile and grew the Rough Purple Chile. From this sort came in 1857 the Garnet Chile; which, in turn, in 1861, was the parent of Early Rose. From Garnet Chile and Early Rose have been developed, in about 80 years, all of the several hundred varieties that constitute the potato flora of the United States.

Modern potatoes are very different. From the first tubers grown in Europe down to the improved varieties of the last half century, the eyes of all varieties were much sunken and the surface was covered with nodules; the tubers are now much more symmetrically formed; the flesh is white, while that of the early potato was yellow; modern American potatoes are light-skinned while there were many dark-skinned varieties a century ago; the older potatoes were shorter, thicker, and more nearly round. In European countries, the varieties of potatoes grown today are still much more like those first cultivated than like the present American potato.

Until some time after 1600, the English writers, when they mentioned the potato, referred to the sweet potato. From the frequency of accounts of sweet potatoes in New England, it is certain that they must have been in rather common use in these northern colonies, although almost never grown north of New Jersey now. The sweet potato is said to have been introduced in New England in 1764. John Lowell, eminent pomologist and one of the founders of the Massachusetts Horticultural Society, said, as late as 1821: 'Sweet potatoes of excellent quality can be raised about Boston, but they are of no agricultural importance in this region.' [16]

In no other part of the world has the pumpkin been used as a food in so many ways and in such large quantities as in New England. In colonial domestic economy, a sauce was made from it; stewed with cider, it became an excellent butter. Pumpkins were also dried for winter; from them several kinds of pies were made, and, mixed with corn meal, half and half, a bread. Colonial members of the Church of England regarded Thanksgiving Day with hardly less favor than the Puritans did Christmas and Saints' days in the Prayer Book. In derision they called it St. Pumpkin's Day, and, indeed, early New Englanders made a saint of old Pompion. One of their rhymes was:

> For pottage and puddings and custards and pies,
> Our Pumpkins and parsnips are common supplies;
> We have pumpkin at morning and pumpkin at noon;
> If it were not for pumpkin we should be undone.

[16] Lowell, John, *Boston Advertiser*, 27 Oct. 1821.

An early New England writer dates an occurrence to 'the times when old Pompion was a saint.' Johnson in his *Wonder Working Providence of Sions Saviour in New England* rebukes the colonists for their dislike of the pumpkin, which he calls 'a fruit which the Lord fed his people with till corn and cattle increased.' During the Revolutionary War, sugar and a sweet syrup were made from pumpkins—very good sweetenings, crude though they were.

The pumpkin pie of colonial New England was a very different product of culinary art from the familiar Thanksgiving pie of today. It was made by cutting a hole in the top of the pumpkin to permit the removal of the seeds and their surroundings, after which the cavity was stuffed with apples, spices, sugar, and milk, and the whole baked. Probably a pastry similar to the modern pumpkin pie was made by those who had flour for the crust.

There is little in the literature of colonial New England about flowers. The best information about what was grown is to be found in advertisements of flower seeds in the newspapers of the eighteenth century. It is to be supposed that until settlements were well advanced and the inhabitants in comfortable circumstances, gardens, if any, were chiefly planted with vegetables and plants grown for medicinal uses. The old herbals gave medicinal virtues to roses, poppies, peonies, marigolds, saffron, and many other plants that are now grown for ornament only. Dried plants, of which there were some flowers, were articles of commerce as 'drugs,' much more commonly found in these earlier centuries than now.

New Hampshire claims the distinction of being the first American home of the lilac, its state flower. The 30 or more species of lilacs are natives of eastern Europe and Asia. The common lilac, *Syringa vulgaris,* probably came from southeastern Europe through central Europe to England in the seventeenth century. Tradition, in New Hampshire at least, says that the first lilacs were planted in America by Benning Wentworth in 1750. During that year Wentworth became Governor of New Hampshire, and added a council chamber and terrace to the house his father had built at Portsmouth in 1690. On the terrace he planted lilacs brought across the ocean in an English ship. Tradition in New

England says that the lilacs planted by George Washington at Mount Vernon were from slips taken from the Wentworth estate. But tradition is often inaccurate. John Bartram, the Philadelphia botanist, wrote to John Collinson, the English botanist, in 1737, telling him that lilacs were well established in the colonies, Virginia in particular, where there was in the garden of Colonel Custis the best collection in the country. Washington, no doubt, got his lilacs from Custis, a friend and relative, and probably lilacs had long been grown in Virginia.

The front-yard flower garden, or forecourt, was common in England in these years when New England was being settled. The English herbals and garden books of the times give full directions for these forecourts for cottages and farm houses. One may see many such gardens, fenced in with stone walls, in parts of Great Britain today. In a modified form, they appeared in every part of early New England.

About small houses, the garden was a parallelogram bounded by side fences that extended from the corners of the cottage to the road, with the front fence close to the road, the gate in the middle. The fence was commonly of white-washed wooden pickets. One may imagine that the earliest settlers of necessity made the boundaries of the yard of rails split from this or that wood. Thus there was privacy to the house and garden even in a town. The flowers were scant in variety—lilies, crown imperials, other bulbs, peonies, pinks, and hollyhocks. At the sides of the gate, two shrubs were planted, the usual choice being lilacs or one of the tall-growing roses. The front-yard path had edgings of pinks, irises, sedums, or other perennials that could stand a little trampling. In temperate New England, near the sea, the edgings were often of box.

It would not be difficult to name fifty or even a hundred country-seats in late colonial New England in which there were fine houses set in landscapes of excellent design, and about which were gardens containing choice fruits, flowers, and vegetables. Not a few of these fine old houses, with remnants of the gardens, yet remain near Boston, at Salem, Newburyport, Portsmouth, and New Bedford.

Noteworthy places in New England before the Revolutionary

War were the Lee house, at Marblehead, Massachusetts, which was said to have cost $10,000; the house of Godfrey Malbone, at Newport, Rhode Island, 'in which was sunk twenty thousand pounds.' In Portsmouth, New Hampshire, were the Cutts house and that of the Pepperwells; and the Wentworth house, the home of governors.[17] We can find but little about the gardens of these fine places. We are told only that these homes rose picturesquely from among the trees; that the grounds were terraced; or that they were laid out with box hedges.

One country-seat of the early seventeenth century was that of the Reverend George Phillips, first minister of the colonial church at Watertown, Massachusetts. The land was a part of a tract in Waltham, then called the Beaver Brook Plowlands, about eight miles from the State House in Boston. The property passed to Christopher Gore in 1791, and became the famous 'Gore Place,' planted, it is said, by an English landscape-gardener in the distinctive style of Humphrey Repton, whose work in England was then creating a new art in land development. The place long continued to be one of the beautiful country show places near Boston,[18] and still is, having been restored in recent years.

Another fine Boston estate in the early part of the eighteenth century was that of Thomas Hancock (uncle of John Hancock), situated west of where the State House now stands, on the south side of Beacon Hill. The garden was laid out in flower beds bordered with box, and planted with fruit trees, hollies, yews, and other evergreens. Thomas Hancock's letter-book came down to posterity, and from it are reproduced three letters written in 1736 and 1737, showing that troubles with seedsmen and nurserymen were much the same then as now. The first letter is dated 5 July 1736. It is an order for trees, addressed to one James Glin, Stepney, England. The letter reads: [19]

I am Recommended by Mr. Thos. Hubbard of This Town to you for A number of Fruit Trees—be pleased to waite on Mr. Wilkes [Mr. Hancock's London correspondent] for the Invo. of them & Let me have ye best Fruit & pack't in ye best manner & numbered, with an Acco't of ye Same. I pray you be very Carefull That ye Trees be Took up in ye Right Season, and if these answer my Expectations I

17 Lodge, Henry Cabot, p. 446.   18 *Garden and Forest*, II: 86.
19 'The Hancock House and Its Founder,' *Atlantic Monthly*, XI: 699, 700.

Ia. Indian (in middle background) smoking. *From Theodore de Bry's* India Occidentalis, 1590-91; *photograph from the Library of Congress.*

Ib. Indians planting corn and beans. *From Theodore de Bry's* India Occidentalis, 1590-91; *photograph from the Library of Congress.*

IIa. Indian gardens on Roanoke Island in 1586. *Drawn by John White for Theodore de Bry's* India Occidentalis, *1590-91; photograph from the Library of Congress.*

IIb. An early picture of Indian corn. *From Johnson's* Herbal, 1633.

IIIa. The Gore Place in Waltham, Massachusetts. *From* Garden and Forest, II, 1889.

IIIb. Clermont on the Hudson, Barrytown, New York, built by Charles Livingstone, a notable horticulturist, in 1776. *From* Garden and Forest, III, 1890.

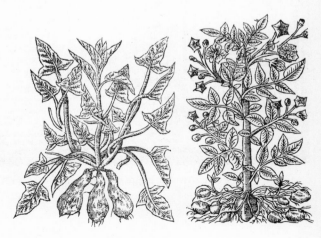

IIIc. Early illustrations of the sweet potato and the Irish potato. *From John Parkinson's* Paradisi in Sole, 1629.

IV. The first catalogue of fruits published in America.

Va. St. John de Crèvecoeur. *From his* Sketches of Eighteenth Century America.

Vb. Residence of St. John de Crèvecoeur, Ulster County, New York. *From* Proceedings of the Massachusetts Historical Society, 1906.

VIa. The Hunnewell Place, Wellesley, Massachusetts. *Courtesy of Mr. Walter Hunnewell.*

VIb. View of Magnolia Gardens, Charleston, South Carolina. *Courtesy of the Charleston Museum.*

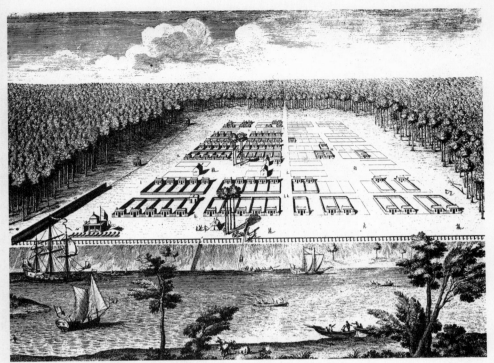

VIIa. Savannah, Georgia, in 1734; from an old line engraving.

VIIb. Elgin Botanic Garden, founded by Dr. David Hosack in 1801 in what is now the center of New York, Rockefeller Center being on a part of the land. *From a sepia drawing by Hugh Reinagle about 1812; photograph from the New York Public Library.*

VIIIa. Flower garden at Mt. Vernon, Virginia. *Courtesy of the Mount Vernon Ladies' Association.*

VIIIb. Rochester, New York, in 1812. *From Henry O'Reilly's* Sketches of Rochester, 1830.

shall want more, and 't will Ly in my way to Recommend Some Friends
to you. I Intreat the Fruit may be the best of their Kind, the Trees
handsome Stock, well Pack't, All No'd & Tally'd, & particular Invo.
of 'em. I am S'r & & T. H.

A second letter followed on 20 December 1736, showing that
Mr. Hancock was so well pleased that a much larger shipment
including seeds and flowers as well as fruit trees had been ordered:

Sir,—My Trees and Seeds pr. Capt. Bennett Came Safe to hand and I
Like them very well. I Return you my hearty Thanks for the Plumb
Tree and Tulip Roots you were pleased to make me a Present off,
which are very Acceptable to me. . . If you have any Particular,
Curious Things not of a high price will Beautifie a flower Garden,
Send a Sample with the price or a catalogue of 'em; pray Send me a
Catalogue of what Fruit you have that are Dwarf Trees and Espaliers. . . My Gardens all Lye on the South Side of a hill, with the
most Beautifull Assent to the Top & it is Allowed on all hands the
Kingdom of England don't afford So Fine a Prospect as I have both
of Land and water. Neither do I intend to Spare any Cost or Pains
in making my Gardens Beautifull or Profitable. If you have any
Knowledge of S'r John James he has been on the Spott & is perfectly
acquainted with its Situation & I believe has as high an Opinion of it
as myself & will give it as Great a Carractor. Let me know also what
you'l Take for 100 Small Yew Trees in the Rough, which I'd Frame
up here to my own Fancy. If I can Do you any Service here I shall be
Glad & be Assured I'll not forgett your Favour,—which being ye need-
ful Concludes,

                    Sr

               Your most Obedt Servant
                         Thomas Hancock.

The third letter was written on 24 June 1737, in righteous
indignation:

Sir,—I Rec'd your Letter & your Baskett of flowers per Capt. Morris,
& have Desired Francis Wilks Esqu. to pay you £26 for them *Though
they are Every one Dead*. The Trees I Rec'd Last Year are above half
Dead too,—the Hollys all Dead but one, & worse than all is the Garden
Seeds and Flower Seeds which you Sold Mr. Wilks for me an Charged
me £6. 4s. 2d. Sterling were not worth one farthing. Not one of all the
Seeds Came up Except the Asparrow Grass, So that my Garden is Lost

for me this Year. I Tryed the Seeds both in Town and Country & all proved alike bad. I spared Mr. Hubbard part of them *and they All Served him the Same*. I think Sir you have not done well by me in this thing, for me to send 1000 leagues and Lay out my money & be so used & Disapointed is very hard to Bare, & so no doubt but you will Consider the matter & Send me over Some more of the Same Sort of Seeds that are Good & Charge me nothing for them,—if you don't I shall think you have imposed upon me very much, & t'will Discourage me from Sending again for Trees or Seeds from you. I Conclude

Your Humble Serv't
T. H.

P. s *The Tulip Roots you were pleased to make a present off to me are all Dead as well.*

Incidentally, these letters contain the first statement telling us that dwarf and espalier fruit trees were being planted in New England two hundred years ago.

Andrew Faneuil built the first greenhouse in New England. It stood on Tremont Street, Boston, between Pemberton Square and Beacon Street. The property on which it was built was at an earlier date the estate of Governor Bellingham, one of the show places of Boston. Faneuil came to Boston as early as 1709 and died in 1737, which is as nearly as the date of the erection of this greenhouse can be stated. A little later, it was said that the only greenhouse in Boston was on the property of Gardiner Green, on Pemberton Hill, the grounds and buildings of which it was a part constituting 'the finest residence in Boston.' [20]

In colonial days everybody believed that all living things are affected by the moon. This superstition goes back to time immemorial. Farmers and gardeners for ages planted their seeds in this or that phase of the moon; orchards were pruned, harvesting began, trees were planted, and weeds were destroyed only when the moon reached its proper quarter. Whether the moon lay upon its back or stood upon its horn governed rain and drought. Diseases attacked plants that were not planted in the old or new of the moon. An almanac was much more important to a gardener than an experiment-station bulletin is today.

20 *Hist. Mass. Hort. Soc.*, p. 18.

The editor of the first general book on farming and gardening published in this country may be cited as a witness for the moon. The Reverend Dr. Samuel Deane (1738-1814), a noted clergyman in Portland, Maine, one-time tutor at Harvard College, later vice-president of Bowdoin College, published in 1790 *The New England Farmer or Georgical Dictionary*. He had the reputation of being a practical farmer as well as a close student of agriculture. Dr. Deane kept a diary, which is still extant. Under date of 4 May 1764, he wrote: 'I planted short beans, sowed cauliflower and apple seeds, being increase of the moon.' [21] His method of harvesting apples so that they would keep was as follows:

I gather them about noon, on the day of the full of the moon, which happens in the latter part of September, or beginning of October. Then spread them in a chamber, or garret, where they lie till about the last of November. Then, at a time when the weather is dry, remove them into casks, or boxes, in the cellar, out of the way of the frost. . .

Some may think it whimsical to gather them on the day above mentioned. But, as we know both animals and vegetables are influenced by the moon in some cases, why may we not suppose a greater quantity of spirit is sent up into the fruit, when the attraction of the heavenly bodies is greatest? If so, I gather my apples at the time of their greatest perfection, when they have most in them that tends to their preservation. I suspect that the day of the moon's conjunction with the sun may answer as well; but I have not had experience of it. The same caution, I doubt not, should be observed in gathering other fruits, and even apples for cyder: But I have not proved it by experiments.

The mallow, *Malva rotundifolia*, reached New England before 1669, if Josselyn, who mentions it in that year, can be trusted. It comes, according to the botanists, from Europe and neighboring Asia, where it is cultivated as a pot herb or for medicinal purposes. In America it is one of our commonest and most pernicious weeds; its flat seeds, called 'cheeses,' are eaten by children, and the leaves are often used for garnishing dishes. This weed has several aristocratic garden relatives, passing under the name 'mallow.' *Althæa officinalis*, the marsh mallow is one of these; the hollyhock,

21 Smith, Rev. Thomas; and Deane, Rev. Samuel, *Journals*, p. 321.

Althæa rosea, is another; while the rose-mallows, beautiful garden plants, belong to the genus *Hibiscus;* and *H. esculentus* is okra or gumbo. All of these plants were grown in colonial gardens, but when and by whom they were brought from the foreign countries in which they are natives we do not know.

Observation early brought New Englanders to the conclusion that the common barberry had something to do with stem rust of wheat. The barberry was brought to the New World with the first importations of ornamental and food plants. It was soon to be found in every dooryard in the northern colonies as an ornamental, a hedge plant, and for its fruits, from which jelly was made. Then came the discovery that wheat growing near barberry bushes did not thrive. A controversy lasting nearly three centuries ensued, about whether barberry bushes had anything to do with the failure of wheat. Finally, at the end of the nineteenth century, when stem rust was causing a loss of at least a hundred million bushels of wheat a year, the question was settled in the affirmative, and wheat-growing states passed laws compelling the destruction of the common barberry, *Berberis vulgaris.*

The first such law was enacted in 1754, when the Province of Massachusetts passed an act 'to prevent damage to English grain arising from barberry bushes in the vicinity of grain fields.' This seems to have been the first of the many pieces of American legislation to control plant diseases. The means of destroying barberries was a subject of articles in almanacs and farm papers for a century and a half.

Tools and implements used by colonial farmers were homemade and differed little from those used in the Middle Ages, or, for that matter, from those in use by Cato and Varro before Christ's time. There is a significant statement in *American Husbandry,* 1775, to the effect that 'gentlemen near Boston, who, having caught the taste for agriculture, which has for some years been remarkable in England, have introduced from there better tools of most sorts and at the same time a much better practice of husbandry.' [22] This was indication that a turn for the better was under way.

[22] *American Husbandry,* p. 60.

3

COLONIAL NEW YORK

THE BEST farmers and gardeners in the American colonies
settled along the Hudson and Mohawk Rivers. These Europeans were Dutch and French Huguenot people who excelled
with the plow, the spade, and the hoe. In other colonies, most
of the English and French, with the exception of the Huguenots,
had impossible dreams of getting rich raising indigo, olives, silkworms, and European grapes, to which the hard-headed Hollanders and home-loving Huguenots were not subject. In the end,
New England took to the sea; Virginia grew tobacco; and in the
deep South men made fortunes raising rice, indigo, and cotton,
each crop remaining profitable for two generations or a little
more.

Dutch supremacy in agriculture goes farther back than the
colonies. Hollanders were the best farmers and gardeners in
Europe at the beginning of the seventeenth century. They had
reclaimed land from the sea and from swamps and morasses, and
had learned to manure it, to rotate crops, to grow cultivated
grasses, to breed animals, and to preserve land. The Dutch were
the first Europeans to import Oriental esculents and ornamentals;
they introduced most of the garden vegetables and sent them to
England and America; they were the largest users in Europe of
hot-beds and greenhouses; Dutch bulbs are still outstanding; many
of the early herbals and books on agriculture were written by
Dutch authors.

The soil and topography of Long Island were like those the
Hollanders had known in the Old World. Soon it was dotted
with bouweries (from *bouwerij,* the Dutch word for 'farm'), and,
no doubt, the gardens blossomed with all the cultivated esculents

and ornamentals of homes in Holland. Settlements were made up the Hudson as far as Albany, and, before a century had passed, north to the Mohawk and westward a hundred miles or more along that river. Walloons, refugees in Holland from France and Flanders, came over. Still later, a colony of Palatinates from Germany was brought to New York by the English. Huguenots came in a fairly steady stream almost from the first to the Revolution. It is remarkable how many different nationalities had a part in the settlement of New York—no other state had quite so many. All learned from the Hollanders how best to grow farm and garden crops.

Peter Stuyvesant arrived in New Amsterdam 10 May 1647, and almost immediately laid the foundation of future domestic happiness by marrying Judith Bayard, a Huguenot. He then bought a farm and built a small brick house. The farm lay north and east of the present Bowery, extending over to the East River, with the westerly portion of the estate marked by a church at the intersections of Stuyvesant Street, Tenth Street, and Second Avenue. The celebrated Stuyvesant pear tree stood near this church, the site of St. Mark-in-the-Bouwerie, for 220 years until 1866, when the tree, a mere shell, was broken down by a dray. On this farm Stuyvesant worked his fields and gardens for many years, then died and was buried in a chapel where now stands the present church.

The pear tree was a Summer Bon Chrétien, said to have been imported from Holland in a tub. Peter Stuyvesant imported, or at least planted, other trees at the same time, not only pears, but apples and cherries. Peaches, a common fruit in New Amsterdam, he no doubt grew from seeds of American trees.

The Bouwerie was large, cared for by 40 or 50 slaves. It was noted for flowers, vegetables, and farm crops as well as fruits. By seeds and cions the plants on the Stuyvesant farm were multiplied and distributed to settlements on Long Island and up the Hudson, where orchards and gardens have been as popular from that day to this as in any other part of America.

Probably there was no settlement and no colony in the country concerning which better records are extant than of New Amsterdam and New Netherland, yet in them there is almost nothing about the details of farming and gardening. Over and over again one may read of homesteads, bouweries, farms, gardens; of rentals paid with animals, grains, butter, fruit, and other produce; of gardens of so many feet frontage and so many feet in depth; of goodly orchards; of speculators in farms; of parcels of land bounded by farms and gardens; various men were spoken of as farmers. It is clear that many crops were grown, but what they were and what care was given them one does not learn.

There was a street in New Amsterdam on both sides of which gardens were laid out; the Dutch name was 'Tuyn Straet'; subsequently the English called it Garden Street. In one of the gardens, yellow celandine was grown so plentifully that the place was called 'Gouwenberg'; the English gave it the name 'Golden Hill,' from which the present irregular street called Gold Street took its origin. The Cherry Street of the present day got its name nearly three centuries ago from the famous cherry gardens of the early settlers.

Adrian Van der Donck, a Dutchman, visited New Netherland in 1655 and wrote that the Hollanders had introduced 'every kind of vegetable which thrive and yield well.' He mentions apples, pears, quinces, peaches, 'morecotoons' [melocotoons, a kind of peach], apricots, plums, figs, 'cornellion cherries,' currants, and gooseberries. A part of his report reads:

> The Netherlands settlers, who are lovers of fruit, on observing that the climate was suitable to the production of fruit trees, have brought over and planted various kinds of apple and pear trees which thrive well. Those also grow from the seeds, of which I have seen many, which, without grafting, bore delicious fruit in the sixth year. . . But in general, grafting is not as necessary here as in the Netherlands, for most of the fruit is good without it. The English have brought over the first quinces, and we have also brought over stocks and seeds which thrive well and produce large orchards.

Of flowers, he writes:

> The flowers which the Netherlanders have introduced there are the white and red roses of different kinds, the cornelian roses, and stock roses; and those of which there were none before in the country, such as eglantine, several kinds of gillyflowers, jessoffelins, different varieties of fine tulips, crown imperials, white lilies, the lily fruitularia, anem-

ones, baredames, violets, marigolds, summer sots, etc. The clove tree has also been introduced, and there are various indigenous trees that bear handsome flowers, which are unknown in the Netherlands. We also find these same flowers of native growth, as, for instance, sunflowers, red and yellow lilies, mountain lilies, morning stars, red, white, and yellow maritoffles (a very sweet flower), several species of bell flowers, etc., to which I have not given particular attention, but *amateurs* would hold them in high estimation and make them widely known.[1]

Even while the English were engaged in war with the French Roman Catholics of Canada, French Protestants were settling in New York. There were Walloons—exiled subjects of the King of France—among the first colonists in New Amsterdam and at Fort Orange, far up the Hudson where Albany now stands. In 1677 a colony of Huguenots purchased a large tract of land in Ulster County and founded New Paltz. From that year to this, New Paltz and the country about it have been renowned for fine orchards and gardens. These New Paltz Huguenots intermarried with the Dutch, and their offspring made wonderfully good farmers and gardeners. They carried the art of gardening far beyond the confines of Ulster County and New York.

Another early settlement of French contributed greatly to gardening in New York. In 1685 the revocation of the Edict of Nantes drove large numbers of French Protestants from Rochelle, France, to England, whence some migrated to New York in 1689 and founded New Rochelle on Long Island Sound, Westchester County. Here they were joined by Huguenots from other parts of France. New Rochelle became another center of orcharding and gardening, one which produced many notable horticulturists.

In every part of the eastern New York of these colonial years, there were poor people who had no land and worked as renters from the rich who owned vast estates and ruled them in the manner of European overlords. The Dutch had established the patroon system; the English lived as did the country gentlemen of Great Britain. They had gardens, orchards, and spacious grounds. The poor lived in cabins, often of a single room, and ate corn, pork, and the produce of their gardens.

[1] Van der Donck, Adrian, pp. 14-15.

That apples were generally grown in early New York is certain. In accounts of the domestic economy of the province, cider is mentioned as a common drink of rich and poor, in towns as well as in the country. As in New England, in market reports in old newspapers it appears more often than any other farm product except butter and eggs. Although the apple orchards must have been chiefly of seedling trees, at least eight well-known varieties originated in New York, along the Hudson, before the Revolution. These are: Esopus, Spitzenburg, Green Newtown, Jonathan, Hawley, Newtown Spitzenburg, Swaar, and Titus Pippin. The first three are still widely grown in the United States, and pomologists would agree that no one of them has ever been surpassed in that combination of attributes that constitutes 'high quality' in the apple.

Probably few Dutch or English settlers had ever seen peaches growing in the open before coming to America. To find this choice fruit growing in such abundance that it could be used freely to make peach brandy was so great a surprise that early visitors from the Old World mention it frequently with praise.

Peaches brought on an Indian massacre in New Amsterdam. Hendrick Van Dyck, a town official, had an orchard in which there were peach trees from which the Indians could not keep their fingers. One evening when the town burgher saw an Indian woman reaching for a peach, he straightway drew bead with his musket and killed her. In retaliation, the next evening 900 Indian warriors slaughtered or carried into captivity 200 settlers. This was the massacre of 1655, one that laid waste to homes in New Amsterdam, on Long Island, Staten Island, and New Jersey, to the great detriment of all farming operations for several years.

The peach did not thrive far up the river. Peter Kalm, the Swedish botanist, who passed up the Hudson on his way to Canada in 1749, speaking of the gardens of Albany says: 'Peach-trees have often been planted here and never would thrive well.' [2] This was attributed to 'a worm which lives in the ground, and eats through the root, so that the tree dies.' Cadwallader Colden wrote in 1737 that cold had killed the peach trees on his place in Orange County the previous winter.

[2] Kalm, Peter, II: 244.

This fruit is much more at home 200 miles west of the Hudson, about the Finger Lakes and on the shores of Lake Ontario. The Indians grew peaches in central and western New York long before these regions were settled by Whites. John Bartram, in his well-known *Travels from Pensilvania to Onondago, Oswego, and the Lake Ontario,* an account of a journey made in 1743, found that apples, peaches, plums, and grapes were being grown in the Indian villages through which he passed. Sullivan's army, which came to this region in 1799 to chastise the Indians, destroyed great numbers of trees of all the hardy fruits. In Conover's *History of Kanadasaga and Geneva*[3] we are told there were several orchards about Cayuga and Seneca lakes in 1790 when the Whites came, and that by 1800 there were 13 distilleries in the region making peach brandy.

The author of *American Husbandry,* writing at the close of the colonial period, found the fruits of New York much superior to those in New England. He wrote: 'Every planter and even the smallest farmers have all an orchard near their houses of some acres, by means of which they command a great quantity of cyder, and export apples by ship-loads to the West Indies.' He speaks of peaches and nectarines and says the fruits are much superior to those grown in England as are 'several articles of the kitchen garden.'[4]

There are no accounts of grape growing by the Dutch in New Netherland, but Jasper Danckaerts and Peter Sluyter, who visited the colony in 1679, said: 'Although they have several times attempted to plant vineyards, and have not immediately succeeded, they nevertheless, have not abandoned hope of doing so by and by, for there is always some encouragement, although they have not as yet discovered the cause of the failure.'[5]

No sooner had the English taken possession of New Netherland than they attempted to grow grapes for wine making. In 1664, Nicholls, the first governor of New York, granted Paul Richards a monopoly on grape growing, stipulating that he could make and sell wine free of impost, and gave him the right to tax any person in the colony planting vines five shillings per acre.

[3] MSS. in the library of Hobart College, Geneva, New York.
[4] *American Husbandry,* p. 76.
[5] Danckaerts, Jasper; and Sluyter, Peter, p. 16.

This was the first attempt to grow grapes commercially in the Province. For a century after, there were spasmodic attempts to raise the Old World grape in the colony, but at the beginning of the Revolution there were only a few small vineyards in what was then New York.

About the year 1760, J. Michel Guillaume St. John de Crève-cœur came into the English colonies by the way of Canada, married and settled down in Orange County, New York. He was deeply interested in agriculture, and, in 1782, published in England *Letters from an American Farmer*. In 1925 more letters from his pen were published, under the title *Sketches of Eighteenth Century America*. After the Revolution he was for a time French consul in New York; he then returned to France, where he died in 1813.

Several distinguished services for American farmers were performed by Crèvecœur during his years in America. He was responsible for bringing André Michaux, a fellow Frenchman and notable botanist, to America; later he helped to lay out a botanic garden at New Haven; he introduced a number of plants in America, among which was lucerne (alfalfa); he corresponded on agricultural subjects with every noted farmer of his time in the country, including Washington and Jefferson; he was the author of a treatise on the potato, published in Caen, France.

Crèvecœur lived in a typical community of colonial New York in the years just before the Revolution. Dutch and English worked their farms side by side on the Hudson and the Mohawk. Not far from Pine Hill were the Huguenots of Ulster County and no doubt a scattering of French Roman Catholics, in which group he belonged. Along the Hudson were many great estates—Dutch patroons and English manors. Crèvecœur wrote at length [6] about orchards, and what he has to say probably applies to all the farm owners, large and small, in eastern New York. Of apples, he says:

Perhaps you may want to know what it is we do with so many apples. It is not for cider, God knows! Situated as we are it would not quit cost to transport it even twenty miles. Many barrel have I sold at the press for a half dollar. As soon as our hogs are done with the peaches we turn them into our apple orchards.

[6] For a further account of Crèvecœur see p. 469.

Crèvecœur gives a good account of how apples, peaches, and plums were dried:

Our method is this: we gather the best kind. The neighbouring women are invited to spend the evening at our house. A basket of apples is given to each of them, which they peel, quarter, and core. These peelings and cores are put in another basket and when the intended quantity is thus done, tea, a good supper, and the best things we have are served up. . . The quantity I have thus peeled is commonly twenty baskets, which gives me about three of dried ones.

Next day a stage is erected either in our grass plots or anywhere else where cattle can't come. Strong crotches are planted in the ground. Poles are horizontally fixed on these, and boards laid close together. . . When the scaffold is thus erected, the apples are thinly spread over it. They are soon covered with all the bees and wasps and sucking flies of the neighborhood. This accelerates the operation of drying. Now and then they are turned. At night they are covered with blankets. . . By this means we are enabled to have apple-pies and apple-dumplings almost the year round.

. . . My wife's and my supper half of the year consists of apple-pie and milk. The dried peaches and plums, as being more delicate, are kept for holidays, frolics, and such other civil festivals as are common among us. With equal care we dry the skins and cores. They are of excellent use in brewing that species of beer with which every family is constantly supplied, not only for the sake of drinking it, but for that of the barm [yeast formed on fermenting liquors] without which our wives could not raise their bread.

Besides drying tree fruits, no doubt these New York farmers dried wild berries, which grew abundantly in the forests and waste lands. Crèvecœur tells us specifically that they dried pumpkins, cut in thin slices, which they used for pies; and that the pumpkin peelings were dried and used in making pumpkin beer.

He tells us also that in near-by New Jersey the art of drying these products was carried to great perfection, some farmers making use of long ovens built for the purpose. These dried fruits, Crèvecœur says, were articles of commerce, especially for shipment to the West Indies.

A paragraph about 'reducing the quantity of cider,' no doubt chiefly to have it keep longer, is of interest:

In the most plentiful years we have a method of reducing the quantity of our cider and of making it a liquor far superior. . . We boil the quantities of two barrels into one, in a fair copper kettle, just as it comes from the press, and, therefore, perfectly sweet. Sometimes I have reduced one barrel and a half into one. This is preserved until the summer, and then affords a liquor which, when mixed with a due proportion of water, affords us an excellent beverage. . . Other people prefer hauling their hogsheads out of their cellars, when it freezes hard. In one night or two the frost will congeal the watery parts. They then draw from whatever remains behind, but this is neither so sweet, nor palatable as the other; it is too potent.

In all newly settled regions, butter is a luxury or wholly lacking, and in its place fruit spreads are largely used. The best substitute for real butter is apple butter, when apples are to be had. Crèvecœur tells how apple butter was made in his neighborhood:

We often make apple butter, and this is in the winter a most excellent food particularly where there are many children. For that purpose the best, the richest of our apples are peeled and boiled; a considerable quantity of sweet cider is mixed with it; and the whole is greatly reduced by evaporation. A due proportion of quinces and orange peels is added. This is afterwards preserved in earthen jars, and in our long winters is a great delicacy and highly esteemed by some people. It saves sugar, and answers in the hands of an economical wife more purposes than I can well describe.

There are several references in these pages of Crèvecœur to other drinks than cider which farmers in Ulster County made from fruits. Apple brandy, the applejack of today, was a favorite strong liquor. Peach brandy was another drink of the people, made in considerable quantities. Crèvecœur found them 'fiery and rough at first, but with age very pleasant.' Besides cider and these brandies, cherry and currant wines were made, their quantities limited 'because of the enormous amount of sugar they required.' Wine made from grapes could be had only if wild grapes were used.

In another interesting paragraph, Crèvecœur tells how colonial farmers kept fruit and vegetables over winter:

We have another convenience to preserve our fruits and vegetables in the winter, which we commonly call a Dutch cellar. It is built at the foot of a rising ground which is dug through, about eighteen feet long and six feet wide. It is walled up about seven feet from the ground; then strongly roofed and covered with sods. The door always faces the south. There it never freezes, being under ground. In these places we keep our apples, our turnips, cabbages, potatoes, and pumpkins.[7]

Strawberries, raspberries, blackberries, gooseberries, grapes, and cranberries were not grown in colonial New York. Strawberries may have been taken from the wild by lovers of this fruit, and set in corners, fence rows, and under hedges, there to grow as best they could. They were so grown in the Old World and the custom probably was brought to the New.

The Hudson was the highway for most of the travel in colonial New York from its mouth to Albany, and on its banks, east and west, every eminence that gave a sightly prospect was capped with a substantial residence, each with its orchard and garden. If one may judge from the reports of visitors, gardens and ornamental grounds about these Hudson River homes were in early days wholly unconventional. Vegetables, flowers, and fruits grew side by side in democratic proximity. There were later, however, not a few patrician gardens about the manor homes along the Hudson and on Long Island and the several smaller adjacent islands. The owners of most large estates planted gardens of formal design, with clipped trees, boxwood borders and hedges, gardens, orchards, and flowers all in proper places. Probably not much that was admirable could have been seen in the seventeenth century, but as the colony became well settled and the people who lived in the manor houses began to have money and time, gardening became an art.

The large tracts of land owned by the great families of the province permitted divisions and subdivisions, especially as marriages between land-holding families took place, so that fine homes and fine gardens multiplied apace as the eighteenth century progressed. Thus there came to be several large estates owned by the Livingstons, the Philipses, the Morris family, and the Schuy-

7 Crèvecœur, *Sketches*, pp. 102-5.

lers, to mention but a few of the historic names with several divisions in the Province of New York.

Of the notable estates on Long Island, comparatively few with fine gardens come within the time covered by this history. One, however, on Shelter Island, between the north and south flukes of eastern Long Island, is noteworthy as the first home of box in America. Nathaniel Sylvester came to Shelter Island on the ship *Golden Parrott* in 1652, founded a manor, and, a little later, set plantations of box around it. The present house is said to date from 1735, a fine example of Long Island colonial architecture, about which are admirably planted grounds, one of whose features is a windmill 145 years old. Dutch windmills, by the way, were long picturesque features of Long Island landscapes.

At the beginning of the Revolution, the city of New York covered only the lower part of Manhattan Island. The streets were narrow and the houses thickly set. Brooklyn was hardly more than a village. The land in what is now Greater New York was mostly open country or rocky, hilly woodland. The roads were passably good and one by one well-to-do New Yorkers bought farms near town to which they might drive from city homes. The country places, one visitor from afar says, 'were elegantly planted with orchards, gardens, and lawns.' Not far from where the present public library now stands, Philip Cortlandt had a country place six miles from the city where he sent his family to spend 'the somer season.'

Public squares in American cities, even in early years, were often bounded with avenues of full-grown native trees and were well shaded by specimen plants. The City Hall Park in New York City was originally a common. Boston Common was specifically dedicated to the use of the public in the early years of the town, and has ever since well fulfilled its function. In the cities on salt water, seaside walks were often parks on a small scale. The Battery in New York is a familiar example of such walks.

Parks had their anti-types in bowling greens, introduced into America by the Dutch in New Netherland. Until after the middle of the nineteenth century there were no athletic fields or playgrounds for games other than bowling.

The little park known as 'Bowling Green' in New York City

dates almost from the time the Dutch established a trading post on Manhattan Island in 1613. On the north of the green a fort was built of logs in 1615. This fort was replaced by a palisaded storehouse in 1626, at which time the green was being used as a drill-ground. In 1647 the fashionable people of New Amsterdam resided along the lower part of Broadway facing the bowling green. This was still the dwelling place of aristocrats in 1710, where lived André Freneau, ancestor of Philip Freneau, poet of the Revolution.

According to an inscription on a plaque in Bowling Green Park, erected in 1939, this was the first public park in New York, established 12 March 1733, when the Common Council passed a resolution reading:

Resolved that this Corporation will lease a piece of Land lying at the lower end of Broadway fronting to the Fort, to some of the inhabitants of the said Broadway in order to be inclosed . . . to make a Bowling Green thereon, for the Beauty and Ornament of said Street as Well as for the Recreation & Delight of the Inhabitants of This City.

There is a stained-glass window in the Bowling Green Building, 11 Broadway, portraying the out-of-doors game of bowling as played 200 years ago.

Almost down to the Civil War, bowling was a fashionable out-of-door game in every part of the country. In the eighteenth century, just before and after the Revolution, it was as popular as croquet a generation ago, and nearly as popular as baseball now. There were greens in the village commons, in the yards of inns, and every large estate had its bowling green. The bowling green had a prominent place on the grounds at Mount Vernon; it lay just north of the vegetable garden, from which it was separated by a brick wall. In private places there were often terraces on one or more sides of the green, frequently with a pavilion from which spectators could watch the game. The bowling green was often a chief feature of fine grounds planted about with trees and shrubs.

Mrs. Grant, author of *Memoirs of an American Lady*, who lived in Albany from 1758 until the Revolution, has much to say in her book about Dutch gardens. The city, when she first saw it, stretched along the Hudson, 'the shore being occupied by gardens.' The town, according to Mrs. Grant, occupied a great space of ground, semi-rural in all its aspects. Every house had a garden, a well, and a little green lawn behind. Before the door a tree was planted, each owner planting the kind that most pleased him, usually something that would shade the open porch before the door. Mrs. Grant goes on to say:

The care of plants, such as needed peculiar care or skill to rear them, was the female province. Every one in town or country had a garden. Into this garden no foot of man intruded after it was dug in the Spring. I think I see yet what I so often beheld—a respectable mistress of a family going out to her garden, on an April morning, with her great calash, her little painted basket of seeds, and her rake over her shoulder, going to her gardens of labours. A woman in very easy circumstances and abundantly gentle in form and manners would sow and plant and rake incessantly.

Mrs. Grant spent much of her time in the home of Colonel Philip Schuyler, which fronted the river some miles north of Albany on the military road to Saratoga, the northern lakes, and Canada. She speaks of gardens and orchards of vast extent, but says very little about them. There was, she tells us, an avenue of Morello cherry trees 300 yards in length, a 'long garden,' and a 'large orchard,' all being enclosed by staked board fences. On each stake of the fence there was the skull of a horse or cow, the jaws fixed on the stakes, the craniums uppermost. These skulls were bird houses, small birds entering through the eye orifices.

We have from Mrs. Grant's book a glimpse of gardening in widely separated places from Canada to the Gulf and from the Atlantic to the Mississippi. Her father was an army officer, stationed for a time at Oswego on Lake Ontario. Then a child with her mother, Mrs. Grant lived here a few years, beginning in 1760. The officers and men of the fort maintained a large garden with fruits, vegetables, flowers, a bowling green, a summer house, and a fish pond. Fruits and vegetables were grown in such abundance that the soldiers dried them for winter use. The practice spread to all the hundred-odd forts then held in America by the British, the officers and men of which knew something about gardening and had more time to plant and care for fruits and vegetables than settlers clearing land.

There are occasional accounts of fruits and vegetables about old forts in state historical publications in New England, New York, and west along the Great Lakes as far as Lake Superior. Early American gardening is indebted not a little to British and French soldiers in the forts of both the United States and Canada. One most admirable garden dating back to an old fort is still maintained at Ticonderoga, New York. Its history is given by Mr. S. H. P. Pell in a letter to the author:

It was laid out by French officers in 1755 or 1756 and named by them the *Jardin du Roi.* The English changed the name to the King's Garden. A map made for General Burgoyne in 1777 shows the plan very carefully and calls it the King's Garden.

My great-Grandfather, William Ferris Pell, about 1820 fenced in part of the old garden and put a cedar hedge around it. The family kept it up as long as they lived there but during the long years when the Pavilion was used as a boarding house and a farm, it was allowed to fall into neglect; but the tenants always planted something. . .

As the French merely took over the old Indian planting ground, the King's Garden may be one of the pieces of land in this country with the longest history of planting.[8]

The Northern Traveler and Northern Tour, a tourist's guide published in 1826, says of this garden:

On a spot formerly occupied as the *King's Garden,* Mr. Pell has a fine garden, abounding in the choicest fruits imported from Europe, and transported from the celebrated nurseries of Long Island. Mr. Pell has been a very successful propagator of the locust tree (*Robina Pseudo acacia* of Linnaeus) thousands of which are growing on these grounds in the most flourishing manner: here is also the *Magnolia Grandiflora,* never before cultivated in so high a latitude; the horse chestnut (*Castanea Equinus*) and upwards of 70 varieties of the gooseberry from Europe. Here also we find the beautiful *Catalpa* and the *Liriodendron tulipefera.* The grounds are laid out in good taste, and are kept with care and in excellent order.[9]

From these early military-post gardens there were a good many escapes from cultivation, and one may find near their sites, even today, some of the hardiest of the run-wilds, as tansey, bouncing-

[8] Under date of April 1939, in a letter to the author.
[9] *The Northern Traveler,* etc., p. 172.

bet, butter-and-eggs, chamomile, live-for-ever, money-vine, cypress spurge, and moss pink. It is said that the situation of old Fort Nassau in Pennsylvania, long in dispute, was finally determined by the garden flowers found on one of the several supposed sites.

Probably nowhere in America have gardens during the two and a half centuries of this history been quite so numerous, so well planted, and so well cared for as along the eastern shore of the Hudson. Fine though they were, the gardens of eastern Massachusetts, of the tobacco plantations of Virginia, of the indigo and later the cotton plantations of South Carolina and Georgia, were, compared to those of the Hudson River Valley, short-lived. The gardens of the Dutch patroons were taken over by wealthy English owners of the great manor estates; these, in turn, were divided into the country-seats of men of culture and of means who, from 1700 to the present time, lived with a degree of luxury, leisure, and refinement scarcely equaled elsewhere in the country.

A good example of the early estates on the Hudson is Hyde Park, the founders of which, so far as landscape gardening is concerned, were Samuel Bard and David Hosack. About 1700 Peter Fauconnier, a Huguenot, who was Samuel Bard's great-grandfather, was given a large patent of land by Edward Hyde, Lord Cornbury, then governor of New York. In honor of the donor, the estate was called 'Hyde Park,' which later became the name of the town. Samuel Bard's father, Dr. John Bard, was living at Hyde Park as early as 1764, developing the farm into a model estate, turning what a few years before had been a wilderness into a well-planted horticultural place with orchards, gardens, and lawns. While Dr. Samuel Bard was living in New York City as dean of Columbia's faculty of medicine, he had among his patients George Washington, who became a friend as well. At Hyde Park, Dr. Bard erected St. James Church, of which President Franklin Roosevelt was senior warden during his lifetime.

David Hosack was a partner, friend, and colleague of Samuel Bard's in the College of Physicians and Surgeons, a part of Columbia University. About 1810, Hosack retired from active work, bought Hyde Park, and hired André Parmentier, sometime between 1824 and 1830, to improve the landscape. The work was so well done that A. J. Downing could write that Hosack's grounds were 'justly celebrated as one of the finest specimens of the modern style of landscape gardening in America.' There were on the grounds a large park, well wooded with native trees; extensive lawns, shrubberies, and flower gardens; several well-filled conservatories; and a large orchard and vegetable garden. Dr. Hosack had many new plants from foreign countries.

Another early landscape of park-like character along the Hudson was De Veaux Park, Annondale, Dutchess County. The place was laid out in 1790 by Colonel André de Veaux, a native of South Carolina. It was planned in imitation of the naturalistic gardens of England and was long noted for its great beauty.

Downing selected several of Dutchess County country seats as notable examples of landscape gardening: Rose Hill, Blithewood, Montgomery Place, The Grove, Ellersie, The Locusts, Hyde Park, Wodenethe, Glenhurst, Netherwood, High Cliff, and Linwood.

The Dutch in New Amsterdam planted formal gardens in the characteristic Dutch style. At least so one may gather from a word here and there and from old sketches. The 'Dutch style' was an exaggeration of topiary work in clipping evergreens, particularly yew and box, in odd and curious shapes, as of animals and birds. This style had been introduced in England by William III but was carried to such an excess that 'Dutch gardening' became the laughingstock of the times and brought about its own destruction. In New York, the growing supremacy of the English soon brought the formal gardens of the Dutch in disfavor, replacing them with English gardens.

Every Dutch garden of note contained at least one sundial. A favorite place for it was the center of a formal design, where decorative lead and iron pieces were also often found. These ornaments, usually vases and statues, though of rough workmanship were often artistic and looked well against backgrounds of clipped evergreen. Nearly all, if not all, came from Holland or England. Some of the sundials and statues survived long after the gardens disappeared, and are occasionally to be found now in antique shops.

Presumably, garden furniture was used much as it is today. Certainly it was made and offered for sale. Andrew Gautier, Prince's Street, New York City, published an advertisement in the *New York Gazette, or the Weekly Post-Boy,* 16 April 1765, which reads: 'A large and neat assortment of Winsor chairs, made in the best and neatest manner and well painted, Vis. High back'd, Low back'd, and Sack back'd Chairs and Settees, or double seated fit for Piazza or gardens.'

The beehive was once a common feature in the furnishings of American gardens. Honey was the chief sweetening in domestic economy, and an ingredient in two common drinks, mead and metheglin. Bees were introduced into New England in 1638 and rapidly found homes in the forests, plains, orchards, and gardens of the New World. Denton in his *Brief Description of New York,* in 1670, says: 'You shall scarce see a house but the South side is begirt with Hives of Bees, which increase after an incredible manner.' And Gabriel Thomas, 1698, writing of near-by Philadelphia, says: 'Bees thrive and multiply exceedingly,—the Sweeds often get great store of them in the woods where they are free for any Body.'

There were landscape gardeners of sorts in colonial New York to cater to the needs of those who desired and could afford fine gardens. Gardeners are mentioned in early books and diaries, and no doubt a search of early newspapers would show advertisements in all the large cities similar to two in New York City in 1758 and 1768. These advertisements give us the best accounts of what early gardens about the homes of the well-to-do were like and particularly how they were furnished. The earlier of the two appeared in the *New York Mercury* of 2 October 1758:

Theophilus Hardenbrook.—This is to give notice that Theophilus Hardenbrook, Surveyor, Designs all sorts of Buildings, well suited to both town and country, Pavillions, Summer-Rooms, Seats for Gardens, all sorts of Rooms after the taste of the Arabian, Chinese, Persian, Gothic, Muscovite, Paladian, Roman, Vitravian, and Egyptian; also Water-houses for Parks, Keeper's Lodges, burying Places, Niches, Eye Traps to represent a Building terminating a walk, or to hide some disagreeable Object, Rotundas, Colonades, Arcades, Studies in Parks or Gardens, Green Houses for the Preservation of Herbs with winding Funnels through the Wall, so as to keep them warm, Farm Houses, Town Houses, Market Houses, Churches, Alter Pieces. . .

Hardenbrook seems to have been primarily an architect, but the second advertiser calls himself a 'Gardener.' His advertisement appears in the *New York Gazette and the Weekly Mercury* of 8 August 1768:

Gardener.—Thomas Valentine, Bred under the ablest master in Ireland, who for some years after his apprenticeship conducted the Gardening Business for the Right Hon. the Earl of Belvedere, a Nobleman remarkable for elegant Taste, extensive Gardens and Plantations, the Major part of which were made immediately under said Gardener's Direction, during his Services with him; and has been employed by several of the Nobility and Gentry, to lay out their Gardens and Improvements. He also surveys Land, makes Copies and traces Maps, draws Designs for Gardens, Plantations, Stoves, green Houses, forcing Frames, etc. etc. He is willing to attend any Gentleman's Gardens within ten or twelve Miles of this City, a Day or two in the Week, and give such Directions as are necessary for completing and keeping the same in proper Order. . .

Another advertisement of this period is of especial interest to gardeners. In the *New York Gazette and Weekly Mercury* of 8 February 1773, Henry William Stiegel advertises glassware for sale at the American Flint Glass Store, 'between Burling and Beekman's Slips in the Fly.' After a list of glassware of many kinds, the advertisement reads: 'Also a variety of English garden seeds of the last year's growth; viz, Early Charlton, marrowfat, badmansdwarf, and golden hotspur peas; winsor, scarlet runner, and large white kidney beans; lettice and cabbages of various kinds, carrot, parsnip, radish, turnip, etc. etc.'

This was the Baron Stiegel whose glassware collectors are now so eager to buy. One finds him spoken of in the newspapers of the times not only as a manufacturer of glassware and a seller of garden seeds, but also as a landscape gardener, an architect, a tinsmith, a military strategist, an iron founder, and a duelist. This man of many accomplishments came to America before the middle of the century, settled in Lancaster County, Pennsylvania, and founded the borough of Manheim, calling it after his native town in Germany. He established there an iron factory and glass works, and as an avocation grew roses. In his old age, fearing a church he had built would be claimed by his heirs, he gave it and the land for a cemetery to the congregation, with the provision that every year a red rose should be given to himself or his heirs. The tribute was paid annually for a hundred years and then fell into disuse. In 1894, a rose festival at Manheim was held, at which the old church was transformed into a bower of beauty, and the custom of paying annually the tribute of a red rose was revived.[10]

Although seeds and plants were nearly all imported in the colonial period, there must have been some nurseries, probably small, and some seed growing. There are a few records, chiefly in advertisements, of exchanges between individuals of plants and seeds.

The Society for the Promotion of Agricultural Arts, an organization in New York City, in the year 1768, awarded a prize of £10 to Thomas Young of Oyster Bay for the largest number of apple trees in nursery rows on Long Island. Young's trees numbered 27,123. There must have been several other nurseries in existence on Long Island at the time, but the only one of note was the Prince Nursery, an enterprise whose fame lasted for more than a century.

The Prince Nursery, founded in 1737 by Robert Prince at Flushing Landing, Long Island, was the first of any importance in the colony and the first of intercolonial trade, later to become international. This famous nursery was carried on by four generations of Princes (see pp. 207-9). At the death of William Prince, the second proprietor, the business was divided between two sons, William and Benjamin. The latter retained the original property under the name 'The Old American Nursery,' while William established at a new location 'The Linnean Botanic Garden and Nursery,' which continued for a half century to be one of the gardening centers of America.

The first known advertisement of the Princes is dated 21 September 1767, and reads: 'For sale at William Princes nursery, Flushing, a great variety of fruit trees, such as apple, plum, peach, nectarine, cherry, apricot, and pear. They may be put up so as to be sent to Europe.'

During the Revolutionary War there was little demand for fruit trees, and the Princes advertised for sale 30,000 cherry trees for use as hoop poles. The nursery was guarded by British soldiers

10 *Garden and Forest,* VII: 250.

during the occupancy of the invaders. So many of the British and Hessian officers wanted trees from this nursery that the business had a splendid revival after the return of peace.

The Prince Nursery was the first in America to advertise ornamental plants in a large way. In an advertisement in the *New York Mercury*, 14 March 1774, are listed Magnolias, Catalpas, and Mulberries, together with several fruits and a filbert.

Possibly the most distinguished botanist in the eighteenth century in New York was Cadwallader Colden (1688-1776), a patron of horticulture as it existed in these early years. Colden was a Scotchman with a medical degree from Edinburgh, who came to America and practiced medicine in Philadelphia from 1708 to 1715. In 1719 he became surveyor-general of New York, and in 1761 lieutenant-governor of the province. His fame as a botanist rests chiefly on a paper entitled *Plantae Coldenhamiae*, published in Upsala in 1742, the earliest contribution to the knowledge of the botany of New York. This paper received high praise from Linnaeus. From 1728 to 1760, Colden lived on a large estate near Newburgh, called 'Coldenham,' the gardens of which were the best then to be found along the Hudson. From 1760 to 1764 he lived in New York City and then moved to Flushing, Long Island, where he lived until his death in 1776.

Colden's daughter, Jane, was also a botanist of note, and together they planted a garden at Flushing, as they had at Newburgh, scarcely surpassed in the northern states. In a letter from John Bartram, dated 24 January 1757, it is noted that Jane Colden was exchanging seeds and plants with both European and American botanists and gardeners, no doubt to the enrichment of gardening in both continents.

The first greenhouse in the city of New York was built in 1764, and was for many years a landmark in the city as well as in the progress of gardening in the country. It was very simple in construction, with a shingled roof, glass being used only for the sides and ends. A little later there were many such greenhouses, differing from this type but little, though often the house was constructed with a story above, in which the gardener lived.

4

THE COLONIES ON THE DELAWARE

THE first settlers in New Jersey were Dutch emigrants from New Amsterdam at the mouth of the Hudson. There were several bouweries on the west bank of the Hudson as early as 1630. These with their gardens of fruits, vegetables, and flowers were not different from those that were in what is now New York.

Contemporaneously with the Dutch, the Swedes settled in Delaware, landing first at Wilmington. The Swedes were good farmers and came to America with a settled policy of practicing agrarian pursuits. They grew all the common farm crops, vegetables, and fruits, and at first made wine out of wild grapes, but soon found cider more to their liking and planted apples.

A hundred years after the first Swedish settlements were made, Peter Kalm visited New Jersey and wrote about the log houses, gardens, farms, and ways of life he saw. He speaks, in particular, of the vegetables and fruits, the quantities of which astounded him, as did the varied uses to which gourds were put by the settlers. He says little of apples and nothing of pears and plums, but much about peaches and cherries. As for flowers, he mentions only those of the woods.

Kalm (1715-79) was a pupil of the great Linnaeus. He was sent to America in 1748 by the Swedish government to report on the natural resources of the country. He traveled widely in the middle and northern states and in Canada, and published *Travels into North America* in 1748-50, the most trustworthy of all the eighteenth-century books on the natural history of this country, and on the domestic economy of the people. Kalm's name is perpetuated by Kalmia, one of whose species is the beautiful mountain laurel of our eastern states, *Kalmia latifolia*.

73

Kalm seems to have been the first botanist to notice the rather pretty striped maple, *Acer pennsylvanicum;* and the silver or soft maple, *A. saccharinum;* by high praise of the fragrant crab, *Pyrus coronaria,* in his *Travels,* he made it popular as a garden plant in both Europe and America. He appears also to have first noticed the sheepberry, or nannyberry, *Viburnum lentago,* the beautiful viburnum so common in the fields and on lawns in the northern parts of the United States.

The first settlements in Pennsylvania were made a little later than those in New Jersey by the Swedes, near the present site of Philadelphia in 1643. In 1655 Swedish authority was overthrown by the Dutch; the Dutch, by the English in 1664. In 1681 William Penn was given a grant from Charles II, which included most of the region that is now Pennsylvania.

The first settlement in Delaware was made by the Dutch in 1638 at Fort Nassau. A little later the Swedes settled on Christiana Creek and named the country New Sweden; the whole region came into the hands of the English in 1664. In 1681 William Penn purchased what is now Delaware from the Duke of York; and, though it was given a separate legislature shortly after, it was in reality a part of Pennsylvania until the Revolution.

Soil, climate, people, and, until the Revolution, the governments of the three colonies were much the same. Few of the colonies offered a more promising home for seventeenth-century emigrants from Europe. The climate was milder than in New England and New York; the soil more fertile; and the Indians much more friendly. In making their settlements, the Swedes chose the banks of the Delaware; the Dutch, land adjacent to New Netherland; the English, mostly Quakers, took lands on the two sides of the Delaware.

Agriculture was almost the sole industry in this area during the colonial period, and was relatively more important than in any other of the colonies. Swedes, Dutch, English, and a little later Germans and Scotch each brought their own agricultural practices and garden crops, which, coming from countries so divergent in soil, climate, and people, enriched the first settlements with a great variety of esculents and ornamentals. Although the Swedes and Dutch came under the dominion of the English, the influence of the agricultural practices of the conquered races have persisted down to the present time.

William Penn, under whom English settlers came to the New World in larger numbers and became settled and at home more quickly than in any other colony, published in England a series of pamphlets telling about the new country. Possibly the best of these is a *Letter from William Penn to the Committee of the Free Society of Traders,* 1683. In it he gives under the heading 'The Natural Produce of the Country, of Vegetables, its Trees, Fruits, Plants, Flowers' a full account of the plants of Pennsylvania, many of which seemed to him to have potential value under domestication. Of the several fruits and nuts Penn describes, he has most to say about peaches and grapes. Of the peach he says: 'not an Indian Plantation without them; but whether naturally here at first, I know not, however one may have them by Bushells for little; they make a pleasant Drink and I think not inferior to any Peach you have in England except the true Newington.' [1]

He describes the 'great Red Grape,' which he says is called 'by ignorance the Fox Grape'; also a 'white kind of Musketel' and 'a little black Grape, like the cluster-Grape of England.' Penn had a Frenchman with him, one Andrew Doz, 'who shews some knowledge in those things.' Doz, encouraged by the wild grapes, planted in 1783 a vineyard on the east bank of the Schuylkill, north of Fairmount, in the manor of Springettsbury, on what is now Lemon Hill, Fairmount Park, Philadelphia. This vineyard with 200 acres of land was patented to Doz in 1690, who paid the proprietor '100 vine cuttings yearly on demand.' This is the first vineyard of which we have a record in Pennsylvania. First called 'Vineyard Hills,' it became from 1770 to 1798 'The Hills,' the country mansion of Robert Morris, the financier of the American Revolution, and, later, 'Lemon Hill Mansion.' For more than two centuries the spot was noted for the beauty of its plantings.

Far-seeing William Penn had in mind in 1683 the possibility of domesticating our American grapes. At the time he argued with himself whether it were better 'to fall to Fining the Fruits of the Country, especially the Grape, by the care and skill of Art, or

[1] Myers, p. 227.

send for foreign Stems and Sets.' He believed in his heart that it would be more satisfactory to work with native fruits than to bring 'another Species of the same kind, that doth not naturally grow there.' He said he intended, 'if God give me Life, to try both, and hope the consequence will be as good Wine as any European Countries of the same Lattitude do yield.' [2]

Unfortunately, Penn seems to have tried planting only the European grape, the result of which, as in innumerable other places, was failure. Had he persuaded his French vigneron, Andrew Doz, to plant and tend any of the wild grapes he so well described, the domestication of native species of grapes might have been put forward a hundred years with great benefit to American grape growing.

Penn, it appears, was well provided with trained gardeners, which few other of the great landed proprietors had. In 1683 there were at least Andrew Doz and Ralph Smith, his first gardener. Ralph Smith died in 1685, but Doz lived long and had children and grandchildren to carry on his name and occupation. In 1685 a third gardener was sent over, 'A good gardner,' writes Penn to his steward, 'counted a rare Artist at it, lett him have at least three hands, for he will put things, I hope, in a very good method, thou will have the tryall of him.' The gardener, James, surname not given, turned out well, for under date of 'Octob. 3, 1686,' the steward could write:

The Gardiner is brisk at work. The Peach-Trees are much broken down with the weight of Fruit this Year. All or most of the Plants that came from England grow, (being about four Thousand). Cherries are sprung about four and five Foot. Pears, Codlings and Plumbs three or four Foot. Pears and Apple Grafts, in Country Stocks, and in Thorns, are sprung three and four Foot. Raspberries, Gooseberries, Currans, Quinces, Roses, Walnuts, and Figs grow well. Apricocks from the Stone fourteen or sixteen Inches sprung, since the month called April.[3]

James, in a letter dated 'the 14th of the month, call'd May, 1686,' first makes plain to the 'People in England' how rich the soil is and how quickly things grow in the salubrious climate. 'Trees and Bulbes are shot in five weeks time, some one Inch,

[2] Ibid. pp. 227-8.   [3] Ibid. p. 289.

some two, three, four, five, six, seven, yea some are eleven Inches. . . And seeds do come on apace; for those seeds that in England take fourteen days to rise, are up here in six or seven days.' The rest of the letter is taken up with what was all-important to American gardeners: 'Pray make agreement with the Bishop of London's Gardiner or any other that will furnish us with Trees, Shrubs, Flowers and Seeds, and we will furnish them from these places. . .' [4]

Ornamental gardening was not neglected in the Quaker colonies. Gabriel Thomas wrote an account of Pennsylvania and West New Jersey in 1698 for William Penn; in that about Pennsylvania, he devotes several pages to fruits and vegetables, as many more to farm crops and animals, and then discusses ornamentals. He says:

There are many Fair and Great Brick Houses on the outside of the Town which the Gentry have built for their Countrey Houses, besides the Great and Stately Palace of *John Tateham* Esq; which is pleasantly Situated on the North side of the *Town,* having a very fine and delightful *Garden* and *Orchard* adjoyning it, wherein is variety of *Fruits, Herbs,* and *Flowers;* as *Roses, Tulips, July-Flowers, Sun-Flowers,* (that open and shut as the *Sun* Rises and Sets, thence taking their Name) *Carnations,* and many more; besides abundance of Medicinal *Plants,* and *Flowers,* found wild in the *Fields.*[5]

Penn had well-thought-out plans for the gardens of Pennsylvania. In 1681, when he received his great grant of land, he immediately laid out 'the City of Brotherly Love.' Among other horticultural features of Philadelphia, there were to be five public squares within the limits of the town and in the center a great square of ten acres. He directed that every man's house 'be placed, if the Person pleases, in ye middle of its place as to the breath way of it, so that there may be grounds, on each side, for Gardens, or Orchards, or fields, yt may be a greene Country Towne, wch will never be burnt and will always be wholesome.'

A glowing account of the fruits grown in the region is given in a letter written by Mahlon Stacy in 1680, a visitor in New

4 Ibid. pp. 289-90.   5 Ibid. pp. 322-32.

Jersey the year before William Penn acquired Pennsylvania. Stacy wrote:

I have seen orchards laden with fruit to admiration, their very limbs torn to peices with the weight, and most delicious to the taste, and lovely to behold; I have seen an apple tree from a pippin kernel, yield a barrel of curious cyder; and peaches in such plenty, that some people took their carts a peach-gathering; I could not but smile at the conceit of it: They are a very delicate fruit, and hang almost like our onions that are tied on ropes. . . My brother Robert had as many cherries this year as would have loaded several carts. It is my judgment by what I have observed, that fruit trees in this country destroy themselves by the very weight of their fruit.[6]

Another account of early orcharding along the Delaware is given by Israel Acrelius, who visited the New World in 1685. Speaking of the Swedish settlements, he says:

Peach trees stand within an enclosure by themselves, grown even in the stoniest places without culture. Many have peach orchards chiefly for feeding their swine, which are allowed to run at large. For apple orchards, not less than two or three acres are taken; some have five or six. The cultivation consists in grafting and pruning in the spring and plowing the ground every five or six years, when either maize is planted or rye and oats sown in the orchard.[7]

New Jersey has always been famous for its cider, particularly that which came from around Newark. Governor Carteret seems to have been the first to praise Newark cider. In a letter written in 1682, he says: 'At Newark is made great quantities of cider, exceeding any that we have from New England, Rhode Island, or Long Island.'[8] The quantity made that year about Newark was 1000 barrels. A hundred years later, 1799, the French traveler, La Rochefoucault-Liancourt, made note that Newark cider was better than that from any other part of New Jersey, although any Jersey cider was better than that produced in any other part of America.[9]

Quakers and Dutch alike along the Delaware grew apples for cider rather than for other purposes. From the planting of the first orchards to the temperance crusade in the early part of the

6 Smith, Samuel, pp. 111-12. See also p. 748 infra.   8 Shaw, 1: 349.
7 Acrelius, pp. 30-40.   9 Ibid. p. 545.

nineteenth century, cider was on tap in every farm and village home, and at every social or political meeting. Brandy was distilled from peaches, apples, wild plums, and wild grapes, and every well-to-do family had a copper still for making these fruit brandies.

We have little precise information about early nurseries in these three colonies. According to Woodward, who does not give his authority, the first nursery in New Jersey was established about the middle of the eighteenth century or a little earlier. He says: 'In 1763, John Wetheriel had a nursery at New Brunswick, judging from an order for 400 apple trees given by Thomas Barton of Perth Amboy. The purchaser specified 100 grafted trees, chiefly Pippins and 300 common trees.' [10]

Agriculture in Pennsylvania, and for that matter in all America, is deeply indebted to the Germans who came from the Rhine to America from about 1690 to 1740. They had been driven from their homeland by religious persecution and by the destruction of their homes in the Rhenish Palatinate in 1688-93. Many of them stopped in Holland for a decade or a generation. Some of them settled in the Mohawk Valley in New York; others in the Shenandoah Valley in Virginia; others in the Carolinas; but they came in greatest numbers to eastern Pennsylvania, forming the religious sects of Mennonites, Dunkards, and Amish. Grouped in nationality as 'Pennsylvania Dutch,' their language is chiefly derived from German. From first to last they have been notable farmers.

The Pennsylvania Dutch were particularly famous in the colonies for their orchard products. They made and sold cider, applejack, apple-butter, dried peaches, and peach brandy. In local markets dried apples were sold as *schnitts*. The process of drying was the same as that described by Crèvecœur for Ulster County, New York. Dried peaches, among the English at least, was known as 'peach-leather.' This product was made by mashing pitted peaches into a thin layer and drying it in an oven. The finished product looked and had the feel of leather, and was edible only after being soaked; it kept indefinitely.

[10] Woodward, p. 21.

It was the Pennsylvania Dutch who started a commercial industry in dried apples. The product was sold in the city markets, in all the colonies, and to ships; large quantities were disposed of in the West Indies. The industry continued until recent years in Pennsylvania and westward in the states to which the Pennsylvania Dutch moved in great numbers. In the 1840's the dried-apple markets were captured by fruit growers in western New York, who constructed dry-houses with an annual capacity of several tons each. Early in the twentieth century, dried apples gave way to canned apples, and an ancient American industry went out of existence.

At the close of the colonial period, truck gardening was better developed in eastern Pennsylvania than in any other part of the Atlantic seaboard. The Pennsylvania Dutch were the best growers of the coarse vegetables that city markets wanted. Philadelphia took most of the produce from Pennsylvania, while that from New Jersey went to New York City. Cabbage was the chief product, and nearly every farmer within reach of a city market grew it. Turnips, onions, parsnips, and carrots followed in the order named.

Writing in 1775, the author of *American Husbandry* depicts New Jersey as a region well planted with orchards, 'surpassing anything in England.' In the orchards were apples, pears, peaches, and cherries. The peaches, we are told, 'are of a fine flavour, and of such amazing plenty that the whole stock of hogs on a farm eats as many as they will, and yet the quantity that rot under the tree is astonishing.' Shiploads of apples were exported to the West Indies, and 'cyder was made in vast quantities.' There were whole fields of watermelons which the country people 'ate at all times of the day, as in England they would drink ale or beer.' [11]

Though settled later than most of the other colonies, Pennsylvania grew most rapidly of all, and long before the Revolution became the wealthiest, the most thickly populated, and the foremost in agriculture. Philadelphia was the metropolis of the New World, the center of life in the colony, and the best market for farm and garden produce in the land. In 1750, as many as 7000 to 8000 wagons, with 4 horses each, coming from as far away as

[11] *American Husbandry*, p. 102.

a hundred miles, were required to supply the city with farm produce.

From Jamestown to the Civil War, America subsisted almost wholly on its agriculture. Washington and Jefferson are generally looked upon as fathers of agriculture in Virginia; and the group of statesmen, jurists, and generals who were gentlemen farmers in New York have had credit given them for their aid to agriculture; but the services of Benjamin Franklin, a Pennsylvanian, have not been so widely recognized.

In the year George Washington was born, 1732, Franklin, under the name Richard Saunders, published in Philadelphia his first almanac. Its publication was continued for 25 years and came to be known by all as *Poor Richard's Almanack,* later as *Poor Richard Improved.* Although the early issues did not contain much information about agriculture, many of Franklin's maxims were drawn from farm life, and from the first the almanac had a flavor of the farm. In *Poor Richard Improved,* short articles began to appear on every phase of agriculture, including the culture of vegetables and fruits. The almanac for 1773 contained this letter:

Courteous Reader:

In my last year's Almanack I inserted several Choice Hints relating to Agriculture etc., which I have the satisfaction to find were acceptable to many of my good Customers. I have this year inserted some more Observations in Husbandry, etc., together with some excellent receipts, hoping thou wilt receive Benefit by them. As it gives me great pleasure to be in any way serviceable in communicating what may be of use to the Public, I shall be very much obliged to any of my kind Readers, that may, from Time to Time, send me such of their own Observations as will be advantageous if published.

I am, Thy Friend to serve,

R. Saunders.

Thus, at a time when there were almost no agricultural publications, Franklin's almanacs, 'vending annually nearly ten thousand,' were important means of agricultural education. But the almanacs were possibly the least of Franklin's services to agriculture in the New World. In letters and writings, he sought to impress upon all his belief that agriculture was the chief source of a nation's wealth. In his travels at home or abroad, he met and discussed agriculture with farmers and scientists, and wherever he went his eyes were open to observe new developments in the field. He took great interest in introducing new seeds and plants, and corresponded with and visited European botanists and horticulturists, bringing to their attention men in America who would exchange seeds and plants with them. He sold in his bookstore European books on agriculture and gardening. Although many of Franklin's biographers give him credit for having bought and managed a farm, beginning in 1747, newly found evidence seems to show that this is untrue; however, his illegitimate son, Governor William Franklin, and his grandson, William Temple Franklin, owned land near Burlington, New Jersey, where they practiced farming.[12]

Franklin was one of the first Americans to suggest formal education for farm youths. In his *Proposals Relating to the Education of Youth in Pennsylvania,* he wrote:

While they are reading Natural History, might not a little Gardening, Planting, Grafting, Inoculating, etc. be taught; and now and then Excursions made to the neighboring plantations of the best Farmers, their methods observed and reason'd upon for the Information of Youth? The Improvement of Agriculture being useful to all, and Skill in it no Disparagement to any.

In 1769 Franklin organized the American Philosophical Society, a union of two other societies. The Society had its headquarters in Philadelphia but it was intercolonial, and had for its chief object systematic correspondence between its members. Among the subjects to be discussed as suggested by Franklin were: 'all new discovered plants, herbs, trees, roots their virtues, uses, etc.; methods of propagating them, and making such as are useful, but particular to some plantations, more general; improvements of vegetable juices, or ciders, wines, etc.' From its beginning, this organization was the means of helping the sciences and the arts dependent on them, of which botany and agriculture, especially gardening, were much favored.

Gardeners are indebted to Franklin for three contributions.

[12] For a full account of these farms see New Jersey Experiment Station Bulletin 451, pp. 11, 12, 13, and 16, and a supplement later sent to librarians, by Carl R. Woodward, author of the bulletin named above.

As early as 1759 he had shipments of Green Newtown apples sent to him in London. He gave samples to his friends, sent some to Court, and thus made popular an apple that is pre-eminently an American fruit, one of the first varieties to have been named in the New World. The Green Newtown became so popular that there was a demand for grafts, and these Franklin's friend John Bartram sent in, one shipment after another. From 1759 to this day, the Green Newtown has been the favorite American apple, if quality and price be the gauges in English markets.

Franklin is also generally credited with having introduced rhubarb in America. The plant was new in England in 1640, according to Parkinson, and was not common in America until the twentieth century. In both England and America, it was at first grown for its medicinal roots rather than for its culinary stalks. Franklin recommended it to American gardeners as an esculent, but did not live to see it widely or commonly grown. Its seeds were sent by him to John Bartram in 1790.

On the authority of Watson,[13] in his admirable *Annals of Philadelphia,* we must give Franklin credit for introducing the osier willow, *Salix viminalis,* long used in the Old World for making baskets. Watson says Franklin found an imported, discarded willow basket sprouting in Dock Creek, Philadelphia, and planted the shoots in the garden of one Norris, where they grew. Soon the tree became popular as an ornamental, and later furnished material for basket-making, an industry popular and profitable in several parts of America as late as 1900.

Colonel George Morgan, a contemporary and friend of Benjamin Franklin, was a prominent experimenter and exponent of agriculture in Pennsylvania and New Jersey in the eighteenth century. Morgan was born in Philadelphia in 1742, and spent his early life as a merchant, an agent for Indian affairs, and as a Colonel in Washington's Army. In 1779 he bought a 300-acre farm adjoining Princeton College, and resided in New Jersey, where for 17 years he wrote and talked on farm subjects. He was an early authority on bees. In 1796 Colonel Morgan moved from Princeton to Morganza, Washington County, in western Pennsyl-

[13] Watson, John F., i: 408; ii: 489.

vania, where, in the next few years, he made his chief contributions to gardening. At Morganza, Morgan established a nursery, and here on the western frontier of Pennsylvania planted a garden and a vineyard. The vineyard is notable as the first to be planted west of the Allegheny Mountains. Grape cuttings were purchased from Peter Legaux, Spring Mill Vineyard, Philadelphia, at a cost of $211.50. There were in all 3480 cuttings, the varieties being Bordeaux, Cape of Good Hope, Champagne, and Burgundy.

Colonel Morgan was one of the American leaders in agriculture, and the brief notice of his work in growing grapes is but a small measure of his services. 'Prospect,' Morgan's home in Princeton, was eventually sold to Princeton University and became a part of the campus. The house of the president of the university was in later years built on the site of Morgan's house, and it, too, is known as 'Prospect.'

George Fox, founder of the Quakers, seems to have brought the idea of a botanic garden to this country. Fox traveled in the colonies in 1671-2. When he died in 1690, he bequeathed to the Quaker Meeting in Philadelphia 16 acres, of which 10 were for 'a close to put Friend's horses in when they came afar to the Meeting, that they may not be Lost in the Woods,' while the other 6 were for a site for a meeting-house and a schoolhouse, and 'for a Playground for the Children of the town to Play on, and for a Garden to plant with Physical Plants, for Lads and Lasses to know Simples, and to learn to make Oils and Ointments.'

In 1694 a colony of Rosicrucians, 'knights of the Rose Cross,' came to America, and early in the eighteenth century planted a garden of medicinal herbs near Philadelphia on the lower Wissahickon River, an affluent of the Schuylkill. The Rosicrucians are a society of philosophers versed in the secrets of nature, and believing that every plant is a part of the 'Master Mind' that created it. These 'Rose-cross' knights claimed to be able to prolong life indefinitely through their medicinal herbs; and, no doubt, the Rosicrucian Garden on the Wissahickon contributed more or less to the knowledge of plants.

The first botanic garden worthy of the name was established and maintained for some years by Christopher Witt in Germantown, Pennsylvania, in 1708. Witt (1675-1765) was an Englishman who came to America in 1704 and joined the Rosicrucians in their colony on the Wissahickon. He was a physician, botanist, and a man of note in Philadelphia. Besides the legitimate professions of medicine and botany, he was a conjurer, fortuneteller, astronomer, and a professor of the black art of hexing. However, it is his botanic garden with which we are concerned, one that antedated John Bartram's famous garden, generally thought to be the first, by 20 years.

In 1718, Witt owned 125 acres of land, but how much was covered by the botanic garden does not appear. At first the plants grown were those used in medicine, but later he collected and grew plants to send to England, especially to Peter Collinson, the English Quakers botanist, by whom, as appears in his letters, Witt was held in high esteem. He was also a friend of John Bartram (1699-1777), with whom he had in later years much intercourse. Bartram wrote a long letter to Peter Collinson, giving an account of Witt as a man and botanist, under date of 11 June 1743.[14] Witt, who died at 90, was the last of the early Rosicrucians.

The next earliest botanic garden in this region of which we have record is described by F. D. Pastorius, a distinguished German horticulturist of the time. Writing to his wife, Pastorius tells her of the garden of Isaac Norris, Fairhill, near Germantown, which, according to him, was as early as 1718 one of the fine gardens in the northern colonies. 'The garden,' the letter says, 'is filled with abundance of rarities, physical and metaphysical,—the other a pretty little garden much like mine own, producing cordial, stomachic, and culinary herbs.'[15]

One of the most conspicuous events in colonial gardening was the establishment in 1728 of the Bartram Botanic Garden at Kingessing, on the banks of the Schuylkill. John Bartram had an early penchant for medicine and acquired sufficient knowledge of it to be rated as a physician; his remedies were mostly herbal, though he seems to have had some skill as a surgeon. He spent

[14] Harshberger, pp. 44-5.   [15] Watson, John F., I: 493.

much of his time in travels in the colonies, collecting for European botanists and his own garden. He became so well known through his correspondence and publications that Linnaeus called him the greatest natural botanist in the world.

Bartram was a botanist, a botanical explorer, and a grower of native and foreign plants at a time when few other Americans cared for them. In his travels in America he met and formed friendships with most of the notable men of the several colonies, and through them, especially through a warm friendship with Benjamin Franklin, he came into correspondence with a great number of men of science in Europe, who stimulated his interest in plants. Throughout his mature years, which covered half of the eighteenth century, he was the largest and most reliable dealer in the exchange of plants between Europe and America. To him European gardeners are indebted for the receipt of many American trees, shrubs, and flowers, and not a few European plants in every field of cultivation were first grown on this side of the Atlantic in the Bartram Garden.

Bartram's botanic explorations began in his own neighborhood, but they expanded to the extent that when he was nearly 70, he explored 400 miles of the St. Johns River, Florida. From his conversations with other botanists came the inspiration to explore the Rockies and the Oregon country, which led to the Lewis and Clark expedition.

Soon after the establishment of his famous garden, Bartram began a correspondence with the witty and wholly delightful Peter Collinson. For more than 30 years the two Quakers exchanged letters, to the great enrichment of the botanic and horticultural literature of the eighteenth century, and to the very great betterment of horticulture and botany on both sides of the Atlantic.

Collinson was never in America, but he had as great an influence on American gardening as any man living in the country. For 30 odd years he devoted time and wealth to importing to England plants from the colonies and sending in return those of Europe. There are few books on gardening and botany more delightful than Darlington's *Memorials of Bartram and Marshall,* which consists largely of correspondence between Bartram and

Collinson and John Ellis, the latter nearly as much interested in American gardening as the former. Collinson is mentioned by Goode as 'instrumental in introducing grape culture in Virginia,' but where or when does not appear.[16]

Again and again in the hundreds of letters that Collinson wrote to Bartram in the years between 1734 and 1768 he mentions seeds of vegetables, fruits, and flowers he is sending (usually with much longer lists of seeds he wants in return), and often encloses parcels for Bartram's friends: he sent a package of seeds in 1737 to Thomas Penn, then proprietor of the province, asking his 'Dear Friend John' to deliver them, and adding, 'Dress thiself neatly in thy best habits, and wait on him for them.'

As early as 1735, Peter Collinson was sending John Bartram grafts of pears, plums, nectarines, and apricots. In a letter dated 16 August 1735, he gives advice about these grafts and adds: 'I am glad to hear that the Medlar grows.' Also: 'I shall be glad and be careful to send the seeds thee mentions, and what other I can collect.' [17] A year later, Collinson sent an assortment of the seeds of these fruits with directions for planting.

A letter of 20 December 1737 from Collinson to Bartram makes plain that lilacs were well-established in America at that time:

I wonder that thou should be sorry to see such a bundle of white and blue lilacs. That wonder might have soon ceased, by throwing them away if you had them already. But as your neighbours of Virginia, in particular Colonel Custis of Williamsburgh, who has undoubtedly the best collection in the country, desired some, I thought possibly you might want them, for I never was over to see. . . I like thy project of planting the white and blue together.[18]

Greenhouses are mentioned in an undated letter (1737?) from Peter Collinson to John Bartram:

I am informed my friend Custis [Colonel Custis of Williamsburg] is a curious man: pray what didst thee see new in his garden? But I am told Colonel Byrd has the best garden in Virginia, and a pretty green-house, well furnished with orange trees. I knew him well when in England; and he was reckoned a very polite ingenious man.[19]

16 Goode, p. 84.
17 Darlington, p. 71.
18 Ibid. p. 108.
19 Ibid. p. 113.

Greenhouses must soon have become common, for in 1760 Bartram writes to Collinson:

I am going to build a greenhouse. Stone is got; and hope as soon as harvest is over to begin to build it,—to put some pretty flowering winter shrubs, and plants for winter's diversion; not to be crowded with orange trees, or those natural to the Torrid Zone, but such as will do, being protected from frost.[20]

Many interesting things come up in the letters between these enthusiastic gardeners. In one of 1738 we find: 'There is a small packet for Doctor Witt. Pray somehow or other convey it to him. Some fine Melon seed for Thomas Penn; some Burgundy Trefoil for J. Logan.' [21] This is the earliest reference to Burgundy trefoil (alfalfa) in this country, although Crèvecœur boasted that he had introduced alfalfa in Orange County, New York, about 1780, and energetic Robert Livingston had 15 acres of alfalfa growing in Jefferson County, New York, in 1790; but if Logan received the seed from Bartram, he was nearly half a century ahead of either.

Lilies must have been commonly cultivated in this period of gardening history. There are some half-dozen native species now under cultivation, and in letters between European and American collectors early in the century there are numerous comments on lilies sent and received. Collinson first grew the beautiful American Turk's-cap lily in Europe. Probably Bartram sent the bulbs to him.

A typical letter is one from Peter Collinson to John Bartram under date of 20 October 1740:

Inclosed is the Mate's receipt for a box of bulbs, directed for thee. Make much of them, for they are such a collection as is rarely to be met with, all at once: for, all the sorts of bulbous roots being taken up this year, there is some of every sort. There is above twenty sorts of *Crocus*—as many of *Narcissus*—all our sorts of *Martagons* and *Lilies*—with *Gladiolus, Ornithogalums, Moleys,* and *Irises,* with many others I don't now remember which time will show thee.[22]

In 1753 Collinson sent to Bartram seeds of the laurel and of the horse chestnut; in 1746, cones of the cedar of Lebanon; in 1760, seeds of geranium; in 1761, carnation seed from the plants

[20] Ibid. p. 224.
[21] Ibid. p. 125.

[22] Ibid. p. 137.

of which Bartram says, 'the brightest colors that ever eyes beheld.' On the other hand, Bartram sent to Collinson the first plants of our splendid cucumber tree, *Magnolia acuminata; M. Fraseri*, the ear-leaved magnolia; the pawpaw, *Asimina triloba*; and a score or more other American plants of lesser note.

Can it possibly be Bartram who grew the first European horse-chestnut tree in America? There does not seem to be an earlier record of it on this side of the Atlantic than 1746, when it came from Europe to John Bartram.

As has been said, Franklin and Bartram founded the American apple export trade to England; in this, Collinson had a hand. In February 1759, Collinson wrote to Bartram: 'Our Friend Benjamin had a fine parcel of apples come over this year, which I shared.' Collinson was so pleased with the apples that he sent Bartram an order for grafts of the variety, the Green Newtown. In 1773 Michael Collinson, son of Peter, wrote to John Bartram, 'Your American apples have been an admiral substitute this season, many of our merchants having imported great quantities of them.'

Bartram's exchanges were not always with correspondents across the sea. In a letter of 21 May 1761, we have an intimation of exchanges between John Bartram and Mrs. Martha Logan, of Charles Town, South Carolina, author of *The Gardener's Kalendar*, the first American book on gardening. Bartram, writing to Collinson about the Carolina Holly, says:

I hope to have plants of it by the favour of an elderly widow lady [Mrs. Logan], who spares no pains nor cost to oblige me. Her garden is her delight. I was with her about five minutes, in much company, yet we contracted such a mutual correspondence, that one silk bag hath passed and repassed full of seeds three times since last fall. I desired her last March to send me some seeds of the Horse Sugar or Yellow Leaf (*Symplocos tinctoria*). She directly sent me a box with three fine growing plants, mixed with several other sorts that she thought would please, and paid freight, with promises to send any vegetable in her power to procure.[23]

The next year, 10 May 1762, Bartram wrote to Collinson again about his Charles Town friends. He says:

[23] Ibid. p. 230.

I have received a lovely parcel this spring, from Mrs. Logan, my fascinated widow. . . I have also fascinated two men's wives, although one I never saw; that is Mrs. Lamboll, who has sent me two noble cargoes. The other hath sent me, I think, a great curiosity. She calls it Golden Lily.[24]

Benjamin Franklin, who both visited and corresponded with Bartram, sent him in 1769 seeds of 'Naked Oats,' 'Swiss Barley, six rows to an ear'; in 1770, 'some of the true rhubarb seed'; 'some green dry Pease, highly esteemed here as the best for making pease soup'; several kinds of turnips, and 'some Chinese Garavances, with Father Navaretta's account of the universal use of a cheese made of them, in China.' 'Garavance' is a Spanish name for the chick pea, but it is doubtful if the Chinese had the chick pea, *Cicer arietinum,* from Spain; however, it is well known that they long have made a sort of cheese out of the soybean, *Glycine Max.* Can it be that Benjamin Franklin introduced the soybean, now of so great value, in America?

One of the plants Bartram discovered on an exploring expedition in 1765 has an interesting history. Franklinia (*Gardenia alatamaha*) is a beautiful, late-flowering, large shrub with pure white, saucer-shaped flowers and large yellow stamens, the flowers appearing in September. Bartram found it in the region of the Altamaha River, in Georgia. In 1774 Bartram's son sent the plant to England; and from that shipment and another in 1778, have come all the plants now known. No one has seen the species in the wild since 1790. It is familiar both in Europe, and in America, where it is found as an admired ornamental as far north as Boston.

John Bartram was the author of one notable botanic work, and joint author with William Stork of another, both of which contributed much to early knowledge of the plant life in widely different parts of North America.[25] The book that Bartram wrote alone was an account of a journey made with Conrad Weiser to study the flora, fauna, geology, climate, and people of central Pennsylvania and New York. In it a good deal is written about the possibilities for agriculture in the country visited.

[24] Ibid. p. 235.
[25] *Observations . . . made in his travels from Pensilvania to Onondago, etc.;* Bartram and Stork, *Description of East Florida, with a Journal by John Bartram,* London, 1769.

As King's botanist, and because of his early botanic garden as well as his correspondence with Collinson and other European naturalists, John Bartram has come down to us a little overrated in comparison with his gifted son, William (1729-1823). There was another son, John, but the mantle of the father, as regards botanic and gardening lore at least, fell upon William, to whom the famous Bartram Garden on the Kingessing River was bequeathed by its founder in 1777.

William Bartram, all students of nature will agree, was one of the best observers in botany and ornithology that America has produced. He loved gardens and seldom failed to call attention to those he visited in his travels, and to the value of the plants he described for cultivation.

He was for some years professor of botany in the Philadelphia College, during which time a number of men who became famous had instruction from him. Meanwhile, at the request and with the financial aid of Dr. Fothergill, a London student of plants, William Bartram traveled through the Carolinas, Florida, and Georgia, collecting and making observations on all that he saw pertaining to plants, animals, birds, and people. Out of this expedition came a book, *Travels through North and South Carolina, Georgia, East and West Florida, etc.*, published in Philadelphia in 1791, which gave valuable information on wild life, Indian agriculture, and the farms and gardens of the early settlers in the southeastern colonies. The book is charmingly written and deserves in American literature a place comparable to that of White's *Natural History of Selborne* in English literature.

In May 1776, William Bartram discovered the mountain magnolia, *Magnolia Fraseri*, on the Keowes River, high up in the Allegheny Mountains in South Carolina, the name *Fraseri* commemorating the services of John Fraser, the Scotch gardener and botanist who introduced the plant in England.

Twelve years after the death of William Bartram, the Bartram Garden passed in 1845 into the hands of Colonel Robert Carr, who married the daughter of the second John Bartram; it was noted for a time for its collection of cacti grown under glass. Later the Garden became the property of a Mr. Eastwide, and then of one owner after another until in 1891 Philadelphia inherited it as a part of a great public park.

Moses Bartram, a cousin of William, was also a naturalist with a fondness for botany. Like his more notable relatives, he was a Quaker living near Philadelphia. He is best known as the author of *Observations on the Native Silk Worms of North America,* published in 1779.

Humphry Marshall (1722-1801), a relative of John Bartram, was another principal botanist of the eighteenth century. He was a farmer in West Bradford, Chester County, Pennsylvania, who, in middle life, his interest in botany being awakened by John Bartram, became a plant collector for European patrons. In 1773 Marshall moved to Bradford Meeting-house and planted a botanic garden at what is now the village of Marshallton. A few years later he began to write an account of the forest trees of America, and in 1785 published a botany. The book is small, 179 pages, entitled *Arbustum Americanum, The American Grove, or an alphabetical catalogue of forest trees and shrubs native of the American United States.* It is a landmark in American botany, containing several of the earliest descriptions of trees and shrubs now used in ornamental plantings. Perhaps the most notable of these is the sweet buckeye, *Aesculus octandra,* handsomest of the several North American horse chestnuts, which he found in the Allegheny Mountains in 1785. The American plum, *Prunus americana,* and the Chickasaw plum, *P. angustifolia,* grown in American orchards and as ornamentals, were first described in Marshall's *Arbustum Americanum.* So, also, was the mountain ash, *Sorbus americana.* Who first described the several species of Vaccinium—the huckleberries, blueberries, and cranberries—does not appear, but it was Marshall who described the only American tree of this species, the farkleberry, *Vaccinium arboreum.* He first described the pecan, *Hicoria Pecan,* though none but early explorers in the Gulf states had as yet seen tree or fruit. The first mention of the bitternut, *H. minima,* was also made by Marshall in his great book, although the common hickory, *H. ovata,* had been grown in England as early as 1629, as well as the white hickory, *H. alba.* Among several oaks valuable as ornamentals is the post oak, *Quercus minor,* of which Marshall published first descriptions.

Marshall, a follower of Bartram, in turn inspired his neighbor John Jackson to plant a botanic garden. In 1777 Jackson began a garden of native and foreign plants about his home at London-grove, which was kept up long after his death by his son William. A century later many of the trees were still growing in good condition.

Perhaps the first collection of evergreens in the United States was begun late in the eighteenth century at East Marlborough, Pennsylvania, by Joshua and Samuel Pierce, who planted them about their residences. As they did not neglect deciduous trees, early in the next century these men had one of the notable arboretums in the country.

James Logan (1664-1751) was a contemporary and friend of Bartram, who may have begun botanic work of merit even earlier. He was one of the fathers of Pennsylvania, who came to America as secretary to William Penn in 1699. He called his estate 'Stenton,' a fine place near Germantown, and here, in 1730, he set out a grand avenue of hemlocks, which a century later was still in good condition. But Logan's chief claim to fame is an account of experiments and observations on Indian corn, in which he supports the Linnæan theory of sexes in plants. He published a paper on Indian corn in 1735, which must have been one of the early botanic publications on maize in America. His house, built in 1771, and a part of the old garden have been preserved.

Robert Morris, at the time the wealthiest man in North America, owned many tracts of land and many houses, several kept for the use of his own family. Two of his estates near Philadelphia had admirable gardens, about one of which, 'The Hills,' on the site of Andrew Doz's vineyard, Morris wrote: 'a spot as beautiful as most places in the world.' Mrs. Morris, too, loved the place and delighted to spend her life there 'in the enjoyment of all that's beautiful to the eye and grateful to the taste.'[26]

'The Hills,' now called Lemon Hill,[27] was a farm on the eastern bank of the Schuylkill River, on which there was a well-administered mansion built on a knoll. About the mansion was a lawn and garden of fruits, flowers, and vegetables. At every turn in the literature of Philadelphia during the Revolution one comes upon accounts of this dwelling place of Robert Morris. In one we find

[26] Oberholtzer, p. 292.   [27] See p. 132.

that 'the grounds were laid out with all manner of trees, shrubbery, and flowering vegetation.' In another that 'There were hothouses for oranges, pineapples and other tropical plants.' From
a third we learn that the gardens were 'under the care of the best
gardeners the country could afford,' one of whom was David
Landreth, founder of the Landreth seed establishment in Philadelphia.

Like New York and unlike New England, there were in eastern Pennsylvania and New Jersey, in the colonial period, many
large estates, some under cultivation and some awaiting division
and sale. But there were also thousands of small farms, on which
buildings were poor and gardens were planted with only the
coarser vegetables. Travelers did not find the farms and gardens as attractive in these middle colonies as in those to the
north. To this statement there are exceptions. The Pennsylvania
Dutch were better farmers but not such good gardeners. There
were few country seats in New England, a somewhat larger number in New York, while in Philadelphia, Burlington, New
Castle, and Wilmington, nearly all well-to-do people had fine
country places with orchards, gardens, and grounds well planted
and carefully cultivated. The best of such places in the North
were about Philadelphia. That city was crowded into a few streets
running parallel to the Delaware—so hot and unsanitary in the
summer that yellow fever was not infrequently epidemic. The
colonial governor, city officials, and merchants set the example of
maintaining estates in the country often 10, 15, or 20 miles away
in West Jersey. On these places gardening in early years came to
full flower.

5

COLONIES ON CHESAPEAKE BAY

G ARDENING by English people, as a continuous occupation, began in the United States at Jamestown. Tilling the soil, however, got off to a poor start at this first permanent settlement of Englishmen in the New World; for, though the planting of crops was the most necessary work to do when the 120 men landed on the shores of the James, it was the occupation about which these men knew least and had the least inclination to be taught. It was several years before there were colonists who wanted to plant gardens in Virginia. Gardening in the colonies to the north was for a century further advanced, and markedly so, even in near-by Maryland.

The Englishmen in the mother country were eager to hear about the marvels of America and to see the strange animals and plants returning ships brought back. There were, as yet, few if any botanic gardens, but men of wealth vied with each other in growing plants from the New World. King James I was an enthusiastic collector. Charles I sent John Tradescant, the younger son of the English botanist, to Virginia in 1637 'to gather all rarities of flowers, plants, and shells.' Johnson's edition of *Gerard's Herbal*, 1636, contains the names of a dozen or more North American plants growing in Tradescant's garden in London. It was John Tradescant, the second, who introduced the tulip tree, *Liriodendron tulipifera,* long a favorite ornamental tree in European and American landscapes. He also introduced the swamp maple, *Acer rubrum,* into England as early as 1656, and, at about the same time, the hackberry, *Celtis occidentalis.* In the earlier part of the century, Tradescant introduced *Platanus occidentalis,* known throughout eastern America as sycamore. The black wal-

95

nut, *Juglans nigra,* certainly, and probably the butternut, *J. cinerea,* were introductions by Tradescant to Europe, though both had been mentioned by American naturalists long before 1650, about the time Tradescant first saw them. According to Sargent, it was Tradescant who sent the bald cypress, *Taxodium distichum,* one of the chief glories of southern maritime forests, to English gardens.[1]

The first Englishman to write an account of the natural history of Virginia, with emphasis on edible plants, was Thomas Hariot. His book was entitled *A Briefe and True Report of the New Found Land of Virginia.* Hariot was a friend of Sir Walter Raleigh's and was sent by him to America to take a hand in founding a colony. Fortunately Hariot returned to England before Raleigh's romantic enterprise came to its fearful end. His book fired the imagination of those who read it and furthered plans for a new settlement, which came to fruition in Jamestown.

Jamestown had been founded 27 years when settlement was made at St. Mary's in Maryland, in 1634. Maryland was at first known as 'Lord Baltimore's Plantation in Maryland,' and then as the 'Plantations,' the name reflecting the fact that the settlers were planters. In truth, the people of Maryland, high and low, lived so close to the land during the colonial period that towns, aside from Annapolis and Baltimore, did not grow. At first, tobacco was less widely grown there than in Virginia, and more land and time were devoted to farming and gardening; a little later, however, tobacco was nearly as dominant in Maryland as in Virginia.

Because nature was so bountiful in the virgin soil of the new country, and yielded such a largess of food both from the forest and the land that was cleared for tillage, these new settlers in the South, for a century to come, practiced for the most part only the crude agriculture of the savages. Fish, game, and wild fruits furnished an abundance of food these people from Europe had never known before.

The marriage of John Rolfe to Pocahontas had a great influence on agriculture and gardening in Virginia. Rolfe and his Indian wife planted a patch of tobacco in 1612. The next year

[1] Sargent, *Silva of North America,* x: 152.

others planted the Indian crop, and soon tobacco was more lucrative for the settlers than the gold mines they had originally been
seeking. In a few years Virginia relied solely on tobacco, the Indian methods of growing having been greatly improved. Once
agriculture was well started, nearly all of the cultivated land in
Maryland as in Virginia, almost down to the Revolution, was
planted to tobacco, to the great neglect of other crops. Jasper Danckaerts, one of the leaders of the Labadist colony in Maryland,
complained of this:

Tobacco is the only production in which the planters employ themselves, as if there were nothing else in the world to plant but that,
and while the land is capable of yielding all the productions that can
be raised anywhere, so far as the climate allows. . . A few vegetables
are planted, but they are of the coarsest kinds and are cultivated in the
coarsest manner, without knowledge or care, and they are therefore,
not properly raised, and do not amount to much as regards to the production, and still less as to their use. Some have begun to plant orchards, which all bear very well, but are not properly cultivated. The
fruit is for the greater part pressed, and makes good cider, of which the
largest portion becomes soured and spoiled, either from not putting it
into good casks, or from not taking proper care of the liquor afterwards.[2]

One turns at once to the works of Captain John Smith to learn
what his fellow Englishmen planted at Jamestown. But Smith's
optimism makes his accounts not quite trustworthy. In one of his
rhapsodies he says, 'Heaven and earth never agreed better to
frame a place for human habitation.' He devotes pages and pages
to the edible wild fruits and herbs in the new land, and by 1629
he could report to the Virginia Company in London: 'Peaches in
abundance; also Apples, Pears, Apricocks, Vines, Figges, and other
Fruits.' Gardens 'were prospering exceedingly,' but the people
'left them to be spoiled by the Cattell that they might attend
their tobacco.'

Despite the abundance that Smith depicts, gardens did not
flourish. Little planting was done at Jamestown in the first years,
and the Englishmen depended on provisions from home and corn
from the Indians. Not only did few of the men sent over know
how to plant and till; but the community plan, on which the

2 Danckaerts, Jasper, and Sluyter, Peter, I: 134, 135.

colony was started, put a premium on laziness. So faint was their purpose that the settlers had come without wives or children, which lessened their responsibilities—all would eat, but few would work. The result was the terrible 'Starving Time' of 1609-10, when, out of 500 inhabitants, all but 60 died. And Smith was in England writing about the abundance of fruits and vegetables.

In 1619 two events had an immediate effect upon gardening in Virginia. A shipload of young women arrived from England and were quickly chosen by men to found homes and families, thereby making a more civilized community, and one much more conducive to the culture of gardens. The other event was the arrival of a Dutch ship that sold twenty Negroes into slavery. Without the aid of Negroes, a plentiful supply of which began coming in, Virginia and the colonies to the south could hardly have planted and maintained the fine estates, built on profits from tobacco, indigo, rice, and later cotton, which brought wealth to the South.

Of the several monuments in print to mark the progress of the colonies in the New World, none is more admirable than *Nova Brittania: Offering Most Excellent Fruits by Planting in Virginia; Exciting All Such as Be Well Affected to Further the Same.*[3] This little pamphlet was printed in London in 1609 and is one of the first accounts of the settlement at Jamestown. It was written before the Starving Time and before the early dreams of an El Dorado had begun to fade. From this pamphlet it would seem that God had denied Virginia nothing in the way of plant and animal life. After enumerating all the plants of England then growing in Virginia, the author writes, with sublime optimism:

We intend to plant there, God willing, great plenty of sugar cane, for which the soil and climate is very apt and fit; also linseed and rape seed to make oils, which, because the soil is strong and cheap, may there be sowed and the oil made to great benefit. We must plant oranges, lemons, almonds, anise, rice, cumin, cotton, caraway, ginger, madder, olives, oris, sumach, and many such like, which I cannot now name, all very good merchandise, and will there grow and increase as well as in Italy or any other parts of the straits, whence we fetch them now. And in searching the land there is undoubted hope of finding

[3] Republished in Force's Tracts: I.

cochineal, the plant of rich indigo, grain, berries, beaver hides, pearls, and rich treasure, and the South Sea leading to China, with many other benefits which our daylight will discover.

Two years later there appeared an account of gardening in Maryland. In 1635, the year after the first settlement at St. Mary's, *A Relation of Maryland* [4] was published, or at least offered for sale, in London by William Pearsley, brother-in-law of Lord Baltimore, the first proprietor. It is comparable for the new province of Maryland to John Smith's *Generall Historie of Virginia* and William Wood's *New Englands Prospect*. The picture of Maryland was just as rosy as were those of Smith and Wood of the lands of their choice, but unless the climate has greatly changed, it is a little exaggerated:

They have made tryall of English Pease, and they grow very well, also Musk-mellons, Water-mellons, Cow-cumbers, with all sorts of garden Roots and Herbes, as Carrots, Parsenips, Turnips, Cabbages, Radish with many more. . . They have Peares, Apples, and severall sorts of Plummes, Peaches in abundance, and as good as those of Italy; so are the Mellons and Pumpions: Apricocks, Figgs and Pomegranates, prosper exceedingly; they have lately Orange and Limon trees which thrive very wel: and in fine, there is scarce any fruit that growes in England, France, Spaine or Italy, but has been tryed there, and prospers well.

Twenty-one years later, 1656, John Hammond published in London his *Leah and Rachel, or, The Two Fruitfull Sisters Virginia and Maryland,* in which Virginia is Leah 'the elder sister,' and Rachel is Maryland. He, too, paints in glowing colors the charm of life in the New World, with definite preference for Maryland, 'the younger sister,' just as Jacob favored Rachel, the younger wife, of whom he was enamored. No more charming account of land for sale has ever appeared in America; the few sentences quoted are too brief for a fair sample: [5]

The Country is full of gallant Orchards, and the fruit nowhere generally more luscious and delightfull than here, witnesse the Peach and Quince, the latter may be eaten raw savourily, the former differs and as much exceeds ours as the best relished apple we have doth the crabb,

---

4 Republished in *Orig. Nar. of Early Am. Hist.*, pp. 63-112.
5 Republished in *Nar. of Early Md.*, p. 291.

and of both most excellent and comfortable drinks are made. Grapes in infinite variety grow wilde, so do Walnuts, Smalnuts, Chesnuts, and abundance of excellent fruits, Plums and Berries, not growing or known in England; graine we have, both English and Indian for bread and Bear, and Pease besides English of ten several sorts, all exceeding ours in England; the gallant root of Potatoes are common, and so are all sorts of rootes, herbes and Garden stuffe.

By 1639, whether they liked or not, the settlers in James-town had to plant gardens. The Virginia Company, realizing the importance of a home-grown supply of food, had a law passed that every man who acquired a hundred acres of land should 'establish a garden and orchard, carefully protected by a fence, ditch, or hedge.' This, seemingly, was not enough, for three years later the home company in London instructed Governor Berkeley to compel settlers to 'apply themselves to the Impaling of Or-chards and Gardens; and that every Planter be compelled, for every 500 acres granted unto him, to Inclose and fence a quarter acre of Ground near his Dwelling House for Orchards and Garden.' [6]

In 1649 the imaginative, sanguine but anonymous author of *A Perfect Description of Virginia*, a pamphlet that seems to have attracted much attention at the time, gives an account of the vegetables grown in the colony. He compared the plantations of Virginia, especially the orchards and gardens, with those of New England, much to the advantage of his home colony. He says: 'There are fifteen kinds of fruits that for delicacy rival the fruits of Italy; in the gardens grow potatoes, turnips, carrots, parsnips, onions, artichokes, asparagus, and better peas than those of Eng-land, with all manner of herbs and physick flowers.' [7] The potato, of course, was the sweet potato, as that was what was meant by 'potato' in the early literature of the South.

The first book written in the colony to speak authoritatively about Virginia was Robert Beverley's *History and Present State of Virginia,* published in London in 1705. He did not withhold censure where it was merited and yet set down admirably what-ever he thought was of good report. We may accept his praises

[6] *Acts of Assembly,* 1639, Robinson Transcripts, 216.
[7] Reprinted in Force's Tracts: II.

of Virginia as fair statements; and when he says he is justified in loving a country where 'plantations, orchards, and gardens constantly afford fragrant and delightful walks,' we may be sure that they were there as early as the time at which Beverley wrote.

In particular, Beverley gives a good idea of the orchards in Virginia, nearly a hundred years after the first settlement at Jamestown. He tells us that: "Peaches, nectarines, and apricots, as well as plumbs and cherries grow on standard trees.' He dwells upon the fact that these stone fruits grow so well that they need not be budded or grafted, and says that he had not heard of anyone who performed either operation 'before the first edition of this book.' The Indians grew peaches and nectarines so commonly and had so many sorts that Beverley believed them to be natives of the country, as did botanists for a century after. He describes 'free-stone' and 'cling-stone' peaches and nectarines, some of which were 'twelve or thirteen inches in girt.' Again we are told that peaches are raised so easily that some 'plant great orchards of them, purposely for their hogs; and others make a drink of them, which they call mobby, and either drink it as a cider, or distilled off for brandy.'

The roseate pictures painted by Lord Baltimore's agents in his Maryland propaganda in England seemed to show a better land than that south of the Potomac, on which better gardens might be expected. Probably that of the Eastern Shore and the Western Shore, the two sides of the Chesapeake were a little better in Maryland than in Virginia. The mountainous parts of the two states differed little in soil. Possibly the rich luxuriant region in Maryland that lies north of Harper's Ferry was better land than any in Virginia. Settlements came a little later in Maryland than in Virginia, and life was no doubt somewhat easier, so that gardens around Baltimore were, in early times at least, a little better than those on the James and the York, with the exception of a few unusual places in Virginia that were quite superior to the average of that state, if we may believe the early accounts.

In Maryland, happily, although there were hardships, there was no Starving Time such as the settlers in Virginia and the Pilgrims at Plymouth had to endure. At St. Mary's, long the most important settlement in Maryland, during that first autumn of

1634, the Marylanders were able to ship a load of corn to New England to exchange for salted codfish. The squaws had taught the white women to make 'pone' and 'hominy,' and cattle and hogs had been brought from Virginia. After a few years, St. Mary's was surrounded by farms and gardens. The colony was much freer from Indian wars than was Virginia, and plantations rapidly spread with the steady inflow of settlers along the shores of the Potomac River and Chesapeake Bay.

The people in Maryland, as in Virginia, were planters until long after the Revolution. Their plantations were scattered through the forests near the rivers, since water was about the only means of communication. These scattered farms were generally large, the landowner often living in a mansion flanked by outbuildings, storehouses, and Negro quarters. Meat, fish, and fowl provided most of the food, with fruit, especially peaches, in plenty. Vegetables were neglected, except for the coarser kinds, and of flower gardens there were almost none in the interior plantations; but, near Annapolis, the capital and largest city, and near the growing town of Baltimore, there were many pretty villas with well-kept grounds and gardens. Like the settlers of every other colony, those of seventeenth-century Virginia and Maryland were paramountly interested in growing grapes. Lord Delaware, early colonial governor at Jamestown, was the first man to promote grape growing in the colonies. In 1616 he wrote to the London Company urging the culture of the vine as a source of revenue. In response, the Company three years later sent to Virginia a number of French vineyardists and a collection of French grapes. The same year the Assembly passed an Act compelling every householder to plant ten cuttings of grapes and the Company made promises of marked favors to all who planted vines. Under these stimuli, vineyards were planted containing as many as 10,000 vines. But quarrels with the French vine-dressers, pests, bad seasons, and the Indian massacre of 1622 destroyed them to the last vine.

In 1639, the Virginia Assembly again tried to encourage vine growing. It passed an Act that read: 'All workers upon corne and tobacco shall this spring plant five vyne plants per pol, and the next year, before the first day of March, 20 per pol, upon penaltie to forfeite one barrell of corne for every one that shall make default.' Later, about 1660, a premium of 10,000 pounds of tobacco was offered for each 'two tunne of wine' from grapes raised in the colony. In spite of these encouragements, grape growing did not flourish. Tobacco was the money crop; the vines did not thrive; and Madeira, 'a noble strong drink,' to quote a colonial historian, 'was cheap.'

In 1710, Governor Alexander Spotswood brought over a colony of Germans from the Rhine and gave them land in Spotsylvania County. These colonists grew grapes and made wine. The Governor's 'red and white Rapidan' became well known and graced his table so often that 'his dinners were pleasing to all his friends.'

In 1769, the Virginia Assembly made a third attempt to encourage the planting of grapes. An Act was passed stipulating that André Estave, a Frenchman, be furnished land, buildings, workmen, and an outfit for making wine, and that if in six years he made ten hogsheads of merchantable wine the property was to be his. The wine was made, but it was poor stuff, and Estave had difficulty in getting the Colony to turn over the property; but the Frenchman was finally paid, all parties attributing the inferior wine to the 'unfitness of the land.'

It is more than probable that all this time settlers in the colonies south of Maryland were growing the Scuppernong grape for fruit. Certainly it was being grown as an ornamental plant on arbors and trellises. This grape, belonging to *Vitis rotundifolia,* grows commonly between sea and mountain from Virginia to Florida. This is the grape that Amidas and Barlow, in 1584, found on Roanoke Island, and reported: 'in all the world the like abundance is not to be found.' On Roanoke Island there is an old vine, gnarled and twisted in trunk, with a great spread of branches, known as the 'Mother Scuppernong,' supposed to be a vine planted by the English in their early landing in 1584. If the Scuppernong was not cultivated, it was because it grew wild so bountifully that all could have grapes for the picking.

Colonel Robert Bolling, living at Chellow, Buckingham County, was the chief patron of grape growing in Virginia in the eighteenth century. He owned a vineyard of four acres of European grapes with which he experimented for many years. At the time of his death, in 1775, he had completed the manuscript of a book entitled *A Sketch of Grape Growing.* Although never published as a book, it was distributed in manuscript form, and parts of it appeared in the *Virginia Gazette,* the *American Farmer,*[8] and the *Bolling Memoirs.*[9]

Efforts were made to grow grapes in colonial Maryland but with no better success than in Virginia. There were some temporary exceptions, perhaps the most notable in the seventeenth century being that of Lord Baltimore, who planted 300 acres to vines in 1662 at St. Mary's. He is reported to have made wine 'as good as the best Burgundy.' An advertisement from the *Maryland Gazette,* 3 December 1761, shows that Governor Blanden, then no longer living, had been growing grapes on a rather large scale near Annapolis.

Orcharding in eighteenth-century Virginia, where most of the trees were grafted, was more advanced than in the northern colonies, nearly all of whose trees were seedlings. Named varieties of all the tree fruits were imported from England to Virginia planters. Gardens and grounds at this time showed the English influence more strongly in both Maryland and Virginia—which had greater wealth and a closer relation to the mother country—than in any of the northern colonies, except perhaps in Pennsylvania, where William Penn's taste for gardening had stimulated gardening.

After the middle of the seventeenth century it is probable that there were few plantations in Virginia and Maryland that did not possess orchards of apples and peaches, and a fewer number had pears, plums, cherries, and quinces. Several writers mention apricots and nectarines. There were far fewer orchard pests at that time than now, and, as long as forests still stood, the climate was probably more equable; certainly the soil was little eroded and, containing much more humus, was more suitable for fruits.

One wonders what the apples in Virginia were like, for, it seems, there were many varieties as well as great numbers of seedlings. Early writers on domestic economy say much about the orchard of Colonel William Fitzhugh, of Westmoreland County. He is said to have had, in 1686, an orchard of 2500 apple trees 'of many varieties, such as mains, pippins, russentens, costards,

8 *American Farmer,* x: 387.   9 Ibid. xi: 172.

marigolds, kings, magitens, and bachelors,' most of them grafted and well-fenced with 'a locust fence.' None of the varieties named survived long in America, and one would have to go to English orchard books to find descriptions of Colonel Fitzhugh's apples, all of which probably came from England.

The men who came from England to settle Virginia drank little water. Those of social standing had been accustomed to wine; the working class to beer. Since domesticated grapes could not be grown, and wine from wild grapes was scarcely drinkable, cider, perry, and peach brandy were made in large quantities. From the founding of Jamestown to the time of George Washington and Thomas Jefferson, on down to that of Robert E. Lee, every plantation owner made cider, drank cider, and bragged about his cider. The fruit of the 1500 apple trees Governor Berkeley had planted about his home at Green Springs in 1642 and that from Colonel William Fitzhugh's famous orchard was used for cider.

That cider in Maryland was still an important article of farm produce is indicated by an advertisement in the *Maryland Journal and Baltimore Daily Advertiser* of 29 April 1783. Edward Dorrey offers a plantation for sale, '20 miles from Baltimore and 10 from Ellicott's Upper Mills.' In describing his plantation Dorrey says: 'There is also an orchard of 600 bearing apple trees of excellent fruit, which yields annually about eight or ten thousand gallons of very fine cider.'

Hugh Jones, the chaplain to the House of Burgesses, one-time professor at William and Mary College in Williamsburg, says, in 1724, a few years after Beverley had written:

Apple-trees are raised from seeds very soon, which kind of Kernel Fruit needs no grafting, and is diversifi'd into numberless Sorts, and makes, with good management, an Excellent Cyder, not much inferior to that of Herfordshire, when kept to a good Age; which is rarely done, the Planters being good Companions and Guests whilst the Cyder lasts.

The grounds about the homes of planters just before the Revolution were pleasant, plain, and simple. There was usually a yard consisting of open lawn, shaded here and there by trees. Near the house was the garden, devoted to vegetables and flowers. Such herbs as sage, thyme, marjoram, and the mints were as common as in England. There were some bush as well as tree fruits; for, as early as 1684, Byrd wrote to his brother in England, thanking him for the gooseberry and currant bushes just received; in the same year he wrote to a second correspondent, expressing his appreciation of a gift of seeds and roots of iris, crocus, tulip, and anemone. The summer houses, arbors, and grottoes, which Beverley says were to be found near all residences, were situated 'in the garden, where they afforded a cool place of retreat on a summer day.' The garden, no doubt, was enclosed by a paling fence to keep out hogs and cattle, which were permitted to wander without restraint. Close to the dwelling were grouped the dovecote, stable, barn, henhouse, cabins for the servants, milk-house, and kitchen. In many yards, a tall pole with a bird house at the top was erected, in which the bee martin might build its nest.

The pictures of Virginia are not all so pleasant. Thomas Anburey, an officer in Burgoyne's Army, published in 1789 a series of letters entitled *Travels through the Interior Parts of America.* He found the face of the country at that time an immense forest, interspersed with various plantations four or five miles distant from each other. On these, he tells us, 'there is a dwelling house in the center with kitchens, smokehouses and outhouses detached, so that each plantation has the appearance of a small village.' At some distance from the houses, he saw peach and apple orchards; and scattered over the plantation, cabins and tobacco houses. In the summer time, we are told, 'the average planter rises in the morning about six o'clock; he then drinks a julep made of rum, water and sugar, but very strong.' Thus attuned, Anburey tells us, 'he rides around his plantation, views all his stock and all his crops, and breakfasts about ten o'clock on cold turkey, fried hominy, toast and cyder; the rest of the day he spends in trying to keep cool.'

From the settlement of Jamestown to the Revolution, ornamental gardening about the homes of the middle classes in Virginia presented a dreary picture. Indeed, flowers, lawns, and landscapes were almost unknown. One looks in vain in accounts of the domestic economy of the Old Dominion for much in the way of beauty except about the occasional home of wealth. Few of the many Europeans who came to America and returned to write about what they saw found ornamental gardens to describe worthy of their pens.

And yet, a hundred historic gardens in Virginia, dating back to the seventeenth and eighteenth centuries, might be named. The Byrds at Westover; the Lighthouses at Tedington; the Eppes at Appomattox Manor; the Carys at Ampthill; the Randolphs at Tuckahoe; the Carters at Shirley; the Lees at Stratford; George Mason, friend of Washington, at Gunston Hall; the Fitzhughs at Chatham; Robert Carter of Corotoman; Landon Carter at Sabine Hall; the Beverleys at Avenel; the Madisons at Montpelier; and the Skipwiths at Prestwould—all had homes in Virginia that date back to colonial times.

The fine places in Maryland were the manors founded in the English tradition. They were the centers in which good gardening practices were learned. There were the notable manor of Evilinton, in St. Marys County; Great Oak Manor, in Kent; Kent Fort, on Kent Island; and Susquehanna Manor, in Cecil County.

It is difficult to learn precisely what these early ornamental gardens in Virginia and Maryland were like. Probably they were very similar to the gardens now to be seen in the reconstructed Williamsburg. It is doubtful whether there was quite so fine a finish in the old gardens, and one may well suspect that the assortment of flowers and shrubs was not so large; but, all in all, specialists in gardening can find little to criticize in the reproductions. There were undoubtedly some gardens in Virginia in the early days even better than those at Williamsburg: far more spacious at any rate.

One may be sure that there was more or less clipping and trimming of trees and shrubs into regular or fantastic shapes. The vogue of thus training plants goes back to the Romans of Christ's time. The yew was the favorite plant for such work, though all narrow-leaved evergreens were used; box was the most satisfactory broad-leaved evergreen. Trees cut in fantastic shapes were the height of fashion in England in the sixteenth and seventeenth centuries, and English gardeners brought the topiary art to Virginia.

The many ancient box hedges about old manor houses, single plants of huge size, gnarled and twisted by age, bespeak the popularity of box, both the tree and the dwarf, in early Virginia gardens. Box trees were used for hedges, as specimen plants, and for topiary work, while dwarf box was used for bordering flower beds. In uncared-for garden sites one often finds 'box-walks,' once the pride of the garden, now so closely grown together that one can get through them only with difficulty. Often, in the center of circles of dwarf box is found a huge box tree, sometimes cut, but more often so neglected for generations that the species can hardly be recognized. Occasionally there are wide *allées* bordered by box trees. It was a common custom to separate the front yard from the back with a row of box trees; or, to enclose the vegetable garden with a tall box hedge.

The first ornamental gardens in Virginia of any great magnitude contained what the English called 'knotted beds,' or 'knots,' then the fashion in British gardens. The outlines of these knots are still to be traced in old gardens in all the Atlantic states; they are mentioned in early books, and their fame has come down in legend and family histories. Indeed, they were common a generation ago from Maine to Georgia and, occasionally, good knots may still be found in old-fashioned gardens. In Geneva, New York, is a splendid example, laid out as late as 1868 by Calvin Vaux, one of the designers of New York's Central Park.

A knot is a cluster of decorative flower beds of more or less intricate patterns, usually with paths of grass or hard walks intervening. The simplest designs are diamonds, crescents, squares, or circles, but there seems to have been no limit to the imaginations of designers in laying out knotted gardens. In some of the arrangements the number of beds was small—6, 8, or 10—but in others there were as many as 50 or 60. In some, the beds were raised, the soil being held in place by bricks, tiles, or other non-living material, but usually in America the patterns were outlined by dwarf box or some other low-growing plant that might be clipped.

Probably early in the eighteenth century the word 'parterre' began to be heard as a substitute for 'knot,' a parterre being a sort of glorified knot, in which there were no restraining walls of brick, tile, or hedges. The designs were more geometrical, and the flowers lower. The walks between the figures were sometimes of turf but often of colored sands. Parterres were very common in England from 1700 to 1900, being superseded somewhat in the nineteenth century by bedded gardens, a modification in which the figures were even more elaborately laid out and the plants lower and more closely clipped.

The maze was another feature of English gardens of the sixteenth and seventeenth centuries. Survivals of mazes are to be found in several Virginia gardens showing that they were once popular on this side of the Atlantic too. Yew and box were favorite plants for a maze. It is said that there was a particularly fine maze at Tuckahoe, the home which Thomas Randolph founded on the upper James in 1674.

Most of the trees that dotted the extensive grounds about Virginia manors for the first hundred years were native. There were available from Virginia forests such splendid trees as the oak, ash, tulip, linden, sycamore, walnut, butternut, honey-locust, dogwood, elm, maple, pine, hemlock, sweet gum, magnolia, and the redbud or Judas-tree. Of several of these there was more than one species. The catalpa and pecan, which were very popular before and after the Revolution, came from farther west and were rarities when George Washington began to plant at Mount Vernon. There is, or was, a famous pecan tree at Brandon on the south bank of the James River, which, in 1889, was sixteen feet four inches in girth four feet above the ground, towering high above its forest associates.[10]

The Williamsburg of colonial Virginia is now familiar, through the Rockefeller restoration, to every lover of gardens. The town was settled, or at least became a fortified place, in 1633, in what was called the 'Middle Plantation' from its situation on a ridge midway between the James and the York Rivers. In 1699 Williamsburg succeeded Jamestown as the capital of the colony. It had a better situation in lay of land, climate, and soil; and gardening was better there than it ever could have been in the old capital.

The plantings about the Governor's Palace in Williamsburg showed gardening at its best. Hugh Jones, in his *Present State of*

10 *Garden and Forest,* III: 598.

Virginia, published in 1724, speaks of the Palace as '. . . a magnificent structure, built at publick Expense, finished and beautified with Gates, fine Gardens, Offices, Walks, a fine Canal, Orchards. . .' The grounds, as originally laid out, covered 370 acres 'more or less.' Besides the ornamental plantings, there were an orchard and a vegetable garden. The grounds were bordered, in part at least, with European lindens, *Tilia vulgaris,* said to have been brought from Scotland. Possibly, these were the first of the popular European linden to be planted in America. The European buttercup, *Ranunculus acris,* is said to have been first planted on the grounds of the Governor's Palace, where it ran riot and eventually became an escape, spreading far and wide.

The grounds about the Saunders house in early days seemed to have ranked next to those of the Governor's Palace. They were notable for well-planned and well-kept terraces, but, from the gardener's point of view, even more so for early plantings of native trees at a time when imported trees had preference in all the colonies. Two large bull bays, *Magnolia grandiflora,* standing a generation ago bespoke early planting of this species; other native trees were the mulberry, locust, and hackberry.

Greens, which foreshadowed parks, were to be found in all American cities and towns of consequence. They were planned as gathering places, for military drilling, for a meeting place of the village band, and for market places. In almost every American town of the first two centuries may be found some such green perpetuated in place or name. In Williamsburg a spacious green was planned in the early days of Governor Nicholson in the center of town. It extended north from Duke of Gloucester Street by the parish churchyard, the planners intending it for a foreground and entrance to the Governor's Palace. Near the center of the old town was another similar green designated in the original plan as 'Market Square.' If plans of other early towns were available, as are those of reconstructed Williamsburg, in all would be found greater or lesser greens.

The historic Wythe house, facing the Palace Green, exhibited quite a different style of gardening. The garden lay at the rear of the house, and was as formal as box, cut trees, and bordered walks could make it. In its later years, this, as well as the other old gardens in Williamsburg, was planted with many foreign species, including a considerable number of lilacs and crape-myrtles.

Ships that voyaged between the colonies and the mother coun-try kept up an uninterrupted communication between American and British botanists and horticulturists. From the time of the first settlers at Jamestown until long after the Revolution, Ameri-cans interested in plants sent an assortment of trees, shrubs, and flowers to England in exchange for cultivated plants from Europe. It was fortunate for such bartering that sea captains were often men of some education and culture who were freely admitted to social intercourse with people of good standing on both sides of the Atlantic. In the several early books on colonial Virginia are accounts of these exchanges. Toward the end of the seventeenth century, William Byrd and William Fitzhugh are mentioned more than once as men diligent in promoting these interchanges.

The first account of the plants of Virginia that brought them to the notice of European collectors was written by John Banister (1650-92), a minister of the Church of England and a graduate of Oxford, who settled in Charles City County, Virginia, in 1678, and there began a study of the plant life of the region. Shortly he began work on a *Natural History of Virginia*, which his un-timely death terminated. Meanwhile he was corresponding with the botanists of Europe and writing papers for scientific societies, the one of greatest interest to American botanists being his 'Cata-logue of Virginia Plants,' published in Ray's *Historia plantarum*.

Banister, in 1688, sent *Magnolia glauca* to Bishop Compton in England, who introduced it to English gardens. Banister appears also to have first described witch-hazel, *Hamamelis virginiana*. It was he who sent to Bishop Compton the curious Hercules club, *Aralia spinosa*, so often seen in gardens in temperate climates. And it was probably he who sent to England the flowering dog-wood, *Cornus florida*, one of the most beautiful small trees in American forests and gardens. The black haw, *Viburnum pruni-folium*, valuable as an ornament and in medicine, first came to notice in Banister's book; also the willow oak, *Quercus Phellos*, a tree often planted in the South. The chinquapin chestnut, *Castanea pumila*, one of the first plants to be sent to England, was included in Banister's *Catalogue of Virginia Plants* of 1688. Banister first sent the northern hemlock, *Tsuga canadensis,* to England, though the earliest settlers in Canada and New England had extolled its virtues.

Another of these early botanists of Virginia was Dr. John Mitchell (1680(?)-1768), who came from England in 1700 to the little village of Urbana, near Richmond, on the Rappahannock. Mitchell was a distinguished physician, an author, a map maker, and a botanist who corresponded with Linnaeus and his colleagues in Europe. In 1738 and again in 1741 Mitchell published botanical papers proposing 30 genera of plants. Eventually he became a member of the Royal Society in London, with whose members he exchanged letters and plants to the benefit of botany and gardening on both continents. In his honor the pretty little partridge berry of cool woods was given the name *Mitchella repens* by Linnaeus. It is probable that Dr. Mitchell was the author of *American Husbandry.*

A third attempt to enumerate and name systematically the plants of Virginia was made by John Clayton (1685-1773), an Englishman who came to Virginia in 1705 and lived on an estate called Windsor, in what is now Matthews County. Here he started a garden of native plants, and was soon in correspondence with Linnaeus, Gronovius, Peter Kalm, and Peter Collinson—botanists of Europe—and with John Bartram and Alexander Garden—botanists in America. Studies of Clayton's field notes and specimens of Virginia plants were published at Leyden by Johan Fredericus Gronovius in his *Flora Virginica,* the first part appearing in 1739; the second, in 1743. Not much is known of Clayton's personal life in Virginia, except that almost from his coming there until his death he was clerk of Gloucester County. Among his American correspondents were Benjamin Franklin and Thomas Jefferson. His name is happily commemorated in one of our prettiest woodland flowers, the little 'spring beauty,' *Claytonia virginica.* Peter Collinson, the Quaker botanist of England, wrote of him in 1764 as 'my friend John Clayton, the greatest botanist in America.'

As we saw in the preceding chapter, a colony of mystics, the Rosicrucians, profoundly influenced gardening in Penn's province. Another sect of mystics settled in Maryland and practiced agriculture and horticulture to the great benefit of both. This colony was founded in France by Jean de Labadie (1610-74), a

Frenchman from whom came the name 'Labadists.' The Labadists practiced the simple life of the early Christians, brought in new practices of marriage, held goods in common, and were gardeners of note, as were their followers. The leaders were Jasper Danckaerts and Peter Sluyter, Hollanders, whose book we have quoted earlier. Though the founder was a Frenchman, his followers had been driven to Holland, whence they came to America.

The site of the Labadist colony was on the Elk River in what was then known as Bohemia Manor, whose owner, one Augustine Herman, gave the community 4000 acres. On Sluyter's death in 1722, the sect came to an end, but the land is still known as 'the Labadie tract.' [11]

By 1770, Baltimore had become the fourth city in the colonies, with a population of 20,000. Its rapid growth was largely attributable to its situation on salt water, whereas its rival, Philadelphia, was on a river. Truck and orchard produce were shipped through the port of Baltimore not only from Maryland but from Virginia and Pennsylvania as well. The trade in farm produce might go to Europe, but fruits and vegetables, fresh and dried, cider, and brandy were sold in the far South and the West Indies.

The garden and orchard crops grown for this trade and for use at home are known from advertisements in papers published before the Revolution. One from the *Maryland Gazette* of 3 December 1776 shows that European grapevines were still being grown in Maryland and that grafted apple trees came from England. Another, in the *Maryland Journal and Baltimore Daily Advertiser* of 8 March 1793, gives a list of garden and flower seeds, grapevines, and fruit trees available at the time:

Maximilian Henisler; Nursery Man and Seeds Man, At his Plantation, on the Main Road to Philadelphia, about a Mile and a Quarter from Baltimore-Town, begs Leave to inform the Public, that he has now on Hand, and fit for Sale, A Variety of Kitchen-Garden and Flower Seeds of the best kinds, and such as can be depended on, viz: Cauliflower Seeds; Roman Brocoli; Cabbage of different Sorts; savoys ditto; Dutch Kale of various Colours; Scotch ditto; German Greens; Hanover Turnips; double Parsley; round Spinach; red English Carrot; the large French carrot; the early Horn Carrot; Parsnips;

11 Fiske, *Old Virginia and her Neighbours*, pp. 124-9.

white Mustard; early Windsor Beans, early Bunch Beans, large Dutch Caseknife Bean, The Lima Bean, The French speckled Bean, the white French Kidney Bean, the small white French running ditto; early Peas; Bunch Peas, Marrowfat Peas, the French Sugar Pea; the early white and red Radish, fit for Hotbeds, the Turnip Radish, Scarlet Radish, Salmon ditto, Common Radish, Summer Radish, the large white and black Winter Radish; Cabbage Lettuce of various sorts, long Roman Lettuce Seed; curled Endive, broad-leafed ditto; Succory variegated; Tongue Grass; Pepper Grass; Leek Seed, red-top Turnips; French celery, Dutch Headed Celery; the French small Soup Turnip; the Dutch white and yellow Turnip; the Roman Thistle; Artichoke; broad-leafed Basilic common ditto; small leaf ditto; an Assortment of Musk Melons, and Cantaloupe ditto, of the best kind; green Cucumber, large Spanish white Cucumber; Asparagus Plants of the best Sort; an Assortment of Flower Seeds, too tedious to mention; double Tuberose Roots; finer and larger than any imported; a large Quantity of different Sorts of Vines, viz: Burgundy, Rhenish, Tokey, Madeira, Muscat, Claret, the Provence or Coast Vine.

He has just received from Europe, A large and general assortment of Bulbous Roots; and expects a Quantity of choice Fruit-Trees, which, when arrived, shall be publicly advertised.

One is surprised to learn that in colonial Virginia vegetables were grown in hotbeds and greenhouses out of season. Dr. Philip Mazzei, an Italian, who came to Virginia in 1773 to introduce plants from Italy, gives us this information.[12] He tells us also that successive plantings of vegetables were made in gardens, a statement substantiated by President Blair [13] of William and Mary, who wrote in his diary that he had had asparagus on his table in March and peas in December.

In the newly settled parts of western Virginia, as in all the frontiers of the colonies, garden produce was scant or non-existent, varying with the wealth and energy of the settlers. In new homes in the backwoods, certainly, there were no hotbeds or greenhouses to provide vegetables out of season. Food in these back-country regions was simple and monotonous, consisting generally of pork and corn products supplemented by game. Pigs ran wild in all of the colonies south of New England, fattening on beechnuts, acorns, and roots, requiring no attention. Corn was grown near

12 *William and Mary College Quarterly,* IX (2nd ser.): 168.
13 Ibid. VII: 137.

every cabin, and was beaten in hand mortars or a hollow in a stump into coarse meal to be boiled as a mush or baked as hoe-cake. William Eddis, who visited the western settlements in Maryland shortly before the Revolution, wrote that Indian corn was the principal food. When salt beef or bacon was added, he declared, 'no complaints were made about their food.' [14] A half century earlier another writer had said: 'Of the meaner Sort you find little else but water amongst them, when their Cyder is spent, Mush and Milk, or Molasses, *Hominie,* Wild Fowl, and Fish are their principal Diet.' [15]

Of the several plants used by the Indians, two, the persimmon and sassafras, were of importance to the people of Maryland and Virginia. No native fruit received more frequent notice by early explorers than the persimmon. Loaves made of persimmons, 'like unto brickes, also plumes of the making and bigness of nuts and have three or four stones in them,' were seen by De Soto on the Mississippi. The persimmon was the 'piakmine,' or 'pessimmon' of the southern states; the 'eugoufle' of Louisiana and Mississippi. It was called 'mespilorum' by Le Moyne in Florida. Hariot found it at Roanoke and wrote of 'mespila,' unfit to eat until soft and tender. Strachey speaks of it as growing on the James River. The colonials in the South made a persimmon beer and distilled a very good brandy from the fermented juice. Yet this promising native fruit has received almost no attention from modern plant breeders. It may occasionally be found in the markets of the South but almost never in those of the North. Oriental species are now raised on the West Coast.

Though never cultivated, sassafras was considered by Spanish and English discoverers one of the most valuable plants in the New World, because it had, so they thought, remarkable medicinal properties. The colonists at Jamestown devoted much of their time to preparing sassafras for shipment to England. Captain John Smith praised a tribe of Indians because they 'did help us dig and carry sassafras.' [16] The bark of the roots contains most of the medicinal oil, but the dried leaves, powdered and sifted, were

[14] Eddis, pp. 57-8.
[15] *William and Mary College Quarterly,* xv: 146.
[16] Smith, John, I: 107.

most used for sassafras tea, which, before the tea and coffee of modern household use, was one of the most common warm drinks in Europe, especially in England, where it was known as 'saloop' and sold in London down to the beginning of this century. The people of the far South still put it in soups, to which it gives a ropy consistency and a much relished flavor. To such soups are given the names gombo file, gombo zab, or gombo sassafras.

When colonists began planting lawns, the sassafras tree, which grows 40 or 50 feet high, became an ornamental plant much used in the South. It was especially desirable because of its handsome, light-green leaves of greatly varying shapes, which in autumn took on orange-yellow and bright red colors, and of its bright-colored decorative fruits.

Another plant common in the gardens of Maryland and Virginia in the first years of the two colonies was the sweet potato. Whence it came does not appear; but since the Spaniards carried it to every part of the world where it could be grown, it is probable that the northern settlements got it from the Spanish in Florida. Now a mainstay in the agriculture of the South, the sweet potato was, until well into the nineteenth century, a garden crop. It would be hard to set a date for the introduction of sweet potatoes into Virginia, but it was certainly before 1650, when Williams says they were under cultivation.[17] Probably it was the sweet potato that was meant in the list of crops in the *True Declaration of Virginia* (1610); they are specifically named by Jefferson in *Notes on Virginia* (1781).

Of the sweet potatoes grown in Virginia, Beverley says: [18]

Their Potatoes are either red or white, about as long as a Boy's leg, and sometimes as long and big as both the Leg and Thigh of a young Child, and very much resembling it in Shape. I take these Kinds to be the same as those, which are represented in the Herbals, to be Spanish Potatoes. I am sure, those, called English or Irish Potatoes are nothing like these, either in Shape, Colour, or Taste. The Way of Propagating Potatoes there, is by cutting the small ones to Pieces, and planting the Cuttings in Hills of loose Earth: But they are so tender, that it is very difficult to preserve them in the Winter; for the least Frost coming at them, rots and destroys them; and therefore People

---

[17] Williams, p. 48.   [18] Beverley, p. 127.

bury 'em under ground, near the Fire Hearth, all the winter, until the Time comes that the seedlings are to be set.

The large, fleshy, tuberous roots of the Chinese yam, *Dioscorea Batatas,* are eaten in many sub-tropic regions. They are but sparingly grown in our South, not yielding to cultivation so well and not so well liked as the sweet potato. One of the yams was found in cultivation at Mobile, Alabama, by William Bartram in 1733. The Chinese yam was introduced into America by the United States Patent Office, but was a failure as a food plant, becoming instead a valuable flowering climbing plant under the name 'cinnamon vine.' Probably one or two other species of yams are more or less cultivated for food or as ornamentals in the South, and have been since the early years of the colonies. Kalm was served yams at the dinner table of Benjamin Franklin in 1749. These, he says, 'Are white and taste like the common potato but are not quite so agreeable.' [19] Probably Franklin's yams came from the South or the West Indies.

[19] Kalm, II: 66.

6

THE SOUTH ATLANTIC COLONIES

O F the Spanish, English, and French expeditions that time
and again sailed along the Atlantic coast of North America,
the French were the first to make settlement. Jacques Cartier
built a rude fort on the heights of Quebec in 1541, around which
a village persisted for a year or thereabouts. In 1562-4, the French
Huguenots established themselves in Florida, only to be destroyed, almost to the last person, by Spaniards.

The emigrants in these French colonies brought implements
of husbandry, garden seeds, and domestic animals. Probably Cartier's short-lived settlement did little in the way of planting crops,
but certainly the Huguenots in Florida and Georgia made a start
in agriculture, and from them vegetables and fruits found their
way into Indian gardens. As an escape into the wild, the peach
and probably the orange found a permanent home in Florida
and in Georgia. There is much to substantiate the belief that the
Huron and Iroquois Indians, notable among Indian tribes as agriculturists, obtained seeds of garden plants and possibly of fruit
trees from the early French settlement at Quebec.

Melendez, the Spaniard, destroyed the Huguenot settlements
in Florida in 1565 and founded St. Augustine. In spite of the
raids of French and English, the Spaniards continued to hold the
old town for two full centuries. Moreover, they established a number of missions at some distance from St. Augustine, to the south
in Florida, north as far as North Carolina, and west into Alabama.
Around these far-flung missions, gardens were planted by the
adventurers of the several nationalities, especially the Spaniards,
who, however, were more interested in trade with the Indians
and the finding of precious metals than in gardening.

Yet gardening in this coastal region was not wholly insignificant. As early as 1577, Bartolomé Martinez, at Santa Elena, could write to the King: 'I Planted with my own hands grape vines, pomegranate trees, orange and fig trees; wheat, barley, onions, and garlic. All the vegetables which were grown in Spain were raised at that fort.' [1] Two years later the garrison at Fort Elena had sown 'much maize' and there 'were beginning to be many of the fruits of Spain, such as figs, pomegranates, oranges, grapes in quantity; besides vegetables including beans, kidney-beans, melons, pumpkins, lettuce, cardoons, onions, and garlic,—all this in abundance.' In 1600 it could be said: 'This garrison and territory is abounding in the fruits of the earth—corn and other vegetables.' [2]

When Oglethorpe brought his English colony to Georgia in 1733 he found abandoned plantations of olives, figs, oranges, and lemons, some of the trees being of great size. He found also, as did the Whites everywhere in the South and as far north as Pennsylvania and west to Arkansas, that the Indians were growing peaches, which could only have come from the Orient by the way of Europe. The early Spanish or French colonists must have planted peach pits, probably brought to the south Atlantic seaboard somewhat earlier than 1600.

The cradle of European gardening in the United States is, therefore, in the coastal region northward from north central Florida, through Georgia, and well into South Carolina. To this region the Spaniards gave the name 'Guale.'

Between Guale and Jamestown lies Roanoke Island, on which Sir Walter Raleigh made two attempts to plant a colony of Englishmen, an island that Raleigh's captains reported as an exceedingly pleasant land, its people being 'most gentle, loving, and faithful, and such as live after the manner of the golden age.' In 1584, two of Raleigh's ships landed a company of men on Roanoke Island, and, a little later, men, women, and children, to found a permanent settlement. Probably, gardens were planted, but their produce did not suffice to keep the colonists alive. Or, were they murdered by the 'gentle, loving' people? Their fate, as everybody knows, is a mystery.

When Florida was ceded to England by Spain in 1763, St.

[1] Connor, I: 245.   [2] Ibid.

Augustine had been the metropolis and capital of Florida for two hundred years. The town, according to the accounts of English visitors, contained in 1763 many orange groves and gardens, in which were planted fruits, vegetables, and some flowers common to sub-tropic countries. Oranges and lemons, it was said, grew without cultivation and 'produced fruit better than those of Spain and Portugal.' Pomegranates, plantains, pineapples, olives, and papayas were to be found growing luxuriantly. Since these plants are not now grown in the old city, allowance must be made for the enthusiasm of the newcomers.

The English took possession of Florida in 1769, and soon after Dr. Andrew Turnbull, an Englishman, brought 1500 Minorcans to East Florida and founded the town of New Smyrna. He had planned to grow indigo and sugar-cane, but neither was successful. After a few years the Minorcans scattered to a dozen or more parts of Florida, most of them to St. Augustine. Wherever they went they grew oranges, lemons, and other sub-tropical fruits. Dr. Turnbull seems to have started the first of the many booms in Florida in the growing of horticultural products.

After several earlier attempts to settle in what is now South Carolina, a permanent settlement, called Charles Town, was made in 1670 on the west bank of the Ashley River. In 1783 the name was changed to Charleston. During the first thirty years the settlers experimented with a great variety of crops, wine and silk being the two products in which they were most interested. But they also planted the European grains, cotton, sugar-cane, tobacco, hemp, flax, ginger, rice, indigo, oranges, lemons, limes, plantains, pomegranates, cassava, capers, Zante currants, and all of the European fruits, vegetables, and flowers. At first, the rice, indigo, and cotton crops, which later brought the Carolinas great wealth, were grown with small success, but by 1700, or a few years later, rice growing in South Carolina had become profitable and soon enormously so.

The first noteworthy account of the agricultural resources of South Carolina is found in Robert Horne's *A Brief Description of the Province of Carolina,* published in 1666. Just two years after the author (there is some doubt whether Horne was author or only publisher) says, speaking of a settlement at Cape Fear:

'There is a colony of English seated, who Landed there the 29th of May *Anno* 1664, and are in all about 800 persons, who have overcome all the difficulties that attend the first attempts. . .' He then describes well, at considerable length, the natural resources of the region about Cape Fear and briefly the animals, crops, fruits, and vegetables being grown.

He tells us that the settlers brought with them many seeds and roots of the Barbados; that they had sweet potatoes; also indigo, tobacco, cotton, lime-trees, oranges, lemons, and other fruit-trees, all of which 'thrive exceedingly': 'they have two crops of Indian Corn in one year,' and 'Apples, Pears, and other English fruit grown there out of the planted Kernels.' [3]

Another account of the gardens of South Carolina is to be found in a pamphlet entitled *Carolina, or a Description of the Present State of that Country,* by Thomas Ashe, 1682, written some 10 or 11 years after the first permanent settlement was made. The pamphlet was one of several written to advertise real estate in the new colony. Probably some of the statements are exaggerations, as were so many of the glowing accounts of early visitors to America, but, taken with a grain of salt, what Ashe says is a fairly good record of what was being grown in orchards and gardens at that time. We are told, for example: [4]

Fruit Trees there are in abundance of various and excellent kinds, the Orange, Lemon, Pomegranate, Fig and Almond. Of English fruits, the Apple, Pear, and Plumb, Cherry, Quince, Peach, a sort of Medlar, and Chesnut. Wallnut Trees there are of two or three sorts; but the Black Wallnut for its Grain, is most esteem'd: the Wild Wallnut or Hiquery-Tree, gives the Indians by boiling its Kernel, a wholesome Oyle, from which the English frequently supply themselves for their Kitchen uses. . .

The Peach Tree in incredible numbers grows wild: Of the fruit express'd the Planters compose a pleasant refreshing Liquor; the Remainder of the Fruit serves the Hogg and Cattle for Provision. The Mulberry Tree every-where amidst the Woods grows wild: The Planters, near their Plantations, in Rows and Walks, plant them for Use, Ornament, and Pleasure. . . The Olive Tree thrives very well. Mr. James Colleton, Brother to Sir Peter, one of the Honourable Proprietors, brought an Olive Stick from Fyall [one of the Western

---

[3] Salley, pp. 67, 69.   [4] Ibid. pp. 142, 143.

Islands] cut off at both Ends to Carolina, which, put into the Ground, grew and prospered exceedingly; which gave so great Encouragement, that since I left the place, I hear that several more were brought there, there being great Hopes, that if the Olive be well improved from thence perhaps as good Oyle as any the World yields.

For the best account of the orchards and gardens of North Carolina, one must go to John Lawson's *History of Carolina*. Lawson was Surveyor General of the colony and his work took him to every part of the Carolinas. He was a lover of nature, a born naturalist, a keen observer, and was interested in the development of agriculture. His book describes all the natural resources of the Carolinas; the Indian races, their customs and industries; and the White settlements, with the manner of life therein. It is the most accurate and detached of the early natural histories of America, and is written in fascinating style. Lawson was later captured by the Indians, his skin stuck full of fat pine splinters that were set afire one by one, so that death came only after hours of torture.

In this history we find our best account of the peaches the Indians were then growing:

All peaches with us are standing; neither have we any wall fruit in Carolina, for we have heat enough, and therefore do not require it. . . Eating peaches in our orchards makes them come up so thick from the kernel, that we are forced to take a great deal of care to weed them out, otherwise they make our land a wilderness of peach trees. They generally bear so full that they break great part of their limbs down. We have likewise very fair nectarines, especially the red, that clings to the stone; the other yellow fruit, that leaves the stone. Of the last I have a tree that most years brings me fifteen or twenty bushels. I see no foreign fruit like this, for thriving in all sorts of land, and bearing its fruit to admiration. . .

The tree grows very large, most commonly as big as a handsome apple tree; the flowers are of a reddish, murrey color, the fruit is rather more downy than the yellow peach, and commonly very large and soft, being very full of juice. They part freely from the stone, and the stone is much thicker than all the other peach stones we have, which seems to me that it is a spontaneous fruit of America; yet in those parts of America that we inhabit, I never could hear that any peach trees were ever found growing in the woods; neither have the foreign Indians, that live remote from the English, any other sort.

And those living amongst us have a hundred of this sort for one other. They are a hardy fruit, and are seldom damaged by the northeast blast, as others are. Of this sort we make vinegar; wherefore we call them vinegar peaches, and sometimes Indian peaches.[5]

Sometime before 1714, Lawson gave this helpful information to his fellow fruit growers in North Carolina:

We have the common, red and black cherry, which bear well. I never saw any grafted in this country, the common excepted, which was grafted on an indian plum stock, and bore well. This is a good way, because our common cherry trees are very apt to put scions all around the tree for a great distance, which must needs be prejudicial to the tree and fruit. . . Our cherries are ripe a month sooner than in Virginia.[6]

Lawson's description of southern wild plums is good. These wild plums, by the way, were among the first native plants to be domesticated: Lawson was the first to make the attempt, with no record of a second attempt until over a hundred years later. Three or four species grow wild in North Carolina, and one cannot be quite sure about the 'several sorts' Lawson thus describes:

The most frequent is that which we call the common Indian Plum, of which there are two sorts, if not more. One of these is ripe much sooner than the other, and differs in the bark; one of the barks being very scaly, like our American Birch. These trees, when in Blossom smell as sweet as any Jessamine, and look as white as a Sheet, being something prickly. You may make it grow to what Shape you please; they are very ornamental about a House, and make a wonderful fine Shew at a Distance, in the Spring, because of their white Livery. Their Fruit is red, and very palatable to the sick. They are of a quick Growth, and will bear from the Stone in five years, on their Stock.[7]

We can be certain about the 'American Damson' Lawson describes. It is the beach plum, *Prunus maritima,* which grows on sandy beaches and dunes from New Brunswick to Georgia: Lawson says these plums are both black and white, and about the size of the European Damson. He was able to grow them from the stone and cuttings; we grow them only from stones. He rightly says: 'They are found on the Sand-Banks all along the Coast of America.' In his orchard they did not grow 'to the Big-

5 Lawson, pp. 181-3.   7 Ibid.
6 Ibid. p. 183.

ness of the other Trees now spoken of.' They are, he says, 'plentiful Bearers.' [8] It is too bad that Lawson chose the beach plum to
plant in his orchard. Out of all our native plums, it has proved
most intractable to domestication. Any other of these wildings
would have given him better results.

Efforts to grow grapes were not pushed quite so vigorously
in the Carolinas as in the northern colonies or even in Georgia.
Probably the great abundance of the Muscadine or Scuppernong
grapes, *Vitis rotundifolia,* which run riot in all the southeastern
states, and make a fair wine, was one reason why the early settlers
in the Carolinas did not experiment with the European grape
quite so enthusiastically. Yet foreign grapes were planted in South
Carolina and Georgia by the first comers from Europe. Thomas
Ashe gives a very interesting account of attempts to cultivate the
European grape in Charles Town previous to 1682. He also reports an effort to improve the native grape 'by Replantation,' the
first effort on record to domesticate any of the many wild grapes
in North America. Ashe says:

Vines of divers rank, bearing both black and gray grapes grow climbing their highest Trees, running and over-spreading their lower
Branches: Five Kinds they have already distinguish'd, three of which
by Transplantation, and if well cultivated, they own, will make very
good Wine; some of which has been transported for England, which
by the best Pallates was well approved of, and more is daily expected, 'tis not doubted, if the Planters as industriously prosecute
the Propagation of Vineyards as they have begun; but Carolina will
in a little time prove a Magazine and a Staple for Wines to the whole
West Indies; and to enrich their Variety, some of the Proprietors and
Planters have sent them the Noblest and Excellentest Vines of Europe,
viz, the Rhenish, Clarret, the Muscadel and Canary, etc. His Majesty,
to improve so hopeful a Design, gave those French we carried over their
Passages free for themselves, Wives, Children, Goods and Servants,
they being most of them well experienced in the Nature of the Vine,
from whose Direction doubtless the English have received and made
considerable Advantages in their Improvements.[9]

The same year Ashe's pamphlet advertising the province of
Carolina appeared in England, another author, Samuel Wilson,

wrote, in pamphlet form also, an advertisement entitled *An Account of the Province of Carolina, in America,* setting forth its 'Commoditys' of grapes. Wilson writes:

There are growing naturally in the Country five sorts of grapes, three of which the French Vigaroons who are there judge will make very good Wine, and some of the Lords Proprietors have taken care to send plants of Rhenish, Canary, Clarret, Muscatt, Madera, and Spanish Grapes, of all which divers Vineyards are planted; some wine was made last year that proved very good both in colour and taste, and an indifferent good quantity may be expected the next year; The Country hath gentle rising hills of fertile sand proper for vines, and further from the Sea, rock and gravel, on which very good grapes grow naturally, ripen well, and together, and very lushious in taste, insomuch as the French Protestants who are there, and are skilled in wine, do no way doubt of producing great quantitys and very good.[10]

In the early days of the colonies, Charles Town was the center of gardening. Nowhere else in America were there colonial gardens as extensive, as well laid out, as well kept, as were those near this town on the Ashley and Cooper Rivers. These early gardens were planted by Englishmen and Huguenots, men of distinction from Europe who acquired wealth in agriculture and trade in the Carolinas and the West Indies, and chose the beautiful country near Charles Town to build fine homes and plant fine gardens.

The Battery in Charleston, one of the most beautiful small parks in the country, goes back to early colonial South Carolina, when it was called 'White Point Garden.' The park is and long has been planted to trees and grass, with few flowers or shrubs. Whether this is the design of Frederick Law Olmsted, who in late years planted the park anew, or is a custom long approved by Charleston does not appear. The absence of large trees permits a perfect view of the river and sea, which adds greatly to the matchless beauty of this small park. Yet there is and ever has been color in the Battery—color supplied by the white woodwork of the houses in the background, with their red brick and pink stucco walls, where vines with colored flowers run riot in season.

Unfortunately, reliable accounts of the old gardens of the Caro-

[10] Wilson, pp. 174, 175.

linas are scant and fragmentary. One gathers, in general, that the earliest plantings were of the Elizabethan type brought from England—the formal gardens of the seventeenth century. Large or small, they were geometric in design and had intricate figures, closely clipped trees of the Dutch and Italian topiary schools, colored tiles and marbles, and all the formal objects the architect could place in a garden.

Happily, formal English gardens were not long the fashion. The vast estates, the great live oaks, luxuriant vegetation, the freedom of the New World were no more compatible with formal gardens than were the laws, manners, and religions of the New World with those of the Old. The geometrical designs, the clipped trees, the statuary, the mounds and terraces gave way to stretches of open space, vistas, and the abundant use of trees and flowers planted naturally. By the end of the eighteenth century, naturalistic gardening had largely taken the place of formal gardens. The change, though gradual, entailed the destruction of avenues of trees, much fine topiary work, parterres and knots, walks, statuary, and temples; but beauty came out of this ruthless destruction.

For a hundred years or more, the early economic life of South Carolina was dominated by rice, much as it was in Virginia by tobacco. The value of the crop was discovered, according to legend, when a ship from Madagascar stopped at Charles Town in 1693 and left a bag of rice, which, planted, produced a crop so beautiful that rice culture quickly became an industry.

By 1720 rice was being grown on all the coastal rivers in the Carolinas. In 1724 some 1800 barrels were shipped from Charles Town, and the industry grew, with several changes in methods of culture and thrashing, until at the peak of its production, about 1850, some 160,000,000 pounds were exported from Charleston. Rice culture was at its best in the early years in inland swamps, where the water was drawn from shallow pools, but at about the time of the Revolution, rice plantations began to move from the inland swamps to the borders of tidal rivers. Here, then, in the swamps and along the rivers, on the rice plantations, the splendid gardens of early South Carolina were to be found.

To a lesser extent, only because there were fewer plantations, the gardens of North Carolina and Georgia owed their beginnings to rice. The relative number of rice estates in the three states is indicated somewhat by the number of plantations in 1850: in that year South Carolina had 446; Georgia, 88; and North Carolina, 25. The Civil War, with its emancipation of slaves, brought to an end the rice plantations of the southeastern states; many of the mansions were destroyed, others fell into decay, and the gardens reverted to rushes, swamp trees, and stagnant pools.

Meanwhile a second plantation crop, hardly less profitable than rice, even more romantic in its rise and fall, had come and gone on the higher lands of South Carolina and Georgia. This was indigo, the culture of which began in 1741 and lasted as a major crop perhaps a century. Indigo was grown most widely just before the Revolution when the annual export was about 1,000,000 pounds. Ramsay, the historian, writing in 1809, said of indigo: 'It proved more really beneficial to Carolina than the mines of Mexico or Peru are or ever have been to either old or new Spain.' [11]

The first indigo grown in South Carolina was planted by Eliza Lucas, notable as a gardener, agriculturist, and woman of affairs. The indigo seed came to her from her father, Colonel George Lucas, a British officer stationed in the West Indies, whose family lived in South Carolina, and who had left his seventeen-year-old daughter in charge of his Carolina plantation. The father had been interested in the introduction of new crops in Carolina, and Eliza seems to have inherited his enthusiasm. In addition to looking after three plantations she tried many experiments, naively professing in her diary to 'love the vegetable world extremely.' Before her marriage, she did most of her gardening and experimental work at Wappoo and Garden Hill, near Charles Town, but later, as the wife of Colonel Charles Pinckney, she used her husband's plantation, some five miles from Charles Town. At these three places, probably beginning in 1741, indigo was first grown in the South, after which it required a few years to learn how to make the commercial product.

Besides introducing indigo, Mrs. Pinckney's estates were long noted for their gardens, especially their trees, shrubs, and flowers.

[11] Ramsay, p. 212.

She planted all the ornamental native plants that could be obtained, and, having many acquaintances abroad, enriched her plantations with exotics. Also, she grew mulberry trees to make silk and actually produced enough for three dresses, which she wore in England.

Rice and indigo made the planters of these crops the dominant class, politically and socially, of the eighteenth-century South. They were the agricultural nobility of the country, if culture, leisure, wealth, luxury, and great estates are taken as criteria. In the nineteenth century these attributes passed to the inland cotton growers on the highlands between the Atlantic and the Mississippi.

Probably the best-known garden of the rice-and-indigo period in South Carolina was Crowfield, on the right bank of Goose Creek, some miles inland from Charles Town. The plantation was started soon after 1700, but in 1722 passed into the hands of the Middleton family, one of whom, in 1729, built a mansion on the estate and planted about it gardens so extensive and elaborate that Crowfield soon became famous in Europe as well as America. Happily, we have a very good description of this celebrated garden from the pen of the gifted Eliza Lucas Pinckney in a letter written in 1742 to a Miss Bartlett in London: [12]

The [Crowfield] house stands a mile from, but in sight of the road, and makes a very handsome appearance; as you draw near it new beauties discover themselves; first the fruitful vine mantleing the wall, loaded with delicious clusters. Next a spacious Basin in the midst of a large Green presents itself as you enter the gate that leads to the House wch is neatly finished.

From the back door is a spacious walk a thousand feet long; each side of wch nearest the house is a grass plot ornamented in a Serpentine manner with Flowers; next to that on the right hand is what immediately struck my rural taste, a thicket of young, tall live oaks where a variety of airey Choristers pour forth their melody, and my darling the mockingbird joyn'd in the artless concert and inchanted me with its harmony. Opposite on the left hand is a large square boling green, sunk a little below the level of the rest of the garden,

---

[12] Ravenel, *Eliza Pinckney*, p. 53. (See this book for a full account of Eliza Pinckney's activities.)

with a walk quite round composed of a double row of fine large flowering Laurel and Catalpas wch afford both shade and beauty.

When Mrs. Ravenel wrote in 1896, she had to say: 'This fine place has long since been utterly destroyed.' When the writer saw Crowfield a few years since, there was little other than a beautiful wilderness—war, fire, earthquakes, and the elements had completely destroyed this greatest of all the early gardens of South Carolina.

A brief contemporaneous description of Crowfield is found in an advertisement in the *South Carolina Gazette* of 23 September 1785:

To be sold, that elegant much admired seat called Crowfield in the Parish of Saint James . . . it contains upward of fourteen hundred acres of land, has a very commodious dwelling house of excellent brick work, having twelve good rooms with fire places in each, besides four in the cellar with fire places also, and wants very little repair. The gardens are extensive, laid out in good taste and are all in tolerable order. The fish ponds and canals are superior to anything in the State and abound with excellent fish. The pleasantess of the Situation, the good quality of the land, the improvements of the gardens, and the vicinity to the Metropolis render Crowfield a most desirable abode, where profit and pleasure may be as well combined as at any one place in the State, at the same distance from Charleston.

Of the score or more estates that were landmarks because of their gardens in the colonies of the Carolinas, two still remain as examples of pre-Revolutionary gardening: Magnolia Gardens and Middleton Gardens, both of which have been, since their owners first laid them out, among the most beautiful in America.

Magnolia Gardens, Magnolia-on-the-Ashley, or Drayton Hall, is some 10 or 12 miles from Charleston on the Ashley River. The place has been in the possession of the Drayton family since 1671. Many of the live oaks, which were fine trees then, still stand along the walks and on the lawns. The magnolias, as large and beautiful as can be found the world over, are said to have been planted toward the end of the seventeenth century. The gardens cover some 25 to 30 acres on which, from time to time since the place was first planted, more oaks, magnolias, flowering shrubs, and box plants have been added.

The plantings that now give the place fame were begun in 1841 by the Reverend J. G. Drayton, who took the place when there was little that was noteworthy beside the oaks, magnolias, and box. Little by little he made new plantings and in 1848 began to set out camellias and azaleas, which in time became the largest collection of these two species in America, numbering each some 300 varieties, not a few of which came into being on the place. Some of the azaleas are 10 to 15 feet high and from 15 to 20 feet in diameter. No better setting for the brightly colored camellias and azaleas could have been used than the dark rich-green foliage of the magnolias.

Many artists and writers at widely different times have painted or have written about Magnolia Gardens. Perhaps the first writer to spread their fame was the Duc de la Rochefoucauld-Liancourt. This famous French writer visited the Ashley River plantation in the spring of 1796 and wrote:

The gardens along this river [the Ashley] are better laid out, better stocked with good trees, than any I have hitherto seen in America. In order to have here a fine garden, one has but to let the proper trees remain, here and there, or in clumps, plant bushes in front of them and arrange other trees according to their height.

The Duke had dinner at Magnolia Gardens (then called Drayton Hall) and wrote of the grounds: 'Dr. Drayton's father, who was a physician, began to lay out the garden on this principle; and his son, who is passionately fond of flowers, has pursued the same plan.'

John Drayton of Drayton Hall (1766-1820), jurist, author, and one-time governor of South Carolina, was a botanist and a horticulturist of note. In his *A View of South Carolina,* published in 1802, patently modeled after Jefferson's *Notes on Virginia,* he describes at some length the flora of his state. One item is of particular interest to gardeners. Here first appears mention of *Lonicera flava,* a well-known garden honeysuckle collected near Greenville. Later, in 1810, John Fraser introduced it to England.

Middleton Gardens, or Middleton Place, on the same side of the Ashley River, 15 miles from Charleston, is scarcely less notable than Magnolia Gardens. The gardens cover some 40 acres and those who see the two gardens year by year say that Middleton

Place is as often as not more attractive than Magnolia Gardens. In the main, the same trees and shrubs and the same style of landscape gardening are found on the two places, though at Middleton Place professional landscaping gives it more of an atmosphere of art. Perhaps no other American garden is quite so typical of the best eighteenth-century gardening as Middleton Gardens. The garden is at its best on a bright day in spring, when the plantings are aglow with color, with a somber tone imparted by the moss-draped live oaks and cypresses growing in dark waters.

This old estate, originally of 7000 acres, was the seat of the historic South Carolina Middletons, one of whom, Arthur, was a signer of the Declaration of Independence, and another, Henry, a governor, a United States senator, and minister to Russia. The original manor house was built in 1741 (destroyed by Sherman's army in 1865), but the garden was started in 1740. It is said that a hundred slaves worked continuously for ten years making terraces, building walks, and planting trees, shrubs, and hedges.

Late in the seventeenth century and early in the eighteenth, several hundred families of French Huguenots came to America, settling in the different colonies. So many of these French Protestants built their homes on the east branch of the Cooper River that the region in the suburbs of Charleston became known as the French Quarter. Wherever the French Huguenots went they contributed greatly to all fields of agriculture and especially to horticulture. Though the gardens on the Cooper River had long before, under the hands of the English, become notable, the French Quarter soon became known for its fine small gardens, and many of the best gardeners on the large estates, as owners or as practitioners, came from these French settlers.

But plantings in good taste were not confined to the great estates on the Ashley and Cooper Rivers outside Charleston. Mrs. Ravenel gives a very good description of the city at the time of the Revolution or a little after. She says:

In the town, behind their high walls, grew oleanders and pomegranates, figs and grapes, and bulbs brought from Holland, jonquils and hyacinths. The air was fragrant with the sweet olive, myrtle and gardenia. There were old-fashioned roses; the cinnamon, the York and Lancaster, the little white musk, and the sweet or Damascus. The glowy-leaved Cherokee clothed the walls with its great white disks, and was crowded by jasmine and honeysuckle. The lots were so large, often a square or a half square, that the yard, stables and servants quarters were quite separate from these pleasant places, where, according to the fashion of the time, there were arbours, in which the gentlemen smoked their pipes, and the ladies took their 'dish of tea' of an afternoon.[13]

American Husbandry devotes several pages to the fruits and vegetables grown at the time in South Carolina. The author mentions all the hardy fruits, including the apricot, citrons, limes, olives, pomegranates, and all sorts of melons. Oranges, sweet and sour, and lemons were grown for export in great quantities. And in the kitchen gardens, we are told, 'are found every sort of useful plant that is commonly cultivated in England.' 'Garden-stuff,' however, 'which will grow at all in the climate (fruits excepted) is preferable more to the north.' [14]

Fruit growing was common in the highlands of the Carolinas, Georgia, and Alabama, when the first Whites settled there, the Creek, Cherokee, and Choctaw Indians having planted apples and peaches about their villages with seeds obtained from the Whites of the coast settlements. Apple growing was carried on by the Cherokee Indians in the mountain regions of Georgia, Alabama, and North Carolina, and the trees were all seedlings. Vestiges of old apple trees originally planted by the Indians are reported as being occasionally found in upper Georgia as late as 1850. Several of the best winter apples in the South are of Indian origin.

Oranges were grown in South Carolina more commonly in the colony than now, perhaps because of a milder climate. As early as 1737 an advertisement appeared in the *South Carolina Gazette,* 12 February: 'To be sold by James Kerr, a large quantity of oranges, all picked by hand as good as when taken from the tree.'

On 20 September 1760 is another such advertisement: 'Any person who will take a quantity of oranges may be furnished at

[13] Ravenel, *Charleston, The Place and The People,* p. 352.
[14] *American Husbandry,* pp. 268-71.

the house where the late Mr. Benoist liv'd up the Path, at Five Pounds per Thousand.'

In the 15 September 1745 issue, one reads: 'To Be Sold by Mr. Richard Lake, at his Plantation on Ashley River, Lemon Trees with Lemons on them in Boxes, Lime Trees and Orange Trees in Boxes, and several curious Plants in Pots, also a variety of Young Fruit Trees, particularly White Mulberry and Orange Trees.'

From an advertisement in the same *Gazette* of 25 November 1777, we learn that European grapes were being planted in South Carolina: 'To be disposed of, One Hundred Plants, bearing Grapes, Of the best Portugal, large black Muscatels, and white Vernasses. The season now proper for transplanting them; directions will be given how to plant, in what ground, and how to cultivate them all the year, by Lewis Motett.'

In the colonies north of Virginia most of the apples and pears were seedlings, but grafted plants are mentioned so often in the South that one may suppose a large proportion of the trees of these fruits were grafted. Such advertisements as the following in the *South Carolina Gazette* of 1 December 1746, are not infrequent: 'To Be Sold, A Choice parcel of Apple and Pear Grafts, from 1 to 3 years old. Enquire of the Printer.'

The following is another advertisement in the *Gazette* of 9 July 1763:

Thomas Young, Sen. has at present a fine assortment of kitchen garden seeds, several kinds of grass seeds, flower seeds and roots, flower glasses, and some garden tools, Lists of which may be seen at his house near the west end of Broad street. He will sell no seeds but such sorts as have grown in his garden, and therefore can be warranted good. Those gentlemen or ladies who want flower roots, must call for them soon as most of them are now out of the ground.

Young was a plant collector as well as a seedsman. One would like to know more about him; none of his fellow collectors in America seem to have known him. He advertised in the *Gazette* 19 December 1768:

OLD THREE RUNS

Thomas Young, continues to collect the curious and valuable Seeds and Plants of this and the adjoining Provinces. He will have a very fine collection in Charleston, about the beginning or middle of December next. Those who please to favor him with orders, may send them to Messrs. Johnston & Simpson, merchants on the Bay, and they will be properly cured, marked and packed for exportation, also the plants shall be put up in the best manner.

There were also several landscape gardeners in Charles Town in the years just before the Revolution. In the *South Carolina Gazette,* 29 December 1768, is this advertisement: 'James Callahan, Lately from Philadelphia, Perfectly acquainted with all branches of gardening would be glad of employ. Inquire at the Printer.' In the *South Carolina Gazette, & Country Journal,* 15 March 1768, one reads:

WANTS A PLACE

A young Man lately arrived from London, who understands Gardening in all its branches, and will be willing to lay out any Gentleman's Garden at a moderate rate. And, as his constant study will be to please those who are so kind as to give him Employ, he hopes to meet with suitable encouragement. For further particulars enquire of the Printer.

Lastly, in the same paper, on 11 June 1771, is this advertisement:

GARDENING

The subscriber takes this Method to acquaint the Public, that he will undertake to make, or put in Compleat Order, the Garden of any Gentleman or Lady in or within two or three miles of Charles-Town, at any easy expense, either by the Day, Year, or Quarter, as may best suit them; and can be well recommended by the Gentleman he came out of England with. Enquire at Mr. Harper's, Taylor, in Church-Street, opposite Thomas Loughton Smith, Esq.

William Bennet

N. B. Seeds to be sold.

David Ramsay gives pride of place to a Mrs. Lamboll as the first woman in Charles Town to have a noteworthy garden. According to this author, Mrs. Lamboll, before the middle of the eighteenth century, 'improved the south west extremity of King street, in a garden which was richly stored with flowers and other curiosities of nature in addition to all the common vegetables for family use.' [15]

Mrs. Martha Logan was a friend and disciple of Mrs. Lamboll, and won greater distinction because, besides being a good gardener, she was a writer. From her pen came *The Gardener's Kalendar,* the first horticultural book published in America, written when the author was 72 years old. Mrs. Logan was a woman of importance in Charles Town, both in her own right and as the daughter of Robert Daniel, a proprietary governor of South Carolina. Her influence in gardening was no doubt stronger because of her high standing in the community. A Mrs. Manigault wrote in her diary in 1763 that she had 'been to Mrs. Logan's to buy roots.' [16]

Mrs. Logan was the 'elderly widow' of whom John Bartram wrote to Peter Collinson (see page 89). It seems that she not only exchanged seeds and plants with Bartram and Collinson, sold roots to gentlewomen in Charles Town, but did a business so extensive that she was able to advertise seeds, roots, and shrubs for sale. At different times her advertisement appeared in the *South Carolina Gazette,* of which one of 15 February 1768 reads:

> Just imported in the Capt. Loyd from London and to be sold very reasonably by Martha Logan at the house in Meeting-street, three doors without the gate:
> A fresh assortment of very good garden seeds and flower roots: also many other sorts of flowering shrubs and box edging beds now growing in her garden.

According to the *South Carolina Gazette,* 6 March 1742, Martha Logan was managing a plantation, selling garden seeds and plants, and boarding and teaching children at her home about ten miles from Charles Town. The same paper in 1752 mentions her as having printed a gardener's calendar 'esteemed a very good one.' *The South Carolina Magazine* [17] says the calendar was reprinted several times and that the author was said to have written a treatise on gardening when she was seventy. Mrs. Logan died in 1779, aged 77 years.

[15] Ramsay, p. 227.
[16] *S. Car. Mag.,* xx: 205.

[17] Ibid.

When, on 12 February 1733, Oglethorpe landed the first English settlers in Georgia on the present site of Savannah, he chose at once ten acres of land for a public garden. By common consent of the colonists, this small tract became known as 'The Trustees' Garden.' It was to be chiefly devoted to the growing of mulberries to feed silkworms, with the hope that the making of silk would become the basic industry. Also to be grown were flax, hemp, indigo, cochineal, olives, sub-tropic fruits, drugs, and spices. The garden was to serve as a nursery and seed farm for all plants that could be profitably grown. The Trustees' Garden was the first organized experiment station in the United States.

Subscriptions had been made in England sufficient to endow the garden liberally, and much was expected from the tests that were to be made. In 1732, a year before the colonists reached Georgia, two botanists had been sent to neighboring sub-tropic lands 'to search for esculent, drug, fibre, dye and ornamental plants' for the testing grounds at Savannah. But through the death of one botanist and a series of mishaps to the other, few plants from the men reached Georgia and neither of them ever saw the Trustees' Garden.

Meanwhile those in England interested in the colony were busy. Plants of the olive were sent over in 1734; the same year, vines of the small grape from which 'Zante currants' are made were sent from Zante; caper plants were sent in 1735: Neapolitan chestnuts in 1736; and in 1737 a box of caper plants came from Marseilles. Other plants from various sources were white mulberry for silkworms, cotton seed, madder roots, bamboo roots, seed of alfalfa, then called lucerne. Several shipments of varieties of the European grape were also received, from which it was hoped wine could be made.

The two lodestones to attract European colonists to all of the southern colonies were silk and wine. Throughout the life of the Trustees' Garden, its land and the efforts of the men in charge were chiefly devoted to these products. The climate of Georgia was that of Italy, where silk was made; of Madeira, whence came the best wine. Why could not these become staple products in Georgia? Neither silk nor wine, then or in several later attempts, was made successfully; nor does it appear that the importation of most of the other crops named amounted to much. While the results of experimentation in the Trustees' Garden thus appear to be negative, it was something to learn what crops could not be grown.

Through the ups and downs of the colony, and difficulties with gardeners and the malcontents of the new settlement, the Trustees' Garden fell into neglect. In 1737 John Wesley visited Savannah and reported that the Public Garden 'was now under no care and half the trees are dead.' The garden lingered as a mulberry plantation until 1747 or 1748, and then seems to have passed out of existence.[18]

A very good idea of the small gardens of Savannah, and probably other towns in Georgia, is to be had from the plan drawn for the city by Oglethorpe in 1733. Each male of age eligible for an allotment of land was given a town lot with a front of 60 feet and a depth of 90 feet; a garden lot of 5 acres; and a farm of 44 acres. At first the town gardens were used for vegetables, and flowers were kept in the small city yards. These small places were walled in with tabby or brick, and in the tiniest there was at least a fig tree and climbing roses, if not other flowers too.

Several pages in *The Garden History of Georgia* are devoted to the gardens of Savannah, in which, we are told, a great similarity of plan prevailed. The home, if a mansion, was set back from the street; a strip of formal planting or a small formal garden enclosed by a wrought-iron fence constituted the front yard. In the rear, between the residence and the servants' quarters and barns, lay another garden enclosed by high brick or tabby walls. In this back garden were flowering shrubs, figs, and citrus fruits; also an herb garden; while arbors covered with grapes or roses sometimes led from one building to another.[19]

It would seem from the various accounts of these early gardens in Savannah that from the first until long into the nineteenth century all well-to-do citizens owned plantations on the river bluffs, to which they could retire in the summer months. The best of the early gardens in these summer homes were never cramped for room, as in the town, and they were planted in the prevailing European style of the eighteenth century, in intricate geometrical

[18] Holland, xii: 271-88.   [19] *The Garden Hist. of Ga.*, pp. 1-14.

beds edged with brick or tile or box, with many clipped trees and shrubs; but more and more, one surmises, the plantings became quite open; and after their introduction, camellias, azaleas, and oleanders became the fashionable flowers, as they are today. Always there were roses, and in time sago palms, bignonias, bananas, the fairly modern wisteria, and other vines and creepers.

Ornamental gardens in the southern colonies differed markedly from those of New England. Northern gardens were small, unconventional, formless, personal, and wholly democratic. Southern gardens were fewer, much larger, more likely to be conventional, formal, of geometric designs, and as aristocratic as the wealth of the owners could make them. But the elaborate gardens of the South were far fewer than the casual reading of garden literature would lead one to believe. As compared with modern gardens, those of the colonies in the North or the South would be conspicuous for the poverty in plants, lack of landscape design, and clipped lawns: the lawnmower was not invented until the middle of the nineteenth century.

The rice plantations in Georgia were along the Savannah and Big and Little Ogeechee Rivers. The gardens on these plantations, some of them rivaling the best in South Carolina, were of the same general character as those in the colony to the north. Probably nowhere in the South do live oaks thrive better than along the Savannah, and these oaks, hung with Spanish moss, were planted in long avenues, so beautiful that they made Georgia gardens famous at home and abroad long before the Revolution. Later, it was found that camellias grew especially well in the riverlands of Georgia, and the Savannah region became famous for them.

One of the botanical landmarks of America in this period was the publication in London, in 1731, of the first volume of Mark Catesby's *Natural History of Carolina, Florida, and the Bahamas;* the second volume came out in 1733. They were large folios with very good color plates, good paper, and fine bindings. Botanists say the descriptions of plants in the work are lacking in completeness and accuracy, but, nevertheless, they added much to botany and to knowledge of trees and shrubs for lawn plantings.

Catesby was an Englishman who came to Virginia in 1712 and

spent seven years in the colony. In 1722 he returned for a shorter stay in the Carolinas. During his two visits, he was much interested in shipping seeds and plants to and from Europe and America. Plant lovers in both continents are indebted to him for making known many beautiful ornamental trees. He published in the first volume of his work a figure of the native common catalpa, *Catalpa bignonioides,* which he says was unknown in Carolina until he introduced it from the remoter parts of the country. This plant was in England as early as 1726. It was Catesby who also first described the umbrella tree, later named *Magnolia tripetala,* one of the hardiest magnolias, much used as a stock for tender species. Another plant first described by Catesby was the pawpaw, now known as *Asimina triloba,* which, because of the beauty of its foliage and its excellent fruits, should be grown as an ornamental and esculent.

This pioneer botanist made known to gardeners the beautiful dahoon holly, *Ilex cassine,* so often found in gardens, especially in hedges, in the South. He sent seeds of it to the Physic Garden at Chelsea, in London, whence it was introduced in European gardens. Two other notable plants first described by Catesby were the laurel cherry, or mock orange, *Prunus caroliniana,* so widely grown in the South; and the pink dogwood, a variety of *Cornus florida,* which some nurserymen would have us believe is now a novelty.

We are indebted to Catesby for the first description and the introduction of the sour black gum or tupelo pepperige, *Nyssa sylvatica,* and its relative the cotton or tupelo gum, *Nyssa aquatica;* the great laurel, *Rhododendron maximum;* the fringe tree, *Chionanthus virginica,* one of the commonest small trees in American gardens; the pignut, *Carya glabra;* the water oak, *Quercus nigra,* a favorite shade tree in the South; and Catesby described in 1763 the cabbage palm or palmetto, *Sabal palmetto,* one of the most conspicuous plants on our southeastern coast.

Henry Laurens, plant collector and nurseryman, about 1755, purchased a lot of four acres in Ansonborough, long called Laurens' Square, in which he grew a notable collection of fruits, flowers, and ornamentals. Laurens was a man of large affairs, a merchant of wealth and influence, and through his wide business

connections was able to bring to his garden nearly all the cultivated plants suitable to the climate of South Carolina. He was
ably assisted in his avocation by his wife, and she in turn by John
Watson, who is spoken of by Ramsay 'as a complete English
Gardener.' [20] The Charleston home of Laurens was in the center
of a square filled with fine ornamentals, cared for by Watson.

Laurens is given credit by Carolinians for having introduced
the olive, caper, lime, ginger, guinea grass, alpine strawberry,
red raspberry, and various varieties of grapes and hardy fruits in
South Carolina. Probably he imported all the plants said to have
been first brought to America by him, but in most cases they were
re-introductions, since the sub-tropical plants, at least, had been
grown in the Trustees' Garden in Georgia long before, and old
olive trees were growing earlier at the northern end of Cumberland Island off the coast of Georgia.[21]

John Laurens, son of Henry Laurens, and the favorite son of
Charles Town during the Revolution, was a soldier, statesman,
diplomat, and war hero. He was of note in gardening only because
when the British were besieging the city, he cut the trees and
shrubs, many of them rare exotics, which grew in his father's garden, to make fascines for the town's fortifications.

John Watson eventually purchased a piece of land stretching
from King Street to Meeting Street, and soon was the largest dealer
in nursery plants and seeds in the South. It was said by his contemporaries that every new meritorious plant that had been found
or introduced from abroad might be purchased in his nursery.
The following advertisements establish pretty well the dates when
Watson began to sell seeds and plants, and give some idea of what
was in demand for South Carolina gardens about the middle of
the eighteenth century, when the colony had not been settled a
hundred years. The first, which appeared in the *South Carolina
Gazette,* 10 December 1763, reads:

John Watson, Gardener from London.
Has imported in the last vessels from London, a proper assortment
of garden seeds, flower roots, etc., which he will sell reasonably at Mr.
Henerson's, Peruke-Maker on the Bay. Gardening in all its various
branches will be done by him either by the day or year.

20 Ramsay, p. 228.   21 *Garden and Forest,* I: 285.

In the *South Carolina & American General Gazette,* 14 November 1776, the following advertisement appears:

As the Season is now approaching for the Transplanting of Fruit Trees, the Subscriber begs leave to acquaint the public in general,

That he has for sale at his nursery, a great Variety of Apples, Pears, Plumbs, Cherries, Nectarines, Apricots, and Peach Trees, all grafted and inoxculated from the best sorts England and America afford: also Sweet Almonds, English Walnuts, Filberts, Hazelnuts, English Quinces, Olives, China Oranges, double flowering peaches, Almonds & Pomegranates, and a great variety of English and American flowering trees, shrubs, evergreens, &c.

John Watson.

The beautiful places planted by Henry Laurens and the nursery of John Watson were destroyed during the Revolution. The grounds of Henry Laurens were never fully replanted, but the nursery of John Watson was revived and continued by the family, and eventually passed into the hands of Robert Squibb, a nurseryman, seedsman, gardener, and author.

Squibb was a collector of Southern plants, which he distributed in Europe, taking in exchange the products of European gardens. His entrance into the nursery business was advertised in the *South Carolina Gazette,* 14 March 1785.

Robert Squibb, Seedsman and Gardener, Upper end of Tradd-street.

Gardens laid out, and put in order in the neatest manner, and at the shortest notice.

Squibb was the author of the *Gardener's Kalendar for South Carolina* (see page 471).

The taste for beautiful grounds and knowledge and love of botany, especially of ornamental plants, were furthered in Charles Town by Dr. Alexander Garden (1728-92), a native of the city who was educated in Edinburgh to be a physician. Garden's father, a clergyman, came to Charles Town in 1719 to become rector of St. Philip's Church. The son, when sent to Scotland to study medicine, was also a diligent student of botany. He returned to Charles Town in 1752, and after a few years as a professor at King's College, New York City (now Columbia University), he returned to Charles Town to practice medicine.

Garden was an enthusiastic pupil and friend of Linnaeus, who named Gardenia, the cape jasmine, *Gardenia jasminoides,* after him. This species should not be confused with the true jasmines, which belong to quite a different family of plants. It came from China, not from the Cape, as its name would indicate. Nor is it the jasmine of botanists.

Garden's botanical work came to an end during the Revolution; a Loyalist, he left South Carolina, never to return. His son fought with the Americans and was never forgiven. A granddaughter, named 'Gardenia,' was never permitted to enter her grandfather's house.

PART II

7

POST-REVOLUTION IN THE NORTH

THE eighteenth century was one of singular lethargy in American agriculture. Crops, methods and tools changed little in this hundred-year period; few new kinds of farm and garden crops were introduced; farm animals remained much as they had been in the preceding century; tools were few and primitive, having changed little for centuries; manures were not spread on the land; chemical fertilizers were unknown; and scarcely anyone had heard of rotating crops. The plows were of wood reinforced with iron on point and share. But often the farmer did not own a plow, and the soil was broken with a heavy man-killing wrought-iron hoe, the chief farm tool on frontier lands. There were no harrows, cultivators, or seed drills. Grain was at first cut with a sickle, then by scythe, and after the Revolution with a cradle; it was thrashed with a flail or tramped out by oxen, as in Biblical times, and winnowed in the wind. Garden tools were as few and primitive as those for general farming. The agricultural legacy of the colonies to the states was scant and of little worth.

American Independence brought the dawn of a better day. Men talked of Invention, Organization, and Co-operation; speculation ran riot in every field of life. In Europe too, the French Revolution had brought a new era in civilization.

Perhaps the immediate, concrete thing that happened for the betterment of agriculture in America was the organization of agricultural societies. In the colonies there had been almost no means of spreading information on farming. Lacking books, papers, and agricultural societies, men could learn what their neighbors were doing only by travel and correspondence. Off the waterways, a horse's back and a slow coach on poor roads were the only certain means of travel, and of posts there were none until Frank lin came on the scene. Agricultural societies sprang up widely in the post-Revolutionary period and facilitated the spread of agricultural knowledge.

At the close of the Revolution, fruit growing and gardening were largely in the hands of men of wealth, who, the country over, vied in becoming patrons of horticulture. One of the first Northerners to begin to plant largely was William Hamilton of Philadelphia. In 1800 Hamilton was growing nearly all the hardy fruit and ornamental trees obtainable in Europe. His estate, called 'Woodlands,' was on the right bank of the Schuylkill, just outside the city. Perhaps Hamilton served horticulture best by the introduction of named varieties of fruits at this time when most orchards were of seedling trees.

Hamilton introduced the Lombardy poplar in 1784 (although some people credit its introduction to André Michaux in 1785) and it was soon being more commonly planted than any other ornamental tree. In 1798, the Prince Nursery advertised 10,000 Lombardy poplars, trees 10 to 17 feet in height. Wealthy landowners planted long avenues of these poplars, and most cottages had a Lombardy or two. For nearly a century this was a favorite lawn and street tree in the northern states; but, in time, the Lombardy began to be ravaged by a disease and a worm, and now for many years this old favorite has been planted hardly at all.

Another notable tree of the many exotic species introduced in the garden of Hamilton, now better known and more largely planted than the Lombardy poplar, is the Norway maple. As the once-popular poplar began to decline, the Norway maple was planted more and more; today, in the northeastern states at least, it is about the best of Old World ornamental deciduous trees grown.

Still another notable introduction in William Hamilton's Arboretum was the Tree-of-Heaven, *Ailanthus altissima,* from the Orient, thence to Kew Gardens, and on to Philadelphia. In spite of a very disagreeable odor in pollen-bearing time, it has long been a favorite ornamental in cities because of its rapid growth and its resistance to the smoke and smut of coal.

Judge Richard Peters was another citizen of Philadelphia who greatly promoted gardening in Pennsylvania. He owned and planted Belmont, a large estate near the city, now a part of Fairmount Park. He was one of the founders of the Philadelphia Society for Promoting Agriculture, organized in 1785, and its first president. Out of it sprang most of the societies that aid agriculture in Pennsylvania today. In collaboration with a committee of the Society, made up of John B. Bordley, George Clymer, and Timothy Pickering, Peters established a number of pattern farms in different parts of Pennsylvania on which 'all foreign and domestic trees, shrubs, plants, seeds, or grains may be cultivated and if approved as useful, disseminated.'

The grounds at Belmont were long considered 'the most elegant to be found in the North.' Judge Peters' taste seems to have been strongly influenced by the gentlemen from the South who planted formal beds, mazes, hedges, and clipped evergreens. On his lawn were also to be found statues, balls, pyramids, obelisks, and similar embellishments. The naturalistic style of gardening then being introduced in the North seems not to have appealed to him.

A Frenchman, Eleuthère-Irénée du Pont de Nemours, founder of the distinguished du Pont family of Delaware, was an early patron of American horticulture. He came to this country in 1799 and established a gunpowder factory on the Brandywine, near Wilmington. This first du Pont, like several of his descendants, was deeply interested in agriculture and horticulture, in both of which he engaged on his Delaware estate; but, in particular, he is notable as the introducer of the European chestnut in this country. The first trees were planted in 1805, and soon their progeny were scattered, under several varietal names, in the regions where the Old World chestnut is hardy.

To the north, in New York and New England, as about Philadelphia, fine country seats were at this time the scenes of much loving horticultural labor. In most cases gardens were laid out and developed by the amateur skill of their owners, and these, oftener than not, showed to advantage when compared with the landscape architects coming in greater and greater numbers from Europe, most of whom required years to learn the plant requirements of American soils and climate.

The first prominent patron of gardening in western New York in the eighteenth century was Charles Williamson, the Scottish-born land agent for William Johnstone Pulteny, an Englishman, who, with several associates, had purchased in 1791 a million acres of land in the Genesee Country. The land was opened to settlers at once, with Williamson in charge of land development. He established himself at Bath and Geneva with ambitious plans for building two cities. Account books show that the home company allowed him plenty of garden seeds, apple and peach trees, and money for cold frames and hot beds. Moreover, in 1793, he brought over an Irish gardener, Edward Quinn, to lay out grounds in the two proposed cities. Quinn's yearly hire was '50 pounds for board and $130 for wages.' When Maude, the English traveler and author, visited the region in the summer of 1820, he found 'two acres of vegetables and melons on Pulteney Square' in Bath, and fruit trees which, brought in at great expense, had 'made a fine showing.' [1]

There was little truck gardening in any of the new states. The people were chiefly occupied in agriculture and there were few cities and towns to buy the produce of gardens and orchards, each community supporting itself. Besides, the people of different states, and even in parts of the same state, knew little about each other, and local prejudices were intense.

John Fiske discusses this sectional hate at some length. Among other examples, he cites that of New York City, which, in 1787, had a population of 30,000. The city was supplied with firewood from Connecticut, and cheese, chicken, fruit, and vegetables from New Jersey. This was ruinous to domestic industry, said the men of New York, and straightway imposed a high protective tariff. The two states thus discriminated against, retaliated, and an economic war was on that sowed the seeds of bitter hatred [2] and almost led to actual war.

Indeed, until the building of canals and railroads there was little incentive for raising farm crops anywhere more than a mile or two from rivers or the sea. There were few roads over which wagons could be hauled, so that it was impossible to transport the surplus of farms not located on waterways. There were a few truck gardens and orchards on the fringes of Boston, New York,

[1] Cowan, pp. 103, 212.
[2] Fiske, *Critical Period of Am. Hist.*, 1783-89, pp. 146-7.

Philadelphia, and cities in the South, where such staples as tree fruits and coarse vegetables were grown for the market, but elsewhere there were no markets except for cider, brandy, and whisky, easiest farm products to ship. By 1800, however, land near large towns was becoming valuable and was being divided into smaller and smaller parcels, so that intensive truck gardening and orcharding were forced upon its owners.

Another factor entered into the farming of the new states: the land was becoming badly run down because of the lack of fertilizers. A smattering of knowledge about the chemistry of soils and their need of fertilizers was spread about in correspondence, through papers read in agricultural societies, and by demonstrations on farms here and there. Franklin and Washington were experimenters and demonstrators in the use of fertilizers. Summer fallowing was being practiced, and experimenters were discovering that clover turned under enriched the soil. More and more, near the coast, fish were used as fertilizer, as Squanto, the Indian chief, had taught the Pilgrims in their first planting season to fertilize corn. Manure, even to street scrapings from the towns, was saved for the land.

According to an observing traveler, the Reverend Timothy Dwight, the farmers on Long Island found the market for garden truck in New York City so favorable that the gardener could buy manure in the town with profit. In 1806, a writer, speaking of truck gardening near Philadelphia, remarked: 'A grandson or great-grandson, at the present day, raises more produce, lives better, and makes a greater profit upon one-fourth of the land once occupied by his ancestors, than his ancestors did upon the whole individual tract.' The kinds of crops grown for the markets were few, chiefly cabbage, beans, turnips, watermelons, and onions; but in private gardens there was an amazingly large variety of vegetables raised.

While gardening near cities and towns had made great progress, as all writers of the times agree, in the post-Revolutionary period in comparison with colonial times, country folk had not yet found the plenty, beauty, and happiness in gardens that people in Europe enjoyed, particularly if they owned land. William Cobbett, best of all the writers who visited America and wrote about farming, set forth clearly the difference between Long Island and Kent or Sussex in farm life, and the reasons why Americans fell short. His comparison is well worth quoting:

Instead of the neat warm little cottage, the yard, cow-stable, pig-stye, hen-house, all in miniature, and the garden, nicely laid out, and the paths bordered with flowers, while the cottage door is crowned with a garland of roses or honeysuckle; instead of these we here see the laborer content with a shell of boards, while all around him is as barren as the sea-beach, though the natural earth would send melons, the finest in the world, creeping round his door, and though there is no English shrub, or flower, which will not grow and flourish here. This want of attention is hereditary from the first settlers. They found land so plenty, that they treated small plots with contempt. Besides, the *example* of neatness was wanting. There were no gentlemen's gardens kept as clean as drawing-rooms, with grass as even as a carpet. From endeavoring to imitate perfection men arrive at mediocrity, and those who have never seen or heard of perfection, in these matters, will naturally be slovens.[3]

We cannot leave Cobbett without giving him credit for popularizing one of our American trees. It is said that no other native of North American forests has been praised more, scattered so widely by cultivation, or had so much written about it as the locust, *Robinia Pseudoacacia*. Cobbett was largely responsible for so great interest in the locust. During his two years' residence on Long Island, 1817 to 1819, he maintained a small nursery for forest trees, and among those he grew was the locust. It had been sent to France as early as 1635 (the genus *Robinia* had been named after Robin, a French botanist) by Linnaeus and was grown somewhat in Europe and the United States when Cobbett began to recommend it in letters, papers, and in his book *The Woodlands*. His zeal in propagation and his enthusiasm made it the most popular of all trees in England for a decade or two; the fashion crossed the Atlantic, and in the half century before the Civil War no other tree was so generally planted in eastern United States as the locust. The species is so preyed upon by several insects that it is now seldom planted, but there are few long-settled communities east of the Mississippi where ancient decadent trees of this once-popular landscape staple may not be found.

[3] Cobbett, p. 14.

One gets an idea of the primitive conditions in Pennsylvania in the post-Revolutionary period from a description of a short tour to the west of Philadelphia in 1794 by Talleyrand. We are told that 150 miles from the capital, all trace of man's presence disappeared; wild nature in all its pristine vigor was found; the forests were as old as the world itself; decayed plants and trees covered the ground. It was hard to get through the intricate bushes that often barred the way; there were no trees on the banks of rivers but large natural meadows; strange flowers were to be found in the forests, and here and there were traces of former tornadoes that had carried everything before them. 'Enormous trees all mowed down in the same direction bear witness to these terrible phenomena.' [4]

As in the colonies, orchards as late as 1800 received little or no care. Pruning was almost wholly neglected, although the reasons for pruning were recognized and the art had been practiced for centuries in Europe. Not until horticultural societies were organized and books and magazines began to give instructions in the nineteenth century did fruit growers begin to prune their trees. Until experiment stations demonstrated its value long after the Civil War, many horticulturists believed that pruning was harmful. Fruit trees were headed high to keep the fruit out of the reach of livestock.

In none of the fruit-growing states were fruit trees cultivated. Nearly always the orchard was used as a pasture for cattle and swine. In the judgment of most early pomologists manures caused trees to overbear. Not even the sod-mulch was used in orchards, since the only grasses were natives, which make poor sod, and red clover was a rarity. Besides, until the nineteenth century, grass and clover seed were to be had only in unwinnowed chaff, for there were neither thrashing machines nor fanning mills. Orchards were often cropped with corn or grains.

Attempts to control pests in orchards and gardens were few and wholly futile. Epidemics of peach yellows, pear blight, apple scab, and other diseases caused by bacteria and fungi were ascribed to 'morbid infections of the air,' or to a 'surcharge of Franklin's electric fluid.' Pear blight was 'a vegetable apoplexy caused by a

4 'The Memoirs of Talleyrand,' *Century Magazine*, XIX: 374.

surcharge of electric fluid.' It could be controlled, it was thought, by hanging in the trees old horseshoes, hoops of iron, pieces of wire, or any metal that would conduct the 'floating electric current' from the trees. In 1837 the Pennsylvania Horticultural Society offered a prize of $500 for an effective remedy for pear blight. The offer brought many panaceas, samples of which are: soaking the ground with soapsuds; hanging iron in the trees; wrapping the branches with rags soaked in brimstone; driving nails in the trunk to give the trees an iron tonic; and 'physicking' the trees with calomel inserted beneath the bark. The award was not made, which speaks well for the intelligence of the society.

Peach yellows began to be troublesome late in the eighteenth century, and peach growers attributed it to an infection in the air. This is one orchard disease that growers then knew almost as much about, and controlled almost as well, as they do now, although its contagious nature was not known so well. The remedy— in 1800 as today—is to destroy the diseased trees as soon as the foliage begins to turn yellow.

Little could be done to control injurious insects until entomologists had studied their life histories and classified them. Not much was achieved in this field until after the Civil War, and spraying for insects and plant diseases has been practiced only during the lifetimes of many men now living. However, early fruit growers and gardeners were not so badly off in the matter of pests, since many of the most troublesome diseases and insects are of comparatively recent introduction. Moreover, faulty fruits made as good cider and brandy as perfect ones.

Nothing was known about the need of cross-pollination for fruits, although a good deal was said in the early publications about 'sterile trees.' 'Excessive growth of wood' was the cause commonly assigned to sterility. Why corn, cucurbits, flowers, and fruits 'mixed' was not well understood even as late as a hundred years ago, and many people doubted the existence of 'perfect' and 'imperfect' flowers in strawberries.

Common springtime visitors in all northern orchards were the itinerant tree grafters, who went from orchard to orchard grafting apples and pears, usually seedlings, often substituting grafts from unknown trees for named varieties. The matter of varieties, however, was of small importance, since most of the fruit grown was used for fermented or distilled drinks. An apple in a colonial orchard, and long after, was but an 'apple'; a pear, a 'pear'; a peach, a 'peach'; to most who planted orchards—a variety name meant nothing. As late as 1843, Patrick Barry, noted pomologist, wrote of the nursery business: 'It is hard to make a start because of the itinerant grafters who make it a business to peddle cions around the country.'

Yet as we have seen there were many European gardeners in America who knew how to bud and graft—the art was described by writers long before the time of Christ. As early as 1736, Peter Collinson was telling John Bartram to 'graft plums and nectarines on peach stocks.' [5] The matter had been under discussion before, for Collinson urges: 'Pray try; I have great opinion of its succeeding.' Ten years later, he writes impatiently: 'Though thou canst not see, yet I have told thee what inoculating a peach stock may do.' [6]

After the Revolution, budding and grafting became much more common. The Princes were the first nurserymen to advertise budded and grafted trees. In their catalogue for 1771 they offer 29 kinds of peaches, most of which appear to be types grown as seedlings rather than varieties. In 1791 they list 35 sorts, with the statement that 'all are inoculated.' John Kenrick, a nurseryman at Newton, Massachusetts, began business in 1790 by planting a quantity of peach pits, the trees from which he sold without budding. Four years later he had learned to bud and began to make a specialty of budded peach trees.

The practice during the colonial period of growing apples from seed had some advantages; in apple-growing states, thousands of seedlings were passed through the sieve of selection, and America by 1800 began to have a long list of good apples. At the opening of the nineteenth century, out of a hundred-odd varieties offered by nurseries, nearly all were of American origin, not a few of which are grown today. Among these one thinks at once of Baldwin, Ben Davis, Early Harvest, Esopus, Spitzenburg, Fall Pippin, Fameuse, Green Newton, Jonathan, Lady, Maiden Blush, Pomme Grise, Rhode Island Greening, Ribston Pippin,

5 Darlington, p. 81.   6 Ibid. p. 177.

Roxbury Russet, Swaar, Sweet Bough, Tompkin King, Wagener, Williams, Winesap, Yellow Bellflower, and York Imperial; of these 22, 19 are of American origin. Of the three European sorts, Lady and Pomme Grise came from France; Ribston Pippin from England.

In the century and a half since the colonial period ended, perhaps as many as 2000 varieties of apples have originated on this continent and at least 100 have been brought over from Europe; yet 10 of the 20 varieties originating by accident in the colonies are still standard commercial varieties, and the other 10 would stand in any collection of choice apples.

The pear did not reach so high estate as the apple in colonial America, and one somehow feels that a great opportunity was missed. French missionaries early planted pear seeds from Nova Scotia up the St. Lawrence to the Great Lakes; along the shores of Ontario and Erie to Detroit; and about the French trading posts in Ohio, Indiana, and Illinois, from which some of the oldest, largest, and most productive pear trees the world has ever known were grown. Moreover, the trees, some of which the author has seen, were free from blight and bore handsome pears of very good quality. Out of the thousands of these old French trees, no named variety arose, and probably all are now lost to cultivation.

Perhaps the reason for the neglect of these French pears was that they were superseded, none having been recognized by fruit growers as especially meritorious, by the very good new varieties introduced from Belgium and France in the first half of the nineteenth century. In *The Pears of New York*,[7] 2,929 varieties of pears are described, of which more than half have been grown in America. Of this number, only the 4 following sorts were under cultivation in 1800: Bartlett, Seckel, Tyson, and White Doyenne. Of the four, Seckel and Tyson originated in America. Bartlett and Seckel are still the most commonly planted pears on this continent. Had seedling pears been grown as commonly as seedling apples, we should have had more American varieties.

The quince, another pome fruit, was relatively more commonly planted in the colonies than the apple and pear. As far as can be

[7] Hedrick, *The Pears of New York*.

made out, the Orange Quince, which comes nearly true to seed and is therefore a group rather than a varietal name, was the only type of the quince known in America until the nineteenth century. This variety is now about the only one planted, and even so, unfortunately, the quince can hardly be found in modern American orchards. Quinces, then as now, were commonly grown from layers and suckers, with few seedlings from which new varieties might originate.

In no other part of the world, as has been said, does the peach grow and bear as well as in favored parts of North America. Wherever grown in the colonies, the peach came from seeds and there were few or no varieties. There seem to have been two very distinct types, and only two, in colonial America, whereas there are now at least six very different groups. The two were the small, woolly, round, streaked, or reddish Indian peach, poor in quality; and the large Melocoton of which the well-known Crawfords, best of all peaches in quality, are the type.

In the author's *Peaches of New York*,[8] 2181 varieties of peaches are described. Unlike any other fruit, almost none of the varieties grown now or in the colonies came from Europe, and only four of this vast number can have been known by old men of this generation; nearly all the others have originated since 1860. Heath Cling, Oldmixon Cling, Red Cheek Melocoton, and Yellow Rareripe are the four varieties, largely grown a hundred years ago, which might have been found in collections as late as 1900. It is doubtful if any could now be found. All originated in America. Unlike the apple, the peach profited little in the way of new varieties from the millions of seedling trees grown in the colonies.

At one time or another about several hundred varieties of plums have come under the eye of the author.[9] These varieties are of 15 species and sub-species, giving probably a greater diversity of fruits in size, color, taste, aroma, and texture than any other hardy tree fruit. Yet before 1800, only 2 species and some 10 or 12 varieties of plums were grown in North America that could by any chance now be found in our orchards. These are Black Bullace, a damson; German Prune, which goes back to the Crusades and is one of the oldest fruits known; Hand, grown

[8] Hedrick, *The Peaches of New York*.
[9] Hedrick, *The Plums of New York*.

by General Hand in Lancaster, Pennsylvania, in 1790; Hungarian, an old prune from Hungary; Imperial Gage, grown by the Princes in 1790; Italian Prune, from Italy; Peach, a European plum; Reine Claude, an old French variety; Shropshire, a damson from England in the seventeenth century, and one of the first plums to be brought to America; Washington, grown in 1790 from the same lot of seeds as Imperial Gage; and Yellow Egg, an old European variety still grown commercially. The plum profited little or not at all by being grown as a seedling fruit, of which, in comparison with the apple and peach, there were few trees.

In modern America, the apricot is grown only on the Pacific Coast, California having about five million trees. California furnishes America with practically all of its fresh apricots, and has a monopoly on the canned and dried products for the whole world. In the Atlantic States the apricot is now found only occasionally in some favored spot, though the tree is as hardy as that of the peach, and might, at least, be grown as an ornamental, for few trees are handsomer either in leaf or flower. It cannot be grown in the East commercially, chiefly because the varieties now known bloom so early that frost nearly every year destroys the crop. Yet the apricot seems to have been grown in colonial America wherever peaches were planted. Perhaps late frosts were less frequent in the more wooded country in these earlier years. The varieties mentioned by early gardeners, all of which came from Europe and can still be obtained, are Moorpack, Peach, and Royal.

So, too, the nectarine, now almost exclusively a Pacific Coast fruit, although of minor importance because the fruits have skins so delicate that they cannot be safely shipped, is little grown. There are occasional references to nectarines in notices of colonial gardens and in the advertisements of early nurserymen. The nectarine is a fuzzless peach, not more different in other respects than are groups of peaches among themselves. Were it not for the thin skin and the curculio, and had there been more work in breeding varieties, the nectarine would possibly have been as largely grown in America as the peach, for it is better liked. It is probable that the curculio was not so common in colonial orchards. Early Newington, Elruge, and Pitmaston Orange are the three varieties that were offered by colonial nurserymen. All came from Europe.

Unlike the apple and the peach, and like the pear, the cherry is distinctively a European fruit in the origin of varieties. The author describes in *The Cherries of New York* [10] 1145 varieties of cherries, of which at least three-fourths came from Europe. Some of the kinds now grown are among the oldest of all hardy fruits, many of them having been brought to North America by the earliest European settlers. Black Heart was, according to Prince in 1832, more widely known than any other cherry in the country; Black Tartarian, still common in every sweet cherry orchard in the country, was brought to this country at the close of the eighteenth century; Carnation, first mentioned by Rea in 1676, was early brought to America; Early Richmond, the second most popular sour cherry in America, was brought to the lower St. Lawrence region as 'French,' and to Virginia before 1700, where it received its American name, its original English name being 'Kentish'; Late Kentish is the sour pie-cherry of early New England, propagated from seeds or sprouts; May Duke, a corruption of Medoc, was said by William Prince in 1832 to be 'among the first of the cherries introduced to America from Europe'; Montmorency, a group name for several cherries as a type, has been cultivated in France for several centuries and was early brought to Canada and New England; and Yellow Spanish, the Bigarreau of the French, goes back at least to the first century of the Christian Era; it was brought to America soon after the Revolution. Not one of these, nor of any other named cherry, originated in the American colonies.

New Jersey cider continued to be the best America produced, as it had been in the colonial period. William Coxe, the pomologist, reported that in 1810 Essex County produced 198,000 barrels of cider and 307,310 gallons of cider spirits (applejack or apple brandy, it would be called now). Woodward reports that in 1812 one citizen 'made 200 barrels of cider daily, the products of six mills and twenty-three presses.' [11] According to the same

10 Hedrick, *The Cherries of New York.*
11 Woodward, p. 21.

authority the pomace was spread on the fields as a fertilizer. Cider and brandy making continued as leading horticultural products until the great temperance movement of the 1830's ruined the business, although, according to Woodward, as late as 1834, there were 388 cider distilleries in New Jersey.

To find out what fruits were being grown in the northern states in this period, what varieties of each, and who the nurserymen were, we must rely almost wholly on the newspapers of the day. There were no agricultural papers or books, and few writers of the time had much to say about horticulture. Happily, the newspapers, in Baltimore and Philadelphia especially, carried advertisements of several nurserymen, which give us some information. Possibly a search through the files of papers in smaller cities might give further information.

A rather wide range of nursery plants is offered in an advertisement in the *Maryland Journal and Baltimore Advertiser,* 1 August 1786. It should be noticed that the advertiser distinguishes European strawberries under the name 'Hautboys' from 'Strawberry Plants of different Kinds.' Just what the 'different Kinds' were would be hard to say. The advertisement reads:

At Timonium, excellent Clover, Timothy and wild Grass Meadow-Pasturage, for Horses and Cattle, at the moderate Price of Seven Shillings and Six Pence each per Month. . .

Likewise, all Kinds of Stocks for Grafting and inoculating, consisting of Apples, Pears, Quinces, Cherries, Plums, Damson's, wild Grapes, Rasberries, Gooseberries, Currants, Hautboys, and Strawberry Plants of different Kinds—Golden and Weeping Ozier, and Filbert Trees—a few bulbous Roots, warranted good of their Kind. Orders left at Mr. Armstrong's in South-Street, will be received and punctually attended to.

Probably none of the nine apples offered in the *Maryland Journal and Baltimore Advertiser* of 28 October 1788 could now be found in any nursery, but trees of six of them might be found in an occasional old orchard. Many older orchardists will remember House, and Hoop (synonym of Honey Sweet), Romanite, Rambo, Newtown Pippin, Spitzenburg, and Redstreak:

For Sale, and now fit to be planted out in Orchards a Variety of grafted Apple-Trees, viz House-Apples, Hoop's, Romanites, Ramboes, English Russetens, Newton Pippins, Spitzenbergs, Redstreaks, and early Codlings. Orders sent in Two Weeks from this Date, mentioning the different Sorts and numbers of each, will be forwarded to the Nursery-man who will bring the Trees in all next month. The Price for those sent to Baltimore-Town, or any other Part of the country, is Ten-Pence a Piece, to be paid on Delivery.

William Russell.

Philip Walten seems to have been the leading nurseryman and florist in Baltimore in the post-Revolutionary period. His advertisements appear in three of the several Baltimore papers published in the 1780's and 1790's. The following list of fruits probably includes about all that could be purchased from American nurserymen at the close of the eighteenth century. The advertisement appears in the *Maryland Gazette and Baltimore General Advertiser* of 7 November 1788:

To Be Sold, by the Subscriber.

A Quantity of Grafted and Inoculated Fruit Trees: Among which are the following kinds, viz.

Apple-Trees—Price 1 s. each

Newtown pipins
Golden Ditto
Orange Ditto
Long Ditto
English Redstreaks
Black Ditto
Priest Apple
English Codlin
English White Apple
Bell Catlin
Summer Pearmain
Cathead Apple
Robeson Apple

Pears—Price 3 s.

Summer Bergamot
French Orange Ditto

Ball Pear
English Summer pound Ditto
Green Chisel Ditto

Cherries—Price 3 s.

May-Duke
Arch-Duke
Carnation
White Heart
Ox Heart
Bleeding Heart
Kentish Cherry
Spanish Heart
French Cherry &c.

Peaches—Price 1 s. 3 d.

Old Newington
New Newington

Peaches—Price 1 s. 3 d. (Cont.)

White Blossom
Early Purple
Scarlet Nutmeg
White Ditto
Green Ditto
Musketong Peach
Red Pine-apple
Green Catherine
October Peach
Rare Ripe Ditto, &c.
Dean or Heath Peach

Roman Apricots—Price 2 s.

Winter Clingstone
White Newington

Plumbs—Price 3 s.

Yellow Bonum Magnum
Green Gage
Prune Monsieur, &c.

Nectarines—Price 2 s.

Red Roman
Yellow Ditto

The above named trees are a small distance from town, and will be shewn to any person inclining to purchase, by applying to the sub-scriber, living in Sharp-street, near the Market-house, Howard's-hill. If any person should be wanting to send any of the Trees above men-tioned, a great distance, great care will be taken to put them up so as to take no damage.

Philip Walten.

Another of Walten's advertisements appears two years later in the *Maryland Gazette,* 30 November 1790, in which an assort-ment of ornamentals and several other fruits are offered:

To be Sold, By the Subscriber

A number of enoculated and grafted Fruit-Trees, and others, Apples, Pear, Plumbs, Cherries, Peaches, Apricots, Nectarines, English Wal-nuts, of the best kind, Gooseberries, Currants, White Muscat Grape Vines, Monthly Roses, Honey Suckles, Catalpa flower Tree, Weeping Willow, Sena Tree, Bitter Almonds, White and Red Althea Fruit, Purple Ditto.

Philip Walten.

Evidently most of the trees offered south of New York were named varieties. In New England and New York seedlings pre-dominated until 40 years later.

An early collector of fruit trees, a benefactor of pomology in his day, was a Mr. Gough, who offers his surplus trees to fellow fruit growers at 'Nine Pence a Tree.' His advertisement appears in the *Maryland Journal and Baltimore Advertiser,* 30 March 1790:

About Two Thousand Apple-Trees for Sale.

As Mr. Gough has transplanted as many Apple Trees from his Nursery at Perry-Hall, as he would wish, the Remainder will be disposed of, promiscuously, at Nine Pence a Tree.—Among them are some grafted and innoculated, so that it is possible a Purchaser may get a curious variety of good Fruit, that Mr. Gough has been carefully collecting, these Fifteen Years, from France, Philadelphia, and New York. As several large Orchards have been planted at Perry-Hall, from the Nursery, the Trees, now for SAle are, in general, not handsome. . . They are already divided into Bundles, containing Twenty-five each, and will be sold in that Situation. The money to be sent by the Persons who take the Trees away. Application to be made to John Norwood, at Perry-Hall.

A nursery in New Castle County, Delaware, was doing an interstate business in 1791. The stock was being grown in Delaware, but was advertised for sale in the *Maryland Gazette,* 18 September 1791. Some of the varieties listed were grown down to the end of the nineteenth century and 8 or 10 of the apples could be found in any one of the northern states today:

Fruit Trees

James Dixon, at his Nursery, in Mill Creek Hundred, New Castle County, Delaware, fourteen miles from Elkton, fifteen from New Castle, seven from Newport, and eight from Wilmington, Has for Sale, a large and general collection of Choice Grafted Trees, of early and late Fruits, now fit to Transplant, viz.

Among which are,

Apples and Pears	Gregg Apple
New-Town Pippin	Late Blossom
Long Pippin	Yellow Vandever
Cart-house Apple	Sweet-Pine
Pennock	Pound Apple
English Redstreaks	Green Roman Right
House Apple	Virginia Crab
Rambos	White Vandever
English Russet	Black Vandever
Vandever	Summer Queen
Priestly Apple	English Codlin
American Pippin	Wilson's Early
Winter-Queen	Meadow Gales &c.

A supply of any number of said Trees can be had on the shortest notice, at said Nursery, on the most reasonable terms; and at a small expense they will be delivered at any of the above places. Directions will be given with the Trees how to plant and cultivate the young orchard. An allowance will be made to such as take a large quantity.

Aquila Jones, on Bowly's Wharf, Baltimore, will receive and forward any order left with him, to said nursery.

In an advertisement in the *Federal Gazette,* Philadelphia, 20 October 1800, the Oldmixon peach is first mentioned in print. Coxe, and Prince, a little later, state that this is the first American-grown peach to receive a name. The variety was named after Sir John Oldmixon, who came to America in the eighteenth century. Downing supposes that he brought peach pits with him, from one of which this variety originated. The variety is more than 200 years old, though it is doubtful if it could now be found. The writer remembers it well, fifty years ago, as a rich, juicy, white-fleshed peach—one of the best of all peaches:

NURSERY

William *Leeson,* Nursery and Seedsman, In the Northern Liberties, opposite the Old Rising Sun Tavern, continues to sell at his Nursery, the following assortment of Fruit and Forest Trees, Flowering Shrubs, &c. such as

Apples, pears, plumbs, cherries, apricots, nectarines, peaches, quinces, English walnuts, almond, filbert, weeping willow, Lombardy poplar, English elms, catalpa, and plaintree, commonly called buttonwood, with a number of other plants, too tedious to mention. The subscriber has in addition to his former collection, that admirable fruit called the Oldmixon Peach, which for beauty, size and flavor, exceeds any of the peach kind that has yet been discovered. He has also a large assortment of Garden Seeds of the last year's saving, fit for the West India Islands. . .

From an advertisement in the *Federal Gazette,* Philadelphia, 20 October 1800, one learns that hedges were coming in vogue in Philadelphia and its environment in 1800. The orange and lemon trees offered were no doubt in tubs so that they might be given shelter in winter:

Sales of Fruit and other Trees, Flower-roots, Garden Seeds, &c. . . . The whole nursery stock of John Lithen, deceased, consisting of a great number of Fruit trees of the very best and most esteemed kinds in this country—a great quantity of Lombardy Poplars, and other ornamental trees and shrubs—a large quantity of white and other Thorns, in excellent order for planting out in hedges—as good Thorns is an article rarely to be met with, it is hoped Gentlemen desirous of introducing the elegant improvement of Hedges (the most beautiful and durable of all fences) on their Estates, will avail themselves of this opportunity of procuring them—a large collection of Flower roots, such as Hyacinths, Tulips, and many other bulbous and fiberous ornamental flowering plants—a large quantity of Garden seeds, of the most useful sorts, fresh and genuine in their kinds, which will be put up in complete assortments and quantities suitable for the use of private families, also in large quantities suitable for the West Indies. . .

A few fine healthy Orange and Lemon Trees, will be offered for sale at the same time.

John Connelly, Auctioneer.

Besides issuing several broadsides, one of which is reproduced in Plate IV, and a series of catalogues, which began as early as 1791, the Princes were large advertisers in the newspapers of the day.

It was William Prince who first grew trees of the pecan for sale. In 1772 he planted 30 nuts from which he raised 10 plants. Eight of these he sold in England at ten guineas each. After this small start, pecans were offered almost continuously by the Prince nurseries, and soon were for sale by other nurseries.

The pecan might have been known to southern explorers, but it seems to have been brought to notice first in the North and in Europe by Captain Wangenheim, an officer in the Hessian troops that fought for England in the Revolution. The captain was a forester and during his stay in America, a period of eight years, he gave attention to the forest trees of this country. In 1781 and again in 1787 he published descriptions of different forest species, one of which was the pecan, *Carya Pecan*. The drawings in Wangenheim's books are poor, and that of the pecan is far from accurate. The nut is made to look like a peanut and is described as 'kidney shaped.' Probably the author had only seen the young trees growing in Prince's nursery. Wangenheim tells us that the pecan was unknown in the American colonies until 1762, when fur traders brought nuts to New York from the South.

This was the Wangenheim to whom Miss Jane Colden transferred her *Flora of New York,* in manuscript and with drawings, with the hope that it might be published. Wangenheim transferred it to the Banksian Library where, unfortunately, it remained in manuscript.

The best if not the only information about the seeds of vegetables and flowers, the bulbs, tubers, and roots of ornamental plants, and the names of seedsmen, for the period between the close of the Revolutionary War and the beginning of the nineteenth century, is also to be found in newspaper advertisements.

In the *Pennsylvania Packet,* 18 December 1781, John Henry Fisher offers an interesting assortment of seeds of vegetables and herbs. Several of them could not be found in seedsmen's catalogues of today:

GARDEN SEEDS

A general Assortment of fresh and valuable Garden Seeds, The best in their Kinds, to be Sold by John Henry Fisher, at Point no Point; Among which are, Early short top purple Raddish, Early do, Salmon do, Winter do, Turnep, *Cabbage,* viz, Green, Savoy, Green or Drumhead, Common white head, Onion, Leek, *Lettuce,* viz Versailles or green Cos, Cabbage, Imperial, Curled, Tongue or pepper-grass, Cellery, Parsley, Summer Savery, Sweet Bazil, Sweet Marjoram, Sage, Pot Marigold, Summer Spinnage, Prickley winter ditto, Parsnip, Carot, Beet, white Asparagus, Cucumber, Squash, Carduus Benedictus, (holy thistle), *Peas,* viz Best early Hotspur, Large green Nonparel, Thick Stalk Imperial, Bunch, Spanish Moratta, Ocra, Kidney Beans, Different sorts, Carolina ditto, Winsor or garden ditto.

N. B. He has also a very curious collection of annual Flower Seeds, Medicinal Herbs, &c. &c.

Another seedsman in Philadelphia just after the Revolution was General Philip de Hass, evidently a retired soldier, but of what army does not appear. The advertisement is in the *Pennsylvania Packet,* 20 February 1781:

ROOTS OF FLOWERS

General Philip De Hass

Just imported into this City, immediately from Holland, a great variety of Roots of Flowers, for the Pleasure Garden; of Bulbous

Roots, undoubtedly the greatest variety ever imported in America, such as, Tulips, Hyacinths, Narcessus, Daffadel Lillies, and all other the most admired Bulbous Flowers now in esteem in the best Gardens in Europe; The Bulbs are flowering Roots and in excellent condition; Likewise an excellent parcel of the Ranoaculus, Anamones, &c. Also a great variety of the most admired flower seeds, and a complete assortment of Seeds for Kitchen gardens of all kinds. All which was collected last fall, out of the most famous gardens in Holland. Enquire at General Philip de Hass, in Third street near Race street.

A few years later a list of flowers and plants offered in the same paper, 30 September 1789, adds a few plants to those in General Hass's list, but is still far too short an enumeration of flowers then grown:

Peter Crouwels, living out Fourth street, at the Place called Hartsfield, one mile from the city, takes the liberty to inform his Customers in particular, and the Public in general, that he intends to sell off, at very low prices, from this time till the middle of October next, a great Variety of Flower Roots, as Hyacinths, Tulips, Lilies, Tuberoses, &c. Also, Plants in Pots, as Oleanders, Geraniums, of different sorts, Myrtle, Egg Plants, Sensative, Jerusalem Cherries, Passion Flower, and a great number of others, too tedious to mention. He has likewise for sale, a large quantity of Flower Root Glasses of the best kind, and all sorts of fresh Garden Seeds.

The five following advertisements are from Baltimore newspapers. One is surprised at the number of varieties of flowering plants and seeds offered by Peter Bellet in the *Maryland Journal and Baltimore Advertiser* under date of 24 January 1786. One is surprised, also, to read that these florists and seedsmen of 150 years ago published catalogues, none of which seems to have come down to us:

PETER BELLET
Florist and Seedsman

. . . Acquaints the Public, that he has yet on hand an extensive Variety of the most rare bulbous Flowers and Seeds, which have not been known before in the Country.

He has also just imported from Amsterdam, the most beautiful Ranunculas, a Variety of 120 Sorts, in all Colours; 60 Sorts of double Anemonies; 25 Sorts of monthly Rose Trees; 11 Sorts of Jessamines;

22 Sorts of Carnations; 11 Sorts of rare bulbous Pyramids; 8 Sorts of Passetouts; 8 Sorts of Tube-Roses; 8 Sorts of double Jonquils, the most rare in all Colours; Hyacinths of the very best Sorts; 40 Sorts of Flower Seeds; all Sorts of fresh Garden Seeds; and Colliflowers. . .

He has Catalogues of the Names and Colours of all his bulbous Flowers and Seeds

John Lieutaud, a Frenchman, advertises in the *Maryland Journal and Baltimore Advertiser,* 2 April 1790, a fine lot of seeds, roots, and bulbs from France and Holland. As was often the case with early dealers in seeds and trees, this Frenchman offers his services in pruning, grafting, and budding:

JOHN LIEUTAUD
Gardner and Florist, from France.

Informs the Public, that he has, for sale, all Kinds of Seeds, Roots, and Bulbs, of the finest Flowers, from France and Holland, and, in particular, 50 different Species of double Hyacinths, 20 Species of Tarcets, 25 kinds of Rose-leaved Carnations, 101 species of fine double Ranunculus, 50 ditto of Candia with a fine smell, 60 Species of double Anemonies, 150 kinds of Seeds of different Fall and Summer Flowers, and 10 Kinds of Roots and Bulbs of different very rare flowers. Also, a great variety of fresh Seeds of the Production of the rarest and best Sallads, Cabbages, Radishes, Carrots, with Pot Herbs, and many other Vegetables too numerous to particularize in a News-Paper. He can procure all kinds of Fruit Trees for such persons as will honour him with their Orders; also, Prune, Graft, and innoculate Trees, the whole at a moderate price. He hopes he will be able to satisfy the Curiosity of the Public, and deserve their Confidence. He lives at Capt. Gould's in Charles-Street, where a printed Catalogue may be seen. N. B. He has, also, a good Collection of Natural Curiosities, from the Province of Dauphiny, very proper for a Cabinet of Natural History.

Here is a short list of vegetable seeds for sale in Baltimore, advertised in the *Baltimore Daily Repository,* 16 March 1793:

The subscriber's Garden Seeds are just come to hand, consisting of early York, early and late Sugar Loaf, curled Green Savoy, Silver skin Onion, Globe Artechoke, long green Cucumber Seed. Solid Cellery, late and early Charleton Peas, long Orange Carrot, and many other sorts, too numerous to mention, to be sold by

James Edwards

From the beginning of gardening in America down to a generation ago, gardens in town or country were always enclosed, because livestock roamed at large and took their will with greenery. Probably the first garden fences were of rails or stone walls. Where stone could be had in abundance, as in New England and parts of New York, stone walls, a soft gray, covered with vines, quickly became popular, though never able to support wall gardens as in the moist cool British gardens. In almost every part of America where settlements were well established and home owners had means, an occasional white-washed picket fence enclosed the garden; and in the northeast, at least, such a fence was very common.

English yew and holly are the choicest plants for British hedges, but neither has been generally grown for hedgerows in America. Washington and Jefferson tried both in Virginia, as did Adams and Quincy in Massachusetts, without success. Since 1900 a number of Asiatic plants suitable for hedges have been introduced, but prior to that the most reliable hedges in the North were barberry, privet, osage orange, locust, and arbor-vitae, to which cypress and cedar might be added for the South. A far greater number of American plants might have been used, but for three centuries, so greatly does custom prevail, the country adhered to the hedge plants of Europe.

An idea of the furnishings of a garden in the Revolutionary period may be had from a description of the garden of a Mr. Bowler, Newport, Rhode Island, written by the Reverend Manasseh Cutler, noted in his day as a clergyman, statesman, and botanist. He says:

It contains four acres and has a grand circle in the middle. Near the middle is an oval surrounded with espaliers of fruit-trees, in the center of which is a pedestal on which is an amillary sphere with an equatorial dial. On one side of the front is a hot-house containing orange-trees, some ripe, some green, some blooms, and various other fruit trees of the exotic kind and curious flowers. At the lower end of the aisle of trees is a large summer-house, a long square containing three rooms, the middle paved with marble and hung with landscapes. On the right is a large private library adorned with curious carvings. There are espaliers of fruit-trees at each end of the garden and curious flowering shrubs. The room on the left is beautifully designed for music and contains a spinnet.

In typical gardens of the eighteenth and nineteenth century, nearly every garden of the well-to-do contained urns or vases, sometimes of marble, granite, pottery, lead, or—in lowly gardens— cast iron. Most often they were filled with flowers, usually stiff and formal plants, as dracaenas, centaureas, or the like; sometimes they were ornaments pure and simple. As formal objects of art their place was usually near the house. There was a time before and after the Revolutionary War when lead vases were imported from England, many of them so beautiful that when now found in an antique shop a good specimen may be counted as a garden treasure. Downing, in his day, scattered urns, vases, sundials, and similar objects of art rather indiscriminately near the house, on terraces, on lawns, and in flower gardens.

8

POST-REVOLUTION IN THE SOUTH

THE fullest and best information we have on horticulture in the South in the post-Revolutionary period is supplied by the diaries and garden books of Washington and Jefferson. Both lived on the land and loved it, setting down in diaries accounts of all their garden operations. Every Southerner knew about the agricultural and horticultural practices at Mount Vernon and Monticello, and followed as far as possible farm operations on these two estates. The cultivated crops of the far South, to be sure, differed from those of Virginia, because the climate and the soil were not the same; but it was the money-making crops, tobacco, rice, and indigo, that were unlike; the garden and orchard crops were much the same.

Yet there were many admirable gardens and orchards in all parts of the South, at least near the Atlantic, when Mount Vernon and Monticello were in the rough; and before Washington and Jefferson died there were a hundred and more estates notable for horticultural arts in Tidewater Virginia; up the rivers of the Old Dominion; up the Carolina rivers; and in the valleys and uplands on both sides of that indefinite range called 'the Mountains.' Many of these great estates showed in their treatment of food plants and ornamentals quite as much individuality as that displayed by Washington and Jefferson. Nevertheless, Mount Vernon and Monticello are examples as good as any and are familiar spots to most Americans.

There are three respects in which none of the gardens, in the North or in the South, surpassed Mount Vernon or Monticello. Few had the physical extent of these two gardens. Many had more acres, but the vistas across the Potomac and from the high

169

hill of Monticello greatly enhance the sense of size of both places. The second feature in which they surpass is their simplicity— grandeur in restraint and balance. The third attribute may seem to contradict the second and would, had not Washington and Jefferson been master gardeners. It is the great number of native plants intermixed with exotics which added variety yet did not clutter the plantings.

We know very well what Washington grew in the orchards and gardens at Mount Vernon, from the diary he kept from 1748 to 1799.[1] He says little about vegetables and flowers, but much about fruits and ornamental shrubs and trees. We learn that Washington became interested in fruits in 1760 when he was 28 years old. At this time, when most orchards in America were planted with seedlings, Washington was enamored with 'wedding' stock and cion by grafting. In March 1760, he began grafting, and ardently continued it for several years. The following is the first of many entries:

21st Grafted 40 Cherrys—viz: 12 Bullock Hearts; 18 very fine early May Cherry; 10 Carnation Cherry. And planted them as followeth: the Bullock Hearts in the first Row next the Quarters beginning at the farthest part thereof, and ending at a Stick. The early May next to them and ending at another Stick, the Carnation finishing the said Row.

21. Set out 55 cutlings of Madeira Grape, viz: 31 in finishing the 2d row where the Plums are, and 24 in the next beginning at the hither end—there from Mr. Green's.

22. Transplanted to the Corner of the Borders by Garden House a Cherry Graft—from the Cherry tree at the Corner of said Bord[er] by the first Fall.

26. Also grafted 10 of a pretty little early Pear from Collo. Mason's and planted them at the end of the Quinces, except 3 wch begin the 4th Row at the other end.

30. Grafted and planted as followeth, vis: 12 Spanish pairs from Colo. Mason. They hang until November and are a very valuable Fruit.

30. Also grafted 12 Butter pears from Collo. Mason's. These esteemed among the finest pears, and stand next the Spanish pears.

---

[1] Fitzpatrick. All quotations from the *Diaries* that follow are from the edition listed in the Bibliography.

30. Grafted 10 black Pear of Worcester from Collo. Mason's next the Butter Pear. They are a large coarse fruit for baking.

30. Grafted 10 of the Winter Boon Ch[erries] from Collo. Mason's—who had them from Colo. Fairfax, who praises them much. These begin the 5th Row next Grass Ground.

30. Grafted 8 of the Summer Boon Ch[erries] next these—from Do. who had them from Do. etc.

80. Grafted 10 Bergamy [Bergamot] Pears from Collo. Mason's next the Summer Boon. These are a very fine Fruit but Cor[ser] than most other English pears.

30. Grafted 10 of the New Town Pippin from Collo. Mason's who had them from Mr. Presd't Blair.

30. Grafted 43 of the Maryland Red Strick [Streak]. Had the grafts from Mr. Wm. Digges. These are the whole of the 6th Row.

In March 1764 and March 1765, Washington had many days of magnificent accomplishment in grafting. For the most part, the kinds of apples, pears, and plums are the same as those grafted in earlier years. The men from whom he got grafts were his old friends, Colonel Mason, Colonel Fairfax, Mr. Green, Mr. Blair, and Mr. Diggers. These men, of course, were grafting and grow-ing the same fruits and varieties, so that grafting must have been a common operation in Virginia at this time.

Washington used much cider. In February 1760, he records: 'Bottled 35 dozen of Cyder,' and in August 1768, he says: 'Began to beat cyder at Dog Run, Muddy Hole, and the Neck.' Probably the apples were crushed in troughs by beating, preparatory to pressing.

One gathers from the Diary that Washington was very fond of peaches. As early as 1760 there is the following record: 'Laid in part the Worm of a fence around the peach orchard.' The fence he speaks of was almost certainly of split walnut rails, laid zigzag. Eventually it became trellised with wild grapes and Virginia creepers; the corners grew up in sassafras and brambles, bordered with white-flowered Jamestown-weed, and goldenrods. The peach orchard was not only a source of fruit, but a beautiful feature of the plantation, which its owner must have enjoyed in his rural rides. Washington does not tell of feeding peaches to hogs as his neighbors did—no doubt his crop went into peach brandy, which he several times mentions.

On 16 December 1771, Washington records in his Diary: 'Finished planting the Grape Cuttings in the Inclosure below the Garden—the first 29 Rows of which, reckoning from the side next the Spring, are the Winter Grape, the other five are the Summer Grape of tolerable good taste and Ripening in October.' It is idle to speculate what the 'Winter Grape' and 'Summer Grape' were. No doubt, at one time or another, he tried a good number of European grapes, as his contemporaries in all parts of America were doing.

In 1774 Washington leased 125 acres in Berkeley County and stipulated that within three years there should be planted 100 apple trees 40 feet apart each way, and 100 peach trees. He required in the lease that the trees be kept well pruned and fenced from cattle.

Washington was still planting peach pits, although the Princes in Flushing were selling budded peaches at this time. On 11 March 1775 he records: 'At the end of the Octagon—left hand side—in the first Row next the gravel Walk, 5 peach kernals, five sorts from Philadelphia. In the next Rows to these 130 peaches, also a fine kind from Philadelphia. Same as Colo. Fairfax's white Peach.'

Little is said in the Diary about ornamental plantings until 1768. Washington then records in several entries that he is setting out trees and shrubs—mostly natives. From then on, his passion for landscape gardening grew, until Mount Vernon at his death was one of the beautiful estates in Virginia.

On 8 February 1765, Washington records that he 'began to wheel dirt into the Ha Has, tho' it was exceeding miry and bad working.' The ha-ha was a common feature of gardens in the post-Revolutionary period, as it had been in England for a century or more. Washington had one at each end of the mansion at Mount Vernon. This gardening device permitted grazing cattle and sheep to appear on the landscape, but, at the same time, kept them from the house. It was a ditch of which the walls were invisible, so named, according to French etymologists, because people exclaimed as they came up to the sudden check, 'Ha!' (It is also spelled 'aha' and 'ha haw.') Thus the ha-ha was a step, one of the first, in the revolution from the old, stiff, formal garden to natural landscape style.

On 18 February 1785, the Diary records that Washington had received 'four Lime or Linden Trees, sent me by Govr. Clinton of New York.' On the 25th, 'Laid part of the Serpentine Road on the South side of the grass plot.' And on 'Saturday 26th, Finished laying out my Serpentine roads.' Then through March and until the middle of April there is almost a daily record of planting along the 'Serpentine roads' in what was now becoming a spacious, planned landscape, including outside the 'Serpentine Walks' what Washington called the 'Wilderness.'

The lists of trees include: Ash, locusts, sassafras, service trees, catalpas, crabs, magnolias, elms, hollies, cedars, pawpaws, pines, hemlocks, poplars, yews, aspens, live oaks, horse chestnuts, tree boxes, mulberries, willows, walnuts, and 'buck eye nuts brought to me from the mouth of Cheat River' (West Virginia). Of shrubs he lists: black haws, large-berried thorns, small-berried thorns, lilacs, 'red-berry bushes,' 'Scarlet or French honeysuckle, Gilder Rose, Persian Jessamine, and Wild Roses for hedges.'

But this enumeration of plants does not do justice to the entries in the Diary. Washington tells who gave him the plants or where he found them in his rides about the country; what condition they were in; and where and how he planted them.

In the spring of 1785, he again planted peaches, and mentions especially the 'Portugal Peach' he obtained from a Mr. Cockburn, 9 of which he planted in the garden, '2 near the Espalier hedge.' In April he had grafted '12 Duke, 12 May Duke, and 12 black May heart Cherries and 12 Burgamy Pairs.' He then adds, 'And my gardener to show his cunning grafted ten Pairs . . . on Plumb Scions.' He does not tell us whether the grafts grew. (No gardener today is 'cunning' enough to make pear cions grow on plum stocks—at least they would not live long.)

On 19 June 1786, there is an entry in the diary about the French botanist, André Michaux, of whom Washington wrote:

A Monsr. Andri Machaux, a botanist sent by the Court of France to America (after being only 6 weeks returned from India) came in a little before dinner with letters of Introduction and recommendation from the Duke de Lauzen, and Marqis de la Fayette to me. He dined and returned later to Alexandra on his way to New York, from whence he had come; and where he was about to establish a Botanical Garden.

Washington had trouble in his orchards because of the neglect by his slaves. In the year of his great planting, 1785, he was away for a few days, and the Negroes failed to water the newly set plants. He records: 'Most of my transplanted trees have a sickly look, the small pines from the wilderness are entirely dead, almost all of my holly is dead, not a single ash tree has unfolded its buds,' and so on through a whole page of disasters such as only a gardener can appreciate.

The landscape gardening at Mount Vernon was an adaptation from the naturalistic style of the English, so skilfully made, however, that it fitted well in the environment of Virginia. Washington followed the style common in Virginia at the time, and the grounds at Mount Vernon were much like those of a hundred other great estates in the Old Dominion at the close of the eighteenth century. But in his gardening, as in his farming, Washington was an experimenter. It would be interesting to know the outcome of experiments he made in planting 'royal palmetos, sand box trees, physic nuts, Pride of Chinas, live oaks, bird peppers, privet, Guinea grass, and a great variety of Chinese grasses.' In an entry in 1786 he reports planting hawthorns, jasmines, pistachio nuts, and 75 European cypresses sent him by the King of France. It is doubtful that the last two species could have possibly been grown in Virginia.

In his Diary from 1748 to 1799, Washington never mentions an herbaceous flower, nor does he often refer to vegetables in the home garden. From time to time there are references to cabbages, carrots, pumpkins, or 'Pumpions,' and 'Water Mellons,' grown in such quantities that one surmises they were to supply the small army of Blacks at work on the several plantations. But there are other sources of information about the flowers and vegetables grown at Mount Vernon.

The Mount Vernon kitchen garden was restored in 1936 by those having charge of the estate. The new design was made from the books that Washington owned and used, from his work accounts, and from his diary and other writings. The garden was .92 of an acre in area and laid out in beds bordered with dwarf box. In both beds and borders, annuals, perennials, vegetables, herbs, and flowers were planted rather indiscriminately. In different places, water was kept 'in Basons . . . where it may be exposed to the open Air and Sun, that it may be soften'd thereby; for such water as it is taken out of Wells, Etc., just as it is used, is by no Means proper for any Sort of Plants.' The following plants were included in the restored garden:

Vegetables

Asparagus
Beans
Beets
Broccoli
Brussels Sprouts
Beans, pole and dwarf
Cabbage
Carrots
Celery
Chives
Collards
Cucumbers
Eggplant
Garlic
Globe Artichoke
Kale
Leeks
Mustard

Okra
Onions
Peas
Peppers
Potatoes
Radish
Rhubarb
Spinach
Summer Squash
Tomatoes
Turnips

Herbs

Basil
Bergamot
Catnip
Germander
Hyssop
Lavender

Lemon balm
Mint
Mugwort
Pennyroyal
Rosemary
Rue
Santolina
Sweet fennel

Flowers

Calendulas
Hollyhocks

Fruits

Figs
Quinces
Strawberries

Although it is not in the lists of those who reproduced the old garden, there must also have been parsnips; and it is doubtful if Washington grew tomatoes as a vegetable. Sage is not in the new garden, but almost certainly it was in the old, to be used in dressings and sausages. There should have been hoarhound, spearmint, and wormwood, all commonly grown in old southern gardens. Spearmint and mints generally were so commonly grown in Virginia for juleps that in the temperance crusade of the 1830's a plank in a political platform was: 'Every bed of mint must be uprooted.'

Because of several inventions and his work with electricity, Franklin is generally acclaimed as America's scientist-statesman. It is doubtful, however, whether he had knowledge of as many sciences as Jefferson. Certainly Franklin did not have Jefferson's knowledge of the natural sciences, including agriculture. In addition to the inscription on Jefferson's tomb that he was the author of the Declaration of Independence and the Father of the University of Virginia, the engraver might have added, 'Patriarch of American Natural History,' a name given him by a fellow naturalist in Europe.

Jefferson's only book of length published during his lifetime is his *Notes on the State of Virginia,* which was published in 1782 and ran through many editions in English and at least one each in French and German. The book is of interest to gardeners because of a chapter dealing with esculent, ornamental, and medicinal plants, some of which were eventually domesticated. In 1944 the American Philosophical Society published in Philadelphia *Thomas Jefferson's Garden Book,* edited by E. M. Betts.

One of Jefferson's fellow gardeners in Virginia was the fourth President of the United States, James Madison. In 1791 Jefferson and Madison visited the North. That their eyes were open to the plants they saw is indicated by Jefferson's enthusiastic letter written in June from Bennington, Vermont, to his son-in-law, another gardener who owned a beautiful estate at Edge Hill, near Monticello:

We have also visited Forts William Henry, and George, Ticonderoga, Crown Point, etc. which have been scenes from early history. . . We were more pleased, however, with the botanical objects which continually presented themselves. Those, either unknown or rare in Virginia, were the sugar maple in vast abundance, the silver fir, white pine, pitch pine, spruce pine, a shrub with decumbent stems, which they call juniper, an azalea very different from the nudiflora, with very large clusters of flowers, more thickly set on the branches, of a deeper red and high pink fragrance. It is the richest shrub I have seen. The honeysuckle of the gardens growing wild on the banks of Lake George, the paper birch, an aspen with a velvet leaf, a shrub-willow with downy catkins, a wild gooseberry, a wild cherry with single fruit (not the bunch cherry), strawberries in abundance.

The garden at Monticello was not started until 1766; and from then until the end of his life, Jefferson, whenever he was at home, jotted down in yearly repetition all the life events of the farm and garden from the opening of buds to harvest time and the fall of leaves. His book shows a fondness for detail and precision rare

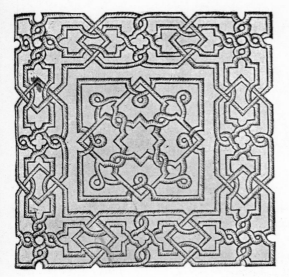

IXa. A geometric flower bed.

IXb. The Mount Hope Nurseries in 1855. *From the company's catalogue of fruits for 1860; courtesy of the Library of the City of Rochester.*

X. Founders of the Mount Hope Nurseries. Upper: George Ellwanger. Lower: Patrick Barry. *Courtesy of Blake McKelvey.*

XIa. Monticello. *From* Harper's New Monthly Magazine, VII: 145, 1853.

XIb. One of the first greenhouses in America, constructed in New York City in 1764.

XIIa. Dougheregan Manor and grounds, the seat of the Carroll family, Howard County, Maryland. *Courtesy of the Baltimore Museum of Art.*

XIIb. Shaker apple dry-house. *Courtesy of the New York State Museum, Albany, New York.*

XIIIa. Backwoodsmen and a steamboat pilot. *From an etching by Basil Hall about* 1830.

XIIIb. Newly cleared land in America. *From an etching by Basil Hall about* 1830.

XIVa. A summerhouse in the North. *From* Garden and Forest.

XIVb. A garden in St. Augustine, Florida. *From* Harper's New Monthly Magazine, L: 1, 1877.

XV. Four American horticulturists. Upper left: Prosper Julius Berckmans. *From* Berckmans American Garden, 1889.
Upper right: Joel R. Poinsett. *Courtesy of Presbyterian College, Clinton, S. C.* Lower left: A. J. Downing. *From Downing's* Landscape Gardening, 1841. Lower right: Charles Downing. *From Hedrick's* Cherries of New York, 1915.

XVIa. College of Princeton, New Jersey, in 1837. *From a lithograph by J. H. Bufford; photograph from the New York Public Library.*

XVIb. William and Mary College at Williamsburg, Virginia, in 1840. *From a lithograph by Thos. C. Millington; photograph from the New York Public Library.*

and hardly to be expected in one who bore the cares of a large estate and great responsibilities in Richmond and Washington.

On 17 March, Jefferson records [2] 'almonds in bloom.' On the first of April the single word 'lilacs' meant without doubt that that shrub was in bloom; late in one October there is an entry, 'walnut and mulberry lost leaves,' and another later in the same month, 'cherry common locust lost leaves. First frost at Montic'; and a week afterwards, 'poplars, white mulberry, wild crab nearly stripped of leaves.'

In a letter to his daughter, Maria, written 9 March 1791, he asks, writing of the appearance of the birds and flowers in Philadelphia:

. . . Have you noted the first appearance of these things at Monticello? I hope you have and will continue to note every appearance, animal and vegetable, which indicate the approach of spring, and will communicate them to me. By these means we shall be able to compare the climates of Philadelphia and Monticello. Tell me when you shall have peas, etc., when everything comes to table, when you shall have the first chickens hatched; when every kind of tree blossoms or puts forth leaves; when each kind of flower bloomes or puts forth leaves.

While minister to France from 1784 to 1789, Jefferson seems to have looked over the domesticated plants in western Europe with the intention of sending to America all that could be grown in the new states. To one correspondent he writes: 'I am sending a collection of vines for wine and the table.' To Monticello he sent 'a packet of the seeds of trees which I would wish Anthony to sow in a large nursery, noting well their names.' He expected much from the olive in America, and wrote to his old friend, George Wythe: 'The olive is assuredly the richest gift of heaven, I can scarcely except bread.' He sent two shipments of about 500 olive trees to South Carolina, but little came from them; in 1813 he wrote 'it is now twenty-five years since I sent my southern fellow-citizens two shipments . . . of the olives of Aix, the finest olives in the world. If any of them still exist, it is merely as a curiosity in their gardens; not a single orchard of them has been planted.' He tried olives at Monticello, but their failure in Virginia was inevitable.

[2] Ford. The quotations that follow are from the edition listed in the Bibliography.

While a diplomat in France, Jefferson spent two months in England, where he visited some of the famous gardens. The Baedeker of English gardens at that time was Thomas Wheatley's *Observations on Modern Gardens Illustrated by Descriptions,* published in London in 1770. Jefferson studied English landscapes with Wheatley in hand, marking passages that might be of use in planting his gardens.

Writing home, he described Hampton Court, Enfield Chase, Moor Park, Blenhem, Wotton, Pope's garden at Twickenham, the Duke of Devonshire's garden at Chiswick, and several other estates considered show places because of their fine grounds. This visit was important for those in America who were planting gardens, since he wrote to his friends telling them of things that might be of use.

A very good description of Monticello is given by Edmund Bacon, long an overseer on the estate. After having served Jefferson twenty years, Bacon moved to Kentucky, where, in his old age, he wrote what he could remember of his years at Monticello.[3]

Bacon places the house, as we know it, far up on the sugar-loaf mountain reached by a winding road. When he came to Monticello only ten acres were cleared and leveled, on the highest point of which the house stood. Under the house and the terraces that surrounded it were cisterns, icehouse, cellar, kitchen, and rooms for all sorts of purposes. These were warm in winter and cool in summer. Here, underground, was storage room for vegetables, fruit, cider, and wood. There were no Negro quarters around the mansion, as there were generally in plantations in the South.

The grounds around the house were planted with flowers and shrubbery. There were walks and borders, and flowers that Bacon had 'never seen nor heard of elsewhere.' Some, he says, 'were in bloom from early in the spring until late in the winter.' A good many of them, the manager thought, 'were foreign.' Back of the house was a lawn of two or three acres where Jefferson's grandchildren played. The garden, which Bacon planted while Jefferson was President, was on the side of the mountain. In it were vegetables of all kinds, grapes, figs, and the 'greatest variety of

[3] These remembrances were published in 1862 by Hamilton W. Pierson, president of Cumberland College in Kentucky.

fruit.' High up on the mountain, out of the reach of frosts, 'fruits never failed.'

According to Bacon, Jefferson sent home a great many kinds of trees and shrubbery from Washington during his stay in the White House. 'I [Bacon] used to send a servant there with a great many fine things from Monticello for his [Jefferson's] table, and he would send back the cart loaded with shrubbery from a nursery near Georgetown that belonged to a man named Maine, and he would always send me directions what to do with it.' The President, his manager says, 'knew all about everything in every part of his grounds and garden. He knew the name of every tree, and just where one was dead or missing.'

There follow in Mr. Pierson's text a great number of letters, mostly from Jefferson, many of them labeled 'Directions for Mr. Bacon' or 'Memorandum for Mr. Bacon.' These memoranda have to do with many things about the farm, orchard, lawn, garden, house, stables, and slaves. Here are a few of the orders for the care of the orchard, lawn, and garden:

If the weather is not open and soft when Doug arrives, put the box of thorns into the cellar, where they may be entirely free from the influence of cold, until the weather becomes soft, when they must be planted in the places of those dead through the whole of the hedges which enclose the two orchards, so that the old and the new shall be complete at six inches' distance from every plant. If any remain plant them in the nursery of thorns. There are 2000. I send Mr. Maine's written instructions about them, which must be followed most minutely. The other trees he brings are to be planted as follows:

4 Purple beeches. In the clumps which are in the southwest and northwest angles of the house (which Wormly knows). There were 4 of these trees planted last spring, 2 in each clump. They all died, but the places will be known by the remains of the trees, or by the sticks marked No. IV in the places. I wish these now sent to be planted in the same places.

5 Prickly ash. In the S. W. angle of the house there was planted one of these trees last spring and in the N. W. corner 2 others. They are dead. 3 of these now sent are to be planted in their places, which may be found by the remains of the trees, or by the sticks marked VII. The fourth may be planted in some vacant space of the S. W. angle.

6 Spitzenberg apple trees. Plant them in the S. E. orchard, in any place where apples have been planted and are dead.

500 October peach stones; a box of Pecan nuts. The nursery must be enlarged, and these planted in the new parts, and Mr. Perry must immediately extend the paling to include these, and make the whole secure against hares.

In other memoranda, quite too lengthy to quote in full, are items such as these:

Keep the thorns constantly cleansed. . .
Wormly must be directed to weed the flower beds about the house, the nursery, the vineyards, and rasberry beds, when they want it. . .
Consider the garden as your main business, and push it with all your might when the interruptions permit. . .

According to Bacon, there were 300 acres enclosed in the tract about the house. 'Mr. Jefferson,' he says, 'would never allow a tree to be cut.' There were roads and paths winding all around and over the estate where the family could ride and walk for pleasure. 'How often I have seen him walking over these grounds and his grandchildren following after him as happy as they could be.'

At one time and another, Jefferson wrote to various Americans about grape growing and wine making, and, we are told by a recent biographer,[4] that he tried his hand at both. Some time before the Revolution, he conceived the idea of growing Old World grapes and making wines on a large scale in the neighborhood of Monticello. To further his plans he persuaded Philip Mazzei to bring over from Tuscany a number of Italian *vignerons*. Vineyards were planted on the hillsides near Charlottesville, but, as was the case with many other such efforts, grapes could not be grown and no wine was made. Several of the Tuscans were employed at Monticello and from wild native grapes they made wine, some of which Jefferson gave to his friends as the product of his own vintage. He continued, however, to stock his own cellar with French wines.

John James Dufour, founder of the Kentucky Vineyard Society, visited Monticello in 1799 and found that the vineyard 'had been abandoned, which proved that it had not been profitable.' Jeffer-

4 Bowers, p. 223.

son did not lose interest in the vine, however, for in 1809 he wrote John Adlum, speaking of the variety Alexander: 'I think it will be well to push the culture of that grape without losing time and efforts in search of foreign grapes which it will take centuries to adapt to our soil and climate.' [5] And, later, he declared that wine made from the Catawba was 'worthy of the best vineyards of France.'

Perhaps there were too many experiments under way at Monticello for good practice in farming. Jefferson, in his last years, when his poverty and destitution were pathetic, wrote to his lifelong friend Monroe: 'To keep a Virginia estate together requires in the owner skill and attention. Skill I never had, and attention I could not have; and really, when I reflect on all circumstances, my wonder is that I should have been so long as sixty years in reaching the result to which I am now reduced.'

Not only his experiments with foreign grapes were a failure, but one suspects from the following quotation that he was not a good grower of the peach, a fruit in which he delighted and often mentioned: 'Five acres of peach trees at twenty-one feet apart will furnish dead wood enough to supply a fireplace all winter, and may be kept up at the trouble of only planting about seventy peach stones a year.' Manifestly, an orchardist who had 'dead wood enough to furnish a fireplace all winter' from a five-acre tract of peaches was a poor grower of this fruit.

Jefferson was the forerunner of the efficiency experts of modern agriculture. His farm book has notes on better methods of plowing, harvesting, thrashing, and other farm operations. Here is a record of the efficiency of the two-wheeled barrow as compared with the one-wheeled:

Julius Shard fills the two-wheeled barrow in 3 minutes, and carries it 30 yards in 1½ minutes, more. Now this is 4 loads of the common barrow with one wheel. So that suppose the 4 loads put in at the same time *vis.* 3 minutes, 4 trips will take 4 × 1½ minutes = 6, which added to three minutes filling = 9 minutes to fill and carry the same earth which was filled and carried in the two-wheeled barrow in 4½.

A. J. Downing is usually considered one of America's first good landscape gardeners. Great he was, but not the first to create beau-

5 Adlum, p. 149.

tiful landscapes in America. Long before Downing lived, there were in Virginia, the Carolinas, and Georgia a hundred landscapes as perfectly planned as any by Downing. Monticello was such a one and it was not the result of happy chance, for Jefferson had studied not only architecture in France but landscape gardening as well. To lay out the grounds and gardens at Monticello required as much study and planning as to build the house.

Under the title 'General Ideas for the Improvement of Monticello,' Jefferson, in 1804, made a memorandum of plans to eliminate the aspect of a farm in the grounds about the house. There were to be lawns and plantings of trees, diversified by thickets, 'all so arranged as to give advantageous prospects' from the roads and paths that circled the little mountain on which Monticello stood. On the lower slopes of the mountain there were to be a park, orchards, and a riding ground. A fish pond was to be built where it could be seen from the house. The park was to be broken by clumps of oaks, elms, maples, and other native trees 'as the open grounds of the English are broken by clumps of trees.' There were to be thickets of dogwood, guelder roses, magnolias, azaleas, rhododendrons, and honeysuckle; there were to be recesses in which to build a 'temple or seat.'

Jefferson's gardening did not end with the landscape. He took great pride in his vegetable and flower gardens, which were also planned for in his 'General Ideas for the Improvement of Monticello.' Unfortunately, his financial resources sank lower and lower from the time he entered the White House in 1801, and his grand plan was never fully carried out, although as long as he lived there were annual additions and improvements.

As President, Jefferson was not too busy to keep track of the green grocery market in Washington. He made a chart showing the dates in the summer months in which garden crops came to market. Those he lists are: lettuce, parsley, spinach, sprouts, corn salad, radishes, sorrel, asparagus, broccoli, cucumbers, cabbages, strawberries, peas, turnips, potatoes, snaps (beans), artichokes, squashes, carrots, parsnips, watermelons, corn, salsify, raspberries, tomatoes, grapes, endive, celery, eggplant, lima beans, cauliflowers, melons, mushrooms, and cresses.

A great opportunity to serve botany and gardening came to Jefferson in 1803 when he obtained money from Congress to send Lewis and Clark up the Missouri and on to the Pacific to explore the Far West.[6] That he had the natural history of the region in mind, especially botany, cannot be doubted, from the fact that Lewis was sent to Philadelphia for nine months to study botany under Barton, leading botanist of the country, to prepare himself in this subject. A great number of seeds and herbarium specimens were collected, which, after several mishaps, came into the hands of William Hamilton and Bernard M'Mahon, gardener and author from Philadelphia, both of whom, after some bickering with other botanists, grew a number of notable plants that were introduced into cultivation. Many shrubs and flowers from the great Northwest were sent to the Prince Nursery for propagation and distribution. Perhaps the most noteworthy of these was the *Mahonia nervosa* or Oregon-grape, which at once became so popular that plants sold for $20 each. It has often been said the Lewis and Clark expedition was planned in M'Mahon's house in Philadelphia. Hamilton, by the way, employed the seedsman Landreth to grow plants from the seeds that came to him.

Until after the turn of the nineteenth century, fruit and vegetable growing for the market hardly existed. Indeed, in these two fields of horticulture there was little change in methods, varieties, and marketing from those of the colonial period. The newspapers carry market reports in which the coarser vegetables are mentioned and occasionally prices of fresh fruits are listed, but more often dried apples and peaches are noted rather than fresh ones. Cider and brandy are found in nearly every market report. Richmond and Norfolk in Virginia and Charleston in South Carolina were the only towns with more than 5000 population in the South in 1800, so that the markets for fruits and vegetables were small.

Besides, there were few good roads in any part of the South at this time. In Virginia, the Wilderness Road through Cumberland Gap was the only well-traveled road for wagons in the state, and at this time it was crowded with a rush of people to Kentucky and Tennessee.

[6] See pp. 331 ff.

Cider and peach brandy were stored in large quantities in the cellars of rich and poor alike. John Joyce, writing to Robert Dickson in 1785, discussing fruits and the drinks made from them, reports:

As to the Drink chiefly used in this collony, it is generally Cyder, every planter having an orchard, and they make from 1000 to 5 or 6000 [gallons] according to their rank and Fortune . . . the Very meanest and hilly Lands are proper for the Peach tree, every planter almost having an Orchard of these trees. The Brandy made from that Fruit, I think, is excellent and they make it in sufficient quantities.[7]

The last large peach orchard planted for brandy making was on the plantation of a Mr. Bayley in Accomac County, Virginia. In this orchard, planted in 1814, there were 63,000 trees, all seedlings. These trees yielded, five years from planting, nearly 10,000 gallons of brandy, or about 15 gallons per 100 trees. Peach brandy sold at the time for $2.00 per gallon.

When the demand for cider and peach brandy had been supplied, the next most profitable use to which apples and peaches could be put was as hog food. Hogs are inordinately fond of peaches and sweet apples, and both are excellent 'fattening' foods. It was said by J. W. Hoff of Birmingham County: [8] 'The sweet apple is very profitably cultivated for stock, especially hogs. One acre of well-grown sweet apple trees will fatten more hogs than five acres of the average farm crops; and the expense to the farmer is nothing in comparison to the latter method of fattening.' Hogs fattened on peaches scarcely less well, and the crops were nearly as cheaply grown.

Apple and peach growers had a third recourse for their surplus crops. Both fruits were dried for home use and sale. In an age when fruits were not canned, either in the home or in canneries, dried fruits were staples, the drying being done on the plantation. Probably most of the apples and peaches were dried in the kitchen or in the sun, though the 'dry house' for fruit was a common outbuilding. In 1859, the Virginia State Agricultural Society offered a premium for 'the best kiln for drying fruit.' [9] The prize was won by Yardley Taylor of Loudon County. Dried fruits were sold

[7] *Virginia Mag. of Hist.*, xxii: 410, 1915.
[8] Fletcher, p. 15.   [9] Ibid.

in considerable quantities in the West Indies and the states to the south.

Landscape gardening on the great estates of the opulent South in the post-Revolutionary period differed little from that of the colonies. The several gardens near Charleston described in an earlier chapter were still patterns to be followed as closely as soil and climate would permit about the homes of the rich, while the small houses and cabins of the poor were wholly devoid of ornamental plantings. A somewhat different type of the gardener's art from that in the Carolinas was to be found in Georgia and northern Florida, especially near the Atlantic.

Pierre Charles l'Enfant, soldier and engineer in the Revolutionary War, painter and architect in Paris before coming to America, remained for some years after the war to practice his professions. His great work in landscape gardening was the plan for the Federal City of Washington, which he was called upon to make by the first President, and the drawings of which are still preserved in the Library of Congress. The essential features of his design were followed in the building of the Capitol. He planned fine houses for several wealthy Americans, among whom were Robert Morris and John Nicholson of Philadelphia, and William Dudley Digges in Prince George's County, Maryland.

In 1901, the Park Commission of Washington recognized the merits of l'Enfant's plan and recommended its restoration and extension. In 1909, l'Enfant's remains were disinterred from an unmarked grave and taken to lie in state in the Capitol, honored by the President and a great concourse of people. The body was then transferred to Arlington, overlooking the city he had designed.

In the South, a sharp distinction was made between arbors, bowers, and pergolas. An arbor might be round or square, but had a domed top; a bower was a long, arched way with a flat top. Both were usually latticed, or either might be enclosed in rustic work. Over the woodwork of both, vines grew. The rose bower was a favorite structure in the South. The pergola was, as now, a much more solid structure, with columns of stone or heavy wood. The 'green gallery' of the South was a pergola. Of trellises and arches, covered with vines, a favorite was a latticed lyre covered with roses.

Much earlier, Crèvecœur described an arbor in Virginia that he visited in 1769. He says:

I am now sitting under one of the most enchanting groves in Virginia; 'tis the work of art, but executed with so much simplicity as greatly to resemble that of Nature. 'Tis an octagon frame round which vines and honeysuckles have been planted. They have grown with such luxuriancy; their limbs and foliage are so interwoven as to refuse all admittance to the rays of the sun, yet leave a free passage to the air. Round this verdant temple at an equal distance, stands a double row of mellifluous locusts, the umbrageous catalpas, and the soft magnolias. Alternately planted, they expand their friendly limbs all round, and repel the scorching rays of the sun. 'Tis a grove of Tempe; 'tis a Druidical temple, in point of gloom, shade, and solitude.[10]

Not quite so common as the beehive in southern gardens, but much more of a feature, was the dovecote. The rearing of pigeons in England was free only to noblemen. When British colonists came to America, they reveled in doing the things they were not permitted to do in the home country; and despite the countless multitude of passenger pigeons, many took pleasure in raising domestic pigeons. The usual architecture of a dovecote was an ornamental box held aloft on a stout post, such as are not infrequently seen to this day in the southern states. There are accounts, especially in the South, of brick or wood dovecotes of considerable size, with shelves and recesses for nests and ladder-like contrivances whereby the squabs might be easily reached.

In the South the first boundaries of fields and gardens were zigzag rail fences, the rails split from walnut, chestnut, or oak. This rail fence is distinctly American, and while scarcely designed for a garden, when planted with bittersweet, honeysuckle, trumpet vine, woodbine, wild grapes or, in the South, Cherokee roses, is an admirable feature in American landscapes—all too rarely seen now that wire fences are so easily to be had, with a great saving of land.

The picket fence, made by nailing sharpened poles to an upper

[10] Crèvecœur, p. 51.

and lower rail, the garden fence almost universally used for small gardens in the nineteenth century, did not become common until sawmills covered the land, well after the Revolution.

Garden walls were commonly made of brick. The serpentine brick wall built by Thomas Jefferson, still standing at the University of Virginia, is probably unique in shape and height, but not in material. The wall is about seven feet high and at one time may have enclosed all the college grounds. The general belief is that its serpentine shape permitted the wall to be built with fewer bricks than had it been straight; but, more likely, Jefferson was following the French fashion of replacing straight lines with more artistic curves, winding lines. Whether straight or winding, the soft-red brick walls of the old South made a pleasing background for plants of any kind.

Garden walls of pink tabby are distinctive features of all the old seaport towns of the South. Behind and above them stand the varied shrubs and trees of the luxuriant land. In small gardens these are mostly oleanders, crape-myrtles, palmettos, acacias, and the smaller ornamental trees. Over the walls, flowering vines of a dozen species furnished splashes of color. Sometimes the walls curved upward to meet the house wall, thus uniting house and garden more completely. These old walls are still common in Charleston, Savannah, Mobile, and New Orleans.

There are to be found in both North and South fine examples of wrought-iron garden gates dating back to the earliest good gardens. It is said that King William introduced finely wrought gates in England about 1700, and that soon no garden of fashion was without one. They became very common in American gardens in the eighteenth century. These gates were often gilded, painted blue or gray, or more often black. Since they permitted views into or from the garden, they were called *clairs-voyées*.

The cities of the South, especially Charleston, Savannah, Mobile, and New Orleans, together with many Southern estates, could, from their earliest years, show many fine gateways that were splendid examples of the iron-master's art. At Westover, early home of the Byrds, was a double-grill gateway which bore the monogram of William Evelyn Byrd. It swung between two massive, square, brick pillars that bore leaden eagles with wings spread for flight, the eagles having been placed there long before this bird was the symbol of the nation. From these gates, iron fences, also works of art, sloped to each side, divided by square pillars, each capped with an emblem of stone.

When made of wrought iron, the gates with their scrolls and patterns were of matchless beauty and have furnished subjects for numberless paintings, etchings, magazine articles, and a book or two. Almost as interesting as the gates were the gateposts, whether massive pillars of stone, or slender iron, or wooden pillars with capitals and flutings. Quite worth notice were the small doors and gates built in the walls for the use of servants and tradespeople, some of which still stand and many others of which are reproductions, the achievements of new owners or modern garden clubs.

Before 1800, the front yards in the towns and cities of Georgia, especially Savannah, or for that matter in most of the cities of the South, were often enclosed with wrought-iron fences of delicate design, which made garden enclosures more beautiful than could be found in the cities of the North. About 1830, cast iron began to take the place of the wrought iron, with great loss in beauty. Gardens in the rear of city homes in the South, in early times, were given complete privacy by tabby or coquina walls, made from broken shells, cement and lime.

No doubt as long as there have been ornamental gardens, water has been used to heighten the effects of artistic plantings. In most gardens, water is and ever has been an accessory to plantings in landscapes, either in fountains, running water, or pools— although, as Bacon says, 'pools mar all.' Fortunately, in America we have had few of the artificial rivulets, cascades, canals, and fish-ponds, which more often marred than added beauty to English country places when gardening was being introduced into America. The exception, perhaps, was in South Carolina, where pools and fish-ponds in early gardens were often features of the landscape.

Dungeness was a good example of the coast plantation of the Far South. It was on Cumberland Island, Camden County, near the Florida line. The southern part of this island, one of the largest on the southern coast, together with Mulberry Grove on the mainland, was given to General Nathanael Greene, a hero of the Revolution, by his admiring friends in Georgia. While General Greene lived at Mulberry Grove, he had a country house on his Cumberland Island estate, where there was a garden famous for its sub-tropical vegetation.

The house, built a few years after the war by General Greene's widow, rested upon an immense shell mound, a relic of Indian habitation, which was leveled to form a terraced base nearly an acre in extent. On the north side of the house was a wide lawn shaded by palms and live oaks; on the south was the famous garden. It covered 12 acres and was enclosed by a massive coquina wall. The garden fell by terraces to a creek. On the upper terrace grew sago palms and crape-myrtles; a second, lower terrace was broad enough to be divided by an avenue of olives; a thickset hedge of mock-orange separated this middle terrace from the third and lowest garden, which was planted to flowers and through which ran an avenue of oranges. In the garden all the flowers suitable for the climate were grown, but it was especially famous for its roses. East of the flower garden was a grove of 800 olive trees brought from Italy. There were, besides, many sub-tropical plants, with oranges and lemons most abundant. The live oaks and palmettos, growing in great profusion, were the grand features of the ornamental trees of Dungeness.[11]

Colonel George Mason, so often mentioned by Washington in his diary, was the owner and chief builder of Gunston Hall, 5 miles below Mount Vernon and 18 miles below Washington, on the Potomac. The manor house at Gunston Hall was built by George Mason in 1755 to 1758, and soon became famous for its orchards and gardens. It was early and long noted for its two rows of box hedge, which eventually attained a height of some 12 or 14 feet. Mason is said to have brought slips of box from England to start the hedge. The plants were much larger and older than those in the famous box plantings at Mount Vernon and it is not improbable that Washington got his box from Gunston Hall. In 1763, Washington writes of grafting plums and cherries from Colonel Mason's plantation.

One of the fine places in Virginia at the close of the eight-

11 *Garden and Forest,* II: 348.

eenth century, more or less the creation of Washington, was Kenmore, near Fredericksburg. Kenmore belonged to Fielding Lewis, who married Washington's sister Betty. Washington helped Lewis plan his house and lay out and stock his grounds, and often mentioned them in his diary and letters. Yet it may be that Lewis also gave Washington ideas and plant material, for his grandfather married Elizabeth Warner, daughter of Colonel Augustine Warner of Warner Hall, in Gloucester County, where Fielding Lewis was born, the owners of which are referred to by more than one writer as fine gardeners. Through this marriage, Warner Hall came in possession of the Lewis family, and in later years was often referred to as a place where 'scientific farming' was practiced.

Two advertisements in Charleston papers show that that city and the surrounding country were supplied by landscape gardeners in the post-Revolutionary period, even as were the cities in the North. In the *Charleston City Gazette,* 6 June 1795, J. Bryant has the following advertisement.

The Subscriber, well acquainted with the European method of gardening, being a native of England, and likewise well acquainted with it in this state, having been in constant practice for some years,—takes this method of informing his friends and the public in general, that he purposes superintending ladies and gentlemens gardens in or near the city whether intended for pleasure or profit—he also plans and lays out gardens in the European taste on moderate terms. He likewise imports on commission, all kinds of trees, shrubs, and seeds, either useful or ornamental, from England, Philadelphia or New York. Any person desirous of employing him in the above branches, by leaving a line at No 131 King Street—at 26 Queen street,—will be duly attended to.

J. Bryant

In the *South Carolina Gazette,* 12 September 1796, another advertisement appears.

Michael O'Brian

Respectfully acquaints the citizens of Charleston, and its environs, that he proposes to undertake the laying out of gardens, in all the different branches, comprising taste and utility. He has been regularly brought up to the above undertaking, and practised in Europe for many years with great success. . .

Gardening in the new states of the Union was well served in the years after the Revolution by André Michaux (1746-1802), a Frenchman, one of the best-known botanists of his time. Michaux came to America in 1785 armed with a commission from Louis XVI and a letter from LaFayette to George Washington. He had been a botanic explorer in Persia for the Jardin des Plantes, Paris, in the years just before coming to America, and it was to continue this work that he came here. He settled first in New Jersey, because of an acquaintanceship with St. John de Crèvecœur, who was then the French consul to New Jersey. As an alien, Michaux could not hold property in the state, and petitioned the New Jersey Legislature for the right to buy land at Bergen Neck, opposite New York City, land now a part of Jersey City. Michaux's qualifications and plans are set forth at considerable length in the preamble of the act that the New Jersey Legislature passed to grant his request. He eventually purchased 30 acres, where he founded a botanic garden that survived only two or three years.

Michaux brought a number of trees and shrubs from Europe, among which was the Lombardy poplar. While the 'Frenchman's Garden' at Bergen Neck made some contribution to gardening, it was poorly kept, so visitors said, and fell far short of the very good gardens later mentioned in Charleston. The land and site were somewhat to blame.

Michaux rendered an important service to American gardening when he brought to this country a really good gardener, of whom there were then very few. The man was Paul Saumier, who carried on the work of his master, and long after Michaux had returned to France this experienced gardener continued to instruct Americans on how to propagate, bud, graft, and care for fruit and ornamental plants. His name is also associated with the introduction of a number of meritorious native plants, most notable of which, perhaps, is the chinquapin chestnut, *Castanea pumila,* a native of southwestern Pennsylvania to the Gulf of Mexico, in dry lands, and west to Texas.

Michaux was interested from the first in southern plants, and in 1787 started a botanic garden in South Carolina. The location was a few miles from Charleston, in Goose Creek Parish, where he cultivated the plants he collected in his excursions in American forests, sending them in time to Europe and taking in exchange rare plants from European gardens. Among the introductions in the South reliably accredited to Michaux is the azalea, which, in the years that have elapsed, has contributed so much to the gardens of Charleston and is a major attraction in both Magnolia Gardens and Middleton Place Gardens. If not the introducer of the first azalea, Michaux brought to South Carolina some new and rare varieties.

Of the many expeditions made by this remarkable man in the ten years of his stay in America, space does not permit a full record. In 1788 he was in Florida; in 1789 he went to Bahama and brought back from these islands to his Charleston gardens 860 trees and shrubs; he made several excursions in the southern Alleghenies; he visited the valleys of Virginia, Maryland, and Pennsylvania; three times he did more or less exploring in New Jersey and New York, traveling once through the Champlain country and on to Montreal and Quebec; in 1793 he made a long journey down the Ohio to Louisville, returning overland botanizing; in 1794 he crossed east Tennessee to Louisville, up the Wabash to Vincennes, Indiana, crossed Illinois, then down the Mississippi to the Ohio, thence overland to Charleston.

From these and lesser explorations, Michaux sent to France more than 60,000 living plants, and when he returned to Paris in 1796 he took with him 40 boxes of seeds. In 1801 he published a very good book on American oaks, with excellent engravings, and prepared the manuscript for his *magnum opus, Flora Boreali-Americana,* but did not live to see the book published. Michaux left Paris in 1801 on a botanic excursion to New Holland but died in Madagascar of a malignant fever on 13 November 1802. In 1803 the book was published by his son, François André Michaux. In it are described 596 genera, and 1740 species. Changes have reduced the number of genera to about a score and the species to about 350.

Michaux was the discoverer of a magnolia that has an interesting history. Sometime between 1787 and 1796, he found near Augusta, Georgia, a magnolia with beautiful cup-shaped yellow flowers, the yellow cucumber tree of nurserymen, which he named *Magnolia cordata.* Either he or the younger Michaux sent it to France; from this shipment came all the cultivated trees of this species, for all efforts to rediscover it at the time failed. Many years later, Louis A. Berckmans, distinguished Georgian botanist, found it in the woods 18 miles south of Augusta. Michaux also discovered the large-leaved magnolia, *Magnolia macrophylla,* near Charlotte, North Carolina, in 1789, and in 1800 it was introduced into cultivation in Europe.

In the early years of his nursery in Charleston, Michaux is said to have planted the pride-of-China tree. Besides the name just given, this tree, *Melia Azedarach,* is known in the South, where it is widely planted from the Atlantic to western Texas, as Chinaberry, China-tree, pride-of-India, Indian-lilac, and in Texas a form is called umbrella-tree. The plant is now a run-wild, as much at home in some parts of the South as any native. From its roots a medicine is made to prevent bots in horses; it is planted near stables to keep away flies; its berries have the reputation of being poisonous, but their seeds are strung as beads for rosaries, giving the tree the name 'arbor sancta.' Perhaps of the many trees introduced by Michaux, this Melia, from Asia, is the most noteworthy.

It was the elder Michaux, also, who introduced the yellow wood or Virgilia, *Cladrastis lutea,* one of the beautiful and valuable American trees, for ornamental plantings. He found it on the limestone cliffs of the Carolinas, Kentucky, and Tennessee. Michaux discovered also the beautiful burr or mossy cup oak, *Quercus macrocarpa,* west of the Allegheny Mountains in 1795. The most beautiful of the chestnut-leaved oaks, *Quercus Prinus,* first described by Mark Catesby in 1731 (and renamed by Nuttall in 1818) and the laurel oak, *Quercus imbricaria,* a desirable ornamental in the South, were introduced by Michaux.

One of the plants Michaux brought to Southern gardens was the crape-myrtle, *Lagerstroemia indica,* which is to the South what the lilac is to the North. Still others are the native spice bush, *Benzoin aestivale,* which many southerners know as the Roman laurel; the ginkgo tree, *Ginkgo biloba;* the varnish tree, *Aleurites moluccana,* and several acacias.

Michaux's son, a botanist of whom we shall hear in another chapter, took charge of the Charleston garden when his father returned to France in 1796, but had no interest in the nursery or in cultivated plants, and little by little the place fell into neglect. By the end of the century it had almost gone out of existence.

One of the botanic worthies of South Carolina in the Revolutionary period was Thomas Walter, who wrote a book published in London in 1787 under the title *Flora Caroliniana,* which gave an account of the plants of his region. His flora, in the main, was comprised of plants growing in an area about 25 miles square on the Santee River. Walter seems to have been a modest man, for he says his collection is 'very incomplete,' though it contained over a thousand species. In the preface he writes that only 'a few are allowed to name,' conceding this right to leaders in science alone, and therefore calls some of his species 'anonymous.' To his name on the title he adds 'Agricola,' thereby expecting us to believe that he was a farmer. A very learned farmer he must have been, for he wrote the book in Latin. It is dated *ad Ripas Fluvii Santee,* 30 Dec. 1787.

Gardeners have good reason to remember Walter because of the rose-red magnolia, a beautiful tree of the Carolinas, which he named, after his friend John Fraser, *Magnolia Fraseri.* In his book is a copper plate with this inscription: 'To Thomas Walter, Esq., this plate of the new auriculated Magnolia is presented as a testimony of gratitude and esteem by his much obliged humble servant, John Fraser.'

Walter's grave is on the banks of the Santee River, St. John's Parish, over which is a monument inscribed with these words:

In memory of Thomas Walter, a native of Hampshire, in England, and many years a resident of this State. He died in the beginning of the year 1788, *Etatis Cir.* 48 *Ann.* To a mind liberally endowed by nature, and refined by a liberal education, he added a taste for the study of Natural History, and in the Department of Botany. Science is much indebted to his labors. AT his desire, he was buried on this spot, once the garden in which were cultivated most of the plants of his *Flora Caroliniana.* . .

John Fraser, gardener and botanist, friend of Thomas Walter, came to America in 1784, and for more than a quarter of a century, 1784 to 1811, made explorations in Newfoundland and the United States. He first spent a season in Newfoundland and then, in 1785, began explorations in the southern states, spending some time in the Allegheny Mountains in 1789. He returned to Europe, but in 1799 again came to the United States and the Carolina mountains, sent by the Russian Government and accompanied by his eldest son. It was on this trip that he found and collected, on the Roan River in the mountains between North Carolina and Tennessee, the magnificent *Rhododendron catawbiensee,* the handsomest of all native shrubs; from it have come many hybrid varieties.

Father and son returned to the Old World in 1802, but came again to America in 1807. They went back to Scotland, where the father died in Glasgow in 1811, after which the son came to continue explorations in this country until 1817.

9

THE NORTH ATLANTIC STATES

1800-1830

PERHAPS greatest progress in agriculture in the first third of the nineteenth century was in the westward spread of the industry. The Royal Proclamation of 1763 forbidding the settlement of land west of the Alleghenies was canceled by the Northwest Ordinance adopted by the United States in 1783, which opened a vast region for farming. In 1803 another immense fruitful territory was acquired by the United States in the Louisiana Purchase. Gardening in this great region west of the Alleghenies will be discussed in other chapters, but here is the place to say something about the horticulture of the hinterland of the states touching the Atlantic.

Settlers had built homes in the Alleghenies and some had crossed before 1800, but there was little gardening to speak of in these early settlements. The food was wild game, pigeons, salt pork, corn, and wheat. Fare was almost devoid of cultivated fruits and vegetables. For the most part, the population was engaged in murderous warfare with Indians, which kept all but the hardiest close to fortified settlements. The pen pictures of these early settlers depict few who would care for gardening. Most of the men spent their spare time in shooting matches, horse-racing, fighting, betting, and gambling, and drank whisky from morning till night. In these people of lawless vigor there was little taste for the elegant art of gardening.

In William Cobbett's *A Year's Residence in the United States of America,* the writer tells of two months' travel in rural Pennsylvania. There is so little about fruits, flowers, and vegetables, of which Cobbett, a lover of all, would have written had they merited praise, that one may be sure there were almost none. He admired the big stone barns in the eastern counties, which he tells us were a hundred feet long, each with a driveway taking wagons up to the wide mows and granaries on the second floor. 'And then all about them looks comfortable, and gives manifest proofs of ease, plenty, and happiness.' Had he visited western Pennsylvania and western New York, his trenchant pen would have found much to say of the dreadful conditions to be found in these frontier regions in the early 1800's as regards ways of living, farming, and gardening.

Yet progress was being made, especially up the Mohawk, in central New York, about the Finger Lakes, and on the shores of Ontario and Erie, in New York, at Pittsburgh, and on the upper reaches of the Ohio. Before 1800 settlements had been begun in all these regions, and in the new decade of the nineteenth century visitors such as Bigelow, Darby, Davis, Dwight, Fearon, Burnaby, Campbell, Cobbett, Combe, Hall, Kendall, Melish, Thomas, Volney, and Weld could all find something pleasant to say about the towns and farms with their gardens.

The year 1800 may be set as the time when horticulture in all its branches began to bud—the full flower can hardly be said to have opened until at least a hundred years later. Fortunately we have a good account of conditions in the Union at this time, written by a man who could write with authority on horticulture. Bernard M'Mahon (1775-1818), an Irishman, came to America in 1796, and went at once to Philadelphia, where he founded a successful seed and nursery business. He served horticulture best by publishing in 1806, in Philadelphia, his excellent *The American Gardener's Calendar*. For 50 years the book was the standard authority in America in the several fields of gardening, its popularity being attested by 11 editions, the last in 1857. The student of horticulture at the present time, however, is most interested in the inventories of cultivated gardening plants found in its voluminous pages, of which there are 648 in fine print.

In the closing pages of *The Gardener's Calendar*, M'Mahon publishes a 'General Catalogue' of garden plants, which is by far the best, if not the only, statement of the plant material in Amer-

ica at that time. It is doubtful whether all the plants in the list
were to be found in America then or at any time since; but we
must take the author's word when he says: 'at present, an immense
number of them are in the possession of, and for sale by, the
Author of this work.'

Under the heading 'A Catalogue of Kitchen-garden Esculent
Plants and Herbs' are listed 67 kinds of vegetables, with many
varieties of the commoner ones. M'Mahon lists all the vegetables
to be found in a modern seed catalogue, except sweet corn; coriander, corn-salad, orach, rampion, rocambole, and skirret, which
he includes, are to be found in few of the catalogues of today.

Kohlrabi and the rutabaga were introduced at the close of the
eighteenth century. Deane, in his *New England Farmer,* says:
'whether kohlrabi, which has but newly found its way into our
country, is hardy enough to bear the frosts of our winters, I suppose is yet to be proved.' As a matter of fact, it is one of the hardiest of our vegetables. However, Deane lists it as a biennial rather
than an annual, which may account for his fear that it might not
stand New England winters.

A curious dispute arose in New York papers in 1818 between
Grant Thorburn, an early seedsman, and William Cobbett. The
latter, who had a seed store in New York in 1818, claimed that
he was the introducer of the rutabaga and sold better seed at a
dollar a pound than Thorburn; but Thorburn retorted that his
seed was better at the same price and that 'in the year 1796 a large
field of these turnips was grown by Wm. Prout on that piece of
ground now occupied by the navy yard, at the city of Washington.' Thorburn was probably right, but the fact remains that
Cobbett in his *American Gardener* and *A Year's Residence in the
United States of America* was a great champion of the rutabaga.

M'Mahon probably went to European fruit books for 'A Select
List of Fruit-Trees.' He names 3 almonds, none of which could
have been grown out of doors in American orchards; 60 apples,
all but a few of which are long since out of date; possibly the
12 apricots listed were grown in regions where the peach is now
grown; the 4 barberries he names were probably grown not only
as lawn plants but also for their fruits; most of the 20 cherries
are familiar names; all of the 5 currants may still be found; the
4 filberts named are now grown; but few of the 119 gooseberries

named were ever grown in America. There is no telling how many of the 55 grapes listed, all European, were tried, but it is certain that none ever lived more than a few years; only 2 varieties of American grapes are listed; probably the 2 medlars he names were tried; the 3 mulberries are still grown; of the 17 nectarines it is doubtful whether more than 3 could now be found; none of the 34 peaches is now grown; a few of the 40 pears are still to be found; perhaps a dozen of the 30 plums are now grown; the 4 quinces were common a few years ago; the 4 European red raspberries long since have disappeared; the 2 sorbuses are no longer grown; and the 5 strawberries named are all species, probably scarcely improved from the wild.

There are no named varieties of the American red and black raspberries; or of the American gooseberries; no blackberries, dewberries, cranberries, blueberries, and no native plums were in this catalogue.

Under 'A Catalogue of Hardy Deciduous Trees and Shrubs,' 442 species, many more than half of them natives, are named. All the native species are found east of the Mississippi.

Under 'Hardy Evergreen Trees and Shrubs,' 99 species are named, about half and half native and foreign. This number would now be multiplied several times.

M'Mahon names more than 1500 trees, shrubs, and herbaceous and bulbous plants for the greenhouse and hothouse. Many of these plants, as the author says, will succeed in open-ground culture in the southern states. It can hardly be supposed that any considerable number of this great array of plants was grown in the small, poorly heated greenhouses in America in 1806, but plant collectors in Europe were then bringing tender plants to their greenhouses in bewildering numbers, and M'Mahon, unwilling that gardeners in this country should be behind their European fellow collectors, lists the plants that were then grown anywhere in greenhouses.

In another section, 28 plants are listed as 'Aromatic, Pot, and Sweet Herbs.' The herbs are: anise, sweet basil, bark basil, caraway, clary, coriander, chamomile, dill, fennel, hyssop, lavender, lovage, pot marigold, sweet marjoram, pot marjoram, winter sweet marjoram, spearmint, peppermint, pennyroyal, horse mint, rose-

mary, sage, summer savory, winter savory, tarragon, lemon tarragon.

Under 'Plants Cultivated for Medicinal Purposes,' 42 species
are named. Nearly all are from the Old World, and nearly all had
long been grown in the colonies, so that some had escaped to the
wild and grew so abundantly that early botanists called them
natives. Later, the Shakers grew more than twice as many medicinal herbs, including those in M'Mahon's list, and a far larger
proportion of American species.

Of 'Hardy Bulbous and Tuberous Rooted Flowering Plants'
there are 116 species, of which less than a dozen are of American
origin. One is surprised at the number of these plants, and if all
were really in cultivation on this side of the Atlantic, gardens
were about as well supplied in 1800 as they are today.

'Hardy Perennial and Biennial Flowering Plants' number 396.
Of these the author says: 'Well adapted for ornamenting Flower-
Gardens and Borders of Pleasure-Grounds.' Not a few in this list,
perhaps 50 or 60, are American wild flowers. A rough guess is
that not half of the 396 species are offered by seedsmen now.

One is rather surprised at the relatively small number of 'Hardy
Annual Flowers' M'Mahon names. He lists only 120, including
twining and climbing plants. These, as the author explains, are
sorts that may be sown in November or early in the spring. A
second lot of annuals are put under the heading 'Tender Annual
Flowers.' These number 80, and are 'such as should not be sown
in open ground in Philadelphia until the first week in May.' Few
of the species of annual plants of 1800 would be rated high in
modern gardens and of varieties there seem to have been almost
none.

An even dozen 'Hardy Aquatic Herbaceous Perennial Plants'
are named. The list includes most of the species that would be
grown in ornamental ponds today. It is evident from the plants
named, and from the author's statement, that water gardens had
some vogue in America as early as 1800.

To collect wild flowering plants must have been an impulse
since civilization began. One is not surprised, therefore, to find a
page in M'Mahon's book entitled 'Collecting Flowering Plants
from the Woods, Fields, and Swamps.' He names half a hundred
choicest wild flowers of the northeastern states as suitable for a

flower garden, and gives directions for transplanting and caring for them.

M'Mahon gives kitchen herbs so much attention in his book that one is led to look up their use in colonial literature. Not much is to be found except the kinds seedsmen advertised. But in all the colonies in the seventeenth and eighteenth centuries, English garden books and cook books circulated freely, and from these it is easy to measure the importance of herbs in the garden.

Cooking, it would seem, attained a high pitch of luxury in the homes of the well-to-do of this period. Ice was the only means of keeping foods cool and it seldom sufficed. To assist in offsetting the taste of tainted foods, spices, vinegar, salt, and herbs were used. There were strange and complex sauces and flavorings in which herbs played an important part. Cookery was an art in which the ornamentation of the dish was looked after assiduously, and garnitures from the garden were indispensable. Game from the woods, wild fowl from the woods and water, fish, and the flesh of domesticated animals and fowls were so plentiful that vegetables, generally speaking, were not eaten in great quantities. It is safe to say that kitchen gardens were chiefly planted to supply herbs, onions, leeks, and fennel for flavorings and stuffings.

Of all kitchen herbs, sage was most commonly grown. Its pleasant-tasting, strong-smelling leaves are used today by people in all countries in temperate climates to flavor sauces, stews, stuffings, sausages, and cheese. No doubt the first settlers in America, from whatever European country, planted sage. There is a tradition that dried sage was taken to China in American ships and exchanged pound for pound for tea. Sage not only was supposed to flavor foods that might quickly go beyond their prime, and to whet the appetite, but was also considered a sovereign remedy, used as a tea, for a number of maladies.

After sage, the mints were grown more commonly in gardens than any other herbs. The several mints were used to make sauces, flavorings for drinks, tea, to be distilled for their essential oils, and to decorate summer dishes and drinks. Two or three kinds of mints were collected as wild plants by Clayton in Virginia in 1739, and they must have been grown long before in that colony. All the old cook books call for mint sauce or mint jelly for lamb and mutton. Mint in tea, essence and oil, was recommended then, as now, for flatulent indigestion.

Fennel was largely grown both for its leaves and its seeds, to give a relish to unpalatable foods, and to relieve the pangs of hunger, especially on days of fasting. Finochio, a form of fennel now very popular with the Italians, was little grown in America until recent years. In its double use of flavoring and garnishing, parsley was another herb. Pot marjoram and sweet marjoram, now becoming so popular in herb gardens, were prime favorites for dressings, sauces, and soups. They were used green and dried. Caraway was grown much more commonly than now, but served the same purposes it does today: its seeds were used in bread, to sprinkle on pastries, for confections, and to make a liqueur, Kummel, which was much liked.

M'Mahon gives dill a good deal of attention. The seeds were used in soups, sauces, dressings, and in making dill vinegar for pickling. Dill pickles were made a century or two ago, as now, by using the leaves, seeds, and stems to make various sorts of fermented pickles.

Balm, lavender, rosemary, tarragon, summer and winter savory, coriander, and thyme were also grown for kitchen uses.

Herbs were dried in a Dutch oven or before an open fire, as the flavor and color were much better when the drying was done by artificial heat than when it was done in the sun. When thoroughly dry, the usual custom was to put the plants, leaves still on the stems, in bags and store in a dry cool place. A much better way was to pick the leaves off the stems and put them in wellstoppered jars. Sometimes they were pounded and put through a sieve before storing in jars. Grocery stores and drug stores kept dried herbs for sale.

Decoctions were made of nearly every herb used for any purpose. In the homes of the well-to-do, a room was set aside in which to make decoctions, essences, and oils. This was called the 'still-room.' One reads of presents of 'sweet waters,' 'essences,' and 'distillations' being given as neighborly gifts. It is surprising how many different plants were used in part, at least, for distilling. Not only herbs and flowers, but fruits, the leaves of some trees, and the roots and bulbs of various plants found their way to the still-room.

Table teas were often made from garden herbs and the leaves and barks of wild plants. Often these were the only warm drinks of pioneers. Of wild plants, bee balm, *Monarda didyma,* and wild bergamot, *M. fistulosa,* were much grown. These and other Monardas were early brought under cultivation under the general name 'horse-mints,' not only for teas but as flowers.

A major event in American horticulture took place in 1784, when David Landreth established a seed house in Philadelphia, regarded as the first concern of any importance in the country to deal exclusively in seeds and to continue more than just a few years. In the first year it would appear that the Landreths (David had been joined by his brother Cuthbert) were truck growers as well as seedsmen; a writer in *The Horticulturist* [1] traces the reputation of Philadelphia for fine vegetables, which he says was 'unrivalled by any city in the Union,' to this seed house. Unfortunately, Landreth did not advertise in the newspapers of the time, nor did he this early print a catalogue, so that what seeds he grew does not appear.

The Landreths were English, the first David having been born in Haggerston, Northumberland County, where he had his training in gardening. He probably had not been long in this country when the seed and vegetable business was established. From the following advertisement in the *Federal Gazette,* Philadelphia, 22 November 1793, one may suspect that David Landreth was one of the gardeners that Robert Morris imported to care for his gardens:

GARDEN SEEDS

A General assortment of fresh imported, likewise a general assortment of this country of my raising, for sale on the lowest terms, both of which are warranted of the first quality, at the place of Robert Morris, Esquire, on the Schuylkill. Orders Executed on the shortest notice by

David Landreth, Gardner

It was the second David Landreth (1802-80) who brought the seed business to its phenomenal development, and made it for many years the leading seed house in America and one of the

[1] *The Horticulturist and Journal of Rural Art and Rural Taste,* IX: 356.

great establishments of its kind in the world. Young David had his first business experience in Charleston, South Carolina, where a branch house flourished for half a century until brought to a close in 1862 by the Civil War. In 1828 the son succeeded the elder David as proprietor of the seed establishments in the two cities, carried on under the firm name of D. Landreth & Co., while the nursery was in the hands of Thomas Landreth.

The Landreth Nurseries specialized at this time and for some time later in roses, camellias, rhododendrons, azaleas, magnolias, and the Osage orange, which had been started from seed brought by the Lewis and Clark expedition and now was being planted in great quantities for hedges in every part of the East. In the greenhouses, great numbers of oranges, lemons, and shaddocks were grown.

The progress gardening was making in the first years of the nineteenth century is well illustrated by the career of Grant Thorburn, who, in 1805, became a seedsman in New York. Thorburn (1773-1863), a Scotchman, came to America in his youth and sought to make his fortune in nail making, the trade of his father. The introduction of machinery ruined his trade and he became a grocer. In his stock he carried flower pots and found that they sold better with plants in them. From this there came in 1802 a plant and seed business, which led to his buying a farm in New Jersey on which to grow his wares. A fire burned his store; he failed and went to a debtors' prison. He persisted, however, and in the course of a decade became well established under the name 'Grant Thorburn, Seedsman and Florist,' which later became 'G. Thorburn & Son,' and still later 'Thorburn & Co.'

It was in 1776 that Ann Lee established a settlement of Shakers at New Lebanon, New York. From here branch communities of the organization were planted in various parts of the United States, until by 1850 there were 56 Shaker settlements in the country. Of these, 4 were in Maine, 6 in New Hampshire, 4 in Connecticut, 10 in Massachusetts, 13 in New York, and 9 in Kentucky. In all Shaker communities meat was used in moderation or banned. Some denied themselves milk, butter, and eggs. Gardens and orchards were prime necessities, and as soon as a Shaker settlement was founded, it became a center for the culture and distribution of vegetables and fruits.

During the first quarter of the nineteenth century, seeds grown by the Shakers were the best to be had in America. Wagons went from village to village, where Shaker seeds were left at stores to be sold on a commission of 25 per cent, taking back in the summer all seeds not sold. The business of growing seeds had been started as early as 1780 and by 1800 was in full swing. Most of the seeds were grown at Watervliet and New Lebanon, New York, but other communities grew them too, and the annual sales amounted to many thousands of dollars.[2] The Shakers were the first seedsmen to put seeds in packets, a practice which soon became universal.

The following memorandum gives the prices charged by the Shakers for seeds about 1807.[3]

40	Bags	of	Red Onion Seed	@	12	$4 80¢
2	do		White do		14	28
20			Blood Beet		8	
1			Yorkshire Cabbage		10	10
4			Winter do		8	32
12			Lettuce		8	96
4			Scarcity		8	32
26			Cucumber		6	1 56
8			Turnip		8	64
2			French do		6	12
2			Sage		8	16
12			Carrot		6	72
12			Parsnip		6	72
14			Radish		6	84
6			Sum^r Squash		4	24
2			Winter do		4	8
8			Watermelon		4	32
8			Musk do		4	32
4			Asparagus		6	24
2			Celery		4	8
2			Parsley		4	8
2			Peppergrass		4	8

2 See also p. 253.   3 Andrews, p. 69.

The Shakers took great pains to improve their animals and fowls through selection of the 'natural creation'; but, it would seem, they did not believe in crossing. A standing order was: 'The different species of animals should be kept distinct, each in its own order. . . No fowls should be set on the eggs of fowls of different kinds.' The improvement of plants followed a similar rule: 'Different species of trees, or plants, may not be engrafted or budded upon each other, as apples on pears or quince; or peaches on cherries, or contrawise.'

It was contrary to orders to grow flowers, but in an intimate glimpse of life in Shaker communities, given by one of the sisters in the magazine *Good Housekeeping* for July 1906, we learn that there were ways of nullifying this rule:

We always had extensive poppy beds and early in the morning, before the sun had risen, the white-capped sisters could be seen stooping among the scarlet blossoms to slit those pods from which the petals had just fallen. Again after sundown they came out with little knives to scrape off the dried juice. This crude opium was sold at a large price and its production was one of the most lucrative as well as the most picturesque of our industries.

The rose bushes were planted along the sides of the road which ran through our village and were greatly admired by the passersby, but it was strongly impressed upon us that a rose was useful, not ornamental. It was not intended to please us by its color or its odor, its mission was to be made into rose-water, and if we thought of it in any other way we were making an idol of it and thereby imperiling our souls. In order that we might not be tempted to fasten a rose upon our dress or to put it into water to keep, the rule was that the flower should be plucked with no stem at all. We had only crimson roses, as they were supposed to make stronger rose-water than the paler varieties. This rosewater was sold, of course, and was used in the community to flavor apple pies. It was also kept in store at the infirmary, and although in those days no sick person was allowed to have a fresh flower to cheer him, he was welcome to a liberal supply of rosewater to bathe his aching head.

Then there were the herbs of many kinds. Lobelia, pennyroyal, spearmint, peppermint, catnip, wintergreen, thoroughwort, sarsaparilla, and dandelion all grew wild in the surrounding fields. When it was time to gather them an elderly brother would take a great wagonload of children, armed with tow sheets to the pastures. Here they would pick the appointed herb—each one had its own day, that there might be no danger of mixing—and, when their sheets were full, drive solemnly home again. In addition to that which grew wild we cultivated an immense amount of dandelion, dried the root and sold it as 'chicory.' The witch hazel branches were too tough for women and children to handle, so the brethren cut them and brought them into the herb shop where the sisters made them into hamamelis. We had big beds of sage, thorn apple, belladonna, marigolds and camomile, as well as of yellow dock, of which we raised great quantities to sell to the manufacturers of a well-known 'sarsaparilla.' We also made a sarsaparilla of our own and various ointments. In the herb shop the herbs were dried and then pressed into packages by machinery, labeled and sold outside. Lovage root we exported both plain and sugared, and the wild flagroot we gathered and sugared too. On the whole there was no pleasanter work than that in the 'medical garden' and 'herb shop.'

The Shakers at New Lebanon began in 1828 to offer dried corn for sale, probably dried in the simple fashion of pioneer families. Later, however, steam-operated corn-cutting machines, steam-boxes for cooking, and kiln drying did the work in a large way. The product was packed in barrels and sold at $20 per barrel. Some seasons more than a thousand barrels of dried corn were sold. Other vegetables, especially pumpkins, and fruits, with the apple leading, were dried for use and sale. Nearly every Shaker community in the northern states had an apple-drying house in which large quantities of dried apples were prepared for market.

The early years of the nineteenth century saw the establishment of a great number of nurseries in the northern states, west to the Mississippi. Three of these, together with the Prince Nursery, founded nearly a century earlier, became of national and international importance. All sold trees in every part of America and exported and imported trees from Europe.

The catalogues of the Prince Nursery from 1771 to 1850 constitute as good horticultural literature as was then to be had in America. In 1828 William Prince published a *Treatise on Horticulture*. William Robert Prince published, in 1830, *A Treatise on the Vine;* in 1831, *A Pomological Manual;* and in 1846, a *Manual of Roses.*

In 1827 the Linnaean Botanic Garden contained more than a hundred species of Australian plants, among which were two species of Eucalyptus and several of Banksia. In 1828 the Garden had for sale more than 600 kinds of roses. The collection of dahlias at one time numbered 350 kinds; and there were, in the latter days of the nursery, enormous collections of camellias and citrus fruits, which were then largely grown as tub plants in cool greenhouses.

William Robert Prince, the fourth proprietor (1795-1869), was the introducer of the Chinese Yam, *Dioscorea Batatas,* and Chinese sugar cane. In common with all other nurserymen in the United States, he was an enthusiast of the mulberry, and in the 1840's grew so many that cuttings of *Morus multicaulis* passed as currency in Flushing. He had plantations of mulberries in other parts of the East, one at Norfolk, Virginia, for all of which he was offered $100,000.

William Robert Prince was a botanist and a botanical explorer as well as a nurseryman. While a young man, he accompanied Professor John Torrey, of Columbia, and again Thomas Nuttall of Harvard, on plant-collecting expeditions in the eastern states, and in 1849 and 1850 collected plants in California, many of which were offered to gardeners from the Prince Nurseries.

The cedar of Lebanon is as renowned as any tree in the world. In Europe, especially in England, few evergreens have been more commonly planted; thousands of magnificent specimens may be seen in parks and gardens. In America, however, this tree is not often seen, though several splendid specimens have been noted in horticultural literature in the Middle Atlantic states for over a century. A. J. Downing, in his *Treatise on Landscape Gardening,* published in 1849, writes of a tree on the grounds of Mr. T. Ash, at Throgs Neck, Westchester County, New York, as the finest in the Union, being at that time 50 feet high. A still older and larger specimen stood in front of the Prince house, Flushing, until a few years ago. Probably the tree was introduced in America by the Princes, for it is early listed in their catalogues.

Three generations of Princes tried to grow European grapes in America. William Robert Prince devoted his life to grape culture. He tried all of the varieties of *Vitis vinifera* to be obtained in the several countries in Europe where grapes are grown, but after fifty years of work with foreign sorts, he gave the rest of his life to improving and distributing varieties of native grapes. Because of his nursery, his book, and his writings, he must be ranked with Adlum and Longworth as one of the three geniuses of American grape growing. His *A Treatise on the Vine* was the first good work to appear on viticulture in America.

To the middle of the nineteenth century the Prince Nursery led all others in size and number of species and varieties offered for sale. In the catalogue of 1841, this nursery had for sale 272 kinds of apples, 420 of pears, 109 of cherries, 156 of plums, 116 of grapes, 147 of gooseberries, with several each of currants, blackberries, red raspberries, black raspberries, and strawberries. Of ornamental shrubs, the nursery had 196 species and varieties of deciduous ornamental trees, 273 of shrubs, 111 of evergreens, 73 of vines, 680 of roses, 85 of culinary herbs, and over 800 perennial flowers. Now, a hundred years later, no American nursery offers nearly so many of any of these plants except of small fruits, and of one small fruit, the gooseberry, not a tenth as many.

After the Prince Nursery, by far the largest and best American establishment of the kind on the continent, was that of the Kenricks, in the towns of Brighton and Newton, Massachusetts, the first large nursery in New England. The founder was John Kenrick. The nursery was started in 1790, but it was not until well after 1800 that it became noteworthy; and it did not reach its greatest fame until William Kenrick, son of John, became a partner in 1823, at which time the Kenricks began to rival the Princes as dealers in nursery stock.

At first the elder Kenrick seems to have grown only seedling trees, but after a few years he learned the art of budding and grafting, and then specialized for some time in named varieties of tree fruits, especially the peach. But when William became a partner, the firm carried a general assortment of fruits. In an advertisement in *The New England Farmer,* in 1823, among tree fruits there were 30 varieties of budded peaches. The firm listed 10 varieties of European grapes, and the Isabella, Bland, Catawba, and Scuppernong among American varieties. The only small fruit was the currant, and of ornamentals the horse chestnut, catalpa, mountain ash, rose, lilac, and a few others. The Kenricks were large growers of currants and in 1824 made 1700 gallons of currant wine; in 1825, over 3000 gallons; and in 1826, about 3600 gallons.

At the time the elder Kenrick started his nursery, the craze for Lombardy poplars was at its height. So many were sold by this nursery that it was said that nearly every family owning land in New England in the first years of the new century planted one or more poplars grown by John Kenrick. The son, in turn, succumbed to the mulberry craze, and in the 1830's was one of the large growers of this tree. In 1832 or thereabouts, William Kenrick introduced the Beurre Bosc pear, still one of the best of all pears, from cions received from Van Mons, the Belgian originator.

In 1833 William Kenrick published *The New American Orchardist,* a valuable contribution because of its full descriptions of many new fruits. In 1835 he published *The American Silk Grower's Guide,* which is, in essence, a treatise on mulberry culture.

The date and place of John Kenrick's birth cannot be learned; he died in 1833 in a mansion near the nursery that had made him wealthy as well as famous. William Kenrick was born in 1795 in the family mansion on Nonantum Hill, on the spot where the Apostle Eliot began his labors for the Indians of New England; he died in 1872, at the age of 77. The nursery was active for an even 60 years, from 1790 to 1850.

Kenrick's nursery may not have come to high estate until toward the end of the period under discussion, for as late as 1822 John Lowell, a leader in agriculture in Massachusetts, complained that New England was utterly destitute of nurseries for fruit trees on an extensive scale; and that cultivators could not buy a supply of the most common plants of the smaller fruits, such as strawberries, gooseberries, raspberries, of the superior kinds; 'that there was no place to which we can go for plants to ornament our grounds; that there was not a single seedsman who could furnish fresh seed of annual flowers on which we can place reliance.'

Very different from the commercial nurseries of the Princes and the Kenricks was that of William Coxe, Burlington, New Jersey. Coxe was one of the first of a number of wealthy patrons of fruit growing in America, who have greatly enriched pomology by introducing and propagating new varieties of fruits from home and abroad.

William Coxe was born 3 May 1762, in Philadelphia, and died at his fruit farm near Burlington, New Jersey, 25 February 1831. He was a man of considerable wealth, a student of books and the arts, and of such charm of personality that throughout his mature life he was one of the leaders in the literary, scientific, and social circles of Burlington and Philadelphia. Fruit growing was an avocation; his vocation was that of a merchant. Coxe was sufficiently wealthy to possess an orchard in which were all of the varieties of fruits to be obtained in America and many imported from Europe. He could say in 1817 that he had been 'for many years actively engaged in the rearing, planting and cultivating of fruit trees on a scale more extensive than has been attempted by any other individual in this country.'

Coxe was not only one of the foremost fruit growers in America, and its best pomological writer in this period, but through associations with prominent men in the country he must have exercised a stimulating influence on gardening. He was a member at one time of the State Legislature of New Jersey, and later a member of Congress, where he was closely associated with Daniel Webster, a horticulturist of note. Coxe was also one of the few men in America to be made an honorary member of the Horticultural Society of London, of which he was for many years a faithful correspondent. He was the author of a notable pomological treatise, *A View of the Cultivation of Fruit Trees,* published in 1817.

In no other state was fruit growing more advanced, when Coxe wrote *A View of the Cultivation of Fruit Trees,* than in New Jersey. There were large orchards of all the tree fruits, the crops of which were sold in Philadelphia and the several prosperous cities near by, including Baltimore. Nurseries were keeping pace with orchards. Of these one of the largest was that of David Smith of Burlington. In 1806 Smith published a catalogue in which were listed 151 varieties of apples, 98 pears, 67 peaches, 43 cherries, 20 plums, 16 nectarines, and 10 apricots.

Another noted nursery was that of Robert Manning, who, in 1823, established his 'Pomological Garden' at Salem, Massachusetts. In this garden Manning attempted to do for Massachusetts what Coxe had done so well for New Jersey—to bring together all the varieties of fruits that would thrive in his region. In time, Manning's collection of tree fruits contained more than 2000 varieties, of which about 1000 were pears, the largest number of varieties of this fruit until then planted in the country. From Manning, men of wealth obtained pear trees for home orchards, which were everywhere in fashion in the northern states. No other American pomologist labored more devotedly to introduce and distribute better pears.

Manning had correspondents in England, France, and Belgium, from whom he received the best varieties of fruits in Europe. In particular, he tested the pears bred by Van Mons, but he also imported many varieties from the London Horticultural Society. Manning was one of the most careful observers among American pomologists, and is said to have had a memory so remarkable that he could long carry in the mind characteristics of trees or fruits he had once seen. In 1838 he brought out his *Book of Fruits* (see p. 483), containing the fullest and most accurate descriptions of fruits that had yet been published in this country.

Robert Manning was one of the founders, in 1829, of the Massachusetts Horticultural Society. He was the father of Robert Manning, Jr., long secretary of the Society, and the author of *The History of the Massachusetts Horticultural Society* (1880), so often quoted in these pages, one of the important contributions to the literature of American horticulture.

The first nursery of note west of the Hudson was that of David Thomas, at Aurora, on the eastern shore of Cayuga Lake, in Cayuga County, New York. Thomas, a Quaker, moved to Aurora in 1805. He was a civil engineer by vocation—one of the builders of the Erie Canal—and horticulture was an avocation. The peach was the fruit he liked best, although he was a large grower of pears, the culture of which was then sweeping the country. Western New York in 1805 was a wilderness, yet Thomas, living in a pioneer community, was a correspondent of many European horticulturists and a member of the Royal Horticultural Society of London and the Linnaean Society of Paris. He was the author of *Travels in the Western Country in* 1816, the record of a journey for the government from Aurora to Vincennes, Indiana. This book, vivid in its descriptions, helped to draw agriculturists to the regions it describes.

John Jacobs Thomas, David's son, was even more noted than the father as a horticulturist. He was born in 1810 on his father's fruit farm at Union Springs, near the shores of beautiful Cayuga Lake, and spent most of his life there, dying in 1895. In his varied career he was a nurseryman, fruit grower, farmer, inventor of farm machinery, speaker on farm topics, and one of the most prolific writers on horticultural and agricultural matters of the nineteenth century. It is as an author of books, as an editor, and a writer for the agricultural press that he gained greatest distinction. Best known of his several books was *The American Fruit Culturist,* which first appeared in 1846. He also wrote *Farm Implements and Machinery* and nine volumes of *Rural Affairs,* issued as annuals. For nearly 60 years he wrote editorials and general articles for *The Cultivator* and *The Country Gentleman,* which, if collected, would make several large volumes. That western New York has for more than a century been a region of orchards, of beautiful farm homes, and of prosperous horticultural industries is largely due to the two Thomases.

Another father and son both with the given name Thomas have been eminent horticulturists and nurserymen in this country. Thomas Hogg, senior, an English horticulturist, emigrated to the United States in 1820, when Thomas, the younger, was nine months old. The father set up business in Manhattan where Twenty-third Street and Broadway now meet (then not in the city), as a florist and nurseryman, at a time when men in his business were few. The Hogg establishment flourished from the start, and, in 1840, more room being required, moved north to Seventy-ninth Street and the East River. Young Thomas and his brother James took over the business when the father died in 1855.

Now began the work that made the Hogg nursery famous in the garden history of this country, although a full account of it does not fall within the range of this history. In 1862 President Lincoln made Thomas Hogg, the second, a United States Marshal, and sent him to Japan, where he spent the next eight years, and returned again in 1873 for a further stay of two years. As a representative of this country he was permitted to go anywhere in

Japan, collecting seeds and plants to his heart's content. These oriental treasures he sent home to his brother James, who grew them to perfection, making the Hogg collection of Asiatic plants the best in the country, one from which American gardens were enormously enriched with trees, shrubs, and flowers.

The few commercial apple orchards in the New World up until 1825 existed almost wholly for the making of cider, although just before and after the Revolution some Green Newtowns were exported to England. Probably the first orchards for the sale of fruit exclusively were on Long Island, in New Jersey, and eastern Pennsylvania, the apples going to Philadelphia and New York. In the 1820's, a brisk trade in apples along the Hudson grew up, and soon the largest apple orchards in the country were to be found near this river. Summer and fall apples as well as winter varieties were in demand. The apples were shipped in 'straw-head' barrels and sold for $1.00 to $1.50 per barrel, the barrels to be returned. The largest single orchard, some 200-odd acres of Green Newtowns, was owned by Robert Pell of Esopus.

P. C. Reynolds, in the northeast part of Dutchess County, owned two orchards in this period. The older was planted in 1775 and contained only seedling trees. In the younger orchard, about 5 per cent were grafted trees; the varieties grafted into original seedling trees were Yellow Harvest, Bough Sweet, Fall Pippin, Westfield Seek-no-further, Black Gilliflower, Rhode Island Greening, and Esopus Spitzenburg. Much of the fruit was fed to farm animals and made into cider. Apple jack was made in large quantities in the neighborhood, the only article of commerce from the apple.[4]

In 1836 Reynolds moved to a farm in Ontario County, in the heart of what is now the famous apple region of western New York. On this farm, also, there were two apple orchards, in which about 10 per cent of the trees were grafted. In 1843 Reynolds began selling apples to a commission man in Palmyra to be shipped on the Erie Canal to New York. The price received was 75 cents per barrel for grafted fruit, including the barrel. In 1848 the seedling trees in the two orchards were grafted to

4 Beach, I: 12.

Northern Spy, Baldwin, Detroit Red, Gravenstein, Porter, and Peck Pleasant.[5]

Despite the many splendid orchards of wealthy amateurs in the early part of the nineteenth century, and of the several very good nurseries, the owners of which were nearly all authors of pomological books, fruit growing was still in a primitive condition. The trees, until as late as 1850, were more often seedlings than grafted varieties; they were neither cultivated nor fertilized; orchards were almost always used as pastures; and there were few markets for orchard fruits.

A picture of fruit growing in New England in 1822 by James Thacher is most depressing. According to him, the most palpable neglect prevailed, in respect to pruning, cultivating, manuring, and of perpetuating choice fruits by grafting. Old orchards were, he tells us, in a state of rapid decay. It was not uncommon to see valuable and thrifty trees exposed to the depredations of cattle and sheep, and their foliage destroyed by caterpillars and other insects. He knew 'of no branch of agriculture so unaccountably and so culpably disregarded.'[6] However, this could be said in almost any age and of any branch of agriculture, an art always far from perfect, and about which pessimism always prevails.

Cider was still a large item in domestic economy. On sale it was always hard cider; the freshly expressed juice of the apple was sold as 'sweet apple juice.' It was still common tender for most services. Even an education might be bought with cider: there being an item in an old account book of 1805 from Bainbridge, New York, 'one-half barrel of cider for Mary's schooling.'[7]

A criterion of the estimation in which cider was held when Coxe published his book on fruit culture in 1817, is the number of pages he devoted to this product. The book contains 30 chapters, 9 of which are devoted to the subject of making and preserving cider. In the 1830's, however, the great temperance movement of the nineteenth century began, the demand for cider fell off, and the profitable cider industry, dating back to colonial days, began to decline. In consequence apple growing suffered, and until transportation for fruits began to be cheaper and more efficient,

[5] Ibid.
[6] Thacher, p. 10.
[7] New York State Historical Association, *Reports*, XXIV: 200.

after the middle of the century, there was not much money in apples.

Agriculture in America has had several glorious sprees in speculation, one of which was in mulberries. The mulberry mania raged from 1825, when the first *Morus multicaulis* trees were set, to 1844, when a cold winter destroyed the last of the plantations. Long Island was the center of mulberry culture, but trees were grown and set from Boston in the north to Charleston in the south, and westward as far as orchards were grown.

Efforts to produce silk began in Jamestown, Virginia, in 1621, at the instigation of the London Company, and continued intermittently for 200 years without much to show in the way of silk, until 1830, when some was really made. Up until this time, failure, it had seemed, resulted from not having the Asiatic mulberry upon which alone silkworms thrive. At last, the tree from Asia was available, and all America believed that success was assured —that a great national industry was to be established.

The French had brought from the Philippines, in 1824, a mulberry tree, *Morus multicaulis,* with enormous leaves, excellent food for the silkworm. The tree grew with amazing rapidity and could be propagated quickly and easily from sprouts that grew from its base. It was this habit of throwing out sprouts that gave the tree its specific name, *multicaulis.* It was said that the tree had come to the Philippines from China, where it had from time immemorial furnished food for the silkworms that produced the famous Chinese silks. In 1826 William Prince & Son, proprietors of the Linnaean Gardens, Flushing, Long Island, imported and began the propagation of this mulberry. The trees grew like weeds and seemed perfectly at home in the New World.

An action of Congress in December 1825 had directed attention to the cultivation of the mulberry and the manufacture of silk. The Secretary of the Treasury prepared an illustrated manual of 220 pages on silk, which was distributed in February, 1828. In August of the same year, the Senate published and distributed another treatise on the subject. The culture of *Morus multicaulis* and the making of silk was discussed in the legislatures of every state in the Union, bringing forth many resolutions and several specific acts. Public meetings were held and for two decades silk culture was everywhere the chief topic of conversation.

No agricultural subject in America has ever had so much attention in the press. Between the years 1828 and 1844, no fewer than 18 books, some of them running through several editions, were published. Newspapers and magazines carried pages of information and advertisements. The catalogues of nurserymen contained for the time being more about mulberries than any fruit or ornamental. The country supported four monthly magazines on mulberries and silk. The following page from the *Flushing Silk Journal* is typical of the publicity given the mulberry, the silk-worm, and silk:

It has been proved that the utmost expense of producing raw silk does not exceed $1½ to $2 per pound, and that it readily commands in our market, from $4 to $5 per pound, and also that at $3 per pound it may be exported to Europe and yield a handsome profit.

Possessing, as we do, every variety of soil, and a climate of acknowledged superiority; with a population rivalling all other nations in skill and enterprize; what room is there left for doubt?

Let each of us therefore commence operations by the erection of a cocoonery of a suitable size proportionate to the number of trees we possess, and provide ourselves with the necessary means to prepare our silk for market. The expense is so trivial compared with the great importance of the object and the certainty of profitable returns that every one should complete his arrangements without delay, and this being done, it will be soon ascertained that far more trees will be wanted than at present exist in the whole country. . .

In all parts of the country where the peach could be grown, mulberry trees were planted, though, as it turned out, the tree is less hardy than the peach. Nearly every garden, in city or town, had its mulberry tree. There is record of one shipload from the East by water to New Orleans and up the Mississippi to Indiana and Illinois—a financial failure, since the silk bubble had burst before the trees reached their destination.

The chief interest to horticulture in this mulberry speculation was growing the plants. Nurserymen who had been growing fruit trees and ornamentals turned their attention to growing mulberries. Even though the trees are easily propagated from sprouts and hardwood or greenwood cuttings, prices were exorbitant. At the height of the speculation, one-year-old trees sold for $2 to $5; for several years the supply was less than the demand. Nurserymen made fortunes in a few years only to lose them when the crash came. There is a record of a nurseryman who grew 30,000 trees on a single acre at a profit of $30,000.

The fury of the *multicaulis* speculation began to subside in the spring of 1839, and before autumn the collapse came. Two unpredictable and uncontrollable natural phenomena brought the speculation to a close. First, the trees could not endure the cold of even mild Long Island; and second, a disease impossible to control appeared and destroyed the trees where climate did permit them to grow. In the spring of 1840, trees went begging for purchasers at a penny each. A cold winter in 1844 wiped out the few remaining plantations in the North, and the amazing speculation in mulberry culture was over.

The seeds offered by the several seedsmen and by the Shakers in the early years of the nineteenth century, and the printed observations of many travelers make plain that vegetables in home gardens were commonly grown in all the old, well-settled communities of the country. It was a different story in new countries where the soil was cultivated only for corn, wheat, and a few fruits. Great strides, no doubt, were being made in vegetable culture in these years through the multiplication of varieties, ease in getting better and cheaper seeds, and the cheapness of glass for cold frames, hotbeds, and greenhouses. There was more wealth so that many could employ gardeners and grow better vegetables. County fairs, exhibitions, horticultural societies, and garden books and papers gave much attention to vegetables.

When Fortescue Cuming visited Pittsburgh in 1807, there was some commercial gardening and orcharding in western Pennsylvania, for in a market report he gives, the following prices are quoted: [8] 'potatoes per bushel .40; onions a dollar; white beans a dollar; dried apples a dollar; dried peaches a dollar; green peaches .40; peach brandy .75 to .80 per gallon; cider 3 to four dollars per barrel.'

[8] Cuming, p. 224.

Little is said, however, in this period about market gardening. Means of transportation were still so poor that vegetables could not be grown far from markets with the hope of profit. Even near large cities and towns, only the grosser vegetables seemed to be raised—cabbage, turnips, parsnips, rutabagas, and the like, were offered for sale in markets. There were market gardeners only in the immediate vicinity of large cities, with those about Philadelphia and New York most numerous. In the newspapers of the times 'greengrocers prices' are so often given that one must believe that there were stores where fruit and vegetables were the chief commodities for sale. Probably there were hawkers who went from street to street selling vegetables and fruits, much as they are now sold in cities of the South.

There is little in print to tell us precisely in what packages fruits and vegetables were sold. The market quotations for apples and pears are usually in 'barrels' and 'casks.' Peaches, plums, cherries, apricots, and nectarines were sold by the dozen or by the pound, coming to market no doubt in baskets and pails which were returnable to the owners. Willow baskets of various sizes and shapes were in use, but they were expensive. Splint baskets, boxes, and crates are modern inventions. Making willow baskets and barrels probably was work for winter days.

Tools are more enduring than packages, and we know from specimens that have come down to us what they were. The cast-iron plow was invented by Jethro Wood in 1819; the only harrow was a heavy wooden-framed tool with teeth a foot in length. As cultivators did not come in use until after the Civil War, the soil was loosened by shovel plows; seed drills for farm and garden crops came after the Civil War. There were no ditching machines until the twentieth century, nor need of them until John Johnson, Seneca County, New York, laid the first tile for draining used in the New World. Despite the great quantities of cider and peach brandy used in the country there was no machinery for crushing the fruit until after the Revolution, the fruit being crushed by pounding in a trough and pressed by simple hand presses.

Garden tools, such as hoes, rakes, sickles, scythes, spades, trowels, shears, clippers, grafting and pruning instruments, watering pots, and hand and wheelbarrows have changed but little in design. They were much the same and quite as numerous in Washington's garden as in modern gardens. Since in the earlier years, down to a generation or two ago, all these tools were made by local blacksmiths and tinsmiths, they were clumsier, more expensive, but more durable. Lawn mowers, hose, nozzles, sprinkling devices, all spraying devices, seed drills, cultivators, manure spreaders, harrows, and horse and power tools are inventions following the Civil War, many of them since the beginning of the twentieth century.

The commonest tool for stirring the soil in orchards and gardens in this period was a heavy hoe made by the village blacksmith. Watering pots of many shapes and sizes were the work of the tinsmith; barrows and carts were homemade; and flower pots in a great variety of shapes and sizes were fashioned by the local potter.

American workingmen in the two and a half centuries of this country did not take kindly to gardening, whether on the lawn or in flower and vegetable gardens. Most of the professional gardeners were Irish, a few Scotch, and still fewer English or German. Wages were lower than for almost any other kind of work and the working day was from sunrise to sunset. In winter, gardeners had difficulty in finding employment. In most places 'gardening' was looked upon as work for old men or boys. As late as 1852, A. J. Downing wrote in *The Horticulturist* that only 3 per cent of the working gardeners in the United States were native or naturalized citizens.

In 1828, when Thomas Green Fessenden's *New American Gardener* was published, the word 'garden' commonly meant the vegetable garden. The author included some account of the flower garden and pleasure grounds but thought that to do so needed an apology: 'Should the agriculturists have no taste for ornamental gardening, yet such is the laudable taste of the fair daughters of America at the present day that there are comparatively few that do not take an interest in a flower garden; and this alone is sufficient reason for these remarks.' A few New Englanders had flower gardens, as they probably had had from the days of Governor Endicott, but they were fewer than in most of the colonies southward.

From the first gardens worthy of the name, however, down to those of today, no large place has been considered quite complete without one or several bowers formed by trees, shrubs, or vines trained over lattice work. Thus was made a leafy roof, under which were seats for resting, or a shaded walk. Such structures have been variously known as arbors, pavilions, summerhouses, and trellises. One reads in descriptions of large places of the 'south arbor' or the 'north arbor,' the 'rose arbor,' the 'honeysuckle arbor,' or the 'rustic arbor,' all variously constructed with foundations of wood or stone, adorned possibly with arches, turrets, and railings. Now and then a man of wealth built a Grecian temple in his garden to serve as a summerhouse. Two quite distinct objects were kept in view in building these structures. One was to have the arbor command a view over lower lands, fields, woods, or water; the other, to secure seclusion.

Probably in no phase of gardening has there been less limit set to imagination than in the patterns and materials of summerhouses. Possibly in no other phase of gardening has there been less taste shown than in building rustic, board, and stone places of this kind. Happily, it has ever been recognized that all must be screened with verdure of some kind, so that nature often makes beautiful that which was ugly when it came from the hand of man.

The orange and lemon were so popular that special houses called orangeries were built in northern climates to shelter them in the winter. The trees, kept dwarf by severe pruning, were planted in wooden tubs, which could be carried out in the summer to adorn the garden. In some of the best gardens, as at Lemon Hill in Philadelphia, there was an orange garden bordered with box set in turfed squares with walks. The owners of conservatories in the early part of the century, Downing tells us, 'were perfectly content if they ripened a washing tub full of Lemons or a few miserable Oranges in a year.' He says, speaking of a time early in the century: 'Astonishment was at its height in Philadelphia, when it was whispered that Mr. Pratt's gardener [at Lemon Hill] picked two wash tubs full of Lemons to make that atrocious mixture called lemonade, for a party.' [9]

[9] Downing, in *The Horticulturist*.

From about 1825 to 1875 or longer, the camellia was the most popular greenhouse flower in the North, as it was as an out-of-door plant in the South. Florists everywhere offered cut camellias for sale, often for a dollar or more for a single bud. Collections were numerous and large, greenhouse owners in the North and plantation owners in the South vying in growing varieties of American origin. Plants of a new variety often sold for $25 each. One of the first books in America dealing with a single species was by General H. A. Dearborn, sometime member and president of the Massachusetts Horticultural Society, who, in 1838, translated from the French Berlese's monograph on the *Genus Camellia.*

The first camellia to reach America was a red-flowered variety with single blooms, imported from Europe by John Stevens of Hoboken, New Jersey, about 1798. In 1800, Michael Floy brought the double-white variety, *Alba Plena,* to add to Stevens' collection. Floy settled in New York and was long a large grower of camellias, although Robert Buist, the Landreths, and others also built up large collections. It was probably the Landreth Charleston branch that introduced the camellia into the South. The plant is a native of China, brought to Europe in 1739. It was named 'camellia' by Linnaeus as a posthumous honor to George Joseph Kamel, a medical missionary to the Philippines who had contributed largely to the natural history of the Far East. Kamel never visited the mainland of Asia and probably never saw a camellia.[10]

Toward the middle of the century, Alexandre Dumas's *La Dame aux Camélias* appeared, from which later came the play *Camille* and the opera *La Traviata,* and the camellia immediately became the flower of flowers in France, England, and America. No dandy considered himself well dressed unless he wore a camellia in his buttonhole. It was the favorite flower for a lady's bouquet or corsage, and has continued from that day to this to be a favorite at weddings.

Next to the camellia, the Indian azalea was the most popular greenhouse flower in this period. The cultivated greenhouse azaleas are hybrids of several Asiatic species, some of which were introduced in the first year of the nineteenth century, but the first exhibition worthy of notice in New England was in the rooms

10 Hume, *Camellias in America.*

of the Massachusetts Horticultural Society, 7 March 1835. From then on, exhibitions were made annually, and in number and beauty of plants competed with the camellia.

As late as 1830, and in many greenhouses to a much later date, heating was done by hot-air flues, which were long pipes leading from a furnace at one end of the greenhouses to the other and back. Hot-water heating began to come in use, in a few houses, at the date given. Steam was not in general use, even for large houses, for another fifty years. The introduction of hot-water heating created a boom in greenhouse building, and by 1840 there were many large glass houses in Boston, New York, and Philadelphia, few towns of any size in the country not having private and commercial greenhouses.

Until toward the end of the century, few vegetables were grown in glass houses, although fruits were widely grown under glass. In late autumn and early spring in northern cities, and throughout the winter in the South, vegetables were forced in hotbeds. Lettuce, radishes, and cucumbers were the crops most commonly forced, but in the spring gardeners more commonly than now used hotbeds and cold frames for forcing or starting other vegetables and flowers.

Long after the Civil War the glass for greenhouses was imported from France and Belgium, that made in America being so wavy, blistered, and spotted, that plants grown under it were burned by sun rays concentrated by the defects in the glass. About the middle of the century, or a little after, there was a craze for blue glass in homes and greenhouses, for which there was a weak imitation in blue whitewash. Not a few greenhouses were wholly or partly thus subjected to blue light. The theory was that the sun's rays were more healthful both to humans and plants when filtered through or reflected by blue.

That fruits and vegetables could be preserved in hermetically sealed receptacles without robbing them of their natural juices, flavors, and aromas was discovered in 1795 by Nicholas Appert, a Frenchman. A little later the process became known in England and in 1810 was patented by Peter Durand, the patent covering the use of tin, glass, pottery, or other material. Ezra Dagget brought the secret to America about 1815, and he and his son-in-law, Thomas Kennett, soon after obtained patents on the art of preserving foods, and canning then began in America, to become within a century a great industry. Eventually much of the produce of orchards and truck gardens was to be put in tin cans, and the welfare of vast areas of agricultural regions was to depend on canning.

Fruits and vegetables were not canned very commonly until long after canning in hermetically sealed jars was well known, however, owing to the scarcity of good cook stoves and the very high cost of glass containers. Commercial canning of fruits and vegetables in the United States lagged until California became a great fruit-growing state and the center of the canning industries of the world.

In *The Cook's Own Book,* published in Boston in 1832, there are 48 pages of 'Receipts for Making all Kinds of Confectionary,' and out of several hundred, nearly all contain tree or small fruits, citrus fruits, nuts, vegetables, seeds of herbs, or a homemade oil or essence of this or that herb. Scattered through the book there are probably as many or more fruit brandies, wines, liqueurs, flings, and bounces. Of preserves, jellies, jams, butters, sirups, compotes, pastes, creams, cheeses, ratafias, candies, cakes, pickles, and ice creams containing fruit, there must be a thousand or more recipes. The use of ice cream with fruits was common, one judges from the many recipes, when *The Cook's Own Book* was written, although in 1744, according to *The Journal of William Black,* it was a rarity, which he reports as a new dish being served with strawberries at the governor's house in Annapolis.[11]

In 1828 the last organized effort to grow European grapes in eastern America was made. In that year the State Legislature of Maryland gave incorporation rights to the Maryland Society for the Promotion of the Vine. The object of the Society was to 'carry on experiments in the cultivation of both European and native grapes.' The secretary of the Society reported in 1831 that there were then under cultivation near the city of Baltimore, several vineyards of from three to ten acres, each, and a great number of

[11] *Penn. Mag. of Hist. and Biog.,* I: 126.

smaller ones.[12] How many of these were Viniferas and how many native varieties is not recorded. Probably most of them were Catawbas and Isabellas, which were then popular wherever grapes could be grown.

The French Revolution drove a wealthy, educated Belgian, André Parmentier, to America. He settled in Brooklyn, where he started a nursery in which was a vineyard. At first, Parmentier's grapes were all European varieties, but later he sold the two American varieties, Catawba and Isabella, which were then becoming popular. One of Parmentier's customers was Robert Underhill, Croton Point on the Hudson, who was induced to plant a vineyard of European varieties. Sooner or later these died, not, however, until Underhill had been fired with a consuming desire to grow grapes. In 1827 he began planting Catawbas and Isabellas. This vineyard of American grapes grew until it covered 75 acres, the product of which was sold in New York City. This was the first large vineyard in the country.

Alphonse Loubat, a Frenchman, planted a vineyard of 40 acres early in the nineteenth century at New Utrecht, Long Island, using European varieties. At one time he had as many as 150,000 vines. He failed completely, however, as did Parmentier, in growing the European varieties, and did not have the wisdom of his countryman to plant American varieties. Loubat published, in 1827, *The American Vine Dresser's Guide,* with 798 pages alternately French and English. The book is chiefly an account of European practices in vineyard culture, of small value for America. At least, Loubat knew why he failed. Diseases and the burning sun, he says, 'were too much for human exertions to overcome.' To protect his grapes from grape mildew, Loubat enclosed the bunches in paper bags, a practice which later became common and is still in use in growing fine grapes.

Prince and Parmentier advertised grapevines for sale in many of the newspapers in all parts of New York State. In one of Parmentier's advertisements in the Geneva, New York, *Gazette,* 23 January 1828, there were 12 European varieties named. In this advertisement, filling nearly a column, native grapes were not mentioned, and the methods of planting and cultivating were all for European grapes.

[12] *American Farmer,* II: 35.

Grape growing, which for many years has been a great industry in the Chautauqua region of New York, the Erie region of Pennsylvania, on west into Ohio, was begun in 1818 by Deacon Fay, a New Englander. Fay at first planted wild vines brought from his New England home. These were unsatisfactory, and at great trouble he obtained and planted in 1822 three varieties of European grapes from which he got little fruit. Still determined to grow grapes, he bought vines of Catawba and Isabella from the Prince Nursery. The varieties grew well, but grape growing did not become commercially important until the introduction of the Concord in the 1850's. Soon this region was growing more vines than any other part of the United States.

About 1818, an enterprising German, Thomas Eichelberger, began growing grapes near York, Pennsylvania, and was so successful that vineyards were planted by many of his neighbors, and this region became an early center of viticulture. The variety most largely grown was Black Madeira, or York Madeira, which Prince, the best authority of the times on viticulture, said was the Alexander, a native variety. Eventually, Catawba and Isabella were grown exclusively about York.

America was now ready for skilled landscape gardeners. From the memoirs, biographies, and books of travel of the times, one gathers that in this first half of the nineteenth century the fever to improve grounds was increased by every visitor to England. One gauges it by such accounts as that of Susan Cooper, daughter of James Fenimore Cooper. The place was Angevine, Cooper's residence from 1817 to 1822, at Mamaroneck, on Long Island Sound, Westchester County, New York.

The improvement of his grounds became a task into which her father entered with instinctive good taste and with all the animation and warmth of interest peculiar to his character, Miss Cooper tells us. The position of the house was fine, we are told, commanding a beautiful view of the low shores of Long Island, with an orchard of Newtown Pippins forming a distant background. Planning a lawn, building a ha-ha wall, and ditching a swamp were Cooper's first tasks. The friends who followed his movements, according to Miss Cooper, often smiled at the almost boyish eagerness with which he watched the growth of the shrubs; or, they shook their heads sagely at the size of the trees he was transplant-ing. Active in all his habits, he superintended the work in all its stages, 'often undertaking some light tasks himself, and never fail-ing to shorten the time by chatting with his laborers—picking up amusement or practical information in this way.' [13]

Though he was in America but a short time (he arrived in 1824 and died in 1830) André Parmentier was the first man really to make a mark as a professional landscape gardener on this side of the Atlantic. Upon reaching this country, Parmentier gave his time and money to found a botanic garden, an indispensable adjunct to his landscape gardening. Parmentier's Garden, as it is still called, is on the outskirts of Brooklyn near the present Brook-lyn terminus of the Long Island Railroad. He began planting in the spring of 1825 on a tract of 23 acres. Here at one time he had, besides pears, grapes, and other fruits, some 400 species of orna-mental trees and shrubs, probably the largest collection of such plant material in America. Among them were many rare intro-ductions from Europe, of which the most notable was the purple-leaved beech, *Fagus sylvatica atropunicea*. There were, besides, some 200 kinds of roses and many flowers, both out of doors and in greenhouses.

In this garden there was a rustic prospect arbor, or tower, a most ingenious piece of work of considerable size and height from which the neighborhood for some miles about could be viewed. This was the first structure of its kind, and was, it is said, copied by Downing and others until, by the middle of the century, there were quite too many rustic towers in American gardens.

Little by little, however, the proprietor of the nursery began devoting his time to landscape gardening. In 1828 he published in his nursery catalogue an essay on landscape gardening, and in the same year the article reappeared in Fessenden's *New American Gardener*. In this article, Parmentier set forth the guiding prin-ciples of naturalistic gardening, which the best American workers in landscape gardening have since followed. His theory was that gardens should be treated like landscapes, whose charms are not to be improved by rules of art. It was strange this should come

[13] Boynton, pp. 68-9.

from the pen of a Frenchman, who, one would have thought, would have advocated the formal modes of Le Notre, the great French landscape gardener, whose work was then foremost in French gardens and parks. M'Mahon and Parmentier brought to America the principles and practices of Repton, the great advocate of the naturalistic style of gardening, though neither could wholly rid himself of the French influence; both permitted the use of what Downing called 'embellishments,' 'niches for statues with draperies, or for busts of celebrated personages,' and of 'rustic arbors,' 'rotundas,' and 'columns.' It was Parmentier whose theories influenced Downing to take up landscape gardening, and thus gave to America her greatest landscape gardener. Parmentier's practice in several estates along the Hudson, notably Hosack's place at Hyde Park, gave Downing his first models in naturalistic gardening.

How many and what places Parmentier laid out one cannot say. Hosack's fine estate at Hyde Park is the best-known example of his work. There were many others, according to Downing, who tells us that he laid out grounds in various parts of the Union as well as in the immediate proximity of New York. He says 'several plans were prepared by him for residences of note in the Southern states; and two or three places in Upper Canada, especially near Montreal.' It was Parmentier's practice to supply plants from his own nursery grounds for the places he planned. Though one cannot now, after the lapse of more than a century, point to places showing his work, we have Downing's word, written a decade after Parmentier's death, that his 'labors and examples affected directly far more landscapes in America than those of any other individual whatever.'

André Parmentier's fame lasted scarcely a century. The reason probably is that three brilliant men—Downing, Vaux, and Olmsted—followed in his footsteps; with better opportunity, and no doubt with fuller knowledge, each made a more lasting impression.

Another architect and landscape gardener who came to America to practice his profession was Joseph-Jacques Ramée. He had done a good deal in landscape gardening in several countries in Europe before coming to this country, and was the author of *Parcs et Jar-*

dins, which became an authoritative work on parks and gardens in the Old World. Unfortunately he lived in America only from 1811 to 1816, but in these few years he did several pieces of work that had considerable influence on the landscapes of the new country. Ramée's most important American work was in revising the designs for the buildings and grounds at Union College, Schenectady, New York. Thus, at a time when college buildings and grounds were for the most part without plan and wholly devoid of beauty, Union was being built on carefully studied and composed plans. Ramée showed his skill in planning at least three other places in this country. In 1816 he laid out and superintended the great estate, Calverton, near Baltimore, for Dennis A. Smith. A little earlier, he designed the less notable estate of Miss Catherine Duane, Duanesburg, New York. He is known to have done some work at Ogdensburg, New York, and on the Ogden estate on Ogden Island in the St. Lawrence, of which, now, nothing done can be identified. French writers say that he laid the plans of several cities in the state of New York, but, if so, there are now no American records of them.

10

THE NORTH ATLANTIC STATES

1830-1860

THE three decades from 1830 to 1860 showed greater progress in horticulture in America than in all the time before. During these years nurseries and orchards increased enormously; landscape gardening became a fine art; a great number of native fruits and flowers were domesticated; many species were imported from foreign countries; greenhouses became common for commercial work and on private places; horticultural societies were organized in every part of the country; gardening books and magazines multiplied apace. It was the primary period for the great era in horticulture that was to follow the Civil War.

In particular, commercial horticulture in all its branches became established early in this period. Orchards, nurseries, greenhouses, and truck gardens dotted the landscape near all cities and towns. Never before had people in all parts of the country been so well supplied with fruits, flowers, and vegetables. Fertilizers, better tools, better transportation, better means of packing, standardized markets in the large cities, and the development of sales agencies marked this period as the dawn of commercial horticulture.

Much progress was made in the study of the life histories of insect pests of cultivated plants during the first half of this century, but knowledge of means to control them was almost nil until well after the Civil War. Four eminent men were studying and teaching the life histories of injurious insects early in the century —W. D. Peck, T. W. Harris, Asa Fitch, and T. Glover, names honored by all entomologists. But none of these men, all great in

their several fields, could or did suggest efficient, practical means
of controlling even the simplest of orchard and garden pests.

It was not that the need of control was not recognized, for then,
as now, in every issue of a farm paper, and at the meetings of
every horticultural society, insect pests and the diseases of plants
were discussed. For insects and fungous diseases alike, the sulphur
plug was a sovereign remedy. The plug was made by boring a hole
in a tree and filling it with sulphur, with a stopper to keep it in.
Bands of tar and mixtures of manure and other disagreeable
substances were spread in rings around trees to keep off worms
and caterpillars. Boards dipped in tar were suspended from plum
and peach trees to trap curculio. Late in this period, jarring the
trees to shake the curculio on sheets spread on the ground came
into practice—a landmark in the control of insect pests in this
country, since it is the first sensible recommendation put into
practice. For a half a century, until the advent of spraying, it was
a fairly efficient means of controlling curculio.

For some reason, curculio was more destructive to plums and
peaches in the last century than it is now, even when trees are
unsprayed. Curculio almost stopped the culture of the smooth-
skinned nectarine, the most delectable of all stone fruits. Two
treatments that preceded the jarring of trees illustrate how little
was known about the insect and how unpractical were the means
suggested for its control. A. J. Downing wrote that an acquaintance of his had 'fenced out the curculio' by building a tight board
fence nine feet high, furnished with a tight gate, about his plum
trees. He says that within the enclosure, 'the trees are loaded
with plums, very few having been stung by the curculio; while
on a few trees on the outside, 20 feet distant, the crops are literally destroyed.' Another method recommended in the press of the
1850's was: 'pave the ground beneath the trees, for a space of 9 or
10 feet wide, lengthwise of each row.'

Even less was known of the diseases of plants. No one knew
much until long after the Civil War about fungi, and no one
had seen or dreamed about bacteria. Epidemics of peach yellows,
pear blight, apple scab, or kindred diseases were ascribed to 'a
morbid infection of the air,' or to 'a surcharge of electric fluid.'
Infestations of insects and epidemics of plant diseases were believed in Puritan New England to be punishments, and prayers

were offered for deliverance from scourges of insects and plant diseases.

In a survey of the progress of horticulture in the swiftly moving second quarter of the nineteenth century, peach culture claims first attention. The remarkable increase in the planting of peaches in every part of America where this fruit can be grown was the most apparent manifestation of growth in commercial fruit growing, whether from the standpoint of financial returns, amount of land involved, or number of people interested. There were, no doubt, more apple trees in the country, and the total quantity grown was greater, but the apple is planted over larger areas.

The superiority of named varieties of peaches over seedlings became apparent following the Revolutionary War, with the establishment of good nurseries in many of the states. As cities and towns grew in size and transportation facilities were improved, peach growing became more and more profitable.

Commercial peach growing on a large scale began in what is known as 'The Peninsula,' the land in Delaware and the eastern part of Maryland lying between the Atlantic Ocean and Chesapeake Bay. The land and climate in New Jersey, near-by Maryland, Virginia, and Long Island is so similar that orchards of peaches were soon being planted in these regions, all of which were grouped in the Peninsula peach belt.

True, there had been large peach orchards in the Peninsula before. For instance, an orchard of 20,000 trees had been set in Anne Arundel County, Maryland, in 1800, the peaches to be used in making brandy,[1] and another of 63,000 trees was planted in Accomack County, Virginia, in 1814, which 6 years later yielded 15 gallons of brandy per hundred trees, worth $2 per gallon.[2] This was the last large orchard planted for brandy making.

The first large peach orchard planted in Maryland for the fruit market was in Cecil County: 50,000 trees set in 1830, owned by a Mr. Cassidy. The fruit from this large orchard was sent to market in sailboats and wagons. In Delaware a 20-acre orchard of budded trees was set at Delaware City in 1832 by Messrs. Reeves and Ridgeway, which, by 1836, had been increased to 110 acres.

[1] Gould, p. 129.   [2] Ibid. p. 130.

The profits were sometimes as high as $16,000 a season. Many orchards of large size were planted in peach soils in Maryland, Delaware, New Jersey, and on Long Island in the 1840's and 1850's, though the era of large fortunes in peach growing in these states did not begin until after the Civil War.

However, there are records in this period of orchards such as those of Major Philip Reybold & Sons, who in 1846 had 1090 acres of peaches near Delaware City, and of John Reed in Kent County, Delaware, who, in the 1830's, had 10,000 trees of Red Cheek Melocotons. In 1848 the peach crop in Delaware was estimated at 5,000,000 baskets. Probably as many more were grown in the other parts of the Peninsula.

Peach growing in New York was not so spectacular as in the Peninsular region, but there has been a peach industry in the fruit belt along the shores of Lake Ontario and about the Finger Lakes since 1800. The peaches in the first quarter of the century went to the brandy still, but the opening of the Erie Canal in 1825 started the growth of many towns and cities in which the product of a half-million peach trees was being sold in 1850, before peach yellows became an epidemic. Across the Niagara River the growing of peaches for city markets did not start quite so soon, but the plantings followed closely those made in New York and became quite as important to Ontario and Canada.

The West, also, had a boom in peach growing. The fruit belt along the eastern shore of Lake Michigan, in that part of Michigan south of the center of the state, furnished peaches to the Middle West almost as abundantly as did the Peninsula to the East. Peach growing in western Michigan had a romantic beginning. In 1775 an Indian trader planted a peach pit near St. Joseph, in Berrien County. Seeds from this tree were planted in several orchards along the lake shore, one of which, at the mouth of the Kalamazoo River, contained 300 trees.

Peach culture as a commercial pursuit had no place in the remote settlements of Michigan in the early years of the nineteenth century, but when towns and cities began to spring up it became established. In 1834 budded varieties were brought from Rochester, New York. By 1840 Captain Curtis Boughton could buy a shipload of the fruit to sell at $45 a barrel in Chicago.[3] At

[3] *Mich. State Hort. Soc. Reports,* 17th Annual Report, p. 237.

once trees were planted in large numbers and a peach boom was on. A hundred nurseries, more or less, began to sell improved varieties, such as Early and Late Crawford, than which no better peaches have ever been grown.

The tales of large plantations; of abundant crops year after year; of high prices and ready sales; and the ease with which peach orchards could be started and cared for, whether in the eastern Peninsula region, western New York, Canada, or Michigan, in this fabulous period, make modern fruit growing seem a slow, tame business. Then the scourge of yellows came and in a very few years the picture was changed.

Judge William Peters of Philadelphia first described and gave name to peach yellows in a paper 'On Peach Trees,' read before the Philadelphia Society for Promoting Agriculture, 11 February 1806. He gave, too, at this early date, the only means so far discovered to check the spread of the disease—the prompt destruction of affected trees. Peach growers generally did not know for nearly a hundred years that the yellows was contagious and that sanitary conditions in the orchard must be provided to prevent its spread. The disease at the time Judge Peters wrote was restricted to the neighborhood of Philadelphia.

Gradually yellows spread into other peach regions. William Coxe wrote to Judge Peters in 1807 that he did not know the disease; in 1817 he wrote in his *Fruit Trees* that it is 'a malady which no remedy can cure nor cultivation avert.' He concluded that 'in New Jersey the peach belongs to the past.' [4] Passing northward from the first reputed center of infection, the disease appeared as early as 1801 on Long Island and along the Hudson, and disappeared only when, in a few years, peach orchards had been destroyed. In 1824 David Thomas planted trees from Flushing, Long Island, on the shore of Cayuga Lake and lost every tree from yellows. The disease, however, was never so common or virulent in western New York as in eastern peach orchards. Yellows did not reach the splendid orchards of the Michigan fruit belt until after the Civil War, when, in a single decade, peach growing was all but destroyed.

The ups and downs in the peach industry in the last century

[4] Coxe, pp. 215-17.

were chiefly the result of peach yellows. When the disease became epidemic in any region, the industry almost disappeared; in a few years, the malady having run its course, peach orchards were planted again. The varieties planted in modern orchards are more resistant to the yellows than those of the earlier orchards; and it is probable that the disease, for the time at least, has lost much of its virulency.

There have been not a few mild manias in horticulture in America. From about 1820 to 1870, the pear was the most popular fruit in the orchards of 'gentlemen farmers,' and nearly as popular as the peach and the apple in commercial orchards. The center of interest in pear culture was eastern Massachusetts, with the Massachusetts Horticultural Society, founded in 1829, as the clearing house for information and exhibits of the fruit. There was scarcely less interest in pear culture in the great estates along the Hudson, and in commercial orchards in western New York, in New Jersey, Delaware, Pennsylvania, with some large orchards in Maryland and Virginia.

There had been much interest in growing this fruit in Belgium, France, and England, beginning about 1785, and from these countries came the urge to plant pears. The man most responsible for the popularity of this fruit in two continents was Jean Baptiste Van Mons, born in Brussels in 1765, who became a student of plants and plant breeding, beginning his work with pears about 1785. Shortly he was growing seedlings by the thousands and by 1825 is said to have had in his nursery at Louvain more than 80,000 seedling trees. Several hundreds of these were named or numbered, the cions of which were sent to the United States. Van Mons' pears began to reach America in 1825, sent to American nurserymen, and brought over by two of his disciples, Parmentier and Berckmans.

André Parmentier grew at one time in his Brooklyn nursery more than 200 varieties of pears. In 1850 Prosper Julius Alphonse Berckmans, another Belgian and follower of Van Mons, came to America and settled at Plainfield, New Jersey, where, with his father, also a distinguished pomologist, he planted a nursery. Here he grew and offered for sale over a thousand varieties of pears and raised many thousands of seedlings.

Besides Parmentier in 1824 and Berckmans in 1850, a dozen or more other American nurserymen were making the pear the chief fruit they listed for sale. One gets a good idea of the popularity of the pear from the numbers offered by the leading nurserymen of the country just before the middle of the century. Robert Manning, the largest grower of pears in the nursery, had in his Pomological Garden in Salem, Massachusetts, in 1842, about 1000 varieties; Prince, in 1841, in the Linnaean Gardens at Flushing, was growing 420 sorts; the Downings at Newburgh, New York, in 1840, were offering 106 varieties; and in the newly founded nurseries in Rochester, New York, and near-by Geneva, it was estimated that more than 600 varieties could be purchased.

At the annual shows of the Massachusetts Horticultural Society, one reads of exhibits of pears beginning in the 1830's on to 1900 that numbered from 40 to more than 300 varieties. Several times we are told proudly in the horticultural papers that this or that show had a greater number of pears than had ever been displayed at the great shows of London, Ghent, or Paris. The pear exhibits of the Western New York Horticultural Society at Rochester were scarcely less notable and of longer duration, though they came a bit later. As late as 1910, at an exhibit of the last-named society, more than a hundred varieties were shown. Alas, scarcely more than a dozen varieties are now to be seen at the exhibits in either Boston or New York.

The many varieties of pears, while the rage for the fruit was on, were largely grown by amateurs. Men of wealth and small growers vied in producing fine pears. Boston, New York, Philadelphia, Rochester, and other cities competed in putting up exhibits of pears, which the garden papers described in detail. Size and color counted far less in awarding prizes than quality. The 'commercial pack' cut no figure.

Yet pears in this period sold for fancy prices. In 1853, Patrick Barry of the nursery firm of Elwanger & Barry, Rochester, New York, wrote:

Sales of pears have been made in Philadelphia this season at prices calculated to give an impetus to their culture. Duchess d'Angouleme pears sold at Isaac Newtown's Fruit and Ice Cream Store, on Chestnut Street, for one dollar each, and smaller specimens at seventy-five cents each. Mr. Newtown was selling a stock of Vicar of Winkfield pears, on

December 2, 1852, at seventy-five cents a dozen, to eager buyers. Our correspondent says he immediately sat down and ordered pear trees for all the vacant spots in his garden. We only add that we think him a sensible man. . . Bartlett pears have been selling on the New York markets at wholesale for $9.00 a barrel. One cultivator of this delicious fruit realized at the rate of $9,200 per acre.

There was much discussion in these years of the best stock on which to grow pears. This fruit can be grafted and on any one of several stocks, and enthusiastic nurserymen tried all. It quickly became apparent that the white thorn, apple, and mountain ash, though they might be productive for a time, made imperfect unions and the tree was short-lived. The only dissimilar stock that produced a long-lived tree was the quince. On this stock pears were easily worked and the resulting tree was not only long-lived but with some varieties was more productive; the fruits grew larger; were of better quality; and the plants were more manageable; more could be planted in an orchard; and the trees came into bearing in fewer years. With these advantages, and since pears on quince to produce dwarf trees was a common practice in European countries, these dwarfs became popular in America.

In the middle of the last century, orchards of dwarfs were a familiar sight wherever pears were grown in this country. Now they are seldom seen, though there were many orchards as late as 1900. This method of growing pears was finally discarded in America because it was found that some of the best liked varieties did not succeed as dwarfs; that the trees varied too much in vigor, health, time of bearing; that they required much more care in pruning, training, and cultivation than do trees on pear stocks; and that they were shorter-lived.

The apple had been an important commercial fruit crop in America for more than a hundred years before the spectacular peach industry began and before the pear turned the heads of amateur growers of fruits. Vast quantities of apples were grown, as we have seen, in the colonial period. Dried apples were sold in all the markets to which cider was sent, and winter apples were sent to the cities of the South by sea and down the Ohio and Mississippi. A considerable trade in this fruit sprang up between America and England, which increased year by year, but of which there are no statistics until 1821. In that year the Treasury Department reported that in 1820 the total export of apples was 68,443 bushels, valued at $39,966.

As yet, however, no large region was growing apples, as was beginning to be the case with peaches; nor were there large plantings until the middle of the nineteenth century, when apples were planted in several counties in western New York. At the same time individual orchards were set out in most of the Northeastern states, from Maine to Michigan.

The first commercial orchard of importance in western New York was planted on Grand Island, the largest inland island in the United States, situated in the Niagara River near Buffalo. The planter was Lewis F. Allen, who afterwards became a noted writer for horticultural magazines, and who, in 1863, published an admirable book entitled *Rural Architecture*. Allen arrived in Buffalo in 1827, bringing with him by way of the Hudson River and the Erie Canal an assortment of fruit trees. The only nursery at this time west of Rochester was kept by Benjamin Hodge of Buffalo, who grew a few apples and pears.

The enterprising Allen purchased several thousand acres of land on Grand Island in 1833, and divided it into farms on many of which were planted peach and apple orchards, so that orchards extended three or four miles along the river shore. The fruit was transported on canal boats and steam tugs to Buffalo, where it sold so well that for 20 years Grand Island was a prosperous fruit region. Eventually the industry became better established on the mainland on both sides of the river. Thus the profitable fruit industry of the Niagara Peninsula in the United States, which persists to this day, was begun. Soon apple orchards were being planted commonly in what is now the fruit belt of western New York. Along the shores of Lake Ontario and about the Finger Lakes, apples and pears largely replaced peaches as the yellows made this fruit less profitable.

The fruit industry in the Niagara River region of the province of Ontario, long one of the most prosperous of the agricultural industries in Canada, was begun by two energetic men who in 1856 formed the firm of Woolverton and Smith. Charles Edward Woolverton (1820-1900), the senior member of the firm, was a Canadian, while Andrew Murray Smith (1832-1910) was an

American, born in Vermont, but who learned how to grow fruit in the Niagara region of New York. The nursery and orchards of the firm were located at Grimsby, in the very heart of Ontario's peach and sweet-cherry orchards and of grape growing and wine making in Canada at the present time. These two men are largely responsible for the development of horticulture in Ontario.

By 1855 fruit growing was an important industry in western New York. By that date seven counties along the shores of Lake Erie and about the Finger Lakes were producing more than a half-million bushels of tree fruits. In Wayne County were grown 28,000 bushels of peaches; Monroe, 22,000 bushels; with Niagara and Orleans scarcely less. Pears, quinces, cherries, and small fruits, while insignificant as compared with apples and peaches, were important as local specialties. In 1860 fruit growing was interrupted by the Civil War, but soon after the war the growth was resumed and shortly became the dominant agricultural industry of the region.

In the Finger Lakes region in western New York, long the seat of the largest champagne industry in America, vineyards were first planted at Hammondsport by the Reverend William Bostwick in 1830, who grew a few varieties in his garden. The commercial industry and wine making were started by Andrew Reisinger, a German vintner, in the town of Pulteney, when he planted a large vineyard in 1853. The making of wine and champagne on a large scale did not begin until several years after the Civil War.

The culture of grapes along the shores of Lake Erie in Pennsylvania and Ohio were later developments—an outgrowth of the viticulture of the Lake Erie region in New York. Meanwhile, grape growing, as we shall see in a later chapter, was becoming important about Cincinnati and along the Ohio River.

It was in the 1840's that crops began to have 'kings.' The horticultural papers and the press generally referred to Robert L. Pell, of Esopus, Ulster County, New York, as the 'Apple King,' and to Dr. R. T. Underhill of Croton Point on the Hudson River as the 'Grape King.' Pell owned an orchard of 200 acres of Green Newtowns, said at the time to be 'the largest apple orchard in the world.' His crop in 1847 was 10,000 barrels. Most of his

apples went to London, where 'he received some years as high as
$21.00 per barrel; when he chose to sell in New York he received
$6.00 per barrel.' Underhill owned 20 acres of Isabella and
Catawba grapes and sent his crop to New York, 'where he found
a ready sale at nine dollars per hundred pounds.' [5]

The interest men of wealth and culture took in growing fine
fruits is illustrated by a statement in Downing's *Horticulturist* in
regard to the varieties of fruits Henry Winthrop Sargent was
growing on his estate at Wodenethe, near Fishkill, New York, in
1847. He was growing in his garden that year 106 varieties of
pears, 60 of peaches, 56 of plums, 14 of nectarines, 12 of apricots,
20 of cherries, 3 of quinces, 6 of raspberries, 4 of currants, 14 of
strawberries, 12 of gooseberries, 11 native grapes out-of-doors, 31
foreign grapes under glass. Apples are not mentioned, as they were
grown in an orchard apart from the garden. Mr. Sargent had on
his place only the choicest fruits known.

Another feature of the garden at Wodenethe was a walk 428
feet in length, bordered with an espalier wall upon which were
grown choice varieties of the several tree fruits. Mr. Sargent's object in growing espalier trees was to show that fruits of larger size
and better color could be produced on them than on standards.
At the end of the walk there was a vinery in which were choice
varieties of European grapes.

During the period from 1830 to 1860 the strawberry and bush
and bramble fruits were becoming popular in American gardens.
It was then that most of them were domesticated, a subject to be
discussed in a future chapter. As late as 1860 the varieties of small
fruits were few and lasted long. In a catalogue of the Prince Nursery in 1815, 18 red raspberries were listed, of which 4 were native.
In 1845, Downing, in his *Fruits and Fruit Trees of America,* listed
12 red raspberries, only one of which was derived from a native
species.

The building of the Erie Railroad proved a boon to growers
of fruits and vegetables in the counties near New York City. For
example, in June 1847, a single train brought 80,000 bushels of
strawberries to New York. Shortly this city became the largest
market for strawberries in the world. It was thought that over-

[5] *The Horticulturist and Journal of Rural Art and Rural Taste,* II: 466.

production would follow; instead the demand increased faster than the supply. Prices came down to about what they are now— very different from prices before railroads, when, as in Baltimore, strawberries sold in May for ten or twelve cents a quart and at the same time in New York City for from one to two dollars per quart.[6]

Gardens and orchards increased greatly in numbers and size in New Jersey in the 'forties, when railroads found it profitable to offer special facilities for shipping farm produce. The Camden and Amboy railroad, running on the east side of the Delaware River, carried so many peas in season that it became known as the 'Pea Line.' A special express train of one or two cars carried vegetables and fruits almost exclusively, although all perishable produce was now so shipped. Because of cheap transportation, New Jersey became more and more noted for its horticultural products, the strawberry, apple, and peach leading among fruits.

A few decades before, at the close of the War of 1812, almost no fruit was to be found in the markets. When New York gave a banquet to celebrate the Treaty of Ghent, raisins could not be found for plum puddings, nor could dried prunes, currants, or cherries be bought. The cooks fell back on dried apples, and it was difficult to get them.

With the opening of the Long Island Railroad in 1836, truck gardeners were enabled to ship to New York in a few hours produce that by boat had taken as many days. Potatoes, then as now, were immensely profitable. The strawberry, from 1840 to 1890, was the chief truck crop, while cauliflower, asparagus, cucumbers, and Brussels sprouts became crops that are still profitable. Possibly no other part of America has produced these crops, together with seeds and flowers, so abundantly and lucratively as Long Island.

Hovey, in 1835, in his *Gardener's Magazine,* remarked upon the lack of vegetables and fruits in country homes, with the further comment that if people of means on farms and in small towns could see the fruits and vegetables for sale in large cities they would be dissatisfied with the turnips and potatoes in their cel-

6 Cummings, p. 57.

lars.[7] At that time it would have been hard to find in any but city markets small fruits or such vegetables as tomatoes, celery, cauliflower, broccoli, or vegetables grown in the winter in hothouses.

As a result of the introduction of new fruits and vegetables, better transportation, and wider experiences of people, at the time Hovey wrote, the consumption of orchard and garden produce was everywhere increasing, though it was still subject to widespread prejudices. Newspapers, books, and magazines contained articles by writers on health condemning the use of fresh fruits and salads, or any product of orchard or garden that had not been cooked. It was held that these esculents uncooked brought on a whole train of summer diseases and should, in particular, be forbidden to children.[8]

Happily, at about this time diet reforms began to sweep over the country, led by Sylvestris Graham and a score of lesser reformers, who wrote and preached that Americans should eat less meat, less bolted white flour and other concentrated foods, and more fruits and vegetables. 'Simple, natural, plain foods' were recommended. 'Bulk,' they said, 'is necessary as nutriment.' There were a dozen such slogans for people who wanted better health: 'Fruits, vegetables and nuts make for temperance'; 'Culinary processes make foods less healthful'; 'Seasonings and condiments ruin the human system.' The controversy waged in papers and magazines and brought forth book after book. The prejudices continued—indeed exist in some degree to this day—but on the whole the use of fruits and vegetables was greatly increased, and that of meats more restricted.

The cucumber, now considered one of the most wholesome vegetables and as easily digested as any other when uncooked, long had a bad reputation: 'Fit only for consumption by cows,' from which came the name 'cowcumber.' Samuel Pepys wrote in his diary on 22 September 1663: 'This day Sir W. Batten tells me that Mr. Newhouse is dead of eating cowcumbers, of which the other day I heard of another, I think.'

Toward the middle of the nineteenth century, western New York, long the seat of a flourishing fruit-growing industry, took

[7] Hovey, I: 44-5.   [8] Cummings, pp. 43-4.

the lead in number and size of nurseries in which hardy fruits and ornamentals were grown. Trees were soon being sold in every part of America. Men came not only from the immediate region and near-by states, but from the Old World as well, to engage in the nursery business. Very fortunately several horticultural papers were started at about this time in Rochester, and enthusiasm for nursery work was further spurred by the organization of county and regional horticultural societies. For more than half a century Rochester was the nursery center of North America.

Although there had been several small nurseries earlier, the nursery business really began in Rochester in 1834, when W. A. Reynolds and Michael Bateman founded 'The Rochester Seed Store and Horticultural Repository.' This enterprising firm issued a catalogue advertising seeds and nursery stock. In 1836 the firm employed a German horticulturist, George Ellwanger, as a foreman in their small nursery. In January 1839, Ellwanger took deed to the five-acre nursery, its stock and equipment, and began the most notable of all American nurseries of any time or place. In May 1840, Ellwanger took Patrick Barry as a partner, the firm took the name Ellwanger and Barry, and the nursery became 'The Mount Hope Botanical and Pomological Garden.'

The Mount Hope Nurseries not only supplied western New York with fruit and ornamental trees and shrubs, but their agents sold stock in every part of the country, especially in the states to the west, and men trained in this nursery started similar establishments in many other regions. In the middle of the century, and for two or three decades after, Ellwanger and Barry grew more trees and shrubs than any other two nurseries in the land combined. The year the nursery was founded there could hardly have been more than 10 or 20 acres of nursery stock in the region. By 1859 this one nursery had more than 500 acres in fruit trees and ornamentals, divided about as follows: [9] standard pears, 69 acres; dwarf pears, 31 acres; standard and dwarf cherries, 25 acres; standard and dwarf plums, 20 acres. Of plants ready to sell: one block of 12 acres contained 130,000 dwarf and standard pears; a block of 8 acres of standard and dwarf cherries, 120,000 trees; a block of plums, 20,000 trees. Unfortunately the numbers of

[9] O'Reilly, pp. 7-8.

apples, peaches, and quinces are not mentioned, but probably apples were grown in largest numbers and peaches second, with quinces least in number of the tree fruits.

Perhaps the most interesting figures in this account of the Ellwanger and Barry Nursery are those pertaining to bush fruits and grapes. The nursery contained 6 acres of currants, chiefly White Grape, Cherry, and Victoria, all old European varieties. The number of plants of currants was 200,000. There were 4 acres of the Houghton gooseberry plants, 70,000 in number. This, the first native gooseberry to be cultivated, originated in 1833. Of the newly domesticated New Rochelle and Dorchester blackberries, there were 100,000 grown on 3 acres. Of American grapes, then in their heyday, there were over 1,000,000 grown on 6 acres. Probably most of the grapes were Isabellas and Catawbas, then the two well-known varieties.

One is amazed at the number and kinds of ornamentals grown by this firm, at a time when nurserymen were just beginning to grow some of the species mentioned. There were 90 acres in ornamentals: 24 in evergreens; 50 in deciduous trees and shrubs; 8 of herbaceous and bulbous plants; 5 in specimen trees; 8 acres of roses; 2 of weeping trees; more than an acre of magnolias; over 4000 plants of the newly discovered sequoia, the giant tree of California.

Space does not permit details about packing houses, greenhouses, hotbeds, cold frames, sheds, stables, employees, methods of work to secure trees true to name, and the regions in which the trees were being sold. Most of the cultivated trees in California and the states of the Far West, until long after the Civil War, went from this nursery, and still later there were many exportations to Japan.

The senior member of this noted nursery was George Ellwanger (1816-1906), who came to America in 1835 and to Rochester in 1836, where he planted a nursery. Barry (1816-90) was born in Belfast, Ireland, and came to America in 1836. After four years in Prince's nursery at Flushing, he came to Rochester. Barry was an editor and author as well as a grower of trees. From 1844 to 1852, he was the editor of the *Genesee Farmer,* and after the death of A. J. Downing he edited *The Horticulturist* for a few years after 1855. In 1851 Barry published his *Treatise on the Fruit Garden,* long one of the best American pomologies.

Of the 104 nurseries reported for New York in 1858, 30 were in Monroe County, in which Rochester is located, and 18 in the city itself. The statement was made in the *Genesee Farmer,* March 1856, that 'more nursery trees were grown in Monroe County than in all the United States besides.' The product of the Rochester nurseries in 1854 sold for more than half a million dollars.

The other centers of the nursery trade in western New York in this period were Geneva and Dansville. Neither could then compete with Rochester in number of trees grown, but Geneva in the latter half of the nineteenth century overtook and surpassed the older center. The leading nurseries in Geneva, late in this period, were those of T. C. Maxwell and Bros. and of W. and T. Smith. Both were established in the 1840's.

In competition with the western New York nurseries during this period, there were in the state the old establishments of Prince, Bloodgood, Parmentier, Floy, and Hogg near New York. Newer ones were those of the Parsons in Flushing, and of the Downings at Newburgh. Two nurseries at Albany, Wilson's and Buel's, catered particularly to northern New York and New England.

Not until well along in the nineteenth century were there nurseries on this side of the Atlantic that specialized in the growing of ornamentals. One of the first such was established by Samuel B. Parsons (1819-1906) in Flushing, Long Island. For some years after its establishment in 1838, this nursery gave especial attention to the growing of native trees and shrubs, and later added the rose and plants from Japan to its specialties. Out of the work with roses came a notable book, one of the first in America on this flower, Samuel Parsons' *The Rose; Its History, Poetry, Culture, and Classification,* published in 1847. Among the Japanese plants came the first importation of the beautiful Japanese maples, an achievement to make any nursery memorable.

Bloodgood's, established in 1798, was another of the famous nurseries at Flushing that grew a general line of fruits and ornamentals, with a strong leaning towards the latter. In 1854, Isaac Hicks, a Quaker, began a nursery on the Jericho Turnpike near Westbury, Long Island, which eventually specialized in evergreens, and became known throughout the land for its wealth of varieties and numbers of evergreens, particularly its coniferous trees.

There was also the Downing nursery at Newburgh, on the Hudson, a poor competitor of the establishments in western New York in selling trees, but surpassed by none in the whole country in regard to the qualifications of the men who owned the business. In 1800, Samuel Downing came from Lexington, Massachusetts, to New York, and in 1801 started a small nursery at Newburgh. He died in 1822 and Charles, his eldest son, took over the business. Andrew Jackson Downing, a younger brother, born 20 October 1815, in 1834 became a partner, and in 1839 became sole owner, continuing as such until his death in a steamboat fire on the Hudson in 1852. Charles Downing (1802-85) became one of the country's foremost pomologists.

The Downing nursery was at its best about 1840, when its catalogue listed and described 140 varieties of apples, 106 pears, 47 peaches, 31 cherries, many small fruits, 50 species and varieties of ornamental trees, 90 shrubs, 17 vines and climbers, 160 roses, and 235 perennials and bulbous plants. In the years this nursery was selling plants, perhaps more went to establish orchards and pleasure grounds along the Hudson than from any other one nursery. A. J. Downing's growing reputation as a landscape gardener made his nursery one from which planters most often chose to buy ornamentals.

A notable and unfortunate innovation in cherry culture took place soon after the appearance of Downing's *Fruit Trees of America,* in 1845. Downing, first of all American pomologists, recommended the Mahaleb cherry, *Prunus Mahaleb,* as a dwarfing stock for sour cherries. Nurserymen who began soon after to grow dwarf sour cherries found that a fairly large standard tree could be grown on this stock much more quickly and more cheaply than on the Mazzard, *Prunus avium,* which had been used from time immemorial as a stock for sour cherries. Soon every nursery in the land was growing sour cherries on Mahaleb stocks, in spite of the fact that sour cherries are short-lived, lack vigor, and are less productive than when grown on the Mazzard. With curious persistency, most nurserymen continue to use this poorer stock, though its weaknesses have been proved over and over.

Besides the several nurseries of the northeastern states mentioned in this and the preceding chapter, one of the later and lesser ones was maintained by Samuel W. Cole, at Chelsea, Massachusetts. Perhaps the Cole nursery would hardly be worth mentioning were it not that the owner was from 1849 to 1850 the owner and editor of the *Yankee Farmer*. He was also the author of *The American Fruit Book,* of which we shall say more later. The nursery was maintained from 1840 to 1850, during which time Cole was a prominent member and worker in the Massachusetts Horticultural Society.

Maine seems not to have had within her borders a botanic garden, as had most other eastern states. Perhaps the nearest thing was the commercial garden and nursery of Stephen Lincoln Goodale, who, in 1841, began business as a horticulturist in Saco, where he grew fruits, ornamental trees, shrubs, vines, and greenhouse plants so extensively that his place became one of note in New England. In 1856 he became secretary of the Maine State Board of Agriculture, and, in the 16 years he held the position, edited 16 volumes of reports that were compendiums of all things pertaining to agriculture, with a strong leaning toward horticulture.

Some six or seven generations of the Moon family, all distinguished Pennsylvanians, contributed much to American horticulture. Of English descent, the family was established in America by James Moon in 1681 on a tract of land near Morrisville, Pennsylvania. A grandson, James Moon, was the first horticulturist of note, and he planted an orchard in Bucks County in 1749, soon raising trees for sale. Not until a hundred years later, 1849, did the Moon nurseries really become notable, at which date Mahlon Moon engaged in the nursery business on a large scale at Morrisville, publishing a catalogue in the first years. But it was as breeders and propagators of ornamentals that the Moon nurseries became famous and continued so through several generations. Mahlon Moon was the originator of the Numbo chestnut and the introducer of *Exochorda racemosa* and *Rhododendron obtusum var. amoenum,* two valuable ornamentals.

Most of the men who were making history in American horticulture in the first half of the nineteenth century had their training in Europe and came to America equipped to make fame or fortune in more than one field. Robert Buist (1805-80), for example, was trained in the Edinburgh Royal Botanic Garden and came to America to work for Henry Pratt, who owned the splendid estate of Lemon Hill, now a part of Fairmount Park, Philadelphia. At that time Thomas Hibbert had a greenhouse and carried on a florist's business in Philadelphia. Buist, in 1830, became Hibbert's partner and took over the business when Hibbert died, soon owning a most successful florist's trade with which he combined the selling of seeds. In time Buist became one of the leading seedsmen in America.

While still a florist, Buist became famous throughout the country for the camellias and roses he grew. It was he who introduced the verbena, which he bred from wild plants into the beautiful flower we now know. When Joel Poinsett of Charleston brought the plant that bears his name from Mexico, in 1833, he consigned plants of it to Buist, who began its propagation under the name *Poinsettia pulcherrima* and soon made it a common greenhouse flower. He introduced from France the Noisette rose, which originated in America but was first grown in gardens in France.

Robert Buist had the happy faculty of gathering about him young men of ability and enthusiasm for horticulture. One of those who became well known and did much in botany and horticulture in this country was Thomas Meehan (1826-1901), who landed in America from England on his twenty-second birthday. Young as he was, he had made a name for himself in England as a gardener and botanist. Under Buist, as superintendent of Bartram's Gardens, and later as gardener for Caleb Cope, near Philadelphia, he was instrumental in popularizing the gorgeous *Victoria regia,* which for half a century was one of the best-liked flowers in America. Not content to work for others, Meehan established, in 1853, Meehan's Nurseries near Philadelphia, which soon became famous for American plants, especially native trees. For 30 years (1859-89) he was the editor of *The Gardener's Monthly*. In 1891 he founded *Meehan's Monthly,* which continued for some years after his death. This remarkable man occupied a number of public positions, was identified with several state and national organizations, and was a plant explorer of note in the Far West and Alaska.

In 1847 seed growing was begun on a large scale in America by the Landreth Company, when, needing more ground than could be bought in Philadelphia, it moved 20 miles away to Blooms-dale, near Bristol. The first purchase was one of 250 acres, soon augmented by 125 more. There were more than a hundred em-ployees, and the paper bags and envelopes required a separate business. The company supplied an almanac gratuitously to cus-tomers, with a description of the mode of cultivating each seed and a calendar of operations for the garden and greenhouse. Landreth's Bloomsdale seeds by the middle of the century had attained a world-wide reputation. They were planted in every state in the Union, in European countries, India, Australia, the West Indies—wherever gardens were grown. It was Landreth's, more than any other seed company, which built up a reputation in the years before the Civil War for American seeds. In the dry atmosphere of the Bloomsdale region, seeds ripened and could be dried better than in the more humid climates of England and continental Europe.

From 'J.J.S.' in *The Horticulturist,* we learn that in the middle of the nineteenth century orders came from the most interior parts of India, from South America, from the West Indies, and from the shores of the Pacific. There was no cause for regret at the costly step taken in the establishment at Bloomsdale, we are told; the huge barns and granaries were soon filled and emptied; 'the iron warehouse at Philadelphia, with its nine floors stored with this novel merchandise, was more valuable than all the silks and haberdashery imported at the cost of millions of dollars for the adornment of our extravagant belles.'

American horticulture is indebted to David Landreth, second in the American line, for more than material wealth from seeds and nursery plants. He was one of the founders and long an offi-cer of the Pennsylvania Horticultural Society. He was a president of the Philadelphia Society for the Promotion of Agriculture, and vice-president of the United States Agricultural Society. In 1832 he started the *Illustrated Floral Magazine,* in folio size, with four color plates in each issue, but as he was unable to obtain artists and printers to do the work well, the magazine was short-lived. Landreth had a ready and pleasing pen and wrote much for horticulture and agriculture, in the latter field being especially interested in Alderney cattle and farm machinery.

In 1853 when Commodore Perry opened the doors for American commerce in Japan, the Landreth seed company was far-seeing enough to send to Japan by Commodore Perry a box of seeds, and in return received Japanese seeds. This was the beginning of importations of seeds and plants from Asia that have brought many treasures and much wealth to American horticulture.

Another Philadelphia seedsman who led the way in seed selling in the early years of the industry in America was Henry A. Dreer (1818-73), son of a German emigrant. In 1838 young Dreer started a small seed store at 97 Chestnut Street, where he carried on business until 1848, when a greatly enlarged store was opened at 59 Chestnut Street. From 1839 to 1850, the Dreer nurseries were at 'The Woodlands,' now Woodland Cemetery. No seedhouse in America was of greater horticultural service to its customers than Dreer's in the last part of the period of which we are writing, its contributions being good seeds and many varieties of vegetables and flowers.

A well-known seedhouse in New York City in the nineteenth century was that of the Bridgemans, Thomas and Alfred, father and son. The elder Bridgeman came to America in 1824, an accomplished gardener and florist. He soon turned his attention to selling seeds and later to growing them, to the end that his seedhouse soon became one of the best known in the country. He was the author of several horticultural works popular enough to pass through a number of editions. When he died in 1850, Alfred took over the seed business for his generation.

The beginning of the mail-order business was a notable landmark in the seed business. The originator of this method of selling garden seeds was B. K. Bliss, a native of central New York, who early moved to Springfield, Massachusetts. Here he founded a seedhouse, into which he eventually took his two sons as partners, under the firm name B. K. Bliss & Sons. Besides the innovation of selling seeds through the mail, the Bliss company was the first seed firm to print a catalogue with colored plates, the earliest of which appeared in 1853. In 1855 the Bliss seed business moved to New York City. In the years that followed, this enterprising establishment introduced many new varieties of seeds and flowers, of which American Wonder and Abundance peas, and *Lilium auratum, L. Krameri,* and *L. Hansoni* were the most notable.

A seedsman and horticulturist of note in Boston during this period was Joseph Breck (1794-1876). The firm he founded is still in business and, according to its records, Breck established a local seed business in Pepperell, Massachusetts, in 1818. In 1822, he moved to Lancaster, Massachusetts. According to the *New England Farmer,* Breck and Edward Chamberlin, Jr., formed Breck and Company in 1836 and purchased the seed store of the late George C. Barrett at 51 and 52 North Market Street, Boston. Included in this purchase was ownership of *The New England Farmer* and of the *Horticultural Register and Gardeners Magazine,* both edited by Thomas G. Fessenden.

This seed store and horticultural and agricultural publishing business had been purchased in December 1832 by Barrett from the then-ailing John B. Russell, who had in 1827 moved the *New England Farmer* to 52 Market Street in the same building with Joseph R. Newell's agricultural warehouse. Here Russell opened a seed store. This information is important because it was in Russell's store and the columns of the *New England Farmer* that the subject of founding a horticultural society in Boston was discussed. Apparently the founding of the Massachusetts Horticultural Society in 1829 was a direct result.

In 1837 Joseph Breck and Company acquired Newell's agricultural warehouse. Later the firm name became Joseph Breck and Son and, still later, Joseph Breck and Sons. Breck was the author of two books on horticulture, publisher of the *New England Farmer* in 1836-46, and its editor in 1844-6. This leading agricultural paper was discontinued in 1846. He also published the *Horticultural Register and Gardeners Magazine,* and was its editor in 1837-8. Joseph Breck was one of the first members of the Massachusetts Horticultural Society and served as its president from 1859 to 1862.

A friendly competitor of Breck & Sons was Fearing Burr (1815-97), also author as well as seedsman. He was a member of the firm of M. & F. Burr, Seedsmen. Burr was a life member of the Massachusetts Horticultural Society, and his name is to be found in the reports of that organization as a judge of fruit, flower, and vegetable exhibits. A book that gave him wide reputation was *The*

Field and Garden Vegetables of America, published in 1865, a little after the period of this history. Throughout his mature life he was a constant contributor to the horticultural press and a lecturer on garden and orchard subjects.

The firm of M. & F. Burr was much interested in introducing new varieties of beans, as may be judged from an account of the vegetable exhibit at the Massachusetts Horticultural Society in 1857: 'The most interesting feature was a collection of sixty varieties of beans from various parts of the United States and Europe, especially France, cultivated by M. & F. Burr, for the purpose of determining their relative value, as well as their synonyms.' The bean was receiving much attention in the middle of the last century. A little later, 1864, at another exhibition at Horticultural Hall, Boston: 'A collection of one hundred and two named varieties of beans, from Lucy H. Brewer of Hingham, a young lady of thirteen, attracted much attention.'

The introduction of the Hubbard squash, long the most commonly grown and best liked of all winter squashes, is one of the landmarks in the development of America's vegetable industry. The history of its introduction is well known from a letter dated 23 December 1857, written by its introducer, James J. H. Gregory (1827-1910) of Marblehead, Massachusetts, for *The Magazine of Horticulture.* The letter reads:

Of the origin of the Hubbard squash we have no certain knowledge. The facts relative to its cultivation in Marblehead are simply these. Upwards of twenty years ago, a single specimen was brought into town, the seed from which was planted in the garden of a lady, now deceased; a specimen from this yield was given to Captain Knott Martin, of this town, who raised it for family use for a few years, when it was brought to our notice in the year 1842 or '43. We were first informed of its good qualities by Mrs. Elizabeth Hubbard, a very worthy lady, through whom we obtained seed from Capt. Martin. As the squash up to this time had no specific name to designate it from other varieties, my father termed it the 'Hubbard Squash.'

In a subsequent publication Mr. Gregory states that the first specimen was brought to Marblehead in 1798 from Boston by a market man named Green. The shape of the fruit brought the remark that it was 'turned up like a Chinese shoe.' It is probable that this variety came to New England from the hands of a sea captain, who found it in trade from the West Indies or South America.

The introduction of the Hubbard and the sale of its seeds made the beginning of an important seed business for its introducer. Mr. Gregory began to have renown as a dealer in reliable seeds, and his seed store became the headquarters for stock seeds for vegetables, many of which were new varieties introduced by him. His farms covered more than 400 acres, and as time went on he branched out into the production of flower as well as vegetable seeds. In the years following those of which these pages are a history, he became an author and lecturer on horticultural subjects, which made his name known in every part of North America.

Along with these professional seed growers the Shakers were developing their seed business. The number of kinds of seeds offered in their catalogue in 1836 was small:—Asparagus, 1; Beans, 6; Beets, 6; Cabbage, 5; Cauliflower, 1; Carrots, 2; Celery, 1; Corn, 2; Cucumber, 4; Lettuce, 6; Melon, 3; Mustard, 2; Onion, 3; Parsley, 1; Parsnip, 2; Pepper Grass, 1; Radish, 4; Saffron, 1; Sage, 1; Salsify, 1; Savory, 1; Spinach, 1; Squash, 4; Turnip, 5. Year by year, however, the list of kinds of seeds and the number of varieties increased, so that in 1890, about the time the business was stopped, the catalogue was nearly as large as those of any of the professional seed growers.

The work of importing seeds and plants and the general encouragement of agriculture now being done so well by the national Government is by no means a new venture. On 26 March 1819, William H. Crawford, Secretary of the Treasury, instructed all American consuls to procure useful seeds, plants, and inventions for distribution in America. John Quincy Adams sent a message to Congress, 6 December 1825, favoring legislation for the promotion of agriculture. Among other things, he asked that consuls be authorized to forward rare plants and seeds for distribution. Long before, however, consuls and naval officers had of their own accord been sending seeds, cuttings, and breeds of fowls and animals.

Congress created the Patent Office as a branch of the State Department in 1836, and Henry Leavett Ellsworth became the first Commissioner of Patents. Ellsworth was a farmer at Windsor, Connecticut, and had long been a contributor on agriculture to the *Connecticut Courant*. He had at this early date traveled in the western states and purchased much land in Michigan and Iowa. In the circumstances, the new commissioner was more interested in agriculture than in inventions, and immediately upon assuming office began to collect 'new and valuable varieties of seeds and plants.' Seed distribution got off to a good start, and in 1840 more than 40,000 packages were distributed; in 1847, more than 60,000; in 1863, 1,200,000 packages of seeds and 25,750 bulbs, cuttings, and vines; in 1877, 2,333,474 packages of seeds and 156,862 plants and cuttings.

As the years passed, the distribution of seeds became more and more a species of petty graft on the part of congressmen, who used their franking privileges to send them to those who would take them. Instead of rare varieties, the packages often contained packets of the commonest and cheapest seeds that conniving seedsmen could supply. It was not until well into the twentieth century that, under the combined forces of farmers, gardeners, seedsmen, and farm and horticultural papers, free seed distribution with its many scandals was brought to a close.

Yet the subject of congressional distribution of seeds and plants must not be left with the impression that no good was accomplished. New and valuable varieties of vegetables, flowers, fruits, and farm plants were ever being introduced through the Patent Office and the Department of Agriculture, which took over the work in 1862. This was especially true of plants. At various times importations of prunes, European grapes, the navel orange, ornamental and fruit trees, sugar-beet seeds, and many choice vegetable and flower seeds came to America, or were distributed through governmental agencies.

Toward the middle of the century, newspapers and magazines began a campaign of advertising that greatly helped gardening, although the method was objected to by nurserymen and seedsmen. Various periodicals offered plants, seeds, and even tubers (as the potato) as premiums to subscribers. These premiums were particularly enticing when the varieties were new and offered opportunities for grandiloquent descriptions. It would be hard to say how many new fruits, vegetables, and flowers were thus offered to American gardeners. As good an example as any was Andrew S. Fuller's Brooklyn Scarlet strawberry, of which more than 300,000 plants were sent out by the *New York Tribune*. This variety, raised from seed by Fuller in 1859, was long a standard strawberry.

Fuller's career was that of many American horticulturists, who, unlike Old World gardeners, seldom began their life's work in growing and caring for plants, but took to horticulture as an avocation. Fuller was first an itinerant carpenter in New York, but finally moved to Milwaukee. Here he built a greenhouse on a city lot, and grew plants so well that his renown came to the ears of the Princes, and they induced him to come to them. After two years with the Princes, he began a nursery business of his own in Brooklyn, specializing in breeding small fruits and nuts. He later wrote a number of books on these and other horticultural subjects, all of which were published in a period later than that covered by this history.

A remarkable change in public taste in one of the fields of landscape gardening began in 1831 in the establishment in Boston of Mount Auburn Cemetery by the Massachusetts Horticultural Society. In all the years preceding, in America as in Europe, burials were made in graveyards, usually churchyards. These burial grounds were seldom cared for and the plants growing in them were the weeds of the locality. A cemetery was as dismal a bit of landscape as could be found in any community, usually made much more so by the slabs and sculptured monuments that marked graves. The rural cemetery now became a distinctive feature of the American landscape.

The man most instrumental in establishing Mount Auburn Cemetery was Dr. Jacob Bigelow (1787-1879), a botanist and physician of Boston, author of *An American Medical Botany,* published in 1817 to 1820 in three volumes, a most admirable work. Had he not taken the matter in hand, it is doubtful whether this cemetery, so important to landscape art, would have come into existence so early in the history of horticulture in America.

Mount Auburn, containing about 80 acres of land, was laid out as a naturalistic landscape and soon became an admirable bit of art, a cemetery clothed by lawns and groups of trees and shrubs in place of the weeds, long grass, and thistles that covered the ground in most cemeteries. For some years the cemetery remained in the hands of the Massachusetts Horticultural Society, receiving the best of care, and was ably administered. Soon it was a model for other cities, and visitors came from as far as Europe to see this new kind of resting place for the dead.

Seldom has there been more universal acceptance of a new form of art, and seldom has progress been more rapid in making a change. Within 20 years nearly all the cemeteries in towns and cities, and many in rural burial grounds, were laid out in natural-istic landscapes. In a very few years, Green-Wood in New York, Laurel Hill in Philadelphia, and Spring Grove in Cincinnati rivaled Mount Auburn in beauty and adaptability. These new burying places were spoken of at the time as 'open cemeteries,' since railings and hedges were not permitted about individual plots. The kinds of monuments and markers and plantings of trees and shrubs were regulated.

Another of the notable naturalistic cemeteries, laid out in 1840, soon after Mount Auburn in Boston, was Mount Hope, Roches-ter, New York. G. M. Hovey thought the scenery of Mount Hope was 'more bold and magnificent than that of the celebrated Mount Auburn.' He believed that 'it can be made one of the grandest places of the kind in the world.' At the time, the site contained about 50 acres clothed with almost every variety of tree and shrub indigenous to this part of the country.

Naturalistic cemeteries became at once a stimulus to the move-ment for public parks in American cities. In Philadelphia, care-takers at Laurel Hill, then four miles outside the city, kept ac-count of the number of visitors in the summer of 1848. Between April and December there were 30,000. It was apparent that even more people would visit a public park—an argument used in the establishment of parks all over the country. Rural cemeteries were not only laid out in good taste in landscape gardening, but, be-sides, contained a great variety of native and foreign trees and shrubs, so that they became notable botanic gardens.

Andrew Jackson Downing's career as a nurseryman has been mentioned on a previous page, but his life and services as a landscape gardener must now receive fuller attention. Downing first came to public notice in 1841 as the author of *Treatise on the Theory and Practice of Landscape Gardening* (see page 485). Later, in 1841, Downing's *Cottage Residences* appeared, a good but not a great work, long since out of date.

Downing's definition of naturalistic gardening may be summed up in a brief quotation: 'the spirit of nature, though softened and refined by art, always furnished the essential charm, thus distinguishing it from the French or Italian style, where one sees the effects of art slightly assisted by nature.' Thus, in theory at least, Downing's ideal manmade landscape was a primeval paradise of unstudied nature; but, in practice, as illustrated by many of the places he planted, there was a good deal that showed very emphatically the handiwork of man.

Critics find much fault with what Downing wrote and practiced in architecture. It was a time when American architecture was at its lowest level and Downing did little to raise it. Even in landscape gardening his practice was not quite up to his theory.

There are many examples still in existence to illustrate Downing's work. Most of these are in the Hudson River Valley. His favorite seems to have been Blithewood, at Barrytown, then owned by Robert Donaldson. A picture of Blithewood was used as a frontispiece in his *Landscape Gardening*. In and near Newburgh are several estates laid out by Downing, one of which was his own residence. Wodenethe, at Fishkill, New York, created for his friend and student, H. W. Sargent, still stands as a monument to Downing's genius.

At the time of his death Downing was engaged in three projects of note in Washington. He had been asked to plan and plant the grounds about the Capitol, the White House, and the Smithsonian Institution. These were perhaps the most important pieces of work he had attempted, the most important of any in the country. His conceptions of what was to be done about these places were eventually carried out in large measure and now show the spirit of the artist.

In Downing's lifetime, no American city had begun to make provision for public parks, although the grounds about the water works, now Fairmount Park, Philadelphia, had been laid out in park-like plantings, and Boston Common was a notable pleasure ground. In 1849, Downing began writing in *The Horticulturist* editorials showing the need of public parks and educating public taste to their desirability. What he wrote has since become a part of common knowledge in every part of the country; but, in the middle of the last century, his essays were unique, fresh, and original. Downing was a graceful, forceful, and convincing writer, and as his essays appeared month after month they were read by a host of readers and were copied by the press, so that the public in New York and other large cities began to demand parks.

In large part as an outcome of Downing's writings, Central Park in New York City was started in 1858; it was soon followed by others, and the admirable park system of the city came into being. It is not too much to say that as a result of the inspiration created by Downing's *Landscape Gardening*, his *Rural Essays*, and his editorials in *The Horticulturist*, the movement for parks in all American cities was begun. Certainly the strongest impulse the movement received at the outset came from him.

The disciple upon whose shoulders Downing's cloak fell was Calvert Vaux, an Englishman, although it might quite rightly be said that the garment was shared by Frederick Law Olmsted, a young American. In 1851, Downing had visited England, where he went to see country places and parks. Much was made of him and he met the British landscape gardeners and their fellow workers in architecture, among others Vaux, then 27 years old, whom Downing persuaded to come to America as his business associate.

Young as he was, Vaux had already attained distinction as an architect and as a painter of landscapes. His tastes and training admirably supplemented those of Downing, and the two men worked together successfully until the death of the senior partner. It was then left for Vaux to finish the work in Washington in which the firm was engaged. He at once took over the task and successfully planned grounds about residences and public buildings, following Downing's principles, though with perhaps a stronger leaning towards formal gardening, especially in embellishments on private grounds.

In 1858 Vaux's great opportunity came. The agitation for parks in cities, which Downing had begun more than a decade before,

had at last awakened public sentiment in New York City to demand parks and pleasure grounds. A long rectangular area of
several hundred acres lying between Thirty-ninth Street and Har-
lem was purchased, and competitive plans were called for to lay
out what was to become Central Park. There were 33 designs, and
one signed 'Greensward,' the joint work of Calvert Vaux and
Frederick Law Olmsted, was accepted. New York's Central Park
as it stands today follows in the main the original features of this
early artistic conception.

Although Vaux had a part in creating parks in several other
cities, served on many important commissions, and acted as a
consulting landscape gardener in laying out the Niagara Falls
Reservation, most of his work was done in the parks of New York
City. He wrote no books and only little for the horticultural press;
but the reports he published, in whole or in part, together with
designs for a great number of parks in several cities, have contributed to the garden literature of America. Like Downing, Vaux
was accidentally drowned in November, 1895.

The third notable landscape gardener in this early period was
Frederick Law Olmsted, who was a little later in beginning professional work than Vaux, and never an associate of Downing, but
certainly a disciple. Olmsted, also, had much to do with the park
systems of New York City, Boston, and, in time, a score or more
other cities in the country, so that during his long life (1822-1903)
he influenced the improvement of landscape planting in parks,
parkways, and about public buildings far more than any other
American. His work as a landscape gardener, however, had hardly
begun in the period covered by this history.

Olmsted, as a student at Yale, studied engineering and agriculture, finishing his studies in 1846. After college he was a farmer
and a writer on agriculture for a few years; and then, in 1850, he
made a journey on foot through Great Britain and parts of Europe to study Old World agriculture. With an engineer's training
and an eye for the beauties of landscapes, he became interested
in ornamental grounds both on private estates and in public
places. Thus, during the years in which Downing and Vaux were
beginning their work as landscape gardeners, Olmsted was for the
most part traveling, studying, and writing books.

Out of the accounts Olmsted gave of four journeys, one abroad and three in this country, made between 1850 and 1860, one gets perhaps the best idea of what rural America was like in the last decade of this history. The four books, all admirable for this study, are: *Walks and Talks of an American Farmer in England,* published in 1852, the year of Downing's death; *A Journey in the Seaboard Slave States, with Remarks on their Economy,* 1856; *A Journey through Texas, or a Saddle Trip on the Southwestern Frontier, with a Statistical Appendix,* 1857; and *A Journey in the Back Country,* 1860. If this history of gardening were to cover the years of Olmsted's life after 1860, it would be well worth while to dwell upon the splendid preparation these journeys were for Olmsted's future work.

Before the end of his ten years of traveling and writing, Olmsted had become nationally known as a landscape gardener. After the acceptance of the Vaux-Olmsted design for Central Park, he was engaged in the construction of the park. Thus began the career of one who had a hand for the next forty years in planning nearly every large city park in the United States or Canada. He also laid out the grounds of many colleges and public buildings, and planned state and national reservations.

Possibly Fairmount Park, Philadelphia, is the oldest of the public parks in America, older certainly than Central Park. Historians of Philadelphia say that the Holmes map, dated A.D. 1687, shows a manor of about 2000 acres called Springettsbury, which contains Faire Mount. The park, however, as a public place, dates back only to 1812, when Philadelphians, hoping to obtain a supply of pure water, purchased the precipitous bluff known from the earliest days as 'Faire Mount,' overlooking the Schuylkill. The first purchase consisted of 5 acres, but by 1824 there were 24. Trees and vines were planted to hide the rugged rocks. Twenty years later, Lemon Hill, belonging to Robert Morris in Revolutionary times, was purchased to protect the water works. The ground was not, however, officially made into a public park until 1855, when an ordinance was passed that 'devoted and dedicated to public use as a park the Lemon Hill estate, to be known by the name of Fairmount Park.'

The park grew in public favor, and one estate after another was purchased by Philadelphia and its public-spirited citizens, till in 1878 there were 2971 acres, a larger area than any other park in this country. At one time or another, Calvin Vaux and Frederick Law Olmsted, as well as other foremost landscape gardeners, had a hand in remodeling and improving this famous park. The great Centennial Exhibition was held there in 1876.

One of the first squares in Philadelphia was the Mall, a sort of inner court to the State House, covering about an acre, and ornamented with trees and walks. It is described in detail by Manasseh Cutler in his diary of 1787. Among other things, Cutler says: [10] 'here is a fine display of rural fancy and elegance. . . The artificial mounds of earth, and depressions, and small groves in the squares have a most delightful effect.' The numerous walks, we are told, are well graveled and rolled hard. They are 'all in a serpentine direction, which heightens the beauty, and affords constant variety.' That painful sameness, commonly to be met with in garden *allées,* and other works of this kind, Cutler tells us is happily avoided here, for no two parts of the Mall are alike.

'The public,' he continues, 'are indebted to the fertile fancy and taste of Mr. Samu'l Vaughan, Esq. for the elegance of this plan.' This Samuel Vaughan was a wealthy merchant from Jamaica who moved first to London, and then, at the close of the Revolution, to Philadelphia, where he became one of the leading men of the city, an intimate of Washington, Franklin, and Jefferson. He was for many years Secretary of the American Philosophical Society, which did so much to improve agriculture and horticulture in the New World. The accounts of his home estate show it to have been one of the fine places of Philadelphia. Besides planning the Mall he took charge of the grounds about Gray's Inn, and with his assistance its owner made it one of the largest and most attractive landscapes in the North at the close of the eighteenth century.

Downing, writing in 1837, praises Philadelphia as 'the first city in point of horticulture in the United States.' [11] He rightly ascribes this pre-eminence to the influence of John Bartram and other early botanists, and of such amateur horticulturists as Wil-

[10] Cutler, I: 262-3.   [11] Downing, III: 3.

liam Hamilton and Henry Pratt, who vied with each other, beginning as early as 1800, in bringing to their gardens every tree, shrub, and flower to be obtained at home or abroad. Both men had greenhouses filled with choice plants, and both opened their grounds and greenhouses to the public and so inspired a taste for gardening among the people of the city. This taste supported many commercial gardens and nurseries in Philadelphia, of which Downing names those of Colonel Robert Carr—possessor of the old Bartram Gardens—Landreth, Buist, and Sherwood as the most noteworthy. The Pennsylvania Horticultural Society, Downing says, with its programs and exhibitions, was another means of stimulating taste for gardening pursuits.

The general results of the efforts of these professional botanists and gardeners and of amateur horticulturists were evident to every visitor to the city who wrote about Philadelphia in this period. Fairmount Park was beginning to take form; there were well-planted public squares; fine avenues of trees bordering the streets; tea gardens and beer gardens; and pots of flowers in the windows and on the balconies of houses.

There seem to have been several privately owned public gardens in Philadelphia, which are mentioned by Hovey, the editor of *The American Gardener's Magazine* in July 1838. These public gardens were found in all towns of any size and were fairly common, one gathers from advertisements, throughout the eighteenth century and down through the nineteenth, until superseded by parks owned by the public. They combined flower gardens, sometimes greenhouses, museums, aviaries, a bowling green, or several of these features with a bar-room, tavern, or in a smaller and more respectable way a tea or coffee-room. Very often a particularly admirable garden in private hands was for one reason or another turned into one of these public gardens for the amusement or recreation of those who could pay. Public gardens are still to be found in many American cities, changing little in spirit but much in material, as tastes in amusements and recreation change.

In 1834 Fanny Kemble, the English actress and author, married Pierce Butler, a wealthy Southerner who had a northern home, Butler Place, six miles from Philadelphia. According to a late biographer of Fanny Kemble, not all the homes of wealthy people about Philadelphia had fine grounds. Butler Place [12] was approached by a short avenue of maples, dusty in summer, muddy in winter, and rough at all seasons. There was a cornfield on one side and an apple orchard on the other, with farm buildings in the background. There was no lawn—the rough grass about the house was mowed only twice a year; no gravel paths; no garden worth the name, just a kitchen garden squared off by a row of mangy box bushes, where flowers grew reluctantly, because, according to the gardeners, 'they were frivolous creatures'; truly, an unattractive picture.

Fanny Kemble thought the farm scenery of the region between Philadelphia and New York unattractive, and the people and their homes unpleasing. Traveling with her father from New York to Philadelphia, she found the land flat; the trees second growth; the cottages few and far between and no better than the huts in France or Ireland. 'Ragged barefoot peasants stood staring as the string of coaches rattled by. There were wild flowers in the underbrush, but no gardens brightened the monotonous expanse intersected by rail fences that went zigzagging across the country like the herringbone on a flannel petticoat.'

On the other hand, according to Mrs. Trollope, who visited America in 1827-9 and wrote so critically of all she saw, there was at this time hardly an acre on Manhattan Island that did not show some pretty villa or stately mansion, the most admirable of which were on the North and East Rivers. To Mrs. Trollope, 'the loveliest is one [Woodlawn] situated in the beautiful village of Bloomingdale. To describe all its diversity of hill and dale, of wood and lawn, of rock and river, would be in vain, nor can I convey any idea of it by comparison for I never saw anything like it.' [13]

Until the improvement of the lawnmower, some years after the middle of the nineteenth century, it was not possible to have such a close-cut, smooth lawn as our modern ones unless the grass was cut with a scythe, an expensive operation even when labor was cheap. An alternative was to keep cows or sheep, using the lawn as a pasture, but this was untidy for home grounds and any but large parks. In the lawns of a century ago, turf seats a foot

[12] Armstrong, p. 186.   [13] Trollope, p. 281.

and a half wide and two feet high, built in a circle around the base of a tree or set against a wall, were common.

Few objects in lawn planting were more admired in the middle of the nineteenth century than weeping trees. They were almost universally planted on American lawns, as they were in European countries, either as single specimens or in groups with trees of normal growth. Drooping trees were pensive forms in nature to correspond with what at this time was the highly regarded 'pensive' in art. Nurserymen in Europe and America kept their eyes open for trees that showed a drooping habit, and immediately seized upon chance seedlings with this tendency. Such trees were of course sports, which then, as now, could not be induced by art, although at that time a good deal of nonsense was written about inducing the drooping habit by inserting grafts in trees upside down.

A search through several volumes of *The Magazine of Horticulture,* 1850 to 1855, brings to light some 30-odd weeping trees, 12 of which were recommended in a leading article by the editor in 1850 as fine ornaments for any lawn. Nurserymen offered at this time weeping forms of several species each of the oak, elm, beech, willow, ash and one or more forms of the peach, cherry, plum, sophora, laburnum, catalpa, and of several conifers. It required some art on the part of nurserymen to grow these weeping trees, since many were grafted or budded several feet from the ground. All weeping trees were thought to be especially well suited for planting in cemeteries.

The editor of *The Horticulturist,* visiting Canada in 1858,[14] found little noteworthy in the provinces of Ontario and Quebec except in Montreal. He entered Canada at Niagara Falls, where there was 'no variety' in planting; noted the grape growing at Hamilton; and found in Toronto, which has long had some of the finest gardens in America, that there were in 1858 'few attractive features.' At Montreal, older than Toronto, he found 'gardening much in favor.' He went on to say, 'There are probably more glass structures for fruit and flowers in Montreal than in any other city of the same population on our continent.' There was a flourishing horticultural society in the city, which received aid

14 *The Horticulturist,* XIII: 395-9.

from the Government, probably at that time the only horticultural society on the continent that received governmental aid.
Some twenty estates having fine gardens are described. One gathers that gardening out of doors and under glass in Montreal and
Quebec at this time compared favorably with that of other large
American cities. But the impression is given that outside of these
two cities, gardening was as little developed in Canada as in the
newer states of the Union.

In the years before citrus fruits could be brought from California and the South by quick transportation, much was grown
under glass. There were orchard houses in which, at first, oranges
and lemons were grown; then grapes caught the fancy of the owners of glass houses; and not a few were built for the culture of
peaches, nectarines, apricots, and to a lesser extent plums and
cherries. Figs, pomegranates, pineapples, and strawberries were
all grown under glass, and fabulous prices were paid for out-of-
season fruits. Two or three dollars for a pineapple or a bunch of
grapes, or a dollar for a peach, nectarine, or apricot, were common prices.

Different kinds of fruits called for special houses. Oranges, lemons, and pomegranates were grown in 'orangeries,' grapes in
'graperies,' and several stone fruits in 'peacheries.' With the coming of the first railroads, citrus fruits were imported from the
South and orangeries passed out of existence. It was a different
matter with grapes. Better grapes can be grown under glass than
in open air, and graperies continue to this day, in fewer and fewer
numbers, to produce wonderful crops in spring and early summer,
although the main supply of greenhouse grapes comes now from
Belgium and Holland. There are still some glass houses in America in which nectarines, apricots, and peaches are grown.

Henry Winthrop Sargent describes at some length his orchard
house at Wodenethe, after expressing the opinion that this was
'the cheapest, in fact, the only way to grow peaches, apricots, and
nectarines.' [15] It was a glass house with a curvilinear roof, 70 by 20
feet, and 12 feet in height. A center and two side benches ran the
length of the house, in which 250 potted trees could be brought
into fruit. The house was lightly heated with hot water. The

[15] Ibid. p. 451.

plants were kept in a cellar until January, when, at intervals of 7 to 10 days, they were brought in by tens and twenties, thus giving a prolonged season.

Scarcely any under-glass work received more attention in the second quarter of the nineteenth century than grape culture. There were at the time only two good grapes that could be grown out of doors, Catawba and Isabella. Grapes could not be imported from California or Europe. If people in eastern America were to have grapes over a long season, some must be grown under glass. John Fiske Allen, in *The Culture of the Grape,* 1847; Chorlton, in *The American Grape Grower's Guide,* 1856; Hoare, in *A Practical Treatise on the Cultivation of the Grape Vine on Open Walls,* 1840; and William Prince, in *A Short Treatise on Horticulture,* 1828; all gave directions for growing grapes under glass, as did many writers in the several horticultural papers.

The popularity of grape growing under glass is indicated by the number of grape houses in Buffalo, a boom city at this time, and not particularly interested in horticulture. Yet there were in this comparatively small city in 1858, according to a correspondent in *The Horticulturist,* 'nearly if not forty glass vineries, many of them large, elegant, and exceedingly attractive, and of course costly.' [16] The typical house is described as being a 'span-roof-octagon-curvilinear-lean-to with varied finish and architectural designs.' These houses were for the most part owned by amateurs, but the 'vinery of vineries' in Buffalo was a commercial house owned by Mr. Horace Williams. It was 700 feet long, 12 feet wide, a lean-to, and in it grew 230 vines. The varieties grown in Buffalo and elsewhere were chiefly Black Hamburgh and Muscat of Alexandria.

There were in these years not a few pineries in the country, hothouses constructed for the culture of pineapples. To grow pineapples under glass is a costly operation. Usually three years are required from propagation to fruiting; the first year in the 'nursing pit'; the second in the 'successive pit'; and the third in the 'fruiting house'; during each stage of growth the heat must be high and the plants attended to with care. In the eighteenth century, English gardeners mastered the details of indoor culture of

[16] Ibid.

this fruit, and during the last half of the century a craze for pine-apples under glass was under way in Europe, where perhaps a dozen books devoted to its culture were printed. The first large pinery in America was built in the 1830's by John G. Cushing, Belmont Place, Watertown, Massachusetts, after which the culture of the pineapple was taken up by many and continued until the fruits could be imported cheaply from Cuba.

Greenhouses in the first 60 years of the nineteenth century were small, crude buildings, of which roofs and sides were usually port-able sashes. The framework of these sashes and of the building was so thick, and the panes of glass were so small and thick, that too little light reached the interior of the buildings. In 1854 William Saunders, a Scotch gardener, entered into partnership with Thomas Meehan of Philadelphia, and soon after built the first greenhouse in America with a fixed roof, a great improve-ment over houses with movable sash. In 1855 Frederic A. Lord built in Buffalo a greenhouse with a fixed roof, with glass of larger size than had been used before, and embedded in putty in-stead of placed on the outside, as had been done in houses with sash-roofs.

Peter Henderson, in his day (1822-90), was the country's best authority on floriculture. Writing in *Garden and Forest* in 1888, he says: 'At the beginning of the present century it is not probable that there were 100 florists in the United States.' [17] He did not think that all their structures could have covered 50,000 square feet of glass. To illustrate fashion in flowers, he writes of a period when camellia flowers brought a dollar and rosebuds would not bring a dime; at the time he wrote, 1888, these prices were re-versed, and the newly come chrysanthemum was more in demand than either of the older flowers.

In all of this period and until well toward the end of the cen-tury, florists' plants were grown in pots and tubs, with almost none in soil-filled benches. Most of the flowers were small and short-stemmed, as camellia, bouvardia, heliotrope, tuberose, and mignonette, which for the closely packed nosegays had to be

17 *Garden and Forest*, I: 2.

wired. Long-stemmed flowers—roses, carnations, and chrysanthe-mums—were little grown until after 1870. There were almost no books for the florist and no magazines on floriculture, although all the horticultural magazines of the latter part of this period gave much space to the subject.

The reports of the Massachusetts Horticultural Society give information on what garden plants were grown under glass in Massachusetts in this period. Thus, for the year 1834, the 'Committee to Name and Label the Plants and Flowers' exhibited at the September horticultural show and listed the following ornamental plants:

There might be seen the Banana of the West Indies, the Fig from Persia, the Coffee from Arabia, the Lemon, Orange, Pomegranate, and Sago palm, with many other interesting plants, natives of a tropical clime. Among those ornamental as well as useful were the variegated Holly, Myrtle, Laurel, Magnolia, Aucuba, Box-tree, Aloes, and the elegant India rubber tree. Some were remarkable for either their curious foliage or flowers, as the Arum, Pourretia, Eucalyptus, Nandina, Cactus, etc; others for their delightful and agreeable odor, as the Hedychinum Gardnerianum, Polianthes tuberosa, Pancratium, Funkia, Jasminum, etc. Those conspicuous for their rich and brilliant colors were the Erythrina picta, nearly eight feet in height; the Vallota purpurea, with six expanded flowers; the Gladiolus Natalensis, with three tall spikes, and numbering nearly twenty open flowers, which for magnificence of bloom can be eclipsed but by few plants at this season of the year. Among the various flowers and charming bouquets which adorned the tables was a large collection of the superbly splendid Georgina (dahlia), amounting, from all the contributors, to nearly five hundred flowers. There was also a beautiful variety of the lovely China and German Asters.

The plants at the beginning of the list would not now be found in private greenhouses, but for most of the last century they were prime favorites. One is surprised to find how many plants were grown for their edible products; how many sub-tropical shrubs, remarkable for their foliage, were grown; how many there were that could be interesting only for the odors of flower and foliage.

A number of plants with ornamental foliage from the tropics were not mentioned in 1834, but were to be found twenty years later when hothouses were better built for higher temperatures;

among these were crotons, dracaeneas, marantas, agaves, and caladiums.

Probably the most generous patron of ornamental gardening in New England in the middle of the nineteenth century was Mr. H. H. Hunnewell, Wellesley, Massachusetts. In 1851 Mr. Hunnewell began to transform some forty acres of his large estate into a garden of ornamentals. The garden soon came to have many features that visitors from afar came to see. Possibly the most spectacular was the Italian garden overlooking Lake Waban, the finest collection of trimmed trees to have been planted in America.

One of the admirable features of the Hunnewell place is a splendid collection of heath plants, rhododendrons, and azaleas, long the finest plantation of broad-leaved evergreens in the northern states and in choice varieties in the whole country. Here, again, the planter set out not only to create beauty on his own estate but to make an educational institution. At the time the collection of broad-leaved evergreens was begun, it was not known what species and varieties of rhododendrons and azaleas would thrive in the trying climate of New England; it was generally thought that but few if any of the choice varieties could be grown so far north. Mr. Hunnewell, persisting through many years, demonstrated that hundreds of sorts were adapted to outdoor culture in that climate.

Another of the three major features of the Wellesley gardens is the pinetum. Later there were to be several such pinetums, as those of Mr. Charles A. Dana on Long Island, of Josiah Hoopes, in West Chester, Pennsylvania, and that at the Arnold Arboretum. Mr. Hunnewell's, the first comprehensive collection, was long unsurpassed in the number of species and varieties, and may never be surpassed in the vigor and beauty of its specimens. This division of the garden, too, has been a source of education and an inspiration to all in America who take an interest in coniferous trees.

Hunnewell was a banker and a builder of railroads. His interest in railroads gave him a chance to help arboriculture. He found that our western catalpa, *Catalpa speciosa,* made good railroad ties, and had some planted in the treeless plains for this purpose.

Eventually, thousands of acres were planted along the lines of the western railroads.

The dahlia has always been popular in autumn exhibitions of the Massachusetts Horticultural Society, although it had not been long in cultivation in America when the first exhibition was held in 1830. The habitat of the dahlia is Mexico, whence it was introduced into Spain in 1789 and named by a Spanish botanist after Andreas Dahl, a Swedish botanist. In Germany this name was afterwards changed to Georgina in honor of a German botanist. The flower was introduced in the United States from Germany about 1810 and was long known as the Mexican Georgina. The first flowers of the dahlia were as round as a ball and so stiff and formal that they were little liked. Eventually there came a break, out of which many types arose, the most popular varieties being flat loose dahlias with chrysanthemum-like leaves in several well-marked colors. In the past hundred years probably as many as 5000 varieties of dahlias have been offered flower growers.

The garden aster, one of the most popular fall-blooming annuals, is a native of China. It was brought from China to Europe in 1731 and soon became popular, especially in Germany, where it evolved from a single flower, white, violet, or blue, to the double aster of many shades and hues of its primary colors. For a century and a half, all new varieties and nearly all aster seed came from Germany. From M'Mahon in 1806 for a half century, all garden writers referred to asters as 'China' and 'German' asters. Asters have had several periods of great popularity in America, possibly being most commonly cultivated in the first years of the twentieth century.

The rose, probably the oldest and certainly the most commonly cultivated ornamental in the United States, has been grown in American gardens since the first Whites made settlements. At least fifty books have been written on the rose in this country in the last hundred years, most of them in the twentieth century; four notable ones were published during the period of this history, each as good for its time as any that has appeared since: *The Rose Manual,* by Robert Buist, 1844; *Manual of Roses,* William Robert Prince, 1846; *The Rose,* Samuel Parsons, 1847; and

American Rose Culturist, 1856. From these four books, with their groups of varieties, we learn what roses were being grown in America before 1860, but perhaps the best evidence is to be found in the catalogue of roses published by the Crapo Nursery, New Bedford, Massachusetts, in 1848. This nursery, owned by Henry H. Crapo, specialized in roses and probably offered under one name or another all the kinds then being grown in North America.

Crapo lists varieties of Bourbon, and Hybrid Bourbon roses, *Rosa borboniana;* Provence or Cabbage roses, *R. gallica,* which the catalogue says was the first rose introduced to this hemisphere, possibly then the most widely cultivated of any species; the Damask roses, *R. damascena,* so called from having been brought originally from Damascus; the Moss roses, *R. centifolia,* var. *muscosa;* the Champney or Noisette roses, *R. Noisettiana;* the Ayrshire roses, *R. arensis,* var. *capreolata,* then the most popular climbing roses; the Chinese ever-blooming or Bengal roses, *R. chinensis;* the Tea or Tea-scented China roses, *R. odorata;* and the Prairie or Michigan rose, *R. setigera;* Crapo does not offer varieties of the Cherokee rose, *R. laevigata,* although that species with its varieties was then being grown in the South; it is not hardy in the North. The Sweetbrier or Eglantine roses, *R. Eglanteria,* not listed, must have been grown also, and probably was then, as now, often an escape from gardens; and the Musk roses, *R. moschata,* must have been grown more or less. Thus we were raising before 1860 all the roses now commonly grown except the Memorial or Wichuraiana roses, *R. Wichuraiana;* the Banks rose, *R. Banksiae;* the Hybrid Teas; the Polyantha roses, a group of hybrids; the crimson ramblers, *R. Gentiliana;* and the Hugo rose, *R. Hugonis.*

The Tea roses, or Tea-scented China roses, belonging to *R. odorata* are natives of China, where they have long been under cultivation. The name comes from the delicate scent, the faint perfume of tea. Tea roses came to England early in the nineteenth century and across the Atlantic before the middle of the century. The Teas bloom more or less continuously through the summer and autumn, and were very popular until the end of the century, when they were pretty well replaced by the Hybrid Teas.

Hybrid Perpetuals, until the advent of the Hybrid Teas, were

long the dominant roses in America. Just when they were introduced and whether from England or France is hard to say—probably from France, whence comes another name for the group,
the 'Remontants.' Botanists agree that there were several species,
four at least, hybridized to form the Hybrid Perpetuals. These,
when hybridized with the Tea rose, combined five species from
half the world to make the dominant class now grown in gardens
and greenhouses. The favorite Hybrid Perpetual varieties, known
wherever roses are grown, are Frau Karl Druschi, Baroness Roth-
schild, and Clio.

Rugosa roses, *Rosa rugosa,* came from the Orient to England
toward the end of the eighteenth century, and shortly afterward
were listed by the Princes. The Hybrid Rugosas, now commonly
grown, came after the period of this history, as did the Hybrid
Teas.

Noisette roses, once popular in northern greenhouses and still
much grown in the South and on the Pacific Coast, have a romantic history. John Champney, a notable lover of plants in
Charleston, South Carolina, was a grower of roses, and in 1810
grew from seed an accidental hybrid, an attractive rose that he
called Champney's Pink Cluster. A florist in Charleston, Phillip
Noisette, sent Champney's Pink Cluster to his brother, Louis
Noisette, in Paris, who renamed the Charleston rose Blush Noisette. A number of similar roses were grown by European rosarians, and the Noisette group came into existence. Eventually many
of these Noisette roses, most of them climbers, came back to
America: Marechal Niel, Lamarque, Ophir, and Solfaterre, white
and yellow varieties, being best known.

From the very first, American gardeners must have grown the
several lilies so widely spread along the Atlantic Coast of this
continent. Certainly the Turk's Cap, *Lilium superbum;* the Orange Cap lily, *L. philadelphicum;* the Meadow lily, *L. canadense,*
with its orange and yellow sub-varieties, var. *coccineum* and var.
flavum; the Southern Red lily, *L. Catesbaei;* and the Carolina lily,
L. carolinianum, were all grown in the gardens of this country
in early years; for, before 1820, all were prized possessions of European gardens. Indeed, *L. canadense* is said to have been taken to
Europe in 1535 by Jacques Cartier and was mentioned both in a

book published in Paris in 1620 and by Parkinson nine years later.[18]

The great wealth of Pacific Coast lilies was not discovered, or at least not introduced into gardens, until after the period of this history, with the single exception of the Leopard lily, *L. pardalinum*, which was introduced in 1848. A dozen or more other western lilies were first introduced into England, and thence came to America as garden plants, as have, for that matter, most of the lilies of the world.

M'Mahon, in his *American Gardener's Calendar*, 1806, lists only 7 lilies, 3 native and 4 foreign species. The 3 natives are the Orange Cap, Southern Red, and the Meadow; the foreign species are the Scarlet Turk's Cap, *L. chalcedonicum;* the Lesser Turk's Cap, *L. pomponium;* the Japan lily, *L. japonicum;* and the Martagon, *L. Martagon*. Before the middle of the century, however, nurserymen were listing 4 other foreign species: the Madonna, *L. candidum; L. bulbiferum;* the Yellow Turk's Cap, *L. pyrenaicum;* the Coral lily, *L. pumilum;* and the showy Japanese lily, *L. speciosum*. Most of these species, native or exotic, it must be remembered, had botanical or garden varieties, making the list much longer.

Still, lilies in America were little grown, in comparison with those cultivated in Europe or now to be found in the gardens of this continent, until after 1860. An amazing number of species were introduced from China to England in the first half of the nineteenth century, continuing to come later, supplemented by another lot from India. At last, in 1861, lilies began to be popular in America. Perhaps the first real stimulus to lily culture in this country was the introduction of the magnificent Goldband lily, *Lilium auratum,* sent by Dr. George R. Hall to Francis Parkman, the historian and horticulturist, about 1860. In 1862 Parkman showed flowers of it at a meeting of the Massachusetts Horticultural Society, its appearance being 'greeted as an event such as could occur but few times in the life of a lover of flowers.' Parkman at once began hybridizing and shortly produced *L. Parkmanii,* by hybridizing *L. auratum* with *L. speciosum*, which was sold to Anthony Waterer, an English nurseryman, for £100. Meanwhile, C. M. Hovey, introducer of *L. speciosum* in 1844,

18 Slate, p. 5.

and editor of the *Magazine of Horticulture*, had begun to send out hybrids. Both Parkman's and Hovey's hybrids quickly 'ran out' for 'lack of constitution.'

The chrysanthemum, which had had a history of several centuries as a cultivated flower in Japan, seems not to have reached Europe until 1789, and shortly after must have come to America, for not much later than 1800 it was being listed by plant dealers. Its growth in popularity was slow. The first record of an exhibition of chrysanthemums appears in the minutes of the Massachusetts Horticultural Society for 1830, when 15 varieties were shown. In the same Society, the first prizes, amounting to $17, were offered in 1861; in 1868 a 'Chrysanthemum Show' was held by the Society with prizes of $55. From then on interest in the chrysanthemum grew apace, until in the 1880's and 1890's it was a favorite flower throughout the country.

The gladiolus, at least the South African species from which came the varieties we now grow, was introduced about 1830. At an exhibition of the Massachusetts Horticultural Society, 9 August 1834, it is recorded that *Gladiolus psittacinus,* one of the leading parents of garden gladiolus, exhibited by the Messrs. Winship, was 'one of the richest and most gorgeous plants which ornamented the hall. It is of late introduction, never flowering here before this season. It will probably be considered one of the finest varieties of bulbs which decorate the flower garden.' Gladiolus had not been mentioned before, but from 1834 on they were exhibited annually, and soon their hybridization became one of the most popular hobbies of flower growers.

In the middle of the century, garden nasturtiums, first the climbing and then the dwarf varieties, began to be listed in seedsmen's catalogues, but who first introduced them is not easy to determine. They were a welcome addition to gardens; the climbing sorts were first found only in greenhouses, where they were greatly admired. When the dwarf ones appeared a little later, their leaves were used for salads and the seeds eaten pickled.

This was the period of bouquets of tightly tied bunches of flowers of many kinds, with arbor-vitae tied in to furnish green.

It was not until towards the end of the century that light, graceful bunches of roses, lilies, violets, orchids, carnations, chrysanthemums, all on their own stems, garnished with ferns and filmy asparagus foliage, made their appearance. Floral designs on wire frames were hardly known until after the Civil War. If flowers were used at all at funerals in earlier times, they were tied to wreaths of wooden hoops or crosses made of laths. Palms, ferns, and decorative plants for weddings, churches, and household decorations belong to the second half of the century.

In a manuscript tucked between pages of a recipe book of 1831, the author found the following recipe for the ingredients of a nosegay: 'Two moss-rosebuds, a small spray of rosemary, six heads of lavender, a cluster of mignonette, a bunch of white jasmine, a sprig of lemon verbena, a cabbage rose or two, surrounded with sprigs of rose leaves.' A typical nosegay of the period contained many times the number of flowers in kinds and numbers as this recipe specifies. Rosebuds formed the base of the popular nosegay. Each flower stem was tied to a stick or wire, and many flowers were compactly bound together in a hemispherical bouquet, the stems of which were hidden by a paper collar. The nosegay might be carried in the hand or worn as a corsage.

Most modern women have lost the art of making potpourri-jars, on which the women of a hundred years ago prided themselves. Early books gave many recipes for them, and jars of rich enameled pottery adorned the homes of wealth, while lesser examples of the art were found in poorer homes. In the days before modern plumbing and refrigeration, potpourri-jars and sachets were prime necessities for those who had delicate noses. No woman a century ago could take pride in her house if she did not have a potpourri-jar in her living rooms and a sachet in every bureau drawer.

Orchids began to be shown in America about 1830. In 1837, Marshall P. Wilder of Boston exhibited the first orchid to be shown at the exhibition of the Massachusetts Horticultural Society, and a few years later had a large collection. Mr. Edward S. Rand, of Dedham, near Boston, became a large collector in the 1850's, and in 1865 gave his whole collection to Harvard University. From this time on the number of collections of orchids increased rapidly. There was no reaction against them in America during the years of this history, such as there was against camellias, asters, dahlias, and zinnias.

The culture of hardy annuals and perennials in flower gardens is now so general that it is hard to believe they were little grown a hundred years ago, or not widely grown until the end of the nineteenth century. The paramount interest in the years before and after the Civil War was in bedding plants. Tastes of garden owners, especially if they were well-to-do, ran to carpet-like masses of low-growing foliage plants with brightly colored leaves that could be clipped in low geometrical designs. For the most part, only those rich enough to employ a gardener and own a greenhouse could make much of a show of carpet-beds; often as not, these were put in the center of the lawn, or, less objectionable, planted as borders along walks or close to the house.

The plants most commonly used in making carpet-beds were alternanthera, echeveria, coleus, iresine, centaurea, ageratum, lobelia, and low-growing feverfews. If height was wanted, geraniums, cacti, begonias, salvias, petunias, heliotropes, fuchsias, cannas, grasses, and such sub-tropical plants as crotons, bananas, dracaenas, palms, castor-oil plants, caladiums, and ferns were planted. These tall plants were used as center pieces. They made work for florists, since most of them had to be started in greenhouses.

The term 'geometric-bedding' suggests the usual forms of 'carpet-bedding.' 'Fancy bedding' referred more particularly to imitations in plants of houses, animals, calendars, greetings to conventions, clocks, names of places at railroad stations, and other such incongruities. This form of gardening went with the chromo age of pictures and the gingerbread era in architecture, happily now little practiced.

During these years a great number of books appeared on flowers, chiefly as superficial, fashionable 'floral offerings.' Among the many, however, there were several that were admirable, considering the primitive state of floriculture at the time. The best were: *The American Flower-Garden Directory,* by Robert Buist, 1832; *The American Flower Garden Companion,* by Edward Sayers, 1838; and the several books on roses mentioned earlier.

11

THE SOUTH ATLANTIC STATES

1800-1860

BEFORE the Civil War, progress in horticulture in the South was not comparable with that in the North. In the northern states orcharding was increasing by leaps and bounds; viticulture, at the end of this period, was profitable in several regions, and grapes were grown in many gardens; large nurseries were springing up; greenhouses for home grounds and florists' establishments were common; horticultural organizations existed in every state and many counties; many horticultural books were being published; there were many farm papers and several horticultural magazines; a number of native plants were being domesticated; landscape gardening had become a fine art; and truck gardening was flourishing near large cities. None of these activities were so far advanced in the South. The only respect in which the South surpassed the North in these decades was in the planting of fine grounds about the homes on great plantations, where soil, climate, and cheap labor gave a great advantage. On the other hand, gardening on farms and in villages was far better in the North.

Two reasons may be given why the South was falling short of the North in horticulture in these years. The chief one was that cotton and tobacco were almost the sole money-making crops in the South; whereas in the North every tiller of the soil was casting about for new crops; this gave northern people an adventurous spirit in horticulture, which the people of the South did not have. The second reason was that railroads, canals, and turnpikes made transportation in the North far superior to that in the South.

The villages in New England and in the eastern parts of New York and Pennsylvania were in these years becoming more and more beautiful. The houses were usually of the simple architectural style we now call 'colonial,' overtopped always by steepled churches. The chief elements in the landscapes were broad streets, the graceful American elm, with an abundance, if not a great variety, of shrubs and flowers. Homes surrounded by plantings of trees and shrubs stood in green lawns. The South had many fine estates, but the homes of the common people and their villages never showed the finish, neatness, and comfort of those of the North.

Of the southern states, Virginia and Maryland had a more varied horticulture than any of the others. Diversified crops, better transportation, and nearness to markets gave them a great advantage in commercial horticulture. In particular, Virginia, in the decades between 1830 and 1860, made great progress in commercial fruit growing and in truck crops. Perhaps it very nearly equaled any of the states to the north in these branches, though it was singularly short in gardening books, horticultural magazines, and horticultural societies.

In the latter part of the period, Virginia took a high place among the apple-producing states through the production of the Green Newtown in the mountains of the Piedmont. This apple, as has been said, originated in Newtown, Long Island, sometime previous to 1750. When the Green Newtown was introduced in Virginia does not appear, but as early as 1773 Thomas Jefferson recorded that in March of that year he had obtained grafts of this variety from Mordecai Debnam at Sandy Point; and that they had been ingrafted and the grafted trees had been set out at Monticello.

The Green Newtown of New York took on new life as the Albemarle Pippin of Virginia in accordance with the following legend: In the first year of Queen Victoria's reign, Andrew Stevenson, whose home was on a mountainside in Albemarle County, Virginia, was minister at the Court of St. James's. He had Albemarle Pippins sent over for his use, and gave several barrels to the new Queen, who was so delighted with this variety that she exempted it from the small tax then imposed on imported apples. At once there began a demand in England for Green Newtowns, which persists to this day. There is no doubt that, as grown in the mountains of Virginia, this variety is better than when grown at its home in New York. There is no doubt, either, that Albemarle Pippin and Green Newtown are identical. Some maintain that the Yellow Newtown is distinct from Green Newtown. The author has grown the three varieties, supposed to be distinct, side by side on the grounds of the New York Agricultural Experiment Station, Geneva, New York, and found them identical when grown in the same soil and climate.

Fruit growing in Virginia did not wholly depend on apples or on the one well-known variety. There was then a greater diversity of tree fruits than is found in the state today. In 1845 the following list of fruits was recommended for Virginia:

Apples: June, Summer Rose, English Codling, Large White, Bell Flower, Wine Sap, Albemarle Pippin, Quince, Spice Crab, Goose Pen.

Peaches: Washington, White Magdalen, White Heath, Lemon, Early Rose, Carolina.

Pears: Seckle, Summer, Viraglea, Winter Viraglea, Bon Chretien [Bartlett].

Cherries: Ox Heart, Tartarian, Yellow Spanish.

Of these varieties, two of the apples, none of the peaches, two of the pears, and the last two cherries are still commonly grown in one part of the country or another, but probably not more than a few trees of any of the fruits excepting Albemarle Pippin and Winesap apples would be found in Virginia. These two are Virginia's best varieties.

In the years just before the Civil War a large and very profitable fruit industry developed in Tidewater Virginia. Apples and pears were grown as early fruits for the North. The apples were summer sorts, the leading varieties being Early Harvest, Summer Queen, Early Ripe, and Red Astrachan. Not infrequently, early apples brought as much as $1000 per acre. In these same years, there were many acres of dwarf pears in Tidewater, planted to as many as 500 trees per acre, of which there are reports of yields of $5 and $6 per tree. Bartlett and Duchess were the varieties most grown. Their culture dwindled during the war but came back with greater plantings and larger profits in the decade that followed. Peaches, which had formerly been much grown in this region, were now little planted. Peach yellows and fungous diseases took heavy toll and no remedies were known.

Probably commercial horticulture was as good or better in Virginia in this first part of the century than in any other part of the Union. All of what is now Virginia was settled before 1800. There were roads of a kind connecting settlements with cities. The population was larger and the wealth greater than in any other state. Certainly it took the lead in agriculture; there were a great number of wealthy people with fine farms, houses, and gardens in nearly every part of the state. Richmond and Norfolk were large cities and Williamsburg, Fredericksburg, Alexandria, Petersburg, and Staunton thriving small cities, in which the produce of orchards and gardens found sale.

Apparently there were few fruits or vegetables, species or varieties, growing in the early nineteenth century that were not in cultivation in the years just after the Revolution. Probably orchards were better cared for in grafting, pruning, and cultivation. Fertilizers were coming into use but as yet consisted of stable manure, plaster, and near the coast, fish; chemical fertilizers were still unknown. There was much talk about the diseases and insect pests of fruits and vegetables with many curious but useless remedies; no one as yet sprayed to check any pest of fruit or vegetable.

Until 1863 West Virginia was a part of Virginia; its agriculture and horticulture were similar to that of the western part of the mother state. Most of this region was covered with mountains, and the mountains with forests. Gardening cut a small figure in any part of western Virginia, even in the river bottoms where agriculture was chiefly carried on in the early history of the state. The settlers were too busy clearing land, to grow crops other than for the bare necessities of life.

Yet in a state that produced four million bushels of apples in 1939, one may be certain that there was some fruit growing a hundred years earlier. The earliest orchards were planted along the Potomac and on the banks of the Ohio. Two fruits were chiefly grown, the apple and the peach. In the first years of orcharding on the Potomac and Ohio, the fruits were floated down the rivers to markets in flat boats, the apples often being carried on primitive boats as far as New Orleans. West Virginia is noted as the place of origin of two of our most popular green apples— Grimes Golden and Golden Delicious. Grimes Golden must have originated soon after the Revolution, for in 1804 it was the favorite apple for the New Orleans traders. Golden Delicious originated just about a century later, although it was not introduced until 1916.

Experiments in meteorology of value to agriculture in America were begun by Commodore Matthew Fontaine Maury, first meteorologist of note in the United States, about 1840. He made plain the differences between temperatures on high lands and low lands, whereby fruit growers could largely escape dangers from frosts and cold weather. His experiments were carried on in Amherst, Frederick, and Albemarle Counties, Virginia. Of his results, as they applied to the apple, Maury said: 'In Frederick County there is an elevated ridge of land on which apples are so generally safe, when all others in the neighborhood are killed by frosts, that it has acquired the name of Apple Pie Ridge.' Similar deductions were made for other fruits and localities.

In 1868 Maury became professor of meteorology at the Virginia Military Institute at Lexington, the first man in America, if not in the world, to hold such a professorship.

An event of major importance in fruit growing took place about 1840, which was to have a profound influence on orcharding in the South. It is difficult or impossible to grow pears south of New York because of pear blight. Fruit growers in the South tried in vain to find a blight-resistant variety. Such a pear appeared at the date mentioned. It was the Oriental, Chinese, or Sand pear, a fruit hardly more edible than a potato uncooked, but fairly suitable for culinary purposes. This pear was introduced into Europe in 1820 by the Royal Horticultural Society of London. Who first brought the pear to America, and when, seem not to have been recorded; but as early as 1840, the Prince

Nursery was offering two, under the names 'Chinese' and 'Sha Lea.' Prince recommended them for their fruit and the trees as 'handsome ornamentals.'

However, it turned out that only the hybrids of the Chinese and the European pear are of much value for their fruit. Of these there are two in general culture that added to orcharding in the South, particularly in Maryland and Virginia: Le Conte and Kieffer.

Le Conte is a hybrid between the Chinese Sand pear and a European variety. In 1850 Major John Le Conte purchased a pear tree from the Hogg Nursery in New York City and took it to Liberty County, Georgia. It was soon discovered that (1) it was resistant to blight; (2) the tree could be propagated from cuttings; and (3) the fruits were good for all culinary purposes, though not a choice dessert pear. In the years that followed, it was about the only pear planted in the South, and by the end of the century millions of Le Conte trees were being grown. Later, Kieffer largely took its place, since it was even less susceptible to blight and its fruit was better.

In connection with the Le Conte pear, the services of the Le Conte family to horticulture must be mentioned. The founder of the American branch of this family came to New Jersey early in the eighteenth century. Eventually one of the Le Contes bought a plantation in Liberty County, Georgia. The estate was called 'Woodmanston,' and in the second quarter of the nineteenth century, under the ownership of Louis Le Conte, a notable gardener and botanist, it became known all over the United States, not only for its gardens, but as the birthplace and home of the famous Le Contes.

The Kieffer is a later pear in point of origin and hardly belongs in this history except to show its relation to the Chinese Sand pear under discussion. Peter Kieffer, a nurseryman living at Roxborough, near Philadelphia, grew and sold the Chinese Sand pear as an ornamental. In his orchard there was a tree of Bartlett. Among chance seedlings, Kieffer found one of peculiar growth, which he saved. The tree bore fruit in 1863, and the new variety was named Kieffer. Soon it was being shown at all the horticultural exhibitions. The Kieffer became popular in the North as well as the South, and it and the Ben Davis apple were for half a century the most pretentious cheats in the orchard. Kieffer is of value in the South as a pear resistant to blight. It is not bad for culinary purposes, but is hardly fit to eat out of hand.

As compared with the North, the South had few large nurseries before the Civil War. Only two were outstanding. About 1850 Franklin Davis started a nursery in Rockbridge County, Virginia, which he moved to Augusta County, and finally to Richmond. Eventually 'The Richmond Nurseries' became the largest establishment growing fruit trees in the South. In some years Davis's output was said to have been more than half a million trees. He seems to have been a grower of apples and pears, for at a meeting of the American Pomological Society in Richmond in 1871, he exhibited 193 varieties of apples and 31 of pears. Trees from the Richmond nurseries were sold far to the west in Kentucky, Tennessee, and Missouri, and as far south as the Gulf. Davis published catalogues, which it would be most interesting to see, but no copies seem to be in existence.

Another nursery in the South that served the whole country as well as the Southern states was Berckmans' Nursery at Augusta, Georgia. While fewer plants were grown, there were more species and greater efforts were made to breed and introduce new varieties than in any other place in the South.

Probably all will agree that Prosper Julius Alphonse Berckmans was the foremost pomologist in the South and one of the foremost in the United States in the last half of the nineteenth century. Berckmans was also a botanist of note, a landscape gardener who laid out several beautiful places in the South, the introducer to America of a great number of fruits and ornamental plants, and a breeder of many varieties of fruits and ornamentals.

The climate of New Jersey, where he had first settled, was not quite suitable for Berckmans' work and he found a site in Georgia more to his liking. Here he established himself at 'Fruitlands,' a place that became famous in the next few decades throughout the whole world for horticultural plants.

In his catalogue of 1861, Berckmans listed upwards of 1300 varieties of pears, 900 of apples, 300 of grapes, 300 of peaches, and over 100 each of azaleas and camellias. Here he originated 12 varieties of meritorious peaches, 7 pears, and a plum. These numbers do not begin to show his full activities in fruit breeding, in the course of which many thousands of seedlings, especially of pears and grapes, were discarded. Berckmans worked in hope of producing varieties of pears and grapes that would grow well in the South, but failed with both fruits.

At Fruitlands there was a 'Mother Hedge' where Berckmans planted in 1860 ten plants of the Amur privet, *Ligustrum amurense,* the first plants of this privet in this country, now grown in many parts of North America. He imported from Belgium, Germany, France, and Japan many varieties of azaleas and camellias, plants he helped to popularize in the South for out-of-door culture.

In 1869 Berckmans introduced to America a peach, the Peento or Java, remarkable in tree and fruit, and one of the curiosities of nature. The peaches are flattened lengthwise. But it is more than a curiosity, however, since its sweet, almond-like flavor makes it a very good dessert fruit. Though its pits had been brought from northern China by William Prince, the indefatigable importer of foreign plants, as early as 1828, Prince could not grow the Peento in the North, but in the hands of Berckmans in Georgia it was at its best. Eventually a score or more varieties were developed from the type.

Two other notable groups of peaches were introduced from the South during this period, one of which, the Chinese Cling group, gave a new turn to peach growing in America. In 1850 Charles Downing, Newburgh, New York, imported potted plants of the Chinese Cling from England. The variety had been sent from China to England in 1844 by Robert Fortune, famous collector of plants, from Shanghai, China. Downing sent one of his trees to Henry Lyons, Laurel Park, Columbia, South Carolina, with whom the variety first fruited in America. It turned out to be a large, white-fleshed, clingstone with admirable tree characteristics. Chinese Cling was the first of the main group of cultivated peaches in America, most of the peaches now growing here having been derived from it.

Chinese Cling came from northern China; but at about the same time Downing got peach pits from southern China through his neighbor, John Caldwell, who had received them from Canton, China, in 1847.[1] Fearing he could not grow them so far north, Downing sent pits to Lyons in South Carolina. These peaches from Canton were very different from the Chinese Cling from Shanghai. They are the elongated, beaked, honey-flavored peaches, now well represented by Honey, Climax, Pallas, and Triana. Grown in the North, they largely lose the long shape, the beak, and the honey flavor.

Captain Henry Lyons, introducer of these two groups of peaches, was a notable fruit grower in the South in the two decades before the Civil War. He purchased a garden, already made famous by Nicholas Herbemont, in Columbia, South Carolina, which he called, or which Herbemont had named, 'Laurel Park,' and was also known as 'Lyons' Garden.' It was a small place of but four acres, but on it Lyons carried on for many years experiments in growing fruits and flowers.

Viticulture is also much indebted to Herbemont, who was the most active and intelligent cultivator of the grape in the South in the first years of the nineteenth century. Just when he began to grow grapes does not appear, but while growing them he was much interested in other fruits and in ornamental shrubs and trees as well. His place was a square on the southeast corner of Bull and Lady Streets, the bit of land that later passed into the hands of Captain Henry Lyons. On this square Herbemont grew, among other things, a collection of foreign and native grapes. Outside the city he had a large vineyard, where he made 'a fair quantity of very fair wine.' To him is due the credit of having made popular the Herbemont and Lenoir, long the two leading grapes in the South for any purpose, and still the best two for red wines. Mrs. Herbemont was a grower, breeder, and disseminator of fine roses and was a leading rose authority in America.

Herbemont was one of the early viticulturists interested in native grapes. In 1820 he sent out a circular asking for cuttings of native grapes, to which he had a gratifying response. In 1828 he began a series of articles in the *Southern Agriculturist* upon the cultivation of grapes for wine. Fortunately he became aware at once that it was useless to experiment longer with European

[1] *The Horticulturist*, I: 382.

grapes and chose for his vineyard the American varieties then to be had, such as Bland, Isabella, Lenoir, and, best of all, the old Warren or Warrenton. To the last-named grape he gave the name Madeira, under the supposition that it had originated on that island. Prince, to whom he sent cuttings, renamed it Herbemont's Madeira, which the public quickly shortened to Herbemont. Later, viticulturists agreed that it is a derivative of one of our native species, long grown in the South before it came into Herbemont's hands.

Bland, popularized by Herbemont, is one of the oldest of all native grapes, grown under several synonyms in the South from the early part of the eighteenth century. It was introduced by Colonel Bland, a Virginian, but where he got it nobody knows. Lenoir, the third of the grapes Herbemont cultivated, is also an unknown but was first grown in the Carolinas and Georgia. There is a tradition that it was found growing in a hedge by a man named Lenoir, who believed that it was a European sort. It is not improbable that all three of these grapes are accidental hybrids of the European grape and a native species.

Late in the 1850's, a grape of superior value was planted in the western part of Virginia and for nearly two decades was as profitable as any then being grown in the eastern part of the state. The variety is Norton, or Norton's Virginia, as it was first called. It is of uncertain origin but was first known and named by Dr. D. N. Norton, Richmond, Virginia, who sent plants to Prince as early as 1830. The grape became popular in Virginia as a source of red wine, and from it, in the hands of good winemakers, the best wine of the claret type made in America is produced. Before the Civil War, grape culture in Virginia and Maryland began to expand, with Norton as the leading variety, Ives and Delaware next. Virginia fruit growers enthusiastically predicted that the state would become 'the wine-cellar of America.' The Rivanna River in Albemarle County was called 'the Rhine of America,' and Charlottesville the 'Capital of the Wine Belt of America.' [2] The grape is now scarcely grown commercially in Virginia, although the Norton may be grown well in favored parts of the state.

[2] Fletcher, pp. 24-6.

The strawberry became a profitable crop in Tidewater Virginia in the 1850's. It was possible to carry this fruit from the ports of eastern Virginia to northern cities by boat, and shipments were begun at this time from Norfolk. Railroads were not equipped for handling perishable produce and, besides, water transportation was cheaper and more convenient. Strawberries from Tidewater Virginia sold in the North for as high as a dollar a quart. The war stopped these shipments for a time, but by 1870, 3,000,000 quarts of strawberries were being shipped annually from Norfolk. In no other part of the South does there seem to have been a commercial industry for this fruit until after 1860.

Eli Whitney's invention of the cotton gin in 1793 changed the landscape of the cotton-growing states in all the regions where this crop could be grown. From the early settlements to the end of the eighteenth century, the wealth of the South was in the coastal plains, where indigo, rice, and sugar cane were the money crops. Cotton plantations brought large fortunes to the interior of the Carolinas and the Gulf states. In 1793, the production of cotton hardly supplied the home demand, but by 1820 exports had risen to twenty million dollars. Except where sea-island cotton could be grown, the great estates of the South, after a long interlude, were moved from the indigo and rice regions of the coast to the higher lands of the interior. With this change in soil and climate, the style of gardening necessarily underwent transformations.

It was on these cotton lands, on plains or river bluffs, that the many-columned white mansions of Southern plantations arose. Often, in the early days, aided by Whitney's cotton gin and labor that cost only the board of the Negroes, a fortune could be made from the crop of one year. The climate is as great an asset to this part of the South as the soil. It is mild and moist, with only an occasional frost or freeze, agreeable to nearly every fruit, flower, and vegetable of the temperate zone, and in favored places those of the sub-tropics. A plantation often numbered a thousand or more acres. There might have been, and in a few cases were, as beautiful gardens as men have ever planted. Land could be had, when settlers first came, for a dollar an acre, or as often as not the settler 'squatted' and the land was his without cost.

For twenty years before the Civil War, Tedington on the lower James was considered one of the finest-kept properties in Virginia. It is an old place, which first came to notice when acquired by Captain Philip Lighthouse about 1700. The first manor house was built in 1717 and from then on it became noted for its lawn and gardens, especially for its box hedges and box trees, which are said to have been the finest in Virginia. Tedington, however, did not reach its highest estate until about 1850, when Colonel Richard Baylor became the owner. The place then consisted of 5000 acres with a frontage of three miles on the James. The grounds are pictured as having been perfectly cared for by slaves and to have had many foreign as well as native trees and shrubs. The orchard and vegetable garden were of the best.

At Petersburg there was in the early nineteenth century the plantation of John Shore, the house and grounds of which were destroyed in the Civil War. We know but little of the details of the plantings on this estate, but here and there in the literature of the times are several references to Shore's great love of plants, especially of ornamental plants. His place was adorned with a great variety of fruits, flowering trees, and shrubs, which he propagated in a small nursery for the sole purpose of supplying friends and family connections with ornamentals. Plantations in nearly every part of Virginia are said to have had from Petersburg fruits and trees, such as locust, horse chestnuts, the several magnolias, hawthorns, crape-myrtles, and acacias.

Weyanoke, on the north shore of the James not far from Jamestown, was another fine place of this period. Sir George Yeardley, when Governor of Virginia, owned the site and began some improvements, which seem to have been of little note. A subsequent owner, William Harwood, about 1740, built a manor house, after which the estate passed through several hands until 1854, when it came into the possession of Fielding Lewis Douthat, whose wife, Mary Willis Marshall, was a granddaughter of Chief Justice Marshall. The estate soon became noted as one of the most beautiful places in Virginia. The gardens were extensive with plots of flowers and vegetables laid off between broad walks lengthwise and crosswise of the grounds. This, too, was a famous distributing place for new and rare ornamentals.

At Appomattox is the Eppes Plantation, on which lived several generations, descendants of Francis Eppes, all of whom seemed to have been gardeners of note. Francis Eppes came into possession of the land, a large grant, in 1635, and at once gardening began. The love of plants ran in the family, and Thomas Jefferson wrote of Colonel J. W. Eppes, his nephew, that he considered him 'the first horticulturist in America.' Why, or what his services to horticulture were, we are unable to learn. Of Dr. Francis Eppes of Appomattox there are, however, quite detailed accounts of his plantings from 1830 to 1860. Possibly the climax to his horticultural career was attained in 1845, when he returned from the Old World bringing seeds and plants of many species with him, some of which, despite the ravages of war, still survive. The Eppes Plantation was noted at this time for its fig trees and a splendid pecan tree from which the variety Appomattox sprang.

A garden in Charlotte Street, Fredericksburg, Virginia, deserves a paragraph, not so much because it was a notable planting in this state of spacious, well-planned gardens, but because it was the home of Matthew Fontaine Maury, the meteorologist, from 1836 to 1842. A granite block in the front of the house reads, after giving the name of the owner,

Pathfinder of the Seas
Projector of the Atlantic Cable
Founder of the National Observatory
Father of Meteorological Science
Commander in C.S.N.

Maury's garden was by no means insignificant. Today, all its grandeur gone, in poor surroundings, long after the plants have ceased to live, it still shows a formal arrangement of ovals, oblongs, and circles, which probably followed in mathematical precision the plans of its owner. A second home in Fredericksburg, a substantial brick in lower Main Street, also had a garden, which Maury planted and tended in the years just before the war, where his family lived as late as 1862.

When one reads the notes of the many visitors to the Cotton Kingdom, one quickly comes to the conclusion that, in spite of the many beautiful estates, in so far as gardening in the Lower

South is concerned, in the first half of the nineteenth century it was, for the most part, a region of lost opportunities. There were, one gathers, many grandiose Southern establishments whose interiors were filled with marbles, mirrors, paintings, glass, tapestries, linen, and silver, but the exterior surroundings were more often than not almost uncared for, made beautiful (sometimes and sometimes not) by live oaks, magnolias, and the many southern shrubs and vines that grow spontaneously.

A traveler in the South in the 1830's might often see huge colonnaded structures of imposing architecture, the homes of the wealthiest planters. But the grounds about these edifices were usually neglected; horses were grazing around the piazzas, over which were strewn saddles, whips, horse blankets, and the paraphernalia with which the planters loved to lumber their galleries. On nearly every piazza, in some states, could be found a washstand, bowl, pitcher, towel, and water-bucket for general accommodation. Here they washed, lounged, often slept, and took their meals. One finds this picture in the accounts of many travelers.

It should not be thought that any great proportion of the population then, or ever, in the Cotton Belt belonged to the great planter group living in mansions and making fortunes every good cotton year. Much more often the Southerner began life in a log house or frame cabin, in which there were rarely more than one or two rooms, to which porches were added and a second story raised if the landowner prospered. The daily fare for the vast majority of the Whites, as of the Blacks, was pork, cornbread, mush, and molasses, with 'greens,' sweet potatoes, and 'roasting ears' as the vegetables. Of flowers and ornamental plants, the vast majority of homes had almost none.

Writing in 1839, Fanny Kemble (Mrs. Butler) paints a rather sorry picture of gardening on St. Simon's Island, one of the islands of fabled wealth on which sea-island cotton was grown. She writes: [3]

I had been anxious to enlist his [her husband's overseer] sympathies on behalf of my extreme desire to have some sort of a garden, but did not succeed in inspiring him with any enthusiasm on the subject; he said that there was but one garden that he knew of in the

[3] Kemble, p. 131.

whole neighborhood of Darien, and that was our neighbor, old Mr. C—'s, a Scotchman on St. Simon's. I remembered the splendid gardenias on Tunno's Island, and referred to them as a proof of the material for ornamental gardening. He laughed, and said rice and cotton crops were the ornamental gardens principally admired by the planters, and that to the best of his belief there was not another decent kitchen or flower garden in the state but the one he had mentioned.

Pierce Butler's overseer could have known little about the gardens of South Carolina, and so well informed a woman as Fanny Kemble must have known that he was wrong. There had been, and there were, many beautiful flower gardens, some plantations of citrus fruits, and good vegetable gardens in every Southern state at the time she wrote. Even on St. Simon's Island there were good gardens.

When Oglethorpe came to Georgia in 1730, he built his governor's mansion, Georgia's first, on St. Simon's Island. His place was named Orange Hall, but was more commonly called 'Oglethorpe's Villa.' There was a farm and a garden of 50 acres about the mansion, in which he grew fruits, flowers, and vegetables, setting an example to his associates. Several good accounts of St. Simon's Island have come down to us, informative, in particular, of the plantings of vines, oranges, and figs. Moreover, we are told that these newcomers found trees of the fig, olive, orange, and peach that had been planted several generations before by the Spaniards. Surely, some of these gardens must have been kept up down to the time when Fanny Kemble visited the island.

The 'Mr. C' mentioned by Fanny Kemble's overseer, with a son who followed him, maintained on St. Simon's Island an experiment station of note. In it were grown many new plants brought in by himself or others, and several notable experiments were conducted. Among the plants he introduced about 1830 was Bermuda grass, which made good lawns possible in parts of the South where previously no lawn grass could be grown. In 1825 he imported 200 olive trees from France for the making of olive oil, of which he made from 200 to 300 bottles annually. He also imported and tried to grow date palms.

Another of the several estates on St. Simon's Island in these years was Harrington Hall, built by Captain Raymond Demere.

The place was notable for its hedge of cassena, *Ilex Cassine,* the beautiful evergreen shrub of the South variously known as cassena, dahoon, and yaupon. The grounds and garden were laid out in elaborate formal designs, reputedly the first formal garden in this part of Georgia. Captain Demere was an officer on Oglethorpe's staff, and his place was near the Governor's Mansion.[4]

In 1774 William Bartram visited Georgia on his botanical journey in the deep South and was a guest at Grange Hall, owned by the President of the Island, James Spalding. He tells us that the Hall was a delightful habitation, situated in the midst of a spacious grove of live oak and palms near the strand of the bay, commanding a view of the inlet. A large open area surrounded the low but convenient buildings, from which a spacious avenue led into the island, terminated by a large savanna; each side of the avenue was lined with beehives to the number of 50 or 60.

Another of the large places on the Island was the Retreat Plantation, owned at one time by Thomas Butler King, during whose ownership Audubon, on his way to Florida in 1831, paid a visit and was entranced with what he saw: 'was fain to think that I had landed on some one of the fairy islands said to have existed in the Golden Age. But this was not all; the owner of the hospitable mansion pressed me to stay a month, subscribed to my Birds of America in the most gentlemanly fashion.' [5]

At the end of the eighteenth century, the Retreat Plantation had been purchased from James Spalding by Major William Page, who began at once to plant trees. The daughter of Major Page, Anna Matilda, as a young woman took charge of the agriculture on this plantation and on another, the New Field Plantation, and showed great gifts in growing all things. In 1825 she married Thomas Butler King, a Northerner, and two years later inherited Retreat and New Field. For a time the Kings lived on other plantations and in the North, but in 1842 returned to Retreat. Mrs. King became one of the best-known gardeners in the South, the fame of her garden spreading to the North and to the Old World. She had many friends among sea captains, and through them imported plants from all temperate and sub-tropic regions. Her rose garden was probably the best in the country. In 1854 Mrs. King

4 *Garden Hist. of Ga.,* p. 10.   5 Herrick, ii: 11, 12.

wrote to her son in Harvard Law School: 'I want everyone to see my garden in its beauty. I have now 92 different kinds of roses in bloom, forming, I may say, *thousands* of flowers—the Honeysuckles, Honeyflowers, Verbenas, Phlox, Nasturtiums and many others the names forgotten, form a perfect blaze of beauty.' During the latter part of the Civil War, the Kings were refugees, and Retreat Plantation was visited by Thomas Wentworth Higginson, the American author, who wrote of it:

> . . . the loveliest tropical garden, though tangled and desolate, which I have ever seen in the South. . . The deserted house was embowered in great blossoming shrubs and filled with hyacinthean odors, among which predominated little Chickasaw roses which everywhere bloomed and trailed around. There were Fig trees and Date Palms, Crepe Myrtles and Wax Myrtles, Mexican Agaves and English Ivies, Japonicas, Bananas, Oranges, Lemons, Oleanders, Jonquils, Great Cactuses and wild Florida Lilies.[6]

St. Simon's Island was famous for its long staple cotton, and that Mrs. King was expert in growing and improving plants may be deduced from her culture of this crop. During the time she had charge of Retreat and New Field, she bred the 'Retreat Brand' of sea-island cotton, improving it so much that it brought seven cents a pound more in Liverpool markets than any other long staple cotton.

Were this a history of gardens, many more pages would have to be devoted to gardens on St. Simon's Island, where, it would seem, soil and climate were nearly perfect for gardening. The brief accounts of the several plantations described serve to show that from Governor Oglethorpe's coming to St. Simon's Island in 1733 to the Civil War, gardening in the United States was at its best on this bit of land off the coast of Georgia. Gardening flourished, in lesser degree, on other islands and in other places in Georgia, where, from early settlements until the Civil War, there was great wealth on the rice, indigo, and cotton plantations.

O. W. Blacknall, a North Carolinian, gives in *Garden and Forest* what seems to be a very good account of the plantings on a

[6] Higginson, T. W., p. 91.

country seat in the Carolinas in the first half of the nineteenth century, when cotton culture was most profitable:

Hedges in the way of enclosures were practically unknown, while ornamental hedges of Box were common. Cedar was also used for this purpose, though to a much less extent on account of the great care necessary to keep it trim. Flowers were nearly all grown in the vegetable-gardens some distance to the rear of the house, but there were always some Roses along the front walk, and often a bush of running Roses trained on one side of the porch. But little attention was paid to pot-plants, the Geranium taking precedence among the few flowers grown. In most yards no sowing of grass-seed was necessary, the native grasses, if protected from weeds, giving usually an excellent sward. Protected by the fallen tree-leaves purposely left in autumn, it remained green from the uncovering in early March till the trees again cast down its winter robe of russet-brown. Few Oak-trees were located in the yard, or at least to the front of the house, on account of their injury to the grass, while under most of the other trees planted for shade or ornament it grew ever more luxuriantly than in the open.[7]

Contrasting the gardens of this period with the earlier ones of Washington and Jefferson, one would probably notice first the astonishing richness of plant material, whether of fruits, flowers, or vegetables. Also, there would be found many more hothouses, vases, iron statues, arbors, walks, and items of lawn adornment, a constant seeking for the unique and novel rather than the perfection for which the owners of Mount Vernon and Monticello strove. The invention of better garden tools, especially of the lawn mower, gave to the gardens of the later period a much finer finish, but most lovers of fine gardens would have preferred the perfection in planting to which Washington gave his attention.

The southern states, one and all, were lacking in lawns. It is not easy to grow good grass—other than Bermuda grass—except in high altitudes, south of the Potomac. Blue grass, best of all American lawn grasses, shrivels and burns at the first blast of summer heat, and other grasses, of which good ones were few, were not introduced until the end of the century. Only the well-to-do attempted to grow grass about their homes. Cottages and cabins were generally surrounded by wind-swept sands or clays. Without grass,

[7] Garden and Forest, v: 459.

it was difficult to find good settings for flower beds, shrubberies, and walks.

In almost every part of America at one time or another, some man of wealth, or a lover of a beautiful spot, or an eccentric, has built a mansion and surrounded it with attractive grounds, which has stimulated a taste and knowledge of gardening in all its branches. Such a mansion, with fine grounds, blooming orchards, and fruitful vegetable gardens, gave a rather splendid horticultural aspect to a bit of the West Virginia and Ohio country at the beginning of the nineteenth century.

Who has not read the story of Harman Blennerhassett and Aaron Burr? Blennerhassett, it will be recalled, was an Irish country gentleman, ostracized in the Old World because of his marriage to his niece. He came to America in 1798 and bought an island in the Ohio River near Parkersburg, West Virginia. Here he built in the wilderness a magnificent place, which was for a decade one of the great estates of America. Aaron Burr visited him in 1805, and Blennerhassett's Island became more famous as the birthplace of the Burr Conspiracy. When the conspiracy collapsed, the mansion and island were occupied and plundered by Virginia militia. The house burned in the winter of 1811-12, and the island was then abandoned.

One may find many descriptions of this superb establishment in the writings of travelers in the western country or the memoirs of settlers, according to whom it was a paradise in the wilderness. Here is an extract of an account by Cuming, who visited Blennerhassett's Island in 1807:

To begin with, in the course of a few years Blennerhassett had developed an extensive and well-kept farm. About the mansion, low, with a broad Italian front, the lawn had been planted in the Italian style, labyrinth fashion, with gravel walks leading through it. The shrubbery was well stocked with flower shrubs and all the variety of evergreens natural to this climate. The garden was not large but seems to have had every delicacy of fruit, vegetable, and flower suited to the climate and soil.

Joel R. Poinsett was one of the leading gardeners in Charleston in the 1840's. During the latter part of his life the two gardens he planted were famous the country over. Poinsett was not only a gardener but a botanist, traveler, diplomat, and statesman as well. He was born in Charleston in 1779, a descendant of a wealthy and well-known Huguenot family in South Carolina. After an education in Charleston, Yale, and London, he spent several years in world travel and then settled down to the career of a diplomat. He was first sent as a confidential agent of President Madison to the South American countries. In 1824, under President Jackson, he went to Mexico as the first American minister to that country. In all his travels he kept a keen eye open for garden material, and sent plants and seeds to American nurseries, always with the thought that he should some time have gardens of his own.

It was in 1833 that Poinsett gave his Charleston friends the plant that bears his name. At first, botanists called the plant *Poinsettia pulcherrima;* then it became *Euphorbia pulcherrima.* Happily, however often botanists may change its scientific name, poinsettia will remain the common name.

Poinsett's garden in Charleston was on the east side of Rutlege Avenue near Radcliffe Street. His house was surrounded by magnolias and live oaks, some of which still remain in the street and in private grounds. In the garden he maintained here he grew the rare shrubs and flowers he had gathered in his travels. Poinsett, in his last years—he died in 1851—bitterly opposed secession, so that his name has long been held in disregard in the South. A larger and perhaps more notable garden planted by Poinsett was at Casa Bianca, on a plantation, the life of which was so charmingly told by Patience Pennington in *A Woman Rice Planter.* This garden was started about 1830, and here, as in the Charleston place, he grew the shrubs and trees he had collected in his travels.

Baltimore had a number of beautiful estates, one of which, Hampton, seat of the Ridgely family, is notable for several historical events in the horticulture of the country. Here stood, as late as 1889, a *Magnolia Soulangeana,* a hybrid of two Chinese magnolias, one of the first specimens, if not the first, in America; a magnificent purple beech; and a splendid cedar of Lebanon, all planted about 1830. Here, also, for a century or more, was a glass-covered orangery, built about 1784, which for many years sheltered one of the best collections of citrus fruits in America. The place, long cared for by professional gardeners, had many other magnificent specimen trees, and a row of very large native cedars, *Juniperus virginiana*, at the top of an old-fashioned garden.[8]

So far, almost nothing has been said of early horticulture in Florida, which is, after California, the chief center for the culture of sub-tropic fruits in America. Attention has been called, however, to the fact that horticulture in what is now the United States was really begun by the Spaniards in Florida; but while the beginning was very early, little progress was made in gardening until the territory was taken over by this country in 1822 and a stable government formed. Still something must be said about the horticulture of the Spanish, who for more than two centuries had settlements, built homes, and planted gardens in Florida, Georgia, and the Gulf states.

It is a common belief that the Spanish conquerors of the New World were a bloodthirsty lot, who, sword in hand, looted the country they entered and left nothing in return. But the early Spanish travelers and historians describe over and over the great achievements of their race in establishing the domestic arts. All the European plants that would thrive on the islands and on the mainland of their American possessions were brought over by the conquerors. To be specific, the Spaniards early introduced wheat, rye, barley, rice, the European bean, chick-peas, lentils, sugar cane, flax, and possibly alfalfa, as field crops. Of hardy fruits they brought apples, pears, peaches, plums, apricots, cherries, nectarines; of nuts, almonds, chestnuts, and walnuts; of sub-tropic plants, oranges, lemons, limes, tamarinds, bananas, mangoes, and the huge grapefruit of the Philippines. The Spaniards introduced many European shade trees, ornamental shrubs, and all the vegetables and flowers of their country. Many of these plants came to Florida, the Gulf states, Texas, New Mexico, and Arizona in the sixteenth and seventeenth centuries and, in due course, to California.

The Spanish city of St. Augustine had an existence of more than two hundred years under Spain, and every year, despite

[8] *Garden and Forest,* II: 298.

destruction time and again by French and English, justified its existence as a place of importance. One learns from its historian that as a Spanish town it was three-quarters of a mile long and half a mile wide, built on a wooded hill with well-shaded streets.[9] The *plaza,* as characteristic of Spanish towns as the green of New England villages, faced the harbor. On one side was the spacious palace of the governor, well covered with vines and set in shrubbery. The houses were built of stone, having two rooms on each of two stories, with balconies and windows for each room, about which were vines and flowers. The entries were protected with stone porticos with stone arches, over which grew vines. In gardens grew the fruits and flowers of Spain—figs, oranges, limes, lemons, guavas, pomegranates, shaddocks, and grapes—with all the familiar vegetables, herbs, and flowers of the homeland. Outside the city walls were fields of grain, and orchards. We are told, however, that the agriculture was insufficient to support soldiers and citizens, and that supplies were brought year after year from Cuba. Be that as it may, gardens, by all accounts, prospered, and from 1665 to the present day, horticulture in its several fields has been a profitable and pleasing art in Florida.

Excellent conditions are found in Florida, and in selected spots in the other Gulf states well into Texas, for growing citrus fruits. From the earliest settlements by the Spaniards, oranges, both sweet and sour, were planted with success in these several regions. Later, lemons, limes, oranges, and grapefruits were planted. The plantations of these fruits now found in the South are for most part later than the Civil War.

It is a matter of record that some of the citrus fruits were grown in the colonies successfully as far north as Charleston at least, where now the same fruits succumb to cold and are seldom planted except as specimen trees.

An event of prime importance to Florida and the Gulf states took place early in the nineteenth century. The grapefruit or pomelo, which was first reported in the United States in 1809, after half a century of culture, began to be popular, then found great favor. Soon the growth of the grapefruit industry became one of the phenomena of American horticulture. Curiously, re-

9 Fairbanks, p. 160.

cent though its introduction, botanists are not yet quite sure of
its botanical standing or where it came from. It was unknown to
early growers of citrus fruits in Europe, and is supposed by some
to have originated as a seedling sport in the West Indies. It is now
regarded as a separate species, *Citrus paradisi.* The shaddock,
C. maxima, near kin to the grapefruit, has long been grown in
the warmer parts of the South for its huge fruits and large, glossy
leaves.

From the earliest settlements in the Gulf states, northward to
Virginia and even to Maryland, fig culture was carried on with
the greatest optimism. All the early writers about products of
southern states say much about the figs grown along the coast and
inland, where the thermometer did not fall in winter to freezing.
Even to the beginning of this century, figs of the Brown Turkey,
Celestial, Brunswick, and several similar hardy varieties could be
purchased as far north as Raleigh for a dollar a bushel. Then California began to grow its hundred or more varieties, especially the
Smyrna fig, which can be grown only when cross-pollinated by
hand or through the friendly offices of the fig wasp. The introduction of this insect in California spelled the doom of commercial
fig growing in the southern states, where soil and climate are not
so suitable and the wasp is less friendly. Figs were grown and probably ever will be in the Gulf states for home use, but never to compete with California in the markets.

It was the fond dream of the founders of the first settlements
in the South that the olive might be grown in commercial quantities. Thomas Jefferson and the sponsors of the Vine and Olive
Colony, on the Tombigbee River in Alabama (see p. 360), in
their turn, as late as the first quarter of the nineteenth century,
persisted in experiments to grow the olive. Though an occasional
tree might be made to live and bear, and some to reach old age,
the olive has never been grown profitably in any of the southern
states. This tree needs a warm, dry atmosphere, a rich, well-
drained soil, and a mild temperature that does not fall below
freezing. California has many regions that fulfil these conditions,
but none of the southern states do.

The other sub-tropic fruits, the banana, pineapple, mango, and
coconut, may have been tried in one or another part of Florida

in earlier times but they do not seem to have become important until well after the Civil War. The pomegranate early caught the fancy of Europeans in the New World, and the fruiting varieties were largely grown for cooking, drinks, and medicinal purposes, while both the fruiting and the non-fruiting kinds have ever been planted in regions along the coast south of Charleston as choice ornamentals.

The avocado or alligator pear, a tree of tropical America, was grown in Florida to a limited extent at least a hundred years ago, but until recent years did not become popular.

The jujube, or Chinese date, cultivated from time immemorial in China for its oblong-globose, scarlet fruits, which differ in shape, size, and color so that the plant runs into many varieties, was introduced into South Carolina early, and again by the Patent Office in 1855 in several of the southern states. It did not succeed in the South but later became well established in California.

The guava, now so largely cultivated in Florida for sweetmeats, jellies, and jams, was early brought from South America, where it has always been cultivated. Wherever it grows in the far South, it is planted as an ornamental as well as for its fruits, its glossy green camellia-like leaves making it a handsome plant.

Just when or by whom the loquat was brought to America does not appear, but its introduction in the deep South at an early date brought us a delectable fruit. Its culture is recorded in Kew in 1787; and, no doubt, before the end of the century its plum-like seeds had been brought by someone to America. At any rate, it is often mentioned in fruit lists in the first half of the nineteenth century, as if well known. It is a decorative plant, easily grown, and soon became a favorite pot-plant in northern conservatories.

The date palm was introduced in Florida before the peninsula came into the possession of the English, but has never fruited well in that state's moist climate. It makes, however, a handsome ornamental tree in any of the South Atlantic or Gulf states, and is a favorite lawn and roadside tree.

The leading agricultural writer in Virginia in the early part of the nineteenth century was John Taylor of Carolina, who wrote under the pen name 'Arrator.' His letters, some 60 or more, were published in the *Richmond Enquirer* in the years 1809 and 1810. These were published in book form in Georgetown, D. C., in 1813 under the title *Arrator; Being a Series of Agricultural Essays, Practical and Political, By a Citizen of Virginia*. One letter was on 'Orchards,' while most of the others had to do with maintaining a supply of vegetable matter in the soil by manures and soiling crops, a practice of which Taylor was America's first advocate.

Taylor had small interest in gardening and orcharding, and his single, short epistle on 'Orchards' is of value chiefly for his point of view. The chief use of an orchard to him was to fill the cider barrel. Two-thirds of this short essay is devoted to his method of making cider and in planning for 'more cider.' 'Good cider,' he says, 'would be a national saving of wealth, by expelling foreign liquors; and of life by expelling ardent spirits.' And again, he says that apples 'are the only species of orchards at a distance from cities, capable of producing sufficient profit and comfort to become a considerable object to a farmer.' He objects to distilled liquors from fruits as being 'precarious, troublesome, trifling, and out of the farmer's province.' He then sums up the value of the apple to furnish some food for the planter's hogs, a luxury for his family in winter, and a healthy liquor for himself and his laborers all the year. Independent of any surplus of cider he may spare, it is 'an object of solid profit and easy acquisition.'

12

THE NORTH-CENTRAL STATES

WHEN Cadillac founded Detroit in 1701, it is on record that he brought with him from Quebec a gardener, one Pierre d'Argenteuil, to lay out gardens and orchards. Probably vegetables and fruits had been planted earlier at French settlements in several states of the central west, but hardly in such numbers or so well established, as to constitute the beginning of horticulture. For a century and a half, Detroit and the regions about it in Michigan and Canada were centers of gardening in this part of America. All the early visitors to the river towns between the lakes Erie and Huron speak of the gardens and orchards that flourished in the settlements. In particular, they mention the mammoth pear trees.

As late as 1900, some 20 of these old pear trees were to be found in the city of Monroe, Michigan. The tallest must have been more than a hundred feet in height. One, said to have been planted in 1772 by a Colonel Francis Navarre, measured 9 feet 10 inches in circumference 3 feet from the ground and bore as many as 150 bushels in one crop. The pears, early or late, were very much alike in size, shape, color, and flavor, as if all came from the same parentages. They were medium in size, turbinate in shape, greenish yellow, sweet and juicy, but so astringent that they were not very good to eat out of hand, although they were excellent for cooking.

While the crowning glory of these French orchards along the Detroit River, in size and productiveness of tree, were pears, apples also furnished the early settlers with choice fruits. From these orchards nurserymen got cions of some very good apples, so that Michigan had in the first half of the nineteenth century about as good a list of apples as the states on the Atlantic Coast. The French orchards furnished the delicious Pomme de Neige, or Fameuse, and the equally well-flavored and handsome Detroit Red, which the old orchardists called Roseau; several Calvilles, red and white apples rather difficult to identify now; Pearmains and Russets, chiefly grown for cider. The seeds and cions of these trees came from the French along the St. Lawrence, who had brought seeds from Normandy and Provence.

The seeds for fruit trees and garden vegetables in the French settlements in the Middle West were brought from Canada, whence came the early French settlers. Records and traditions, substantiated by many old trees, establish the fact that by the middle of the seventeenth century orchards and gardens had been planted by the French in Nova Scotia, Cape Breton, Prince Edward Island, and on the shores of the St. Lawrence, especially at Montreal. From these plantings near the sea, seeds were carried far inland by traders and missionaries.

At the beginning of the eighteenth century what was called the 'Illinois Country' was an undetermined territory stretching from the Alleghenies westward beyond the Mississippi and from the Ohio north to Canada. The principal settlements were at Vincennes, on the Wabash, Kaskaskia, and Cahokia, settled at the close of the seventeenth century, on the land of 'the American Bottom' along the lower Illinois and the Mississippi. Farms in these French towns were laid out as in the *habitant* towns in Canada. The cultivated fields ran in long strips with a few rods frontage, the farm being marked by furrows. In the front of the fields there were fences to keep the cattle out. A wooden plow with an iron point was the only tool to scratch the virgin soil. Plows and two-wheeled carts were drawn by oxen with a bar fastened across their horns, or Indian ponies driven tandem by voice and whip. Fields were held in common, a man's farm for the season being determined at a springtime village meeting.

Under such conditions agriculture and horticulture were most primitive. Spring wheat was grown as the commonest farm crop, with some oats, hemp, hops, and tobacco. The French, unlike the English, grew little corn. A little butter was made by shaking cream in bottles. Melons, beans, pumpkins, and squashes were the chief vegetables. Apples, pears, peaches, and a few grapes were the only fruits. Vines grew poorly and wine was made from wild grapes. Surplus wheat and apples were floated down the Mississippi to New Orleans, the capital of the region after 1731.

The several towns of the Illinois Country were much alike—all typical of French villages in the New World. In the center of each was a grass-covered square with narrow streets running at right angles from it. Houses were built of hewn wood, low with pointed roofs covered with bark, which, extending over the front, made a porch. Most of the houses were of one story. These were set close to the street, near to each other in friendly fashion, and enclosed by picket or palisade fences, which also surrounded fruit trees, vegetables, and, it may be, an occasional flower garden. According to the accounts of early visitors, these French homes were far more comfortable, and the horticulture at least, if not the agriculture, was better than that of English settlements in the Kentucky and Ohio regions, which came a little later.

There were trees of apples and pears of enormous size and venerable age in Indiana, Illinois, and Missouri, as well as in Michigan, when English settlers came to these states early in the nineteenth century. A pear called the Prairie du Pont originated at Cahokia, Illinois, in 1780, from seed planted by M. Girardin, a native of France. The tree grew to be very large, was blight-proof, and bore small, round, lemon-colored pears, fit only for cooking. This Frenchman was the largest planter of apples and pears in this great region. He set out an orchard in 1780 of which it was said he brought the trees from France—more likely he brought seeds. As late as 1868, some of the pear trees in this orchard were alive, of immense girth and height, still healthy, and bearing fruit every year.

By 1735 there were a number of French families settled about the fort and trading post at Vincennes, Indiana. One may be sure that these French, lovers of gardens, were soon planting fruits, vegetables, and flowers. As late as 1825 a gnarled cherry tree of great size and age stood in Vincennes, known as the Roussillon cherry. It bore sweet cherries of dark, ruby color, and is the tree described in *Alice of Old Vincennes*.[1]

A pear tree at Vincennes is said to have been one of the largest

[1] Thompson, pp. 1-16.

XVIIa. The graveyard at Westover, Virginia. *From* Harper's New Monthly Magazine, XLII: 805, 1871.

XVIIb. The Miami apple tree. *From* Harper's New Monthly Magazine, XXIV: 738, 1862.

XVIII. Four early, well-known Eastern horticulturists. Upper left: C. M. Hovey. Upper right: William Robert Prince. Lower left: Edward Staniford Rogers. Lower right: Marshall P. Wilder. *Photographs from the Geneva Experiment Station, Geneva, New York.*

XIX. Four early American seedsmen. Upper left: Joseph Breck, founder of Joseph Breck and Sons, Boston, Massachusetts. Upper right: James John Harvard Gregory, founder of J. J. H. Gregory & Son, Marblehead, Massachusetts. Lower left: D. M. Ferry, founder of D. M. Ferry & Co., Detroit, Michigan. Lower right: Peter Henderson, founder of Peter Henderson & Co., New York, New York. *Photographs from the four companies.*

XXa. Campus of Harvard College in 1726; from a line engraving. *Photograph from the New York Public Library.*

XXb. Campus of Yale College in 1832; from a lithograph. *Photograph from the New York Public Library.*

XXI. Four pioneer horticulturists in the West. Upper left: John McLoughlin, Vancouver, Washington. *Courtesy of Department of Agriculture, State of Washington.* Upper right: William Meek, Hayward, California. *Courtesy of Department of Agriculture, State of Washington.* Lower left: G. B. Brackett of Iowa. *From* Iowa State Horticultural Society, 30, 1915. Lower right: John Lewelling of Indiana, Iowa, Oregon, and California. *Courtesy of H. M. Butterfield.*

XXIIa. John Bartram, the botanist. *From* Harper's New Monthly
Magazine, LX: 322, 1896.

XXIIb. Johnny Appleseed. *From* Harper's New
Monthly Magazine, XLIII: 830, 1871.

XXIIc. Kansas City, Missouri, in 1853. *From a line engraving by Hermann J. Meyer;
photograph from the New York Public Library.*

XXIIIa.   Sacramento, California, in 1849. *From a lithograph by G. V. Cooper; photograph from the New York Public Library.*

XXIIIb.   Tucson, Arizona, in 1854. *From a lithograph by Sarony & Co.; photograph from the New York Public Library.*

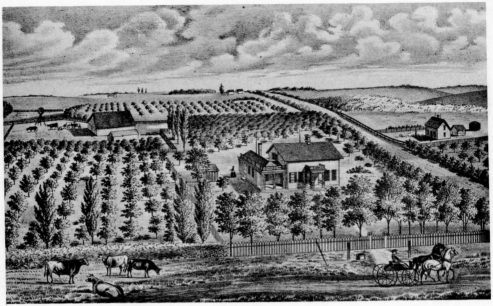

XXIVa. House and orchards of Joseph Munger, an early settler in Poweshiek County, Iowa. *From the* Historical Atlas of Iowa, 1875.

XXIVb. Old olive and date trees on the site of the San Diego Mission, San Diego, California. *Courtesy of the Division of Horticulture, College of Agriculture, University of California, Los Angeles.*

of which there is a record and was long one of the sights of the old town. The tree was a seedling brought from Pittsburgh before 1800 and planted on the grounds of a Mr. Ochletree. In 1855, the trunk measured 10½ feet in circumference at the smallest place below the branches; the top had a spread of 75 feet; the height was 65 feet. Its record-breaking crop was borne in 1837, when 140 bushels of pears were picked. The tree was destroyed by a tornado in 1867.

Westward lay the Illinois towns, Kaskaskia, Cahokia, Prairie du Rocher, and St. Philip. In 1800, there were some 4000 French people in this inland empire. Many were traders and trappers, but many others were tillers of the soil, and while their farming was primitive, and the men much given to lying in the sun smoking, they planted gardens and orchards and were pioneers in horticulture in these two states.

These were times of constant strife between Whites and Indians, English and French, when the palisaded village with its blockhouses was the only place in which safety, peace, and retirement, even of small degree, could be found. To settlers, trappers, explorers, priests, and traders, how peaceful these gardens must have seemed! These palisaded villages in every part of the Middle West where Whites built homes served agriculture and horticulture, for a shorter time and in a lesser way to be sure, quite as did the monasteries in Great Britain during the centuries of the retreat of the Romans, after the Roman Conquest.

Another seat of orcharding and gardening in Indiana, a little later in its establishment than Vincennes, was near Fort Wayne at the junction of the St. Mary and St. Joseph Rivers, where the two form the Maumee. Here there stood for much more than a century a famous apple tree called after the Miami Indians, the 'Miami apple tree.' Doubtless it grew from a seed planted by some missionary explorer. In 1860, this tree had a trunk more than 3 feet in diameter, and at that time was said to have been bearing fruit for more than a hundred years. About this tree the cabins of Little Turtle, famous as the leader of the Indians who massacred General Harmar's troops in 1791, were clustered. Near by Captain Wells, white brother-in-law of Little Turtle, planted an apple orchard in 1804, which was long pointed out as the oldest apple orchard in Indiana.

Gardening in the Middle West by real tillers of the soil, who produced gardens quite different from those of traders and trappers, began soon after the close of the War for Independence. Westward migration had begun in Tennessee and Kentucky after the treaty of 1763, which closed the French and Indian War and gave England all the French possessions east of the Mississippi. These first English settlers had their hands full in fighting Indians—there was little time for gardening. But after the Revolution, in the formative days of the young republic, westward migrations thronged along the valley of the Mohawk; to the heart of the West by the way of the Potomac; from Pittsburgh down the Ohio; and over the Carolina mountains. The westward settlers of these later migrations were soon secure enough in their new homes to plant gardens.

At the close of the Napoleonic Wars, William Faux, an English farmer, crossed the Atlantic to 'shew Men and Things as they are in America.' He published his observations in London in 1823 under the title *Memorable Days in America*. In general what he wrote is so distorted and ill-natured that one must put the author down as a man with a jaundiced eye and a malicious pen; yet, what he writes of what he saw in Ohio, Indiana, and Illinois, a generation after the Revolution, is substantiated by so many other visitors of the times that one can hardly question his veracity.

His picture is so repellent that one cannot believe that gardening or any other trade or profession could have had a place other than to minister to direst necessity. Of a forty-mile ride between Vincennes, Indiana, and Princeton, Illinois, he writes:

I saw nothing but miserable log houses and a mean ville of eight or ten huts or cabins, sad neglected farms, and indolent, dirty, sickly, wild-looking inhabitants. Soap is nowhere seen, or found in any of the taverns, east or west. Hence dirty hands, heads, and faces everywhere. Here is nothing clean but wild beast and birds, nothing industrious generally, except pigs, which are so of necessity.

How could gardening flourish?

William Cobbett, who described the English countryside so admirably in his *Rural Rides,* a man 'bred up at a ploughtail,' who wrote so pleasantly in his *A Year's Residence in the United States of America* on farming on Long Island, and who found agriculture in Pennsylvania not too bad, could say little in praise of agriculture farther west. He visited the Illinois settlements early in the nineteenth century, and, like Faux, expatiated upon their social crudity, dirt, disorder, remoteness from markets, and the lack of pleasant living in the frontier places where he stopped.

The early explorers and travelers in the Northwest Territory and prairie states, and people there for trading purposes, speak poorly of the agricultural possibilities of the parts that are now good farming regions. Pike, who crossed northeastern Kansas in 1806, expressed the opinion that it might some day be habitable for goats. As late as 1847, Horace Greeley visited northern Illinois and informed his readers in the *New York Tribune* that 'deficiency of water was a great drawback' to farming, a deficiency that he did not believe would ever be remedied. Debaters in the Wisconsin Constitutional Convention, in the middle of the century, described the region between the Wisconsin River and St. Paul as a wilderness 'uninhabited and uninhabitable.' To go back to a much earlier date, Thomas Jefferson, usually so optimistic, wrote in his *Notes on Virginia:* 'It will be two centuries before civilization reaches the Mississippi and four centuries before it extends to the Pacific.'

As late as 1846, Thomas Allen, from St. Louis, Missouri, and a writer in *The Horticulturist,* could say little in praise of the gardens of the Mississippi. He tells us that gardening is generally known in the West as 'tending a truck patch.' The object of having such a garden, he says, 'is the daily plentiful supply of "garden truck" in the kitchen pot.' Field crops were the main reliance and received most attention. He repeated instances of very good farms destitute of any sort of garden whatever. He found an abundance of corn and potatoes, sunflowers and cabbages, beets, parsnips, onions, eggplants, tomatoes, squashes, and 'gourds of almost incredible dimensions, in the very shadow of the wilderness.' Here and there he saw 'orchards of apples and peaches, and strawberry patches of no small extent, or perhaps the beginning of a vineyard.'

Yet there must have been east of the Mississippi better orchards and gardens than west of it; for, in the same volume of *The Horticulturist,* Henry Ward Beecher takes the editor to task for his 'amiable fondness for the localities of the Hudson River,' and says that 'the western states, say Ohio, Indiana, Kentucky, and portions of Illinois, are, the whole range of the orchard being considered, better fruit-growing States than New York or New England.' [2]

Gardening and orcharding began in Ohio at Marietta, its earliest settlement, founded by the Revolutionary soldier, General Rufus Putnam, 7 September 1788, on the banks of the Muskingum River, in the southeastern part of the state. Under General Putnam's vigorous management, the land was quickly cleared and farmers began to build homes and plant gardens and orchards. A year or two later the Reverend Manasseh Cutler visited the new settlement and in his diary tells of a visit to General Harmar, who had come to command the garrison. The laconic description of the visit shows that there were gardens and other amenities of life at Marietta as early as 1788. The entry in Cutler's diary reads: 'Genteel dinner; fine fruit. Mrs. Harmar a fine woman. Beautiful gardens.' [3]

In the early 1790's a colony of 800 French settled on the Ohio, in Gallia County, naming their settlement Gallipolis. Fortescue Cuming visited the town in 1807 and said: 'the place abounds with fruit of which French settlers always pay great attention.' [4] Early horticultural records of Ohio mention Gallipolis as a horticulture center of southeastern Ohio at the turn of the nineteenth century. The peach seems to have been a favorite fruit here, and Thomas Ashe says of these French in his *Travels in America in 1806*: 'They cultivate little more than fruit and vegetables, and they depend on the exchange of these for bread and other necessities to be had of boats descending the river.' The peaches grew so well that an old settler had stills and made brandy, which, 'at a tolerable age, is of a very fine quality.' He made 400 gallons of peach brandy each season, which he bartered for flour and corn at the rate of one dollar per gallon for the liquor. He then could sell his flour and corn for chickens, hogs, and garden produce, which he sold at a cheap rate to boats on their passage down the river. He was very much of the opinion that 'were it not for the

---

[2] *The Horticulturist,* I: 112.   [3] Cutler, I: 417.
[4] Cuming, *Sketches of a Tour to the Western Country,* etc.

prospect of bringing the peach brandy into success, Gallipolis town and settlement would be abandoned.' [5]

Twenty miles down the Ohio, 'opposite the Little Sandy Creek,' the French had made another settlement in which the peach, according to Ashe, was the only crop grown with success. He thought the French had talent in the management of peach orchards and these, he says, 'they bring to profit and perfection.' At this town down the river from Gallipolis, he found 3000 gallons of peach brandy, 'the amount of which furnishes the settlement with coffee, snuff, knives, tin ware, and other small articles in demand among French emigrants.' [6]

A common complaint in every newly settled region was that there were no nurseries from which trees and shrubs could be obtained. At a time before railroads, when wagon roads were difficult to travel, there had to be local nurseries before there could be much planting of fruits and ornamental trees. The men who established nurseries were usually the leaders in every division of gardening in a new country. Such a man was General Rufus Putnam, who planted the pioneer nursery of Ohio near Marietta.

It was an event of no small moment in the horticulture of Ohio, when, in 1796, Israel and Aaron Putnam, sons of Rufus, brought cions of the Roxbury Russet, one of the best of all apples, from the orchard of their uncle, General Israel Putnam, Pomfret, Connecticut, to their home in Ohio. Soon the Roxbury Russet was distributed in all the new settlements of Ohio and became the most popular apple in that state. Settlers from North Carolina brought cions of Rawles Janet and Limber Twig, which, with standard varieties from New York and Pennsylvania, soon gave the Putnam nursery a good assortment of apples, ever the standard fruit of Ohio. This was the earliest nursery west of the Alleghenies. It continued to supply settlements in Ohio and all its neighboring states with trees until 1821.

Of several other early nurserymen in Ohio at early dates, two were outstanding. In 1810, Silas Wharton, a native of Bucks County, Pennsylvania, emigrated to Waynesville, near Dayton, and established a nursery. Wharton was a friend of William Coxe

[5] Ashe, *Trav. in Am. in* 1806, etc., pp. 167-8.
[6] Ibid. p. 176.

and from him obtained cions and trees of many good fruits. He published the first catalogue of nursery stock in the state. In 1824, he listed 92 varieties of apples and 58 of pears. Ohio, the western part in particular, and Indiana were greatly indebted to Wharton for fine fruits at this early date.

Another early nurseryman in Ohio was Zebulon Gillet of Quaker Bottom, Lawrence County. Gillet and his son started a nursery in the first quarter of the nineteenth century. In 1848 this nursery became famous as the place of origin of the Rome Beauty apple, which has ever since remained a standard variety in the state.

One of the most pleasing chapters in the history of Ohio and American horticulture is the work of Johnny Appleseed, an eccentric and lovable pioneer who for 46 years traveled through the wilderness from Pennsylvania to Illinois planting apple seeds. He was born Jonathan Chapman in Leominster, Massachusetts, in 1774; and in early manhood began his work of planting apple seeds, preaching, warning settlers of Indian raids, and befriending men, birds, and beasts.

Just when Johnny Appleseed began his pilgrimages in the great region between the Ohio River and the northern lakes does not appear, but in 1806 we find him loading a canoe with apple seeds from cider mills in western Pennsylvania. Thence, he floated down the Ohio to the Muskingum, up which he paddled into the very heart of Ohio, making the branches of the Muskingum his waterway. He gave his seeds to any settler who would plant them and promise to care for the young trees. Here and there he planted a patch of rich, loamy land from his stock of seed, covered it with brush to keep animals out, and told farmers to help themselves to the young trees.

Sometimes he used a canoe, but usually he traveled on foot, feet and body bare except for a coarse bag with holes cut in it for his arms. He went barefoot until winter, often so late in autumn that he walked on frozen ground and in snow. What little money he required for the simple necessities of life came from donations from farmers or the occasional sale of young apple trees. As settlements became thicker in eastern Ohio he moved westward and on into Indiana, leaving orchards in his trail over an area of more than a hundred thousand square miles. Johnny Appleseed lived to be 73, dying in 1847. At least 40 years of his life were spent in planting apples.

In Johnny Appleseed's philosophy, it was wrong to injure any living thing. He would not kill a snake, a bee, a fly, a mosquito, or any other of the animal and insect enemies of mankind. He believed that pruning and grafting were wicked, and left behind him thousands of acres of seedling apples, most of which produce apples fit only to make cider. There is no record of any of his seedlings now in cultivation.

By the second quarter of the century, Cincinnati was the horticultural center of the Ohio Valley and, for that matter, of all the region drained by the Mississippi. In it were planters of orchards, vineyards, and vegetable and flower gardens; in or about it were the best nurseries of the Middle West; in it lived the most notable authors on gardening subjects—Longworth, Warder, Ernst, Buchanan, and Hooper. Lastly, the Cincinnati Horticultural Society was one of the best in the country and was long a clearinghouse in the whole Middle West for horticultural information.

Cincinnati was the first center of a grape and wine industry in America. Nicholas Longworth introduced the Catawba in this region about 1825 and in a few years the Ohio River became known as the 'Rhine of America.' According to Robert Buchanan [7] there were 1550 acres of grapes within 20 miles of Cincinnati in 1850. Longworth's winery is said to have cost $60,000 and Buchanan's half as much.

Horticulture in the whole country was greatly enriched in the first half of the nineteenth century by the work of Nicholas Longworth, who has three great accomplishments in horticulture to his credit: the establishment of commercial viticulture, with its accompaniment of wine making; proof of the fact that many varieties of strawberries are infertile with themselves and must have pollenizers; and the introduction of the first variety of the black raspberry, *Rubus occidentalis*. One might easily name a score of lesser achievements that this remarkable man, not a professional horticulturist but a banker, lawyer, and man of large business, accomplished in his avocation.

[7] Buchanan, p. 61.

Longworth (1783-1863) was a native of New Jersey, but in 1803 moved to Cincinnati, then a log village of 800 inhabitants. Here he began the practice of law, and his first fee, for the defense of a horse thief, was two secondhand copper stills, which he traded for 33 acres of land, later valued at $2,000,000. He bought a cow pasture for $5000 that reached a valuation of $1,500,000. Soon he was paying more land tax than any other American except William Backhouse Astor. Great as was the worth of his lands, the value of his experiments in growing gardens, vineyards, and orchards yielded far greater profits to the people of the country, and no doubt to his own happiness. In 1828 Longworth retired from business and devoted himself to grape culture and wine making. For his first ventures in viticulture he imported 1500 plants of some 20 varieties of European grapes, none of which lived for more than a few years. He then began experimenting with varieties of native species and soon was planting Catawba, which he received from its discoverer, John Adlum. The Catawba turned out to be quite at home in the region along the Ohio River, and Longworth became its promoter and distributor. Before 1840 he was making wine on a large scale, his product rivaling that of Europe. A gift of wine to Longfellow inspired the poem, 'Catawba Wine.' When the census of 1859 was taken, it was found that there were 2000 acres of grapes within a few miles of Cincinnati.

After grapes, Longworth was fondest of strawberries, but had poor success in growing them. Among the market growers about Cincinnati, only Abergust, a German, grew strawberries well. One day Abergust's son, visiting Longworth, told him that his crop would be small, as nearly all the plants were self-sterile. This chance remark led Longworth, a keen observer, to study strawberry blossoms, with the result that he concluded self-sterile and perfect-flowered varieties must be interplanted for successful strawberry culture. He published his discovery and precipitated in 1842 the 'Strawberry War,' which lasted for at least two decades, as some of the foremost horticulturists in the United States opposed Longworth's theory. Probably the fact that Cincinnati strawberry growers soon became the best in the country was proof that the two forms of strawberries must be interplanted. At first, Longworth denied the value of bi-sexual varieties of strawberries, but later admitted that he was wrong in this contention and introduced one such, the Longworth Prolific.

The third most notable of Longworth's horticultural achievements was the introduction of the Ohio Everbearing black raspberry, the first named variety of this fruit to be grown in gardens. Longworth found the berry in the interior of the state in the autumn of 1832, and in the winter of that year began its propagation. Yet with all his prestige as a grower of fruits, he could not persuade gardeners to plant black raspberries. Wild plants were too common, the fruit was not well liked, and its varieties were difficult to propagate; yet eventually improved varieties made it one of the popular bramble fruits.

Longworth seems to have had a passion for growing things and a gardener's touch for all cultivated plants. As has been said, he devoted most of his time to grapes, strawberries, and the black raspberry, but he also planted an orchard of many varieties of tree fruits. His was the first conservatory built in Cincinnati. According to Harriet Martineau, he had the finest vegetable and flower gardens in the city in 1834. She says of him: 'He employs four gardeners, and toils in his grounds with his own hands.' Again: 'he has succeeded in making twelve kinds of wine, some of which are praised by good judges.' [8]

Newspapers and horticultural papers of Ohio and the country at large were much enriched by Longworth's pen, which, at one time or another, furnished information on nearly every phase of gardening. In 1846 he published a booklet entitled *The Cultivation of the Grape, and Manufacture of Wine*. Another publication of note was *Character and Habits of the Strawberry Plant*. He also contributed a chapter, 'Culture of the Strawberry,' to Robert Buchanan's *Culture of the Grape*.

Dr. John Ashton Warder was almost as notable a member of the Cincinnati school of horticulture as Longworth, its founder. Warder (1812-83) was a physician, born and bred in Philadelphia, where in his father's house he had known the younger Bartram, the younger Michaux, Audubon, Nuttall, and lesser scientists. He came to Cincinnati in 1837 to practice medicine and almost

[8] Martineau, *Retrospect of Western Travel*, II: 51.

at once became interested in horticulture. He was associated with Longworth and others in founding several scientific societies, two of which, the Cincinnati Horticultural Society and the Wine Growers Association, were related to horticulture. In 1850 he became the publisher of *The Western Horticultural Review,* which, in its life of four years, was the mouthpiece of the gardeners of the Middle West. In one number of this magazine is the first description of *Catalpa speciosa,* named by Warder. This species is a valuable shade tree, a native of the Mississippi Valley from Indiana to the Gulf. In 1858 Warder published *Hedges and Evergreens;* and, in 1867, his greatest work, *American Pomology—Apples,* which made him a national authority on fruits. He was a militant forester and a strong advocate of rural cemeteries. He helped to plan and maintain Spring Grove Cemetery, considered one of the most beautiful burying places in the country.

Somewhat lesser men than Longworth and Warder in this group of famous Cincinnati gardeners were Robert Buchanan, the author of *The Culture of the Grape, and Wine-Making,* published in 1852; F. R. Elliott (see page 492), who, in 1854, published *Elliott's Fruit Book; or the American Fruit-Grower's Guide;* and Andrew H. Ernst. Ernst was a German nurseryman and pomologist who conceived the plan of the Spring Grove Cemetery, and, helped by Warder and others, brought it into being a little before the middle of the century. In turn, Ernst gave Warder valuable assistance in writing his fruit book.

Horticulture in Ohio in this period, 1800-1860, was not confined to Cincinnati. In particular, good work was being done in growing grapes in other parts of the state, the grape, perhaps, for a time, being the favorite fruit in Ohio.

It was found that Kelley's Island in Lake Erie, near the city of Sandusky, containing about 3000 acres, had a soil and climate well suited to grape culture and that very superior Catawba grapes could be grown there. Eventually the whole island and the country for miles around, on islands and the mainland, were planted to grapes. These plantings were begun in 1846. Grape growing and wine making in this region have flourished, with some ups and downs, to the present time.

One of the leading horticulturists in northern Ohio in the second quarter of the century was Dr. Jared P. Kirkland of East Rockport, who in the 1830's began to breed fruits and flowers. In pomology he gave special attention to grapes, raspberries, pears, and cherries. He named and distributed more than 30 varieties of cherries, Wood, a sweet cherry, raised in 1842 and still grown, being his greatest success. He was also a successful peony hybridizer, but in the field of ornamental horticulture is best known for introducing foreign magnolias. He is given credit for having been the first horticulturist to bud and graft magnolias, making possible their cultivation where otherwise they could not be grown.

Orcharding, other than the planting of a few trees in the gardens of early French traders, began in Indiana when Reuben Ragan (1793-1869) planted a nursery in Putnam County in 1820. Ragan was a Virginian who had served an apprenticeship in the Old Dominion under Edward Darnaby. From 1820 to 1850, the Ragan Nursery was one of the largest and best in the Middle West. From it the choicest hardy fruits to be found in America were sold in Indiana and neighboring states. Reuben Ragan was the father of William Henry Ragan (1836-1909), who, during his later years, became the accepted authority on the nomenclature of fruits, serving for many years in important positions having to do with pomology in the United States Department of Agriculture.

A second notable family of nurserymen came early to Indiana to enrich the state with orchards. In 1825 Meshack Lewelling,[9] a physician, moved from Salem, North Carolina, to Washington County, Indiana, and founded another town of Salem. Here he planted a nursery and an orchard. From this early nursery the south-central counties of the state blossomed with all the tree fruits. The restless feet of Lewelling's three sons soon carried them westward to Iowa to start new plantations, and then on and on to Oregon and California, where they became truly great men, as we shall see, in the garden enterprises of the Pacific Coast.

By the middle of the century there were many nurseries in Indiana and trees were dirt cheap. Henry Ward Beecher, writing

[9] Some spell the name Luelling, but the sons spelled it as given above.

in 1844,[10] says that finely grown apple trees, not under 10 feet high, could be purchased for 10 cents each, and pears at 20 cents; and in some nurseries good apples could be had at 6 cents. According to Beecher, 'at least 100,000 apple trees had been planted in 1843, and in 1844 that number would be surpassed by 25,000.' Pears were in these years little grown in Indiana; the numbers a few years before had been in the ratio of 100 apples to 2 pears, but Beecher thought that nurseries in 1844 were selling apples and pears in the ratio of 100 to 20.

Long before there were nurseries and orchards in Indiana, there was a vineyard of some note. In 1801 John James Dufour, a Swiss, had founded a colony of his relatives and countrymen some 15 or 20 miles from Lexington on the Kentucky River in Kentucky. The location did not please some of the colony, especially since the vines did not thrive, and in 1802 they went down the Kentucky to the Ohio, ascended the larger river a few miles, and near the present city of Vevay, Indiana, 45 miles below Cincinnati, planted a vineyard, the first in the state. After a few years the vines began to die and in a few more only a remnant of the plantation was left.

The settlers in these states had to trust for a generation to seedling fruits. The early settlers could not bring from the Atlantic states grafted trees, and if fruits were to be grown they must plant seeds. That which was begun of necessity was continued through inaction, and even until the Civil War there were in all the states in the Middle West many seedling trees, although splendid nurseries had long since sprung up.

Out of these seedling apples a few good varieties came. Beecher, writing in 1845 for *The Magazine of Horticulture,* said of them:

An immense number of seedling trees are found in our State. Since the Indiana Horticultural Society began to collect specimens of these, more than 150 varieties have been sent up for inspection. Of the number presented, not six have vindicated their claims to a name or place—and not more than three will probably be known ten years hence.

Henry Ward Beecher (1813-87), the great clergyman, was the most conspicuous figure in early Indiana horticulture. In 1839 he

[10] *Mag. of Hort.,* II: 53.

became pastor of the Presbyterian church in Indianapolis. Almost at once he took up horticulture as an avocation. The *Indiana Journal* printed in its regular issues a column or two, which was reprinted in magazine form under the title *Indiana Farmer and Gardener,* later changed to *Western Farmer and Gardener.* Of this publication Beecher became editor, and soon the paper was the most popular farm magazine in the Middle West. Beecher's style was direct, pithy, humorous; his material was taken largely from eastern and English publications, but was selected with much common sense. Eventually, in 1859, the best of his articles were collected and published in a book, *Plain and Pleasant Talk about Fruits, Flowers, and Farming.*

We have in articles by Beecher some interesting figures in regard to prices of apples. 'During the season of '43-'44 apples of the finest sorts (Jennetin, green Newtown pippin &c) sold at my door for, as late as April, at twenty-five cents a bushel—and dull at that.' At this time, we are told 'corn brings from twelve to twenty cents a bushel; wheat sells from forty-five to fifty; hay at five dollars the ton.'

In these years in Indiana, as elsewhere, apples were still largely grown for cider or for home and local use. Fruits were not in great market demand, as were grains and meats. Beecher prophesied that this was to be speedily changed, even in newly settled Indiana then so far from markets. He was convinced that apples grown in Indiana would soon be shipped on the Ohio River, the Great Lakes, and by canal to eastern markets. He predicted that 'Fruit will become more generally and largely an article, not of luxury, but of daily and ordinary diet.' In a few years the apple crop, he thought, 'would be a matter of reckoning by farmers and speculators, just as is now the potato crop—the wheat crop—the pork &c.'

Mr. Beecher, however, became a little over-enthusiastic about the apple, his favorite fruit, when he predicted that should he live threescore years and ten 'the apple crop of the United States will surpass the potato crop in value, for both man and beast.' A statement of fact connected with this prophecy is of more importance. The writer says:

If not another apple tree is set in this county [Marion County], in ten years the annual crop will be 200,000 bushels. But Wayne County has

double our number of trees—suppose, however, the 90 counties of
Indiana to have only 25 trees to a quarter section of land, i.e. to each
160 acres, the crop of 15 bushels to a tree would be nearly *two millions*.

One gets from this article by Beecher the best account extant
of small fruit culture and flower culture in Indiana in 1844:

The year has greatly increased the cultivation of small fruits in the
State. Strawberries are found in almost every garden, and of select
sorts. None among them all is more popular, or more deservedly so,
than Hovey's Seedling. We have a native white strawberry, removed
from our meadows to our gardens, which produces fruit of superior
flavor and fragrance. The crop is not large—but continues gradually
ripening for many weeks. The blackberry is introduced to the garden
among us. The fruit sells at our market at from three to five cents,—
profit is not therefore the motive for cultivating it, but improvement.
I have a *white* variety. . . *Assorted* gooseberries and the new raspberries, Franconia and Falstaff, are finding their way into our gardens.
The Antwerps we have long had in abundance. If next spring I can
produce Rhubarb weighing two pounds to the stalk, shall I have surpassed you? I have a *seedling* which last year without good cultivation
produced petioles weighing from eighteen to twenty ounces. My wrist
is not very delicate, and yet it is much smaller in girth than they were.

Early writers say almost nothing about ornamental plants and
flowers in the Middle West. Beecher, continuing in this article
in the *Magazine of Horticulture,* tells us a little something about
flower gardens and lawn plantings. He tells us that in no department is there more decided advance than in floriculture; that
towns, yards, and gardens are choicely stocked; that hardy bulbs
are sought after; that ornamental shrubs are taken from our forests or imported from abroad in great variety; that the althea,
rose, acacia, jessamine, calycanthus, snowberry, snowball, sumach,
syringa, spicewood, shepherdia, dogwood, redwood, and other
hardy shrubs abound. The rose, he says, is an especial favorite.
'The Bengal, Tea, and Noisette bear our winters in the open garden without protection. The Bourbon and Remontants will, however, drive out all old and ordinary varieties.' The gardens of
Indianapolis, he thought, would afford about 60 varieties of roses,
which would be reckoned first rate in Boston or Philadelphia.

Michigan, now noted for its apples, peaches, cherries, grapes, a great variety of truck crops, and vegetables and flowers under glass, did not cut much of a figure in horticulture before 1860. To this statement there are two exceptions: the beginnings by the French in and about Detroit gave the state an early reputation for fruits; and the peaches on the shores of Lake Michigan, described on another page, were of remarkably good quality and widely planted and sold. But certainly Michigan before 1860 had no such standing in horticulture as Ohio or Indiana. One could not name a dozen writers in the state as one could for this period in Ohio, and there was no man in Michigan to compare with Henry Ward Beecher as a horticultural authority.

Perhaps an occasional adventurous farmer made his home and planted an orchard in one of the southern counties of Michigan soon after the War of 1812; but even feeble pulsations of immigration from the East were not felt until 1820-25, these to be followed more and more rapidly till they culminated in the Michigan Land Speculation of 1836 and 1837. Then it was that horticulture in all its branches took on new life. It turned out that the southern half of the Lower Peninsula was admirably suited in soil and climate for tree fruits, the small fruits, and all northern vegetables. Peach yellows, plum curculio, pear blight, apple scab, and the dozen other pests of orchard fruits had not yet put in an appearance, and a cultivated plant in the virgin land of the region grew like the proverbial bay tree. Apple trees grew wild, bearing every year.

The great drawback to fruit growing in Michigan in these early years was the lack of uses to which the fruit could be put, other than for consumption by the families of the growers. The towns were of small size and offered little for commercial fruit growing. Until after 1850, there was no transportation by rail and water to larger cities, east or west. The temperance movement, begun in the 1830's, was sweeping the whole land and there was no market for cider or apple and peach brandy, as there had been in the eastern states. Nor does the surplus seem to have been fed to pigs, as it was in so many of the Atlantic states. Later, after the Civil War, a number of commercial fruit dryers helped to take care of surplus fruits.

Monroe, in the southeastern part of the state, was, in these first days of horticultural enterprise, the nursery center of the state, as it has been in all the years that have followed. The city is on the Raisin River, so named by the first French visitors because of the grapes growing abundantly on its banks. It was here, on the banks of this river and near the shore of Lake Erie, that the French planted orchards and vineyards more than 200 years ago. The first nursery was conducted by a man known as 'Variety' White, who deviated from the usual course of growing seedlings by bringing in varieties of tree fruits from the East. White's nursery was started in 1840, and a few years later I. E. Ilgenfritz established a nursery that for over a hundred years has furnished Michigan and neighboring states with fruit and ornamental plants. From this time on, nurseries, large and small, multiplied in the four tiers of counties in southern Michigan.

Probably the first commercial orchard worthy of note was planted in what is now a part of the city of Detroit. William Woodbridge, an early governor of the state, in 1824 or 1825, bought 2000 apple and pear trees from Grant Thorburn, the New York seedsman, which he planted on his Detroit farm. This importation included all the standard varieties of the East, and was supplemented by the several old French sorts then being grown about Detroit on both sides of the river. It is said that Governor Woodbridge found a good market for his fruit on the ships then carrying cargoes and passengers through the Great Lakes.

A second orchard and nursery center in Michigan in the first settlements in the interior by Whites was in Lenawee County. As early as 1830, there were several orchards and small nurseries under way in this county. Possibly the nursery most worthy of note was that of Nathaniel P. Hoag, who, in 1833, began operations by planting a bushel of apple seeds. The next spring he bought cions from the Prince Nurseries, in sufficient numbers to graft 12,000 trees. The varieties included all the standard apples of the East, the introduction of which was a great boon to apple growers in the state. This enterprising nurseryman, in the next few years, imported varieties of plums, cherries, peaches, quinces, and the Isabella and Catawba grapes, probably the first named grapes to be planted in Michigan.

Michigan had few pests on fruits before the middle of the century. In 1834, however, southern Michigan and especially Lenawee County had orchards nearly destroyed by the seventeen-year locust, a pest now not troublesome to fruit growers. The next pest to appear, one now easily controlled by spraying, was the canker worm, which defoliated most of the orchards in Michigan several times between 1840 and 1860. These two insects were the most troublesome pests in the Middle West during the infancy of orcharding.

In what is now the famous Fruit Belt of western Michigan, formed chiefly by the counties of Berrien, Van Buren, Allegan, Ottawa, Kent, and far to the north Grand Traverse, there was little commercial fruit growing, except in Berrien County, until after the period of this history. The success of small nurseries and home orchards in all these counties from 1830 to 1860 fore-shadowed the great industry that was to come.

A notable event in Michigan horticulture was the establish-ment in 1844 of testing grounds in the orchards of Theodorus Timothy Lyon (1813-1900) for varieties of apples and pears. Up until that time most of the orchards in Michigan had been of seedling fruits or of local varieties. Lyon proposed to find out what apples and pears would grow in his orchards at Plymouth, near Detroit. He corresponded with nearly every pomologist in the East and brought from their orchards practically all the varie-ties of these two fruits for his trial grounds. In the years that followed, he made exhibits of Michigan-grown apples and pears, not only in Michigan but at pomological meetings in eastern cities, with the result that even before the Civil War the state began to have a reputation for its fruits. As a member of the American Pomological Society, Lyon had charge for many years of the preparation of the *Fruit Catalogue,* copies of which are full of pomological history, especially of varieties of apples and pears. He was the author of the first set of rules adopted by the American Pomological Society governing the nomenclature of fruits, to secure uniformity in which he worked for years. In his later years, he made further contributions to horticulture as superintendent of the fruit-testing sub-station of the Michigan Agricultural College at South Haven.

Another event of note in the horticulture of Michigan was the establishment of the well-known seed house of D. M. Ferry & Co., in Detroit. The seeds of this firm long have been sold in all parts of America, but particularly in the central states. It had its beginning in the small establishment of M. T. Gardner & Co. In 1852 Dexter Mason Ferry came to Detroit from New York State to seek his fortune. He at first worked as a bookkeeper in a bookstore, but soon began keeping the books of the Gardner seed establishment as well. In 1856 he became a partner in the seed store, which later took the name of D. M. Ferry & Co. This firm is particularly noted in the annals of the seed business as the founder of the 'commission box' business. Seeds were put up in packets, attractively illustrated, usually with descriptions of the mature plant and often with directions for growing. These packets were in turn put up in large, good-looking boxes for display in the stores of the country.

From the *Transactions of the Illinois Horticultural Society* for 1870, we get a number of facts and dates in regard to the early history of horticulture in Illinois.[11] One of the first nurseries in the state was started by Joseph Curtis—a man to be remembered, as we shall see—at Paris, in 1818. Before 1820 William Archer, Clark County, and John Smith, Bond County, had started nurseries. Whether or not these nurserymen sold seedlings or grafted trees does not appear, but since a great point is made later of the importation of grafted trees, one may assume that the first orchards from these nurseries were of seedlings. One of the earliest orchards, after those of the French, was planted by Abraham Eyman, near East St. Louis, from seedlings of trees planted by the French.

Samuel Ogle, of St. Clair County, we are told, went to New Jersey in 1819 and brought from there the first grafted trees planted in the southwestern part of the state. The same year, George Hart brought from Georgia the Red June apple, a variety long the standard early sort in America. Other orchards mentioned in this historical sketch were planted in 1817 by Daniel Lane, Elijah Austin, Colonel J. Mayo, and John Stratton. The year 1819, according to this article, was one of magnificent accom-

11 *Ill. Hort. Soc.*, pp. 277-80. 1870.

plishment. Colonel J. W. Blackburn, General J. Sanford, William Murphy, Laban Burr, and E. Purnell all set out large plantations of trees, and Joseph Capps planted currants and grapes in Sangamon County for wine. After 1820, one gathers from all sources, fruit plantings multiplied rapidly. Flowers and vegetables are not mentioned until much later, though gardens of them there must have been.

A man of note in the early settlement of Illinois and Iowa was George Davenport, who helped to found Davenport, Iowa, and Moline, Illinois. He came to this region as a commissary of the fort on Rock Island, but eventually became an Indian trader, in which occupation and as a dealer in real estate he became a man of wealth. Davenport was a native of England and no doubt brought to America a love of horticulture, which, in old age, he turned to as an avocation. In the 1840's, his estate on Rock Island was the showplace of the Mississippi. He maintained a garden of fruits, vegetables, and flowers, and on the lawn were, besides trees and shrubs, an arbor of Isabella and Catawba grapes, and a number of peach and cherry trees.

As in all new states, it was difficult to know what varieties to plant. Cold winters, hot summers, and a soil vastly different from that of the eastern states made the environment of Illinois a difficult one for varieties suited for the East. In common with other states of the Middle West, Illinois became a testing ground for varieties. Some orchards contained as many as 150 varieties of apples. To make matters worse, some varieties were introduced under several names. When a variety was not liked, the trees were speedily grafted to other kinds, so that grafting was a major orchard operation in these new states. In fact, grafting was about the only operation apple trees received. Until the end of the century there was no spraying, little pruning, almost no cultivation, and no fertilizing except by animals pastured in the orchard.

After all, horticulture could hardly have had much of a start in Illinois and the states bordering it until the Erie Canal was finished and the ports on the Great Lakes and the Ohio had the trade of steamboats. Settlers largely came from New England by the Erie Canal and from the Middle Atlantic states on the Ohio. Until quick and easy transportation by steam was available, it was not possible for settlers to come in large numbers, and the few who came had not the means to bring fruit plants. Almost up to the middle of the century, states west of Michigan, Ohio, Kentucky, and Tennessee were mostly primitive. Forest and prairies covered much of the land; level lands were swampy; wild animals, snakes, mosquitoes, and malaria, in consequence, were abundant; and Indians were, to say the least, bothersome. Civilization conducive to gardens and orchards had not yet arrived.

Down through the ages, gardeners have paid much attention to grafting. Garden writings from Theophrastus and Pliny to recent experiment-station bulletins contain information on the subject. In one book or another, centuries ago, nearly every kind of grafting now known had been described. Yet it remained for an American youth, a century ago, to add a very great deal to our knowledge of grafting and of a process so valuable that the propagation of nursery stock was revolutionized. The discovery of this new kind of grafting was made in Ohio, but it was put in practice and brought to the attention of fruit growers in Illinois.

The inventor, Joseph Curtis (1786-1882), though born in the East, was a man of the Middle West, a man not well known, yet one who should be remembered with gratitude by all planters of trees. He was taken by his parents from New Jersey to Manchester, Ohio, in 1786. Here, in 1802, when he was 16 years old, he began planting an orchard. A brother-in-law, a nurseryman, had taught the boy how to bud, cleft-graft, and splice-graft, commonest forms of grafting. Because each of these methods required a stock for every cion, young Curtis became impatient, stocks being difficult to obtain. It occurred to him that he might cut in pieces the apple roots being plowed up by his father and make a stock of each piece. The grafts he thus made grew and the trees from them were as good as any in the orchard. The method quickly came into use in all nurseries as 'root-grafting' and 'piece-root-grafting.'

Later, Curtis developed and made popular collar-grafting, in which cions are grafted on seedling trees at the dividing line between root and top. Still later, he came to believe that trees on their own roots were better than those on other roots—true in some species and varieties—and sought for a method of propagating them on their own roots other than starting them from cuttings. He found that by setting the graft deep in the ground he could grow trees on their own roots. Probably this method had been known for centuries but was little practiced; certainly Curtis brought it to the attention of American nurserymen.

Chicago in 1860, 30 years after its founding, had a population of 110,000. It had by this time achieved a world-wide reputation for its stockyards, farm machinery, railroads, and banking. It was the 'Bovine City' and the 'Queen City of the West.' It was also, then as now, a city of gardens, so that it was often called the 'Garden City,' noted for its summer and winter gardens, where one might eat and drink surrounded by ornamental plants. Even then, parks were being planned and trees planted along city streets. Probably in no other city west of the Atlantic seaboard were grounds about private homes more enthusiastically cared for or better planned. Local nurseries, florists, and seedsmen thrived, though many of their wares were imported from the East.

One of the most notable nurseries in the north-central states was one founded in 1848 by Robert Douglas (1813-97) at Waukegan, Illinois. Douglas was born in Scotland but came to Canada in 1836, thence to Vermont in 1838, then on to Waukegan in 1844, where, after a few years' adventuring in California, he established a small nursery. The nursery grew apace, and after a few years Douglas was growing forest tree seedlings by the millions with a special bent toward coniferous trees, on which he soon became America's chief authority. He planted forest trees in many midwestern states, and was a consulting forester for many large enterprises in all parts of the Union. At one time he was a large grower of *Catalpa speciosa* in Kansas.

Many new western trees were first grown, in quantities at least, at the Waukegan nurseries; in particular the Douglas spruce, the Colorado blue spruce, and the beautiful concolor fir, not to mention blocks of the commoner white spruce, and the Norway spruce. It was long the practice of the Waukegan nurseries to take contracts for planting forests of either coniferous or deciduous trees, in which they prepared the ground, set the trees, and kept track of them until they were established. They once planted 3,000,000 catalpa trees in one county in Kansas.[12] Few other nurs-

---

[12] *Garden and Forest,* v: 274.

eries in America have named so many horticultural varieties of deciduous and coniferous trees; Mr. Douglas had a keen eye for any variation that would make a tree valuable.

Another notable contribution to American horticulture was made by the Waukegan nurseries under Robert Douglas. When he began his nursery work it was the practice of American nurserymen to import stocks for apples and pears, as well as of other trees, from Europe. Douglas began at once to grow his own stocks of apples and pears, though told by all that he could not succeed, and in 1863 was growing 50 acres of seedling fruit stocks; and so, though he is best known as a grower of forest trees, he has been a great benefactor of orchardists as a grower of stocks and trees of fruits.

The first settlers in Missouri were Frenchmen from Canada. French adventurers, trappers, and missionaries founded Ste. Genevieve in 1755, and St. Louis became a trading post in 1764. Undoubtedly seeds of apples and pears and of garden plants were planted by these French settlers as they were in Illinois and Indiana, although there seem to be few accounts of such plantings. Soon both French and Spaniards came from the lower Mississippi bringing grapes, peaches, roses, ornamental vines, and shrubs. Missouri became a part of the United States in 1803 through the Louisiana Purchase. The first American settlers were from Kentucky and Tennessee; and undoubtedly they planted gardens, but there appears to be nothing in print to show what they did.

Thomas Ashe, who visited St. Louis in 1806, speaks well of its horticulture. He says: 'The environs are full of gardens and fruit trees, which in the proper season must perfume the air and be highly pleasing.' One of the entertainments of the inhabitants, he tells us: 'is to roam in the fields and gardens after sunset, and enjoy the delightful odours of the flowers, and refresh themselves with fruits of exquisite taste and flavor.' [13]

Gardening had not advanced far in Missouri, when, in 1820, Captain Edmund Bacon, manager of Jefferson's farm at Monticello, visited the state to buy land. Fortified with a letter from Jefferson to Governor Clark, of Lewis and Clark expedition

[13] Ashe, *Trav. in Am. in* 1806, etc., p. 291.

fame, with whom he stayed in St. Louis, Bacon had a good opportunity to see this metropolis of the West. He says little about orchards and gardens, but from his account of the town itself, one would not expect much in the way of horticulture. At that time, Bacon says: 'St. Louis was a dingy little settlement, not much larger than a good negro quarter.' There was only one narrow street, three or four hundred yards long. The houses, we are told, were mostly old-looking, built of rock in the roughest manner possible. A few of them were plastered. They were all one story. The fences around their truck patches, Bacon wrote, 'were a kind of wicker-work made of posts stuck into the ground, and brush wattled into them.' [14]

Nurseries and fruit growing seem to have been started in Missouri by James Hart Stark, a Kentuckian, who came to Pike County, Missouri, in 1815. Stark, who was a son of Captain James Stark, at once planted a nursery and an orchard from seeds and cions brought from Bourbon County, Kentucky. The Pike County orchard of about 50 acres was the first commercial plantation in Missouri and brought buyers from afar, the crop often amounting to several thousand barrels. The nursery has been maintained by the descendants of this first Stark, enlarged from year to year, and is now one of the oldest in America to have had unbroken existence.

Although there was not much interest in agriculture in Wisconsin and Minnesota before 1860, what there was centered especially in grains, livestock, and vegetables. As in the other states of the Middle West, the French, who made the first settlements about their trading posts, planted grains, vegetables, and probably tried tree fruits without success. On the western shore of Lake Michigan, especially at Green Bay, apples, pears, and sour cherries were planted and grew lustily, supplying fruit to less fortunate settlers to the north and west.

There were few white settlers in either of these two states until after the Civil War. Those who came to practice farming found the climate too cold for the cultivation of tree fruits, though they could readily grow small fruits and even early hardy grapes, if

[14] Pierson, p. 32.

they gave them winter protection. They found such an abundance of wild raspberries, blueberries, strawberries, American plums, frost or river grapes, and Juneberries that they did not suffer from the lack of fruits. Vegetables of all the kinds grown in the northern states were easily raised and were as freely planted as in any other new state.

The first settlers in Wisconsin and Minnesota came from New York and New England. Ignorant of the cold winters, and of the prevalence of fire blight on apples and pears, they planted eastern varieties of tree fruits, nearly all of which quickly succumbed to cold or blight. Pioneers came to believe that tree fruits could not be grown in these states, a hasty conclusion that greatly delayed orcharding.

Peaches, sweet cherries, European plums, and pears were rarely successful in any part of either state. Early Richmond, Montmorency, and Morello sour cherries were grown by pioneers wherever the apple could be grown. Varieties of several American species of plums, some of which originated in this northern region, furnished the first settlers with plums.

There is well-authenticated record of the first market gardener in Minnesota. In 1854, when there were only 12 or 15 families in the settlement, Wyman Elliot came with his father to Minneapolis and began raising vegetables for sale. Later, his place became known as the 'Minneapolis Garden Nursery,' from which were sold fruit and ornamental trees, shrubs, and flowers. Elliot was a charter member of the state horticultural society founded in 1866.

One of the men whose unwearied feet took him as a pioneer to several states in the Middle West, and who planted gardens in at least two, was John S. Harris. He was a soldier in the Mexican War and then became a prospector for land in Illinois, Iowa, Wisconsin, and Minnesota. Finally he settled in La Crosse, Wisconsin, in 1851, as a market gardener, but in 1856 removed to La Crescent, Minnesota, and engaged in nearly every field of horticulture —in all so successfully that for nearly half a century he was one of the most noted horticulturists in the upper Mississippi Valley. Harris helped to organize the Minnesota State Horticultural Society and was proud of the fact that his was the first name on the roll of members. He used to boast, also, that he had tried in his orchard every variety of apple that gave promise of standing the cold climate of Minnesota.

Another pioneer from the East who made a name for himself in horticulture was Orville Morrell Lord, a New Yorker, who, in 1852, settled in Winona County, Minnesota. Lord's specialty in horticulture was native plums, concerning which he became widely known as an authority. He was the originator of the Rollingstone, one of the best of the American sorts. For many years he maintained a test orchard for native plums, growing all the varieties obtainable, and published the results of his experiments in *Farm, Stock and Home,* of which he was for some years the horticultural editor.

As in most of the states in the Middle West, French Canadians were the first fruit growers in Iowa. While the lands of what is now Iowa were owned by Spain and the inhabitants were all Indians of the Ioway tribe, Julien Dubuque, born in Canada, but of French descent, settled in 1783 near the Mississippi in the county that bears his name. Dubuque mined and smelted lead in the several regions on the Mississippi where lead is found, and became immensely wealthy. On the banks of the great river he built a fortified settlement about which he and the Canadians that followed him cultivated fields and orchards. He, or one of his compatriots, planted an apple orchard, or at least an apple tree; for, when English-speaking settlers came to Iowa in the 1830's they found an apple tree 14 inches in diameter that bore fine winter-keeping apples.

Another early French Canadian planter of fruit trees in Iowa was Louis Honoré Tesson, son of a St. Louis trader, who planted an apple orchard at the head of the Des Moines rapids in the Mississippi on the site of the present town of Montrose. It is reported that in 1799 Tesson formed a settlement near the mouth of the Des Moines River on a grant of land he had received from the Spanish Government. The terms under which the grant was made included planting and sowing seeds. He enclosed his house and, within the palisades, planted an apple orchard. When settlers came to the Territory, Tesson had long been gone and many of the trees were missing, but 15 were still bearing. The last was cut down in 1895. The site of the orchard is marked by a monument erected in 1930 by the Montrose Woman's Civic Club, built by a subscription raised by the club, the Iowa State Horticultural Society, the Historical, Memorial and Art Department, and by the public.[15]

George Davenport (see page 323) was one of the beginners of horticultural activities in Iowa as well as Illinois. From his orchards and gardens on Rock Island, while Iowa was still a territory, plants and seeds found their way to many Iowa homes. In particular, by example and precept, he started Antoine LeClaire, a half-breed, a friend, and an associate, on the road to horticultural fame in Iowa. LeClaire was the owner of a famous hotel and was postmaster in the early years of Davenport. About 1840, he imported 400 apples from Cincinnati which he planted within the limits of what is now Davenport.[16]

Henderson Lewelling (1809-78) is most notable of the early horticulturists in Iowa. He was Iowa's earliest nurseryman and the earliest planter of fruit trees. Iowa had been owned in turn by Spain, France, and the United States; and, as a part of the latter country, had been in the territory of Louisiana, Missouri, Michigan, and Wisconsin. It was to the last-named state that Lewelling had come in 1836 to found in what became Iowa territory in 1838 the town of Salem, where he planted his nursery and orchards.

This pioneer horticulturist, however, belongs to the nation rather than to Iowa alone. The son of Meshack Lewelling (see page 315), he began his tree planting as a youth in Salem, North Carolina. Henderson and at least two brothers, John and Seth, were nurserymen and orchardists.

The Lewellings spent only ten years or thereabouts in Iowa, but during this time they seem to have been most active. It is said that they made yearly trips to eastern states for nursery trees. In their Iowa orchard they planted 35 varieties of apples and a large assortment of pears, peaches, plums, cherries, and quinces. Through the Lewellings Salem became the nursery and fruit-growing center of early Iowa; and, until the Civil War, fruit and trees were distributed far to the north and west. Meanwhile, the population was doubling every decade, the demand for trees was growing in proportion, and Henderson Lewelling became so well-

[15] Pellet, pp. 5, 6.   [16] Ibid. pp. 7, 8.

to-do that before he left for the Pacific Coast in 1847 he had built an imposing stone house.

Another of the early nurserymen in Iowa, like the Lewellings pioneering in several states, was James Smith, a Kentuckian, who established a nursery in Illinois in 1834 and then moved to Iowa, where he started a nursery and orchard at Des Moines in 1847. At various times this energetic man had as many as seven nurseries in seven counties in the state. At the age of 70, in 1879, the tireless old nurseryman moved to Brookings, South Dakota, and planted another nursery.

Out of the score or more national figures in gardening in Iowa, the most notable was Gustavus Benson Brackett (1827-1915). His father, Reuben Brackett, a Yankee clockmaker in Unity, Maine, moved to Ohio to turn farmer and nurseryman, then made another move to Denmark, Lee County, Iowa, in 1841. Sixty-two years later, 1903, the younger Brackett, writing *A History of Horticulture in the Middle West* for the American Pomological Society, says of his father's moving: 'He located at Denmark, settled by three families from New Hampshire who had travelled across the country by wagon train. With half a bushel of apple seed washed by myself from pomace of a cider mill in sight of Cincinnati, my father started the first nursery in Lee County.'

Young Brackett joined his father in growing nursery stock and orchards in Lee County, but was interrupted by the Civil War. After he returned, as a Colonel on General Grant's staff, he specialized in orcharding, especially in pear culture, until called by the state to take charge of exhibits in several successive world's expositions. In these he distinguished himself by exhibiting in large numbers nearly perfect wax fruits. Later, at the age of 70, he became a worker in the United States Department of Agriculture, and, until his death in 1915, was an authority on the nomenclature of fruits.

There is little to say about gardening in Kansas, Nebraska, and the Dakotas in the years of this history. With the exception of Kansas, to which New Englanders came a little earlier to keep that state free from slavery, their settlement, by tillers of soil at least, had scarcely begun when the Civil War broke out. The Northerners in Kansas planted gardens of vegetables and flowers and tended them so assiduously that the Southerners who had settled there were astonished at the results. It was not then supposed that fruit and ornamental trees would thrive on the open prairie in this vast region, where now are many orchards and lawn trees.

Happily, two men in the early years of the settlement of Kansas had faith that it was worth while to plant trees and shrubs on prairie lands as well as along wooded rivers. These two are perhaps the founders of orcharding in Kansas. The earlier was G. C. Brackett, a brother of Colonel Brackett of Iowa, who in 1860 planted an orchard at Lawrence, Kansas, with trees from his father's nursery in Denmark, Iowa.

The second man to grow a nursery and an orchard in Kansas was Welcome Wells, living near Manhattan. At the beginning of the Civil War he had a commercial orchard of 40 acres; but the varieties were poor and, as he himself said, 'about all that was accomplished was to demonstrate that hardy fruits could be grown in Kansas.' After the war Wells planted a test orchard in Kansas and tried variety after variety, to the great enrichment of fruit growing in the prairie states.

An event of major importance for orcharding in the colder parts of the north-central states was the introduction of Russian fruits, the hardiest tree fruits under cultivation. As early as 1832, John Kenrick described two Russian apples, which quickly became standard sorts when the region under discussion was ready for orchards. The two were the well-known Oldenburg and Alexander. A few years later Red Astrachan and Tetofsky were brought from England, where they had been grown for a decade or two. These apples were the forerunners of a vast number of varieties of the common tree fruits, including apricots and mulberries, which had their origin in Russia.

Probably, Russian fruits would have received scant attention in America had it not been that in Wisconsin, Minnesota, Iowa, Kansas, and Nebraska, which were being settled in the years 1830-60, hardy Russian fruits could stand cold winters and hot dry summers. During the time covered by this history, few varieties were imported; but in 1870 the United States Department of Agriculture made importations of many varieties of the several fruits;

and, a little later, Professor J. L. Budd of the Iowa Agricultural College and Charles Gibb of Abbotsford, Canada, went to Russia, and large importations of apples, pears, cherries, plums, apricots, and mulberries were made. Few of the several hundred Russian fruits proved adaptable to the soil and climate of this country; and, after voluminous writings and discussions, Russian fruits came to little except to furnish a dozen or two fruits and many hybrids for the cold Northwest.

Toward the middle of the nineteenth century, one of the cheapest and commonest nursery plants was the osage orange, then used in hedges everywhere from the Gulf as far north as the peach is hardy. Wire fences were unknown and farmers in the prairie states found hedges cheaper than wooden fences and more enduring. For garden fences, 'every man taketh what liketh him best' as an old English gardener, Thomas Hill, wrote in his *Gardener's Labyrinth* in 1563. Then, as now, a score of evergreen and deciduous trees and shrubs were planted. For farms in America, however, two vigorous thorny plants were most suitable; these were the osage orange and the honey locust, of which the former was the favorite.

The osage orange hedge was almost the only fence farmers in the prairie states could afford. The plants grew like weeds and were set by the million. The rich green of the foliage and the large orange-like fruits made a handsome hedge. A native of Arkansas and Kansas, the osage orange was one of the many valuable plants brought back by the Lewis and Clark expedition. The Landreth Nurseries in Philadelphia were early and large growers of it in the East, but in the West it had a special champion. In 1833 Professor J. B. Turner, a graduate of Yale, came to Illinois to teach in Illinois College, which had just been founded. He was interested in agriculture and became an ardent believer in the value of the osage orange as a hedge plant, and for years spent much of his time writing and talking about it. By 1860, there were thousands of miles of fences in the Middle West made of this thorny tree, until eventually the wire fence was found to be cheaper and better. Professor Turner planted many other trees for the Middle West, both in his trial grounds and for sale from his nursery. He is said to have had the finest collection of ever-greens to be found in America at the beginning of the Civil War.

Countless artifices have been used to persuade people to plant trees. It would be hard to say how many trees LaFayette is supposed to have planted in his last tour of America. Presidents, governors, generals, and other distinguished men and women have, from the time of Washington, planted trees as memorials of one kind and another in every part of America; cemeteries have memorial trees; and there are trees on nearly every college campus to commemorate years of graduation. But all these many memorials put together are far fewer than the forest and fruit trees planted in every state in the Union on Arbor Day, the name applied to an annual tree-planting day in every part of the United States.

Arbor Day originated a few years later than the period covered by this history, but its originator was an early fruit grower in Nebraska. Julius Sterling Morton (1832-1902) was a New Yorker who moved to Michigan in 1834, and then on to Nebraska in 1854, where he entered politics and public life. He lived on a large farm near Nebraska City, upon which he planted 500 apple trees in 1859. Almost at once he began to sponsor a day for planting trees under the direction of agricultural societies. In 1872 he urged that the state set aside one day for tree planting, to be known as 'Arbor Day.' This the State Legislature did, designating 22 April, Morton's birthday, as the day. From Nebraska the idea spread to other states and to Canada. The day was observed at first by scattered farmers' organizations, but soon it was recognized the country over as a school festival.

13

THE SOUTH-CENTRAL AND GULF STATES

TENNESSEE and Kentucky were the first of the south-central states to be sufficiently well settled to enjoy the luxury of gardens. By 1860 fruit and vegetable growing was much further advanced in the northern states than in Tennessee and Kentucky, but in the matter of ornamental grounds, the latter states had far more and far better plantations. At the beginning of the Civil War, there were as many well-planted and well-cared-for grounds in these two states as in any other parts of the United States in proportion to the population.

Upon consideration, the reason is obvious. The rich valley lands of Tennessee and Kentucky were settled earlier and by an energetic, virile people from the Atlantic Coast. As early as 1810, more than 260,000 people had immigrated to these two states. Over 40,000 of them were slaves, who were a great economic asset in clearing and farming the new lands. The crops were far more diversified and valuable than in the states to the north. Here were grown not only corn, grains, fruits, and livestock, but the immensely valuable crops of cotton, tobacco, flax, and hemp, which, with slave labor, often brought fortunes in a few years. The ideal life in the South, of which so much has been written, came nearer existence, actually, in Tennessee and Kentucky in the decade or two before the Civil War than in any other of the southern states. It was a pleasant life; money was never lacking, in the pockets of landowners at least, and the well-to-do lived at ease in great houses surrounded by beautiful grounds.

There were not, at this time, or ever, nearly so good orchards as in the north-central states, where soil, climate, markets, and transportation were more suitable to fruit growing, but still there

was an abundance of fruit for home and local use. On every plantation there were home orchards of apples, pears, cherries, and
peaches. In many parts of these states peaches grew wild, often
the so-called Indian peaches, blood-red within, streaming with
juice. These fruits, at first, as in all newly settled lands in these
early years, were seedlings, though, as years went by, grafted trees
came from Virginia, and in time there were a few good nurseries.

All the vegetables and flowers that would grow in the temperate
and hospitable climate of these two states were quickly introduced; and with the trees, shrubs, and vines native to the region,
among which were live oaks, magnolias, rhododendrons, catalpas,
and the southern hemlock, horticulture was well developed. Several features of home grounds were more marked than in most
other states, even in the South. Usually there was a race course for
the blooded horses so common in Tennessee and Kentucky.
Judging from descriptions, one might count upon a greater number of arbors, pergolas, and summerhouses than on the grounds
of estates to the north and east; and conspicuous objects in the
landscapes of most large places were the family graveyards, with
monuments and ornamental plantings.

Perhaps we have given too favorable a view of the gardens in
these states, especially in the first fifty years after their settlement.
(The first permanent settlement by Whites was made in Tennessee by Englishmen on the Wautauga River in 1769; in Kentucky,
at Harrodsburg in 1774.) By contrast, the reports of three notable
travelers seem to indicate that fruits and vegetables were little
grown generally in the period of this history.

Ashe, who passed through Kentucky at the turn of the nineteenth century, wrote that the people in the settlements 'ate salt
meat three times a day and had no fruits or vegetables.' They
drank 'ardent spirits,' he relates, 'from morning until night.' [1]
Ashe is not considered a very reliable reporter, but Harriet Martineau, who was most accurate in her statements, gives some sub-
stantiation to Ashe in the matter of a lack of fruits and vegetables.
She spent some time in the South and writes in her *Society in
America*,[2] 'corn was more valuable than gold—everything eats corn
from slave to chicks.' A still later visitor reports the same condi-

[1] Ashe, *Trav. in Am. in* 1806, p. 241.
[2] Martineau, *Soc. in Am.*, II: 43-4.

tions. Frederick Law Olmsted, traveling in the south-central states in the 1850's, found that country people lived almost wholly on salt pork and corn bread, with now and then bacon and hominy. Sometimes the fare was made a little more tasty with turnip greens, coffee sweetened with molasses, and sweet potatoes in season. Fruits and vegetables, he wrote, were generally neglected by the 'poor whites' and Negroes.[3]

The earliest record of gardening in Tennessee and Kentucky seems to have been made by Gilbert Imlay, who traveled through these states in the 1790's and several times mentions orchards and gardens. He tells us—hardly possible to believe when Indians were still on the rampage and food hard to get—that 'gardening constituted one of the amusements of both sexes. Flowers and their genera form one of the studies of our ladies, and the embellishment of their houses with those which are known to be salutory constitutes a part of their employment.'[4] Imlay mentions a surprising number of flowers then being cultivated in these states—practically all that then grew in Virginia and Carolina gardens.

To these busy pioneers, no doubt, fruits and vegetables appeared to contain so little to sustain hard-working men that they were not worth the labor of growing. In the South, corn, beans, turnips, and later sweet potatoes were cultivated, but the pumpkins, parsnips, potatoes, and cabbages grown in New England and stored for winter were seldom to be found supplementing the hearty corn and pork. On the farm such spring greens as dandelion, cowslip, lambs-quarter, and pigweed, which could be had for the picking, were eaten. Wild berries were abundant in spring and summer; and, as farming advanced, apples and peaches were raised for cider and brandy. Indeed, there was a prejudice against people so 'elegant' as to eat garden vegetables or to cultivate strawberries or raspberries; in 1840 the Whigs, in conducting the 'log cabin, hard cider' campaign of Harrison against Van Buren, attacked the latter for using public money to raise 'garden sass' for the White House table.

Gardening with fruits and vegetables, as one might expect, followed as soon as settlements were established, but it is a surprise to find that in many early settlements ornamental gardens were

[3] Olmsted, p. 396.
[4] Imlay, *Description of the Western Territory of the United States*, etc., p. 156.

planted by a few, while the places were little removed from wilderness trading posts. Cuming, who visited Louisville in 1808, 20 years after the first house had been built, gave a pleasant account of the town, which he found most delightfully situated 'on an elevated plain to which the ascent from the creek and river is gradual, enough to admit of hanging gardens with terraces, which doctor Gault at the upper, and the two Messrs. Buttets at the lower end of the town have availed themselves of in laying out their grounds very handsomely and with taste.' [5]

The growth and prosperity of Nashville and Memphis in the first quarter of the nineteenth century were phenomenal. Nashville long took the lead, and early in its history gardening was recognized as a chief recreation of wealthy men. Fine country places sprang up about these cities, which compared favorably with estates in Virginia and the Carolinas. Of orchards in these early years of the century, it is to be supposed that seedling trees were the rule here, and that named varieties, if any, came from Virginia.

In the mountainous hinterland west of the cotton lands—in the Carolinas, Kentucky, Tennessee—what we now call the Southern Highlands, gardening hardly existed in this period nor has there been much down to the present. In these regions corn was and is the staple crop. Hogs could then, and can even now, be raised for the trouble of turning them loose to forage in the forests. Corn is easily stored, to be ground as needed, and pork can be salted or smoked and the fat used in many forms of cooking. Why raise a garden?

The woods furnished the pioneers 'sallets' of cress, poke-weed, cowslips, and various other greens; and, as time went on, after the first settlements in the vast mountain regions of these states, there was a fenced-in garden patch in which were cabbage, collards, turnips, beets, pumpkins, cushaws (squashes), and melons. Roasting ears were taken from field corn. Beans in variety were obtained by the first settlers from the Indians, the taste running almost wholly to the pole which could be eaten as string beans or shelled and dried for winter. Herbs, such as sage, thyme, the

[5] Cuming, p. 234.

mints, and rue, were grown for cookery and medicine. Pumpkins were sliced and dried in the sun or before the fireplace. Onions and peppers could be found in some households all the winter, but winter vegetables were to most mountaineers a luxury.

The only fruits planted in the highlands of these states were apples and peaches, usually seedlings. Wild blackberries, strawberries, huckleberries, and grapes furnished vitamins in summer, and thrifty housewives presumably dried them as they did further north. Covered wagons filled with green and crimson apples are a familiar sight in the mountain towns of this region now and no doubt apples have been grown from the first, the trees unpruned, ungrafted, untilled, uncared for in any way.

Who can now tell whether the wives of the first settlers in the Southern Highlands grew flowers? Probably not many. In order to exist at all, early settlers had first to think of food crops, and these had to be those most nutritious and most easily grown. It was only after a time that women brought from the coast settlements bulbs of tulips, daffodils, and a few of the most common and most easily grown garden flowers. After all, in a land where azaleas and rhododendrons crowd the cabins, and where the woods are full of wild flowers and a hundred species of ornamental vines, shrubs, and trees, it is difficult to compete in the garden with wild plants.

One vegetable was probably more often raised in Kentucky and Tennessee in their early settlements than in any other parts of the South, common though it was in all the southern colonies. This was the gourd, which was grown not as a food, but to furnish receptacles. To bring copper, iron, brass, or other metals across the mountains from Atlantic ports was prohibitive in cost. The hard-shelled gourd furnished dippers, dishes, food containers, seed containers, ornaments, and, in its diverse shapes and sizes, a great variety of other things. It would have been hard for a woman to keep house without an assortment of gourd utensils, most of which she grew in her own 'patch.'

Accounts of orchards and nurseries in the south-central states are pitiably scant and fragmentary. The first grafted trees in Tennessee and Kentucky came from Virginia and North Carolina, as did the nurserymen, who, in turn, sold top-worked varieties to the states south and west. A good many trees came south from Ohio

and Indiana, where good nurseries quickly followed early settlements. In all these southern states, the silk industry is occasionally
mentioned. To grow silk worms there must be mulberry trees,
and these were probably grown in local nurseries. Wherever cotton could be grown, figs might be planted with assurance of fair
success in growing them to be eaten fresh, if not to be dried. Fig
trees probably came from local nurseries.

The first orchard of grafted trees planted in the south-central
states seems to have been that of Captain James Stark, who came
to Kentucky in 1785, a year after the first settlement was made at
Harrodsburg. Captain Stark's orchard was at Hutchinson, Bourbon County. A nursery is mentioned in the early annals of Kentucky as existing in Anderson County, owned by John Lightfoot.
In 1790 there was a nursery of state-wide fame in the Great Bend
of the Kentucky River planted by Edward Darnaby, a nurseryman
from Virginia. He grew 'all the tree fruits and some grapes.' One
wonders what the grapes were and how well they succeeded.

For that matter, one wonders what the cherries and pears were,
for neither of these fruits grows well south of the Ohio River,
if we except the Kieffer, Le Conte, and Garber pears, none of
which were grown until after the middle of the century. Most of
the peaches were seedlings, as were many of the apples. The apples
grown between 1800 and 1860 were mostly Early June, Summer
Rose, Early Harvest, and in the last years Red Astrachan for summer. The late varieties were House, Willow Twig, Limber Twig,
Rambo, Bullock, Ralls or Rawles Janet, Nickajack, Romanite,
Carthouse, Buckingham, Winesap, Paragon, Pennock, and Smokehouse, all varieties well adapted to southern regions.

Kentucky was the home of the most notable single experiment,
whether by an individual or by corporate authority, in growing
grapes in the United States in the whole period of this history.
Out of the many attempts to establish the wine grape in America
on a profit-making basis, a venture in Kentucky, made by John
James Dufour, was the most carefully planned and best carried on
of any. Certainly it was the most romantic. And, certainly, the in-
tentions of the leaders of the enterprise were the most commend-
able. Dufour believed that the use of wine would lessen intemper-

ance from drinking distilled liquors. He became interested in grape growing in America through reading accounts of the Revolutionary War in Swiss papers. He was struck, in particular, as he tells us in his *Vine Dresser's Guide*, by the complaints of French officers that wine was not to be had in the American colonies. It seemed to him, he says, that since much of the continent was in the same latitude as the wine-producing countries of Europe, with similar climate and soils, there were no reasons why grape growing and wine making could not be successfully carried on here too.

Dufour, the second of that name then living, landed in Philadelphia in August 1796, and immediately began to look up land for grape growing in the newly founded United States. During the next three or four years he visited every part of the country in which there were settlements, from Massachusetts, New York, Pennsylvania, and Virginia, westward to the Mississippi. His object was to visit the vineyards then in existence, or places where grape growing had been tried, and to look up localities that seemed suitable for his venture. The task was discouraging, for he found no place in the entire country a good vineyard, and scarcely a dozen healthy plants of European wine-making grapes. Most of the places where vineyards of European grapes had been planted were covered by forest undergrowth or rank weeds. A few European varieties, the vines poor specimens, were growing in gardens in New York and Philadelphia.

Only at one place was wine being made. French settlers at Marietta, Ohio, were making some wine from wild grapes growing on islands in the Ohio River. These, of course, were native grapes, but not so recognized by the French, who believed them to be derived from French stock once grown at the old French fort, Duquesne.

To these poor vineyards there was one exception. At Spring Mill, on the Schuylkill, near Philadelphia, there were a few vines being grown by a Frenchman, Peter Legaux, which seemed to Dufour to be most promising. This vine of promise was the Cape, the history of which is worth recording. From grapes obtained from Legaux, including the Cape, Dufour was able to begin his grand experiment to provide the American people with wine to take the place of whiskey, rum, peach brandy, and apple jack, distilled liquors which were making drunkenness intolerable in the new country.

Dufour chose as the most favorable spot for his experiment a piece of land in the Great Bend of the Kentucky River, some twenty-odd miles from Lexington. He then organized 'The Kentucky Vineyard Society,' which he says was 'an organization for the culture of the grape in Kentucky.' The society was organized in 1798; and in January 1799 Dufour went to Philadelphia and bought 10,000 grape vines and some fruit trees. Of grapes there were about 35 varieties, planted in the spring of 1799, on 5 acres of land on the Association's property at Great Bend. In 1801 some 17 of Dufour's relatives came to join in the enterprise. The grapes did not thrive, the Kentucky Vineyard Company failed, and, after a lingering death, the Dufour vineyard reverted to the wild.

It was thought that soil and climate in Kentucky might not be favorable, and in 1802 another plantation was made in Vevay, Indiana, where the company had the privilege, granted by Congress, of buying 2500 acres of land. Here, again, there was failure, only the Cape or Alexander growing well. In 1835 the Vevay planters gave up.

Perhaps the best result of Dufour's work with grapes came from a book, *The Vine Dresser's Guide,* which he published in 1826. It is an account of what he saw on his tour of inspection of vineyards in the United States, with advice on how to improve grape growing in the country. But the book was a poor thing for those who wanted to plant grapes; they could get little information that was helpful. Kentuckians were not inspired to plant grapes.

As in other states in the South, physicians in Tennessee and Kentucky grew a wide assortment of plants for medicinal use. Some of these constituted quite notable botanic gardens. One such was that of Dr. Darius Waterhouse, Washington, Rhea County, Tennessee. In his garden were grown rhubarb, elecampane, rue, mustard, horseradish, mullein, dittany, aloes, squills, horehound, sweet fennel, peppermint, coriander, digitalis, thyme, and other medicinal herbs. The Waterhouse estate was noted far and wide, also, for its vegetable garden, ornamental plantings, and summer-houses.[6]

Many homes contained copper stills for the making of essences and perfumes. Probably the women most often tried their hand at making rose water, for which one may find several recipes in private notebooks and diaries. At Belair, near Nashville, Tennessee, the home of William Nichol, built in 1838, it was a custom to give a bottle of rose water to departing guests. The Belair rose water thus became famous.[7] This seems a small matter in horticultural history, but rose water, perfumes, and distilled essences require such great quantities of flowers that without slaves to care for the plants and gather the flowers the preparations could not have been made. Belair is also important to gardeners in Tennessee because of a Scotch gardener, Daniel McIntyre, who early came to take care of the grounds and greenhouses. He imported many rare plants, which were freely distributed within the state. He and his descendants contributed much to gardening in Tennessee.

The first frame house in the great territory west of the Allegheny Mountains was that of Governor William Blount,[8] built in Knoxville in 1792. Here was born on 1 June 1796, the State of Tennessee, from which the Blount House has been called 'The Cradle of the State.' It was probably also the cradle of gardening in East Tennessee. The Blounts belonged to a family of wealth and prominence in North Carolina; and, sooner or later, Governor Blount brought to Knoxville all the fruits, vegetables, herbs, shrubs, and flowers that gardeners grew in the older state. In its early years, the house was placed in the center of commodious grounds, which extended to the river in terraces. There old-fashioned shrubs and flowers bloomed in profusion. The garden at the rear was laid out in rectangular beds in which fruits and flowers vied in luxuriant profusion.[9]

Another of the very early gardens of East Tennessee was Rocky Mount, the home of William Cobb, at Kingsport. The house was of white oak logs, built in 1770. At the right was an 'orchard of apples, plums, cherries, pears, and quince trees.' This must have been one of the earliest orchards in the state. Rocky Mount, how-

---

[6] *Tenn. Hist. of Homes and Gardens*, p. 98.
[7] Ibid. p. 195.   [8] Ibid. p. 65.   [9] Ibid. p. 65.

ever, seems to have been most noted in pioneer days for its herbs. In the flower garden were all the old-fashioned annuals and perennials. From the orchards and gardens planted by William Cobb, it may be supposed that all Tennessee sooner or later benefited from the distribution of seeds, cuttings, and cions.

Still another of the old houses notable for its gardens in this part of Tennessee was Old Ireland, established as the home of John Rhea, in his day prominent in government, and the largest landowner and wealthiest man in the state. The place was noted for its 'Formal Flower Garden . . . boxwood gardens, and gay flowers'; also for a 'cocoonery lot from which the Rhea sisters made silk for their dresses.' [10]

Out of the many other estates of this region, perhaps as notable an example as any from a horticulturist's point of view, was Elmwood, the home of Charles Fleming Keith, built in 1819 at Athens. Eventually there was a beautiful garden, admired in later years for its borders of box. The place was said to have been laid out from plans made by L'Enfant, whose work in Washington is so well known.[11]

The home of John Clemens, father of Mark Twain, founded in 1825 or 1826, at Jamestown, was noted for its orchards and flowers.

On the grounds of President Andrew Johnson's old home, at Greenville, is a willow tree said to have been grown from a cutting of a tree growing at the grave of Napoleon at St. Helena.

The earliest garden, and long the most notable one, in middle Tennessee, was at Travelers' Rest, the home of James Robertson, one of the founders of Nashville. The house was the first brick one in the Cumberland region. The Robertsons had come from North Carolina to east Tennessee, thence to Nashville, bringing with them in the two moves the vegetables, flowers, and herbs of the older state; from these the gardens of middle Tennessee were early supplied.

One of the fine early gardens near Nashville was at Belle Meade, laid out in 1806 by John Harding, lover of horses, who developed the first thoroughbred breeding establishment in America.[12] A gardener from Switzerland soon took charge of the grounds and

10 Ibid. pp. 93, 111.   11 Ibid. p. 43.   12 Ibid. p. 125.

gardens, bringing them to so high a state of perfection that, together with the rolling acres, its race track, and fine horses, the place became known as the 'Queen of the Southern Estates.'

Belmont was another of the many famous places near Nashville in the Old South. The estate dates back to two military tracts of 640 acres, grants for which were issued by North Carolina in 1784. The Belmont mansion was built in 1850, at which time the house and grounds were considered among the finest in America. The ornamental ground covered 180 acres, features of which were a woodland, deer park, orchards, flower and vegetable gardens, formal gardens of shrubs and flowers, and walks bordered with magnificent box. There were three greenhouses, 300 feet in length, one of the specialties of which was a large collection of camellias. In a pool, with fountains that were works of art, plants of *Victoria regia,* the red-flowered, royal water lily, said to have been the first to flower in the United States, were grown.[13] In the greenhouse, tropical fruits and hothouse grapes were grown as well as flowers. A high water tower supplied water for irrigation.

The grounds of President Johnson's home have been mentioned. Those of two other Presidents from Tennessee are worthy of note for their gardens. The Nashville house of President James K. Polk, called 'Polk Place,' purchased in 1840, four years before he became President, was surrounded by a bluegrass lawn on which were fine shade trees, flowers, and shrubs, cared for under the eye of Mrs. Polk. The flower garden in its prime was noted, in particular, for its pinks, phloxes, jasmines, and lilies.

Most celebrated of the estates of the three Tennessee Presidents, however, was Andrew Jackson's 'The Hermitage.' In 1791 'Old Hickory' bought a tract of land 13 miles from Nashville, built a house, and planted orchards and gardens. At this early date Jackson was unable to make Hunter's Hill, as he called the place, an especially fine estate, and in 1795 financial difficulties caused him to sell this plantation; in 1805 he bought the land on which the Hermitage now stands. Here he lived in a clutter of log houses until after the War of 1812, when, his fame and fortune in the ascendant, he built a brick house that is a part of the present Hermitage Mansion.

13 Ibid. p. 133.

Plantings at the Hermitage are especially noteworthy for beautiful trees, many of which were planted under the supervision of the owner. There are 28 species on the grounds, most of them native, constituting an arboretum of the trees of middle Tennessee, with some from other states, and a few foreign species. The magnolias, walnuts, hickories, redbuds, and dogwoods are all especially good specimens. A feature of the grounds is a double row of cedars lining the guitar-shaped drive leading from an iron entrance gate to the mansion. There was, also, a fine vegetable and flower garden. The grounds and gardens are said to have been laid out by Ralph E. W. Earl.

An estate in middle Tennessee, Clifton Place, Wales, Giles County, was laid out by an architect and landscape gardener from abroad. The place was founded by Tyree Rodes in 1809; an English gardener was brought over in 1812. The garden of Clifton Place, in the years of the Old South, was among the finest.

The gardens in west Tennessee for the period covered by this history are fewer and not so remarkable as those in the middle and eastern parts of the state, as would be expected, since settlements and developments came much later. Memphis, however, was on the site of an old Spanish fort where there were orchards and gardens.

Thomas Ashe visited Memphis in 1796 and describes a Spanish-made garden that adorned Spain's Fort, San Ferdinand, on Chickasaw Bluff. After describing the fort and its site, he writes: 'The land is as rich as possible; and in a garden belonging to the garrison, all kinds of fruits and vegetables succeed to a perfection seldom obtained elsewhere.' Again, 'the gardens and improvements are elevated and extreme.' [14] These two statements give evidence that gardening began early in western Tennessee, and that forts of any nationality, if garrisoned long, were often centers of agriculture and horticulture.

Two features of west Tennessee are noteworthy. Box grew especially well, and in many of the old gardens of this region there are magnificent box borders and specimen plants. The Meux Place, Stanton, Haywood County, has a walk 150 feet long, bor-

---

[14] Ashe, *Trav. in Am. in* 1806, etc., pp. 297-8.

dered with box over a century old, 15 feet high, 10 feet wide. At
the Pillars, Bolivar, Hardeman County, the home of Major John
H. Bills, is a box plant 17 feet high and 55 feet in circumference,
more than a hundred years old.[15] Another of the features of west
Tennessee gardens are living cedar summerhouses, much like similar summerhouses made of box in Virginia. In these houses,
cedars are closely planted in squares or circles. Within, branches
are smoothly clipped, thus making a dense, green, aromatic wall.
The boughs above thickly interlace and provide protection against
sun and rain.

Gardening in Kentucky differs little from that in Tennessee.
Since the state was settled and developed a little later than Tennessee, it might be expected in its earlier years to be somewhat
behind the older state in its horticulture. Tennessee, farther
south, is a little richer in the southern flora of fruits, vegetables,
and ornamentals. The Bluegrass Country in Kentucky has better
lawns. Bluegrass, a native of all North Temperate regions where
grass can be grown, is at its best in the cooler parts of these two
states, and, with rock fences built in slave time, gives landscapes
of both states the look of England.

Ashe visited Lexington, Kentucky, about 1806 and says of its
horticulture: 'Gardens produce with great and excellent abundance. Melons, cucumbers, etc. grow in the open air, without
manure or attention. Grapes cluster in the woods and peaches and
pomegranates flourish in cornfields.' [16] But Ashe, newly arrived
from England, was a bit confused. He saw native grapes, no doubt,
in the woods, and corn might have been grown in peach orchards,
or wild peach trees may have been left in cornfields, but what
plant he found flourishing in cornfields and mistook for the pomegranate it is impossible to say.

Lexington was in 1800 the outstanding city in Kentucky in
wealth and culture, and in or near it were many fine gardens.
Most noted was Henry Clay's Ashland, the grounds and gardens
of which were planned by Major L'Enfant. Clay was often, in the
battles of his varied political career, 'tempted to become a quiet

[15] *Tenn. Hist. of Homes and Gard.*, p. 305.
[16] Ashe, *Trav. in Am. in* 1806, etc., p. 195.

country gentleman.' In Clay's *Private Correspondence* he wrote in 1830: 'My attachment to rural occupation everyday acquires more strength, and if it continues to increase another year as it has the last, I shall be fully prepared to renounce forever the strife of public life.'

Not far from Ashland is Mansfield, noted for house and garden, and built by Henry Clay for his son, Thomas Hart Clay. The land purchase dates back to 1784. It was bought by Henry Clay in 1800.

Gardening was at its best about Lexington from 1840 to 1860, but there are no discoverable features of it that stand forth as remarkable except good planning and fine finish in workmanship. A score of fine places are described by writers, some of them dating back to 1800, and as many more might be named for other parts of what is known in Kentucky as 'The Bluegrass.'

Near Bardstown, Nelson County, is Federal Hill, the house in which Stephen Collins Foster wrote *My Old Kentucky Home.* The estate was founded by John Rowan in 1783; the house, one of the three earliest brick houses built in Kentucky, was built in 1795, and from then throughout the period of this history was of note for its park-like grounds, its bluegrass lawns, its great variety of native trees, and its gardens of vegetables, herbs, and flowers. In the old days Federal Hill was a place from which were distributed a great variety of horticultural plants.

In the vicinity of Louisville are a great number of beautiful estates, a few of which are worthy of note. One of these was the home of President Zachary Taylor. The estate was an original land grant to President Madison, who, in the 1780's, gave it to Colonel Richard Taylor, father of President Taylor. The original mansion was built in 1785. Almost at once the place became a center of horticultural interest, noted in the years before the Civil War for twin giant bald cypresses, a large ginkgo, which must have been one of the first in Kentucky, and fine specimens of box.

One of the oldest homes in Louisville was the Gwathmey place, founded by John Gwathmey, who came to Louisville at the beginning of the nineteenth century. The original house was built in 1806 and was the first brick house in the city. The house with its lawns, its huge forest trees, and its plantings on lawns and in gardens made this one of the show places of old Louisville—an inspiration to early planters of lawns and gardens.

Most of the old gardens have vanished—who planned them, what was in them, and what they looked like in their best days are matters unrecorded. One can only say the splendid gardens in Kentucky at present bespeak a worthy past.

John Law's notorious West India Company made feeble attempts to grow fruits and vegetables on their plantations on the Mississippi as early as 1718, but with the bursting of the 'Mississippi Bubble' the orchards and gardens disappeared. Le Page du Pratz, a Frenchman, went to the Louisiana territory in 1718 with a colony of 800 men, sent by the West India Company, and established a number of agricultural colonies. He remained there for 16 years in charge of these plantations. Out of this experience came his *History of Louisiana* in 1758, which contains the first account of the agricultural possibilities of Louisiana and Mississippi, but in which there appears little of note regarding horticultural plants. Of the plants mentioned nearly all have disappeared; the olive and date are wholly lost.

When Charlevoix visited New Orleans in 1722 it was a 'wild lonely place' with about a hundred huts set down among trees and underbrush; but shortly the town began to grow and soon gained ascendancy over other Gulf settlements. Later, the yards, surrounded by sharp-pointed picket fences, were well planted with fruits, shrubs, and flowers, with vegetables in a rear garden. The streets were planted with sour orange trees, which loaded the hot, moist air with heavy perfume. Slaves vended fruits and vegetables from near-by plantations, although the grosser vegetables, as potatoes, turnips, and the hardy apples and pears, came down the Ohio from faraway Virginia, Ohio, Illinois, and the upper Mississippi. One suspects that until cotton brought wealth in the nineteenth century, horticulture received scant attention in New Orleans.

About New Orleans Charlevoix saw groves of oranges growing well; orchards of figs, some peaches, and apples; but the olive, date, and grape did not thrive. He saw a date palm 30 feet high in New Orleans, a staminate plant that produced no fruit. He made the significant remark: 'But little pains as yet have been taken to introduce into this country, though so thickly settled, the ornamental and useful plants which it is calculated to sustain.'

The agriculture of these states of the lower Mississippi at the time of Thomas Nuttall's visit in 1819 seemed to be almost wholly concerned with sugar cane and cotton. Gardening and orcharding had small place in the domestic economy of the people; though Nuttall may have expected too much or have been there at a poor season of the year, for gardens there certainly were in 1819.

One of the early accounts of horticulture in the Gulf states was that written by William Bartram (see page 91). He records that at the confluence of the Coosa and Tallapoosa Rivers, in Alabama, he saw several large apple trees planted by the French who had made settlements in Alabama in 1702. In 1777, in a garden in Mobile, he found the yam, *Dioscorea Batatas*, under cultivation. At Pearl Island, near New Orleans, there were peaches, figs, grapes, plums, and other fruits 'in the utmost degree of perfection.' In a plantation near Baton Rouge, on the Mississippi, he found many useful and curious exotics, particularly the tuberose, 'which grew from five to seven feet high in the open ground, the flowers being very large and abundant.' [17]

Through the Louisiana Purchase in 1803, the United States acquired from France a vast tract of land in the Mississippi Valley. In the region, three states—Mississippi, Louisiana, and Arkansas—are producers of cotton, and soon after the land was acquired cotton was much planted, especially in the rich soil of the Mississippi delta. There had been plantations under French, British, and Spanish rule, but the wealth of the first owners had been insignificant compared to that coming from the new cotton plantations.

Cotton culture did not reach its zenith until 1840 but continued to be exceedingly profitable up to the Civil War. With the access of riches from 1800 to 1860, a great number of fine plantation houses, and some town houses, were built in all parts of the Mississippi cotton belt. The Victorian movement against classicism had not yet reached the South, and the admirable houses were mostly of the Greek Revival type, such as now remain museum pieces; these might have been surrounded by lawns and gardens, but seldom were, through lack of taste on the part of their owners.

[17] Bartram, William, pp. 421, 427.

The climate and soil of these states are as well adapted to the production of fruits, vegetables, and flowers as those of Georgia and the Carolinas; but as settlements, except along the coast and at the mouth of the Mississippi, were made much later, early garden history is scant and fragmentary. The fact that the region in which these states are located was successively under the flags of France, Spain, Great Britain, and the United States delayed permanent stability until other states of the South were prosperous commonwealths.

Indeed, the possibilities of gardening were far from being realized in Mississippi and Louisiana in the period of this history. In every division of horticulture, these states fell far short of their sister states to the east and north. The taste of the people of the region must be blamed for the shortcomings in horticulture; for, in a soil and climate where the live oak and magnolia flourish; where the orange, the lemon, and the pomegranate bear fruit; where the artichoke and okra, as well as the vegetables of the North, and a thousand shrubs, vines, and flowers are now grown; surely there might have been fine gardens, had they been desired.

One of the vegetables of the Gulf states, okra, finds no other place in the world more suitable for its needs. It would be interesting to know who brought okra to America and when and whence it came. Could it have come from Africa on the slave ships? It is a favorite vegetable with Negroes and its name as well as its synonyms, gombo and gumbo, have the sound of Africa. The plant is a favorite food in Nubia, and it grows wild, according to the botanists, on the White Nile. At any rate it came to the New World in the colonial period, for Kalm saw it in Philadelphia in 1784, Jefferson mentions it as cultivated in Virginia in 1781, and M'Mahon lists it in 1806. Curiously enough, it is esteemed only in the South, though it can be grown in the North in warm soils wherever the muskmelon and watermelon ripen. In Louisiana and Mississippi, it is one of the commonest and best-liked inhabitants of the vegetable garden.

When the Americans took over Louisiana in 1803, the people of New Orleans could boast of their live oaks, magnolias, oranges, and myrtles; of roses that grew in prodigal abundance, 'literally embowered in roses,' as one visitor wrote in 1804; of sub-tropical vines, a score of species; and of their famous 'gallery gardens'— galleries enclosed in wrought iron over which vines climbed and within which flowers were planted. But there was almost no landscape gardening, or orchards, or vegetable gardens worthy of note. There were, it is true, a few exceptionally fine places that showed well what could be done in the soil and climate that produced in nature magnificent forests and wild gardens.

Fortescue Cuming made a voyage down the Mississippi in 1807 and gave an alluring picture of the gardens on the banks of the river as the boat approached New Orleans. After landing, he walked through fine orange groves, plucked fruit, then pushed off, and 'continued floating through a country lined with small plantations, and beautiful houses screened from the sun by orange trees, whose fruit we saw hanging everywhere in the greatest abundance.' He says: 'Here indeed the banks of the river have a beautiful appearance, elegant houses encompassed by orange groves, sugar plantations, fine gardens, shady avenues. . .' [18]

The Boré plantation at the beginning of the period under consideration was the show place of the sugar plantations. Etienne de Boré, a Frenchman, was the first man in Louisiana to make sugar, though rum and syrup had long been made from sugar cane grown on the delta of the Mississippi. A few years later this region was the sugar bowl of America, the wealth of cane growing helping greatly to supply the means to build mansions with fine grounds. The mansion of the Boré plantation was six miles from the cathedral in New Orleans, above the city on the left bank of the Mississippi. The following description of it was written by Charles Gayarre, who knew the place before and during the War of 1812:

This plantation was sagaciously and tastefully laid out for beauty and productiveness. The gardens occupied a large area, and at once astonished the eye by the magnificence of their shady avenues of orange trees. Unbroken retreats of myrtle and laurel defied the rays of the sun. Flowers of every description perfumed the air. Extensive orchards produced every fruit of which the climate was susceptible. By judicious culture there had been obtained remarkable success in producing an

[18] Cuming, pp. 331-2.

abundance of juicy grapes, every bunch of which, however, when they began to ripen, was enveloped in a sack of wire to protect them from the birds.[19]

Harriet Martineau, writing of a visit to the battlefield of New Orleans in 1837, presents a pleasant picture of gardening in the South at that time. She says:

. . . Gardens of roses bewildered my imagination. I really believed at the time that I saw more roses that morning than during the whole course of my life before. Gardens are so rare in America, that, when they do occur, they are a precious luxury to the traveller, especially when they are in their spring beauty. In the neighborhood of Mobile, my relative, who has a true English love of gardening, had introduced the practice; and there I saw villages and cottages surrounded with a luxuriant growth of Cherokee roses, honeysuckles, and myrtles, while groves of orange-trees appeared in the background; but not even these equalled what I saw, this warm 4th of May, on our way to the Battle-ground.[20]

Most of those who planted still liked the elaborate gardens of the rice and indigo plantations, with their parterres, avenues of live oaks, formal beds, walks bordered with box, and masses of azalea; or plantings of camellias, crape-myrtles, jasmines, and other flowers and shrubs—a blaze of color. On the other hand, the owners of many of the plantations in the cotton belt in the Mississippi Delta were bred in the states eastward, and in these newer gardens there seems to have been a mixture of the formal elements of the old school and of Jefferson's newer school.

In New Orleans and other French and Spanish towns, the Mediterranean tradition placed the house in a courtyard that was, in all the well-kept homes, an enclosed garden where fruits and flowers predominated, with perhaps a live oak and a palm or two. The houses in these places of luxury in vegetation were vine-clad, with galleries well covered with foliage to keep out the insistent sun. It is probable that late in this period, just before the Civil War, there were no other cities in the world that surpassed half a dozen of those between Charleston and New Orleans in the beauty of gardens of inhabitants who had wealth and leisure. And possibly,

[19] Gayarre, p. 608.
[20] Martineau, *Western Travel*, I: 274.

in America at least, there were no other cities in which the gardens of the homes of the poor were more unattractive.

About some of the fine homes were ample lawns, avenues of live oaks, pleached *allées* of box and holly, pleasing groups of a great variety of native and foreign trees and shrubs, and gardens of fruits, flowers, and vegetables. In all the world, gardening has seldom found so auspicious an environment as on the cotton plantations of the South between 1820 and the Civil War.

In this grand period of Mississippi and Louisiana cotton and sugar plantations, the best gardens in the region were in and near Natchez. There was much wealth in Natchez, and several men of means were enthusiastic patrons of horticulture. Some of the early grounds had been laid out by landscape gardeners from Europe, under whose supervision the Negro laborers, of whom there were an abundance in these years before the war, became expert gardeners. A visitor to Natchez in 1858 [21] states that the most beautiful place in the city and the region was Laurel Hill, owned by Dr. Mercer, a man of great wealth and many cultural attainments. Laurel Hill was some ten miles from Natchez, the road passing through many fine plantations, one of the finest being Gloster Place, the home of Winthrop Sargent, the first governor of the territory.

One feature of Laurel Hill was a hedge, 'miles upon miles of the Cherokee Rose,' described as having a breadth of 10 feet. Another was the magnolias, of which 'thousands lined the road.' The lawns were notable for their live oaks and magnolias. In the gardens were camellias 15 feet in height. There were hedges of Japanese quince and crape-myrtles, 20 feet in height; coral plants, pittosporums and similar greenhouse pets (with us) ran riot. Natchez, at the time, according to this correspondent, was the 'Persia of roses. In no other part of the Union have we ever seen them attain such perfection and beauty.'

This correspondent, on another page,[22] mentions the remarkable rose gardens of Andrew Brown, at Natchez, and then the beautiful estates of Governor Quitman at Monmouth; Mrs. Williams at Ashland; Mrs. Ogden at Kenilworth; Mrs. Dunbar at

---

[21] *The Horticulturist,* XIII: 71.   [22] Ibid. p. 126.

Hawthorn; Judge Boyd at Arlington; Major Chotard at Somerset; Mr. Duncan at Montrose; Mr. Marshall at Richmond; Dr. Duncan at Auburn; Mr. Shield at Montebello; Mrs. Elliot at Devereux; Mr. J. P. Walworth at The Burn; and Mr. Sargent's Clifton. In recent years many of these Natchez gardens have been restored—probably changed for the better, for they are less formal and more naturalistic, with a greater wealth of plant material now than they had a hundred years ago. There is enough of the old, however, to say that Natchez at that time had gardens unsurpassed by any others in the South.

Thomas Nuttall visited Natchez in 1819 and made notes on the horticulture of the region. He found the peach, pear, quince, and fig growing well. The peach grew spontaneously in Arkansas, to the north, and very well in the gardens of Natchez. Apples grew only fairly well. The cherry, currant, and gooseberry were thriving in plants but bore little fruit. The pomegranate and myrtle grew and fruited as well as in their native climate. Grapes were not a success. Oranges and lemons required some shelter. The olive could not be made to grow, nor could the date. Magnolias, royal palms, wax myrtles, sassafras, wild olives, and dogwoods were all commonplace plants, and every householder had his garden, large or small, in which the orange was the favorite fruit, and the rose, lily, and hibiscus the favorite flowers.[23]

One of the first large orchards in Mississippi was planted by Dr. M. W. Phillips in Hinds County, not far from Vicksburg. Phillips was a well-to-do farmer and cotton planter, who, in 1849, planted an orchard of 40 acres with more than 300 varieties of apples, peaches, plums, and apricots. He had a ready pen and set forth his experience in testing these fruits in several southern agricultural papers, especially in the *Southwestern Farmer,* published in Raymond, Mississippi, for which he was one of the editors from 1841 to 1846, as he was of the *Phillips Southern Farmer,* published in Memphis, Tennessee, from 1868 to 1872.

Alexander Gordon, a botanical collector and writer of note, who lived in Baton Rouge, Louisiana, described, in 1849, a garden owned by a Mr. Valcouran, in the Parish of St. James, 60 or 70 miles north of New Orleans, which he thought was 'unsurpassed,

[23] Nuttall, p. 301.

if equalled by any in the Union.' [24] This garden, according to Mr. Gordon, was but one of the many fine ones that then existed about New Orleans and for 130 miles up the Mississippi.

The Valcouran garden was of vast extent with a large collection of trees, shrubs, and flowers, together with hothouses and ornamental buildings. The landscape gardener who had laid out the place 'had designed it in the English style.' Mr. Gordon thought he had not been successful, and wrote that most of the large gardens in Louisiana at that time were in the formal French style, many of them 'very ornate.' 'The magnificent groves of live oaks and magnolias, with other choice trees and shrubs,' the writer says, 'with thinning out and the construction of walks and drives would have made perfect English pleasure grounds.'

As late as 1851, gardening in Mississippi and Louisiana, according to a horticulturist living in New Orleans writing under the pen name 'Sylvanus,' was not far advanced. He wrote at length about how well nature had adorned the region, but says that 'art has done little or nothing.' One of his sentences is: 'Notwithstanding all the praise bestowed upon the sunny south, in this part of it, at least, Landscape Gardening is half a century behind the age.' According to this writer, again: 'Even to the wealthiest planters, those who count their slaves by hundreds and their acres by thousands, and have the incomes of the nobles of England, a garden seems a superfluity, except indeed a kitchen garden, and even that is left to the care of some superannuated slave who can no longer work in the field.' [25]

There was, according to 'Sylvanus,' a public park six miles from the city where thousands flocked on Sundays 'to get away from the heat and stench of this dirtiest of all cities.' This public garden, we are told, possessed no horticultural or botanical attractions, but was a source of profit to the railroad company that owned a hotel where liquor was sold.

This writer devotes some space to the vegetable markets, which he says were poorly supplied. Cabbage was the most common vegetable; artichokes, okra, figs, and oranges could be had in abundance; strawberries were scarce; watermelons could be grown but were insipid; muskmelons were abundant and delicious;

[24] *Mag. of Hort.,* xv: 245-9.   [25] *The Horticulturist,* vi: 220-24.

olives and bananas could not be grown except as curiosities. Considering that the land was fertile beyond belief and everywhere in nature there was a riot of foliage, flowers, and fruits, it hardly seems that this report could be true; moreover the cooks in New Orleans had mastered the art of cooking, their cookery being famous the world over. Sylvanus may have been a Northerner who had not found his way into southern homes.

Another writer in *The Horticulturist* who made a tour of the southern states in 1858 finds little to commend in the gardens of Louisiana and New Orleans. He writes: 'As a general thing, gardening about New Orleans is not much studied.' There were no good public gardens, no horticultural society, but some beautiful plants gave him the impression that 'more variety of planting might be studied with advantage.' [26] The reason for this neglect was attributed to the transient character of the inhabitants, the city being occupied in winter very largely by people who sought to make a fortune and had no civic pride. The place, too, he thought was easily and constantly supplied with fruits and vegetables from the North by rail and from the tropics by boat.

When horticulture began in Arkansas is hard to say. Although the French established a settlement in 1685 at Arkansas Post, there are no records of cultivated plants of any kind about the post. Presumably, fruits and vegetables were planted, as they were wherever the French stayed long; but these early gardeners, if such there were, made no impression on later settlements. Arkansas formed a part of Louisiana until 1812, and horticulture there—such as it was—existed only in the settled parts of the territory in the southeast until a much later date. From 1812 to 1819 Arkansas was a part of Missouri Territory, and probably the rather sparse settlements were influenced in the northern part at least by the Missourians.

In the lowlands of the southeastern half of Arkansas, near the Mississippi especially, where the first settlements were made, horticulture has never been remarkable. In the northwestern half, particularly the Ozark region, where now there are thriving horticultural industries that raise all the hardy fruits and ornamental

26 Ibid. XIII: 70.

plants, there were few settlements until after the range of this
history. There were, before 1860, few nurseries and orchards; and
residents on the land, so far as records show, planted vegetables
and ornamentals sparingly. And yet there must have been a good
many people, for in 1836 Arkansas became a state, and agriculture
was its chief industry.

The horticulture of Alabama is very like that of Georgia on
the east and Mississippi on the west. In its early history, southern
Alabama was part of Florida, and the northern sector, most of the
state, belonged to France until 1763, when England came in possession. In the early settlements there were both Spanish and
French influences in horticulture: as in all the domestic economies
of the people, influences still to be traced in the older towns. At
the close of the Revolution, what is now Alabama became a part
of Georgia and remained so until 1802, when it was ceded to the
Territory of Mississippi, from which it was separated in 1817. In
1819 it became a state, closely molded in all its arts and industries
by the two older states of which it had been a part.

The first permanent settlement in Alabama was made by the
French at Mobile in 1711, and gardening in southern Alabama
probably began at once. Sooner or later the homes, the public
buildings, the ornamental gardens, and the home plantations of
sub-tropical fruits were scarcely inferior to those of any other city
in the South. There were few other places where horticulture
could flourish in southern Alabama, for this part of the state,
a hundred or more miles inland, was an almost unbroken forest
of long-leaf pine, with magnolias and live oaks bordering the
water ways.

North of this great forest region is a broad belt of what was once
chiefly prairie land. Here, cotton was the staple crop for half a
century before the Civil War, and brought wealth to the owners
of land. Although one can find less about them, here were the
same plantations with mansions and occasional fine grounds and
gardens that gave fame to other states in the cotton belt. For the
most part, the owners came from the Carolinas and Georgia and
brought with them the styles in gardening, the plant materials,
and the methods of culture that were in vogue in these older
states.

Northern Alabama, especially in the fertile Tennessee River Valley, which now has a large and flourishing nursery business, with some fruits and vegetables, did not assume importance in horticulture until after the Civil War. Meanwhile the region about Mobile has become one in which great quantities of fruits and vegetables are grown for northern markets, but these industries hardly existed within the period of this history. Hardly a state of great importance horticulturally until recent years, Alabama is now outstanding for the nurseries and fruit plantations in its northern part and its vegetables and beautiful ornamental grounds in the southern part.

Mobile has long been noted for its ornamental gardens, made world-famous in the last few years by the Bellingrath Gardens, twenty miles south of the city near Mobile Bay. But the same plant material has been for two centuries in the gardens of southern Alabama. It is doubtful if anywhere a greater abundance of camellias, azaleas, crape-myrtles, gardenias, oleanders, allamandas, hydrangeas, cypresses, magnolias, live oaks, to mention but the most commonly grown woody plants, could be found or have been longer grown. Sub-tropical and northern herbaceous plants are as commonly grown and have been grown as long. Other features of Mobile homes, besides the plant material, are the old iron gates, galleries, fences, and the stonework of houses and walls.

Southern Alabama has long been famous for its azaleas, which are rather more at home here than in any other part of America, not excepting Charleston. The citizens of Mobile believe that this plant was first brought to America by a Frenchman, named Langloise, in 1711, Langloise's grandfather, they say, having originally brought them from China to southern France. But it is probable that the azalea came to America at a much later date, introduced by two or three plant importers in South Carolina.

As romantic a tale as can be told of gardening in any part of the United States is that of a colony of Frenchmen who, followers of Napoleon Bonaparte, came to America in 1816 to find sanctuary from persecution from French royalists. For the most part they were officers from Napoleon's army, unskilled in the arts of peace, impoverished, and many of them no longer young. American sympathizers organized them to attempt some agricultural pursuit. It was decided that they should grow olives and grapes as main crops, with oranges and lemons in subsidiary plantings. The organization was completed in the autumn of 1816, the colony having decided to settle on the Tombigbee River in Alabama. Congress gave them a grant of four contiguous townships of land, some 10,000 acres, on the site of their choice, and the great adventure began.

In 1817, 150 French settlers left Philadelphia, taking with them an assortment of grape and olive plants. In a report to the government in 1821, it was said that there were in the colony 81 planters, 327 persons all told, 1100 acres under cultivation, on which were 10,000 grape vines. It was apparent from the first that olives could not be grown. After a few years, it became certain that the grape could not be made to flourish; and that the scant crops could not be used for wine because the grapes ripened in the heat of the Alabama summer. The colonists met failure at every turn and finally disbanded and scattered, after having spent $150,000 in the venture. Had they planted American crops, the settlement might have succeeded, poorly fitted as these French officers and their families were for farming of any kind.

The failure of the many earlier attempts to grow European grapes and olives in the East makes all the more pathetic the story of the Vine and Olive Colony on the Tombigbee. Yet from these French settlers came some good. Many of the leaders had been officers of high rank. They and their families were of good French blood. Some remained in Alabama; others scattered through several states, North and South. Wherever they went they carried a love of gardening.[27]

In 1536, more than four centuries ago, a Spanish explorer found an Indian village on the present site of San Antonio, Texas, which makes it one of the oldest communities in the United States. The place was named in 1691, after St. Anthony of Padua. Its recorded history goes back to 1718, when Spanish soldiers established a fort and settlement there, from which time there has been a military post under the flags of Spain, Mexico, Texas, the Confederacy, and

[27] For fuller accounts of this French colony, see *The Bonapartists in America*, A. B. Lyon, *Gulf State Historical Magazine*, March 1893; and *The Vine and Olive Colony*, T. C. McCorvey, *Alabama Historical Reports*, April 1885.

the United States. For more than two centuries there have been from one to several missions at San Antonio, about which, though there seem to be no descriptions of them, there must have been orchards and gardens, centers of distribution of fruits and vegetables to other missions, military posts, and settlements.

The region about El Paso was one of the earliest seats of agriculture and horticulture in Texas. When Baron Humboldt visited the Spanish colony of Juarez, soon after the turn of the nineteenth century, he had words of praise for the settlements on both sides of the Rio Grande, and mentions the vineyards. E. N. Plank, a keen botanical observer who visited southwestern Texas in the 1880's, found a rather high state of irrigated agriculture, with fields of grain, alfalfa, venerable pear trees two or more feet in diameter, the largest apricot trees he had ever seen, old apple orchards, quince trees, and large vineyards of Mission grapes. A Dr. Alexander had 30,000 vines of Mission grapes. The property on which he lived had been bought from the 'son of a priest who had entertained Baron Humboldt.' [28]

Perhaps gardening in Texas began even earlier than the dates mentioned. A farm at El Paso has been cropped, according to a statement in the *United States Census Bureau Report,* since 1540. Reading this, one suspects at once that orchards, vineyards, and gardens, big or little, have existed in Texas for 400 years, for wherever the Spaniards settled they planted gardens.

Permanent gardening and orcharding began in Texas in the Republic, which was founded in 1836 and lasted until 1845. Hither came several thousand Germans and other European settlers, skilled gardeners, laborious, eager to accumulate, and far better farmers and gardeners than Mexicans and Americans. The Germans not only settled in the towns near the coast, such as Galveston and Houston, but went inland and made several settlements of which New Braunfels, near San Antonio, possibly contributed most to horticulture, through the several botanical explorers who made this town their headquarters from time to time.

In 1839 at least four German naturalists whose names are well known in botany—Ernst, Lindheimer, Fendler, and Ervendberg— were engaged in market gardening near Houston, all of whom

[28] *Garden and Forest,* IX: 193.

eventually moved to New Braunfels. These men were botanical collectors for European and eastern American botanists, knew plants, practiced market gardening, and no doubt furnished material and information to settlers in the parts of Texas they visited. New Braunfels was but one of several towns settled by Germans, some founded while Texas was a republic. Many of these men were from German universities, who sought a political haven in the New World.

Nor were German naturalists the only ones who worked in Texas in these early years, forwarding knowledge of botany and stimulating a desire to cultivate plants wherever they went. To name botanists only, besides those mentioned, there were Jean Louis Berlandier, a Swiss who explored Texas for plants in 1828-30; Dr. John Milton Bigelow, botanist of the United States and Mexican Boundary Survey and the Pacific Railroad Survey, 1850-53; Dr. George Thurber, botanist on the United States and Mexican Boundary Survey, 1850-53; Charles Wright, who came to Texas in 1837 and collected plants for Asa Gray, 1844-52; and Gideon Lincecum, who collected plants for several American and English botanists from 1848 to 1874. Every one of these botanical explorers made substantial additions to botany and indirectly to horticulture. Their names belong in these pages because their presence and their activities in the settlement of Texas help to account for the development of horticulture in that state, beginning just before the Civil War and growing year by year down to the present, when Texas must be considered one of the great horticultural states in the Union.

Two of these men, though best known as botanists, were outstanding gardeners. Friedrich Ernst (d. 1858), one of the first men to explore Texas for its botanical treasures, was by profession a gardener. He had been a gardener for the Grand Duke of Oldenburg, but in 1831 migrated to Austin County, Texas, and founded the settlement of Industry. Here in a school he introduced scientific agriculture. He is reputed to have tried to teach his students how to raise tobacco and to make cigars, and is said to have been the introducer of fruit and garden plants in assortment. Farmers in Austin County took kindly to his teachings and that part of Texas became an early garden spot.[29]

29 Geiser, pp. 136, 321.

Even more notable was Ernst's friend and student, Louis Cochand Ervendberg (1809-63), who came to New Braunfels in 1849. The plants that the Germans at New Braunfels were trying to grow came mostly from eastern and northern states and did not thrive in the soil and climate of Texas. Ervendberg experimented with plants and seeds from regions more like the one to which these Germans had come. He became a botanical collector for Asa Gray, then the leading botanist in America, and to him wrote for seeds of plants having medicinal value. Soon he had experimental plots of many esculents and economic plants, some of which became of great value to the new state.

Ervendberg was an early religious and educational leader in Texas. He was a pastor in the German Evangelical Church and made an attempt to found a university, to be called, as specified in the charter for which he asked the Texas Congress, Hermann University, in which scientific agriculture would be taught. His educational enterprise, at least his dream of a university, failed; but he, with other German naturalists of the new state, drew together a considerable body of good farmers and gardeners.

Of these German gardeners in early Texas, at this time an independent state, the British consul, William Kennedy, wrote in 1844, in a diplomatic dispatch to the Earl of Aberdeen: 'Among the European settlers, the Germans have the reputation of being the most successful.' He found them laborious, persevering, eager to accumulate, and orderly. 'They have formed,' he said, 'thriving communities at different points in the interior, and they constitute a considerable proportion of the trading and working population of the towns adjacent to the Coast. In common with the French, they become Market-gardeners.' [30]

Finally, a part of Ervendberg's dream came true. In 1850, after the Republic of Texas had become a state in the Union, he secured the passage of an act in the legislature establishing the Western Texas University, which contained provisions for an agricultural school. In May 1852, he helped to organize the *Land- und Gartenbau Verein* of Comal County. Meanwhile, he had established the *Waisenfarm,* which Frederick Law Olmsted visited in 1854 and described in his *Journey through Texas,* commenting

[30] Ibid. p. 117.

favorably on the farm, the plantings, and an open-air theater among the trees.[31]

Ervendberg's life ended in a sad fiasco. He ran away with an orphan girl from the asylum he maintained, settled in Mexico, where he again collected plants for Asa Gray, and again established an experimental farm. In 1863 he was shot down by bandits.

The only man who could be called a fruit grower by profession in Texas before the Civil War was Gilbert Onderdonk, a New Yorker who moved to Texas in 1851. Onderdonk became, in turn, cowboy, rancher, fruit grower. He found that in many parts of Texas native grapes and plums ran riot in luxuriant growth and abundant production, and this impressed him with the possibilities of fruit culture there. Beginning in 1855, he tested nearly every hardy fruit to be purchased in America and Europe. Eventually he confined his work to peaches, plums, and grapes. From his orchards came a number of varieties of these three fruits. In improving the plum he hybridized native sorts with Japanese varieties, thus starting an entirely new group of plums to the enrichment of American horticulture.

[31] Olmsted, *A Jour. through Tex.*, p. 185.

14

THE FAR WEST

THE pioneer colonist in California was Junipera Serra, a Franciscan, who established a mission at San Diego in 1769, after his order had taken over Jesuit establishments in this part of the world. One after another, this Franciscan planted a string of 21 missions between San Diego and Santa Rosa, far to the north. For his work as a colonizer, those who till the soil in California call Junipera Serra the patron saint of agriculture.

The Franciscans brought to their missions in Upper California from Mexico all the garden and orchard seeds and plants that would grow. The agriculture of the time was crude; but, notwithstanding, when in 1850 California became a state, the gardens and orchards were among the wonders of this fabulous land. Probably in no other part of the world have missionaries so greatly enjoyed the comforts of a genial climate, a generous soil, and labor without cost, as did the Catholic Fathers in California.

As everywhere in Spanish possessions in the New World, the Indian was a serf. From the priests, Indian neophytes learned agriculture, crude though it was, and helped to maintain the farm, orchard, and garden for the food that the missions dispersed with hospitality that became proverbial. It does not appear that the Indians, left to themselves, put in practice much that they learned at the missions, but rather that they quickly reverted to their old food habits. Wild food plants, fish, and game were so plentiful on the Pacific Coast, even as far north as Alaska, that the several Indian tribes were well supplied with food without the necessity of tilling the soil, which faced so many of the eastern Indians.

Accounts of the missions make plain that oranges, figs, olives, grapes, and all the hardy fruits were grown in early orchards. A varied assortment of vegetables accompanied the fruits. These and all agricultural products, it would seem, were grown only about the Church establishments and near the coast. In the early years, at least, there were few if any privately owned places, and no attempts seem to have been made to explore the interior regions.

It was not until after 1800 that vessels from New England began to visit the 'North West Coast,' as North America's Pacific Coast was then called to distinguish it from the 'South Seas' of the Pacific. They came for furs, hides, tallow, and wine, or in search of adventure. It is said that the Mission of San Gabriel then made from 400 to 600 gallons of wine, and other missions nearly as much.[1]

Wickson, in his *California Fruits,* gives an account of California orchards shortly before American occupation, which he had had from General Bidwell.[2] He says:

The Mission of San Rafael had the best grapes—the 'mission grape,' but better than elsewhere. It had also apples and pears.

The Mission of San José had an orchard and vineyard, five or six acres perhaps. The principal trees were olives and pears. The best early pear was called 'Pera de San Juan.' This mission I first saw in 1841. The trees were mostly seedlings, I think, at least the fruit was mostly inferior.

The largest orchards, as well as the largest trees, mostly pear trees, were at Santa Clara and San José (now the city of San José). There were also grapevines. All, both trees and vines, had belonged to the mission, and were of the kinds found at other missions.

The Mission of San Juan Bautista, near Pajaro Valley, had also an old orchard, at least a few trees.

In January and February, 1845, I saw more or less of attempts to raise vines and fruit trees at other points, namely, Missions of San Miguel, San Luis Obispo, and Santa Ynez. The trees, like the missions, were in a condition of neglect and ruin.

Santa Barbara was better cared for; but the state of all the missions that I saw was, to a greater or less extent, that of neglect and decay, including San Buenaventura, San Fernando, and San Gabriel.

At the Mission of San Luis Rey . . . there were the remains of olive orchards, even then gone to utter ruin, hundreds of acres in extent. Pala and Temecula were dependencies of that gem of a mission.

[1] Cronise, p. 15.   [2] Wickson, *Calif. Fruits,* p. 70.

The old Mission of San Diego had the finest of olives and pomegranates. . .

A good account of mission gardens is given by Guadalupe
Vallejo, niece of General Vallejo and a member of one of the
notable Spanish families in early California. It reads:

I have often been asked about the Mission and ranch gardens. They
were, I think, more extensive and contained a greater variety of trees
and plants, than most persons imagine. The Jesuits had gardens in
Baja California, as early as 1669, and vineyards and orchards a few
years later. The Franciscans in Alta California began to cultivate the
soil as soon as they landed. The first grapevines were brought from
Lower California in 1769, and were soon planted at all the Missions
except Dolores, where the climate was not suitable. Before the year
1800 the orchards at the Missions contained apples, pears, peaches,
apricots, plums, cherries, figs, olives, oranges, pomegranates. At San
Diego and San Buenaventura Missions there were also sugar cane, date
palms, plantains, bananas, and citrons. . . I remember that at the
Mission of San José we had many varieties of seedling fruits which have
now been lost to cultivation. Of pears we had four sorts, one ripening in early summer, one in late summer, and two in autumn and
winter. The Spanish names of these pears were *Presidenta,* the *Berga-
mota,* the *Passa,* and the *Lechera.* One of them was as large as a Bartlett, but there are no trees left of it now. The apples, grown from seed,
ripened at different seasons, and there were seedling peaches, both early
and late. An interesting fruit was that of the Nopal, or prickly pear.
This fruit, called *tuna,* grew on the great hedges which protected part
of the Mission orchards and were twenty feet high and ten or twelve
feet thick. Those who know how to eat a *tuna,* peeling it so as to escape the tiny thorns on the skin, find it delicious. . . The old orchards
were pruned and cultivated with much care, and the paths were swept
by the Indians, but after the sequestration of the Mission property they
were neglected and ran wild. The olive-mills and wine-presses were
destroyed, and cattle were pastured in the once fruitful groves.

The flower gardens were gay with roses, chiefly a pink and very
fragrant sort from Mexico, called by us the Castillian rose, and still
seen in a few old gardens. Besides roses, we had pinks, sweet-peas,
hollyhocks, nasturtiums which had been brought from Mexico, and
white lilies. The vegetable gardens contained pease, beans, beets,
lentils, onions, carrots, red peppers, corn, potatoes, squashes, cucumbers, and melons. A fine quality of tobacco was cultivated and cured

by the Indians. . . Other kinds of plants were grown in the old gardens, but these are all that I can remember.[3]

According to the author just quoted, the potato was brought to California by La Perouse, the French navigator, from Chile to Monterey, in 1786.[4]

At which of the missions orange seeds were first planted is not known, but California horticulturists generally agree that the first orange grove was planted at the San Gabriel Mission. This orchard is supposed to have been planted in 1804 or a year or two later. It contained about 400 seedling trees planted on 6 acres of ground. Some of the trees are said to have continued to bear as late as 1885. The orange, a favorite fruit of the Spaniards, was no doubt planted commonly about all the missions, since early travelers report them from the most southern to the most northern establishments.

The San Gabriel Mission orange grove is of note as the parent of the orange industry of the Pacific Coast. From the luxuriant growth of its trees and its abundance of fruits, all could see that the climate and soil of this part of California were well suited to citrus fruits. Oranges were soon being planted in the courtyards and gardens of ranchos for home use. The first commercial orange grove in California was the offspring of the San Gabriel Mission grove. This fruit, as in the case of most others, was in these first years propagated only from seeds. At what date varieties and the art of budding and grafting were introduced does not appear.

The orange industry of California seems to have been started by John William Wolfskill, a Kentucky trapper. Wolfskill, trapping in the Far West, drifted into Los Angeles in 1831, and ten years later planted two acres of oranges from seed obtained from the San Gabriel Mission. The demand for the oranges was so great that the small grove was increased little by little until it covered 70 acres. The first full car of oranges was sent to eastern markets in 1877. They were sold in St. Louis, having been a month on the road.[5]

Wolfskill, by the way, was one of the early orange growers, if

3 Vallejo, xix: 188-9.   5 Coit, pp. 2-3.
4 Ibid. p. 188.

not the earliest, to name a variety of this fruit. Rather late in his career—nowhere does the exact date appear—he introduced a seedling called Wolfskill's Best or Wolfskill's Favorite. Wickson says in 1889, '[the] original tree now stands over thirty feet high, and as large as any tree of its age. . . Ripens ahead of all other native varieties; is largely cultivated in this State; the choicest of all native varieties.' [6] Several other growers of oranges in these early years introduced varieties, the first trees of which appeared in seedling orchards.

Wickson was told by General Bidwell that in 1845 'The largest orange groves at that time were those of Wolfskill, Carpenter, and Louis Vigne. The next year I saw oranges growing at Williams' ranch [about thirty miles from Los Angeles], also a vineyard and trees at Ocampo's ranch. Ocampo had wine and brandy which he had made.' [7]

From this time on, orange groves increased apace for home use, for the local markets, and to supply ships that were coming year by year in greater numbers. By 1860 there were plantings of them in central and northern California, a large grove having been planted at Bidwell, Butte County, in 1859. By the time railroads were carrying perishable fruits, there were groves of oranges and lemons in scattered locations from San Diego to Shasta County in the north.

Lemon culture began a little later than that of the orange, though the plantings of the latter for commerce were not extensive until after the introduction of the Washington Navel in the 1870's.

One may be sure that peaches were early planted in Spanish mission gardens. According to Butterfield, some of the early Spanish peaches had red flesh, as did those 'Indian peaches' introduced by the Spaniards in southeastern America. Butterfield tells us further that as early as 1805 Manuel Higuera asked permission to make peach brandy from surplus peaches grown near San José.[8] Sir George Simpson, the head of the Hudson's Bay Company, saw peaches in 1841 at missions Santa Barbara, San Gabriel, and San Buenaventura. John Marsh, writing to Governor Lewis Cass of

---

[6] Wickson, *Calif. Fruits*, p. 469.
[7] Ibid. p. 71.

[8] Butterfield, pp. 14, 15.

Michigan, in 1842, said that apples, pears, and peaches were plentiful in the Mt. Diablo country.[9]

Several authorities say that George Yount planted peaches at Yountville as early as 1841. Probably Yount's peach plantation furnished pits for other orchards; it is on record that in 1851 J. E. Pleasant got peach pits from him to plant in Pleasant Valley. About 1851, General Bidwell started a nursery at Chico, in which he grew all the tree fruits, no doubt getting peach pits from Yount. At about the same time, 1851, Captain Sutter, of gold fame, planted an orchard of 3000 trees, among which were peaches and nectarines. It is a matter of common record that the Russians planted an orchard of tree fruits and vines near Fort Ross between the years 1814 and 1848, getting the trees from mission gardens to the south. In 1851, Seth Lewelling brought peach trees from Oregon to California.

The peach was the fruit of fruits to the miners in early California. A peach tree or peach orchard seems to have been a veritable gold mine. Wickson tells of trees in early days in which the peach and gold were closely related. According to him, there was in old Colona, where gold was discovered, 'a peach tree which bore four hundred and fifty peaches in 1854 which sold for $3.00 each, or $1,350 for the crop of one tree, and in 1855, six trees bore one thousand one hundred peaches, which sold for $1.00 each. These trees are said to be still living and bearing fruit [1891].' [10]

Charles Howard Shinn, a pomologist of note a generation ago, gives a very good account of a Spanish and American orchard near the Mission San José, planted soon after the gold rush of 1849, which must have been one of the remarkable plantations of youthful California. The place lay within 35 miles of San Francisco. The following description is much abridged:

The ranch was planted by E. L. Beard, who began farming in Santa Clara Valley in 1849-50. In 1852 he established a nursery, sending an agent to the Atlantic states for seeds and cions, which were brought to California by way of Panama. In 1853 the price of a one-year-old cherry, peach, or pear tree was $5. Those who

9 Ibid.   10 Wickson, *Calif. Fruits*, p. 293.

set out orchards at this time found that in 1857-8 the fruit brought 25 cents or more per pound. Mr. Beard and his stepson, Henry Ellsworth, developed an orchard and wheat farm of over 2000 acres in and about the Mission San José. It is the landscape plantings, however, which made the place particularly noteworthy, one of the first ranches to have ornamental grounds.

To the grounds about the dwelling were brought nearly all the native conifers of California and many of the deciduous trees and shrubs. Eventually all of the spruces, firs, and pines that could be had from eastern nurseries were planted. These two energetic men seem to have been the first to import the many trees and shrubs from Japan and Australia which soon were to enrich the gardens of California. Olives and oranges were planted in groves and avenues; large groves of figs and many palms were set; chestnuts, walnuts, and other nut-bearing trees found a place in this remarkable plantation. A large vineyard stretched down the valley which covered more than six hundred acres.

Eventually the place was purchased by Juan Gallegos, a wealthy Spanish gentleman from Costa Rica, who took great pride in the orchards, ornamental grounds, and vineyards, greatly extending their limits and the kinds of esculent and ornamental plants, so that the whole place became and was for years a demonstration farm to Californians. In particular the new owner was devoted to the old olive, pear, grape, and orange trees set out by the early padres, so that the place became a fruticetum where old Spanish varieties of the several fruits might be studied.[11]

All the varieties of hardy fruits grown in the East were quickly introduced in California. An early report of the American Pomological Society listed 1186 varieties as having been tested in the state, of which 561 received approval, according to Cronise, writing in 1868. Of these '561 sorts, 178 were apples, 122 pears, 55 peaches, 43 cherries, 33 plums, 11 apricots, 18 native and 22 foreign grapes, 25 strawberries, 18 currants, 13 gooseberries, and 12 raspberries.'[12] Not a few, and the sub-tropic fruits as well, were imported from Europe and a little later from Asia and Australia.

It was quickly found that fruits from the Old World other than olives and members of the citrus family could be grown in the Far West that could not be planted with success across the conti-

[11] *Garden and Forest*, VII: 434. [12] Cronise, p. 362.

nent. Most notable of these were European grapes for wine and raisins; the small, seedless Corinth grape for the dried currant of commerce; almonds, apricots, and nectarines; chestnuts, English walnuts, and filberts; and plums for making prunes. Figs were early grown but were not at first of good varieties, nor were they successfully cured. At once it was discovered that the enormous crops could not be wholly used fresh, and experiments were started in the 1850's to find out how they might best be preserved.

One might fill pages with accounts of famous fruit trees dating back to the years when the Gold Rush was at its height. One of the most noted of these was a Black Tartarian cherry brought from France by Dr. L. E. Miller in 1854. It was planted just below Rattlesnake Bar, on the American River. In 1890, it was described as being 65 feet in height, with a branch diameter of 60 feet, and a girth at 6 feet above ground of over 10 feet. The following records of yield are given: '1886, two hundred boxes of ten pounds each; 1887, one hundred eighty; 1889, two hundred and twenty; and 1890, three hundred boxes.' [13] In an orchard near Woodside, San Mateo County, there are cherry trees, said to have been planted in 1853, which have trunks over two feet in diameter.[14]

The world began to have official knowledge of horticultural crops in California in 1851 when A. Williams of San Francisco gave a report in the second part of the *United States Patent Office Report* for that year on the produce of the Horner ranch in Alameda County near Mission San José. According to this report, 800 acres planted in vegetables brought in a return of more than $200,000. The crop consisted of 124,300 bushels of potatoes, beets, turnips, and tomatoes. What must have seemed to Easterners a tall story was the tale of an onion weighing 21 pounds. Two years later an even taller story came in the account of the Fair of 1853, at which were exhibited a turnip weighing 33 pounds, a squash that weighed 131 pounds, and a tomato that tipped the scales at 5½ pounds.

Some surprising horticultural statistics were published by the

[13] *Pacific Rural Press*, 20 Dec. 1890.   [14] Wickson, *Calif. Fruits*, p. 272.

Secretary of State in 1852. The profits from orchards at that time were given as $366,910, with an item of 1370 barrels of olives in Santa Barbara County worth $27,500. Garden items listed in this report were '460,000 pumpkins, worth $46,000.00; 5,000,000 pounds of onions worth $186,000.00; and 30,000 bushels of beans worth $72,000.00.'

As early as 1857, when California had but lately entered the Union, there was an article in *The Horticulturist* entitled 'The Way They Talk in California,' which gives a good picture of fruit growing in California at this time. We are told that the lemon, lime, the citron, the mango, the sapota, the pepper tree, cotton, foreign vines in every variety, the soft-shelled almond, sugar cane, pomegranate, pineapple, and the olive are among the products that do well or promise to do well.[15]

At Marysville, according to this article, Beach and Shephard had 40,000 peach trees, 5000 apples, 5000 pears, 3000 cherries, 2000 plums, and 40,000 grapes. G. G. Briggs had nearly 200,000 peaches, 20,000 nectarines, and apricots. Mr. Delman had 80 varieties of grapes, 24,000 vines in all. We are told that peach trees, budded the previous year on small seedlings, in 12 months were 18 inches in circumference at 6 inches above the ground; that fruit of four old pear trees grafted with Bartletts 18 months had sold for $160. 'Mr. Lewellyn [Lewelling], it was said, 'has 25,000 apple-trees, and grew three apples upon grafts inserted the previous winter'; that Messrs. McMurtrie were offered $10,000 for the produce of 1000 acres of potatoes; that Messrs. Thompson have 18,000 trees, and a vineyard of 8000 vines; 'their orchard, which the previous year looked from a distance like rows of half-grown corn, was the next, a forest in which a man may hide himself.' One optimistic statement was that 'Major Barbour fully expected to realize from $15,000 to $20,000 from two acres of melons, selling two to three hundred dollars worth a day.' What seemed the tallest story was: 'Twelve pumpkins raised in Los Angeles weighed over fifteen hundred pounds.' It was said: 'Saurevain Brothers have 60,000 vines and made two thousand and eighteen gallons of wine, and some brandy; Mr. Caldwell raised a sweet potato weighing twenty-three pounds. Mr. Smith raised a

15 *The Hort.*, XII: 314.

beet measuring three feet six inches in circumference.' Last but not least: 'In two small valleys are found one million grape vines.' *The Horticulturist* believed that some of the statements in this *Official Report* were exaggerated.

It may be thought that the horticultural industries of the Pacific Coast began with the coming of Easterners in the Gold Rush of '49. This is not quite true, however, for while the gold fever lasted other ways of making money were ignored. The buckskin bag was the symbol of gold-mining. Then a second era followed in which grain culture—its symbol, the grain bag—was the leading industry from Canada to Lower California. It was not until the 1880's that products of the soil, other than grain and cattle, assumed national importance commercially.

In the pioneer years of the Pacific states, well into the 'eighties and 'nineties, urban and rural dwellers alike were so poorly supplied with ornamentals that Californian homes were supreme in desolation. The country in these years of gold mining and wheat growing was a barren waste over which sheep and cattle ranged, eating grass, flowers, and shrubs. Nowhere in America could desolation have been more marked. No garden, tree, or shrub relieved the hot, dry, brown earth in summer. On wheat ranches the grain was in season beautiful to look at, but about the dingy little cabins, with few exceptions, there was nothing in the way of a garden for food and beauty.

The old order changed when fruit growing became an industry. Good fruit land is valuable. The vast ranges for cattle and the square miles in wheat farms were divided into much smaller tracts, which orchardists kept clean, orderly, and well planted with ornamentals. The slovenly homes of cattle rancheros and wheat growers became as beautiful as any rural homes in the world. By the end of the century, gardening in country and city began to approach the greater perfection of the East. Of modern gardens, in this region of plants and trees, everything that can be grown is now to be found. Those who knew California only when cattle, sheep, and grain were at their peak in production could not have dreamed of the beauties of California gardens half a century later.

Toward the end of the period covered by this history there were perhaps a dozen flourishing nurseries in California, which greatly forwarded every branch of horticulture. Three of these establishments, in particular, enriched the Pacific Coast with fruits, trees, shrubs, and flowers. All Californians would at once select as the leaders the nurseries of John Rock at Niles; Frederick Christian Roeding, of the Fancher Creek nursery, near Fresno; and James Shinn at Niles. Of the three, only the nursery of Shinn, founded in 1855, was of importance until after the Civil War, and the introduction of cultivated species and varieties that make the work of all three men remarkable was done from 1870 to 1890.

These three, while the most prominent of the early nurserymen, were not the earliest. Who brought the first budded or grafted trees to California, or buds and grafts to work on seedlings, will probably never be known. An early date for grafted varieties is 1846, when Martin Lelong, according to his son, B. M. Lelong, one of the leading horticulturists in the young state, brought a number of French varieties of tree fruits and planted them in Los Angeles. They were not particularly well adapted to soil or climate, but were quite superior to the seedling trees grown at the missions, and a good many orchards were planted with these French varieties.

A little later, in the fall of 1849, W. H. Nash and R. L. Kilburn ordered 36 fruit trees from a nursery in western New York. These were packed in a box of moss and shipped around Cape Horn. Most of the trees survived the journey and were planted in Napa Valley in the spring of 1850. The shipment included such standard sorts of eastern America as Rhode Island Greening, Roxbury Russet, Winesap, Red Romanite, and Esopus Spitzenburg apples; Bartlett and Seckel Pears; and Black Tartarian and Napoleon cherries.[16] Sooner or later the Napoleon cherry became in California the Royal Ann, long the most commonly grown sweet cherry in the state. This shipment of grafted trees was followed, year after year, by other importations of named varieties.

Before these varieties came to California there were shipments of fruit-tree seeds from the eastern to the western states. In a report of the California Agricultural Society, several such importa-

16 Wickson, *California Fruits*, p. 74.

tions are noted.[17] A Mr. Barnett, it is said, planted seed from Kentucky at Napa in 1847. T. K. Steward reported that in 1848 he brought 200 pounds of vegetable and fruit seeds, the latter including seeds of the apple, pear, and peach. These seeds were planted on the American River, within the present limits of the city of Sacramento, in the spring of 1849. The same year he planted seeds of figs and olives and in 1851 seeds of oranges. Seedlings of all these fruits became bearing trees.

According to Butterfield, Warren and Sons Garden and Nursery of Sacramento was in all probability the first nursery to print a catalogue in California. Colonel Warren had been in the seed and plant business in Boston and is now remembered for his having taken a wide variety of camellias, including the famous varieties Wilder and Miss Abby Wilder, to the West Coast. Sacramento, which is proud of its camellias, now gives him great credit.

Warren, who later became editor of the *California Farmer,* sent out a catalogue listing 53 varieties of pears, 16 cherries, 37 apples, 20 peaches, 6 figs, and 18 plums.[18] In the 1850's nurseries in the East began to sell fruit trees to Pacific states. In particular, Prince of Long Island and Elwanger and Barry of Rochester made large shipments to California nurseries, sending them around Cape Horn, across Panama, and overland. Nearly every nursery on the Pacific Coast advertised trees from some eastern nursery.

In 1851 Seth Lewelling, brother to Henderson, came to Sacramento from Oregon, bringing with him a box of grafts of apples, pears, plums, peaches, and cherries. Oregon, as we shall see later (page 386), already had grafted trees in bearing and nurseries well started. The pioneer nurseryman in Oregon was Henderson Lewelling, who, in 1847, brought grafted trees to Milwaukee, near Portland. Seth Lewelling was joined by William Meek, who had become a partner in the Oregon venture, in selling trees brought from the home nursery to San Francisco, thence distributed through the valleys of the state.

In 1854 Henderson Lewelling moved his nursery from Milwaukee, Oregon, to Alameda County, California, and in 1859

---

[17] *Calif. Ag. Soc. Rpt.* 1870, p. 250.   [18] Butterfield, pp. 4-21.

William Meek came on to plant a nursery near by. These two nurseries were for some time among the best in the state. John Lewelling, another of the Oregon partners, had previously, in 1853, come to California to go into orcharding, and had helped to establish the famous orchards of Beard and Lewelling in several localities.

Henderson Lewelling's nurseries were pioneer establishments for growing trees in four states—Indiana, Iowa, Oregon, and California. In California the sale of trees brought him wealth, enabling him to build a palatial home in the town of Fruitvale. A few years later his pioneering spirit led him far south to found a new horticultural project in Honduras, but here, for the first time, he met failure. His colony in Honduras did not succeed and he lost all his money. Next he is found as the renter of a patch of land in San José, Santa Clara County, near the scene of his California triumphs. Here, in burning weeds and grass on his bit of land, in December 1878, he burned to death. The woman's club at Oakdale, in 1924, planted two redwood trees on the old Lewelling California estate as memorials to Henderson Lewelling and Luther Burbank.

In the 1850's there are records of importations of several lots of trees besides those of Lewelling. Possibly the most notable of these was the one by G. G. Briggs, who had made a fortune out of watermelons. An account of the melon venture in a report of the California Agricultural Society [19] states that Briggs planted 25 acres of watermelons at Marysville in 1851, from which he realized $17,000. With this money he sent to New York for his family, who brought with them 50 peach and a few apple and pear trees. The next year the peaches and pears bore fruit so fine that he ordered 1400 peach trees from western New York, of which only 400 came safely around the Horn; these were planted in December 1853. The next year they bore a crop that sold at the rate of $1.50 per dozen fruits, realizing $2800 from 50 trees.

This phenomenal success stimulated Mr. Briggs to go into fruit growing on a large scale. In 1858 he had 1000 acres in orchards and nurseries, the trees consisting of peaches, pears, nectarines,

[19] *Calif. Ag. Soc. Rpt.* 1858, p. 169.

apples, apricots, cherries, and plums. In 1858, the yield of the several fruits was 587,628 pounds of fruit, which sold at an average of 16 cents a pound, and, after expenses were paid, left him a net profit of $58,762. That year Mr. Briggs was awarded a medal by the state agricultural society for 'a first class orchard.' [20]

In the 1850's Felix Gillette came from France to California and set up a barber shop in Nevada City, Nevada County. Gillette, a born plantsman, became in time a nurseryman, and out of his meager savings bought a piece of barren land on the outskirts of the town. He sent to France for $3000 worth of nursery stock and on his bit of land founded the Barren Hill Nursery. Soon he was an authority on the Pacific Coast on prunes, grapes, almonds, filberts, walnuts, chestnuts, and grew other fruits and many ornamentals as well. Moreover he was pleased to impart his knowledge to visitors, in the press as on the platform. The barren hill became a paradise of trees and shrubs, and its owner one of the notable horticulturists of America. His contributions to the knowledge of plums and prunes were especially valuable.

The plum deserves special attention as one of the major deciduous fruits of California, grown both as a dessert fruit and for prunes. The early mission orchards contained plums of European origin, brought in by way of Spain to Mexico, thence to California. When the missions with their orchards were abandoned in 1834, a few plums survived. One variety was distributed from the mission at Santa Clara until as late as 1870, under the name Mission. Plum culture, however, really began on the Pacific Coast in Oregon through the efforts of Lewelling. Neither Seth Lewelling nor any of those who bought his plum trees in California thought of that state as a promising region for prunes.

The introduction of plums for prune-making was made by a Frenchman, Pierre Pellier, of San José, who, in 1856, brought to California cions of the Agen, plum *par excellence* for prunemaking in France and America. The variety takes its name from Agen, France, a district famous for its prunes, and is one of the oldest plums under cultivation. In California the Agen became known as the 'French Prune' and the 'Petite Prune.' A few years

[20] Ibid. 1881, pp. 169-70.

after Pellier planted his orchard, California-cured prunes were on the market, coming chiefly from the Santa Clara Valley, to this day a center for prunes. Pellier, by the way, established on the site of what is now the city of San José a nursery that became one of the best on the Pacific Coast.

The success of these several early nurseries and orchards dispelled all doubts about the possibilities of growing fruits in California. In spite of the fruit gardens at the missions, the climate, with its summer droughts and winter rains, so different from that of the eastern states, and the very different soils had given the impression that hardy fruits—apples, peaches, pears, and plums—could not be grown in California. There was also the matter of irrigation. Some nurserymen and fruit growers advocated irrigation; some believed that irrigation was impracticable. It soon developed that fruits could be easily and well grown with water artificially supplied, though it long was a matter of controversy whether deep and frequent cultivation to conserve moisture was not better than irrigation.

Another moot question among both nurserymen and fruit growers was that of dwarf *versus* standard trees. In the eastern states, dwarf trees were being planted by many fruit growers, and were especially well liked by nurserymen who could grow and deliver them to fruit growers rather more cheaply than they could standards. Dwarf trees come into full bearing more quickly than standards, which commended them to Californians, who were seeking the high prices fruits commanded in markets as yet not well supplied. There were in the years from 1852 to 1858 small areas of dwarf apples and pears planted at San José, Oakland, Stockton, and Sacramento. A Mr. Fountain, near Oakland, in 1857 had the finest orchard of dwarf pears and apples in the state. It consisted of three acres of two-year-old apples and pears, numbering 1608, 4 feet high. J. R. Lowe of San José had two acres, upon which, 'besides his house and barn, were over twenty-four thousand fruit trees—cherry, plum, pear, peach, apricot, and nectarine, many of them in bearing.' Another famous but small orchard of dwarfs was that of Thomas Fallon of San José, where there were 'on less than twenty feet square, fifteen pear trees, of several varieties, bearing more fruit than wood. Some fruits weighed more than two pounds; one limb eighteen inches long, bore twenty-two pears, each weighing over one and one-half pounds. The fruit of this little garden of fifteen trees sold for $1,600.00.' [21]

So popular were dwarf trees that a nurseryman in Sacramento in 1858 offered in his list of stock 'ninety-five standard and eight thousand and sixty-eight dwarf pear trees.' [22] The craze for dwarf trees soon ran its course, and all plantings of any considerable size, even in these early days when the yield of several gardens of dwarfs was one of the marvels of horticulture in the state, were of standard trees.

One of the curiosities of early horticulture in California was an orchard laid out by General Sutter on the west bank of the Feather River, eight miles from its juncture with the Yuba. The orchard of several acres was to present all the features of a landscape garden of ornamentals. 'The arrangement of the fruit trees is peculiar, a large portion of them being set on either side of the broad avenues opening through the extensive grounds in various directions, imparting to the whole an air of picturesque beauty seldom seen.' [23] But General Sutter's landscape-garden plan for orchards did not appeal to commercial growers of fruit, nor, with the wealth of native trees, shortly augmented by exotics, did it seem to please planters of ornamentals.

Possibly the most notable early patron of ornamental gardening in California was General John Bidwell, an Ohioan, who emigrated to Missouri, thence to California in 1841, and entered the service of General Sutter. A few years later General Bidwell became the owner of a ranch of 26,000 acres of forest land at Chico, Butte County. Here, eventually, he built a mansion and laid out grounds, giving his estate the name 'Rancho Chico.' General Bidwell, as early as 1856, began, under the direction of a Scotch gardener named Carmichael, to plant native and exotic trees, including some fruits, and so established an arboretum that later was the delight of botanists, visited by Asa Gray, John Muir, and C. C. Parry among many others. At rancho Chico might be

[21] *Calif. Ag. Soc. Rpt.* 1857, pp. 42, 49.   [23] *Calif. Ag. Soc. Rpt.* 1858, p. 167.
[22] Wickson, *Calif. Fruits*, p. 79.

found the firs, pines, and other conifers of California; the oaks, deciduous trees, and shrubs of the region; a vast number of exotics; and hardy and sub-hardy fruits. The grounds were open to the public and were, in the years that followed, of great educational value to all planters of trees.

When California was admitted to the Union in 1850, Los Angeles was the center of grape culture in the state. Vineyards were so plentiful in and about the town that it was known as 'the City of Vineyards'; though, at that time, the primitive place was far from being a city.

Of the men who planted and cared for these vineyards the name of but one is memorable. Colonel Agoston Harazthy was for some years the chief authority in southern California. In 1856, he moved from Los Angeles to Sonoma to engage in grape growing on a large scale. Soon after coming to Sonoma, Colonel Harazthy was commissioned by the governor of California to go to Europe to get information on grape growing. This visit to Europe by a trained California viticulturist turned out to be an event of importance for the grape industry. His reports to the governor and a book, *Grape-culture, Wines and Wine-making*, published in 1862, helped greatly to extend grape growing and wine making in California. Another outcome of this visit to Europe was the introduction of a large number of European grapes for wine making and table use, one of which, Zinfandel, is still a leading wine grape. Colonel Harazthy and his son Arpad were the first successful champagne makers on the Pacific Coast. His brand, Eclipse, was long the only California champagne on the market.

The Horticulturist for January 1855 records an interesting item of viticultural history from California. The editor had received by express, in October 1854, two bunches of grapes packed in redwood sawdust, from Los Angeles. This is probably the first record of grapes shipped from California to the Atlantic Coast; it is probably the first record of the use of sawdust, so largely used later, as a packing material for California grapes. The note accompanying the grapes gives the names of Don Louis Vignes, Dr. Hoover, and Mr. Wolfskill as growers of grapes and makers of wine and brandy in Los Angeles. Don Louis Vignes is said to have been the first maker of commercial wines in California. According to the correspondent, an ocean steamer was freighted for San Francisco every week in the grape season, beginning in August and ending in October.

Another early patron of viticulture in California was A. Delmas, of San José, who early came to believe that the soil and climate of California were especially well adapted for this industry. In the early 1850's, he sent to France for cuttings, which, packed in boxes, withstood the six months' voyage around the Horn. From this and other importations Mr. Delmas had in 1858 a hundred fine varieties of European grapes growing in his vineyard.

Previous to the importations of the European grape by Harazthy and Delmas, the Mission grape, of European derivation, the exact origin of which is not known, was the standard variety and almost the only one. It was grown for table use, being sweet, juicy, and delicious; and for wine and brandy, for both of which it was fairly well suited. No grapes derived from native species were grown until long after pioneers came from the eastern states, and none have ever been widely grown.

The raisin industry in California, now amounting to many millions of pounds annually, was founded by Colonel Harazthy in 1852, when he imported vines of the Muscat of Alexandria from Malaga. From year to year, other importations were made, but there is no record of cured raisins until 1863; the industry did not begin until the 1870's, several years being required to teach grape growers the difference between raisins from raisin grapes and dried grapes from varieties not suitable for raisins. Methods of curing, grading, and packing had to be adapted both to California conditions and to the requirements of eastern markets, which had long been accustomed to raisins produced in the Old World.

From the first settlements in the several southern states, efforts were made to cure figs, as has been done in the Mediterranean countries from time immemorial. Figs grow and fruit well in all the Gulf states and in the North along the Atlantic as far as Maryland, but all efforts to dry them for a commercial product fail because of the humidity. For figs to supplant the imported product, long used in America, the country had to await the twentieth century and California, whence now comes an abundant supply. The fig was introduced in California by the earliest missionaries from Spain and Mexico, but proper varieties and the method of caprification practiced in Asia, whence the best dried figs long came, are introductions in California of the years since 1890, at which time George C. Roeding, of the Fancher Creek Nursery, first practiced caprification on trees brought from Smyrna.

Perhaps the tree gave the fig greater popularity in early days than the fruit. As everyone knows, the fig tree is one of the most magnificent of all orchard trees where it grows well, as it does in most parts of California. Its great size, symmetry, and dense foliage make it a choice tree for either beauty or shade. There are many fig groves in California dating back to the old missions; and, of course, still more that were planted by pioneer horticulturists. One such grove is at Knight's Ferry, Stanislaus County, planted in the 1850's, of which, though the trees are 60 feet apart, the branches form a network through which, in the summer, light cannot pass.[24]

There are single trees that add even more to the fame of the fig in California than the groves. Perhaps as famous as any is one on rancho Chico, near the residence of General Bidwell. It was planted in 1856, and by 1889 had attained a circumference, a foot above the ground, of 11 feet. The branches had taken root like a banyan tree, and the tree was over 150 feet in diameter. It was loaded with figs every year. Another tree Wickson mentions was at Knight's Ferry in the orchard of George A. Goodell. It was 60 feet in height, with branches 70 feet in diameter, and trunk 11 feet around at the base, with 7 or 8 large branches, each of which was nearly 5 feet in diameter.[25]

Probably the first date palm planted in the state was at the San Diego Mission where, in 1889, the tree was reported to be more than a hundred years old. There were other date palms of long standing at Ventura at the site of the old Mission of San Buenaventura. These trees are described as being 40 feet in height and as putting forth leaves at a height of 30 feet. In 1858 or 1859 J. R. Wolfskill planted date seeds taken from market fruits near Win-

[24] Wickson, *Calif. Fruits*, p. 411.   [25] Ibid. pp. 411, 412.

ters, California. The mission date palms never bore fruit, or at least the dates did not ripen, and the several trees at Winters did not bear well, so that the date, until comparatively recent years, was planted for most part only as a curiosity, or for the beauty of the palm with its long, graceful, fern-like leaves.

The date in recent years has been successfully grown in the state, but the early planters failed miserably because they did not have the right varieties, did not understand their culture or the requirements for proper pollination to secure a good setting of fruit. As a matter of historical interest, it should be said that some early growers at least understood that artificial fertilization of the flowers is needed. It was practiced by Wolfskill in his plantation near Winters. It should be said, also, that there are records of many other locations in the state where date palms were early planted, notably at Santa Barbara, Fresno, and Santa Ana in Los Angeles County.

Of the pomegranate, Butterfield writes:

The pomegranate is one of the oldest fruits known and was brought to California by the first Spanish settlers when Mission San Diego was founded in 1769. Like the quince, the pomegranate may be propagated from cuttings or by seed and the plants will survive under adverse conditions.

The American settlers before 1850 were attracted by the pomegranates seen about the Spanish missions and in private rancho gardens. . . After California became a state, in 1850, some of the old Spanish Dons continued to grow the pomegranate, Don Lorenzo Soto of San Diego County, for example. American settlers, like Dr. Thomas J. White of Los Angeles, included the pomegranate in their family fruit orchard. Pomegranates planted by the padres survived for many years. In 1859 there were 3,149 pomegranate trees in California. The pomegranate was sometimes exhibited at fairs. W. E. Cameron of Yuba County received first premium for his pomegranates at the State Fair in 1858 and Gen. Sutter second premium. But there is no evidence that the pomegranate did more than hold its own in plantings for the first 60 years after California became a state.

Nut growing got off to a slow start on the Pacific Coast. There were early plantings of both walnuts and almonds, but no one knew what varieties would grow best, what soils and situations were most suitable, or how to care for the ripened crop. Besides, markets were well supplied in the East by Europeans. Nevertheless, importations of varieties of these two nuts were made in the 1850's, and plantings are recorded as early as 1853 of the best European varieties in Santa Barbara, Ventura, and Los Angeles Counties. For the most part these first varieties were irregular in bearing, and since there were no machines to hull the nuts, or experience in sulphuring to bleach them, there was little enthusiasm about growing them.

Early horticulturists in California were so successful in growing pome, drupe, vine, and citrus fruits that they were inclined to plant any and all trees bearing edible products. Besides almonds and walnuts, they also imported varieties of chestnuts, pecans, pistachios, and filberts. All could be grown, but none was particularly successful, and none could then, or now, compete with European nuts—or, in the case of the pecan, with those of the states bordering on the Gulf of Mexico.

Immigration to Oregon and Washington began about 1840 from the eastern states. The region now covered by the two states was then called 'Oregon.' By 1844 there were so many Americans on or near the Columbia River that a demand for a definite boundary between the United States and Canada became the campaign slogan—'Fifty-four forty or fight.' This issue was settled and Oregon became a territory in 1848, a state in 1859; Washington became a territory soon after Oregon, but not a state until 1889. Thus, the northern Pacific Coast in the United States had a start of several years over California in the matter of settlements by Americans. Another advantage of the northern region was that the first settlers came to till the soil, while early Californians came to mine gold.

The first gardens in the Northwest were planted at the trappers' posts of the several fur companies that were established by Americans and British who came to this region in the early part of the nineteenth century. At Astoria, Vancouver, Walla Walla, and the dozen or more other permanent posts in what is now Oregon, Washington, and Idaho, vegetables and seedling fruits were planted. In particular Dr. McLoughlin, who came to Vancouver in 1824 to take charge of the Hudson's Bay post, is to be credited with plantings of not only fruits and vegetables but flowers as well. With the coming of Whitman, Spalding, and Lee, early missionaries, further introductions were made, and the Indians were instructed in the arts of gardening.

Fruit growing in the Pacific Northwest began in Oregon in 1847, when Henderson Lewelling transported 700 grafted fruit trees in an ox wagon over the Great Plains and the Rocky Mountains by way of the Oregon Trail from Iowa to Oregon. On 17 April 1847, Lewelling started from Salem, Henry County, Iowa, with a wagon load of trees, pulled by three yokes of oxen. He was accompanied by his family, and at the start had a partner. There were seven wagons in the party from Henry County, all headed across the Great Western Desert for Oregon, but, after crossing the Missouri, this small caravan joined a larger wagon train taking the Oregon Trail for the Pacific Coast.

The trees were planted in two boxes set in the bottom of the wagon, which contained a compost of charcoal and earth. There was a general variety of apples, pears, quinces, plums, cherries, and some 'berry bushes'—700 in all. The trees ranged from 20 inches to 4 feet in height. Around the wagon box a rack was built to protect the trees from the oxen.

The adventures and hardships of the journey were all that usually fell to the lot of transcontinental travelers by ox wagon in the 1840's. The plains were hot, dry, and dusty, and it was with difficulty that the trees were kept alive. They had to be watered every day, and often the water had to be carried a mile or more. Lewelling's partner died on the Platte River when the journey was but begun; two of the oxen died on the Sweetwater. Indians were troublesome. Lewelling's fellow travelers insisted that the trees should be thrown away, declaring that they could never get them over the mountains; he would not give up, and was left behind to travel the long trail alone much of the way.

Lewelling reached the Dalles on the Columbia River early in October, and the remainder of the journey was easy. After a rest, the outfit took a boat down the Columbia and a little way up the Willamette. On the shores of this river, on 17 November, seven months from the day they had started, the family made settlement. What of the trees? About half had died; some had grown amazingly, and all alive had leafed out and a few had borne blossoms; some of the berries had fruited in the heat of the desert. These were the first grafted trees of eastern fruits on the Pacific Coast.

The same fall William Meek, another Iowan, arrived in Oregon with a few varieties of fruits. Lewelling and Meek pooled their stock, and in the moist soil of the Willamette Valley founded the first nursery on the Pacific Coast. For want of seedling stocks, the young nursery could not increase its trees greatly, and in 1850 Seth and John Lewelling brought a bag of apple seeds from Iowa. A man named Pugh had brought apple seeds to Washington County, which he had planted in the spring of 1850. These, having grown well, were purchased by the firm of Lewelling and Meek. Orcharding was off to a flying start in Oregon.

In 1850 J. W. Ladd brought from the East by water, and across the Isthmus, some 2300 fruit trees. These were the first fruit trees that lived ever brought to the Coast by the Isthmus. The difficulties were nearly as great in bringing them through the tropics as across the plains. Many were lost because of poor packing, and whole boxes were purloined by treacherous carriers. Of those that arrived, there were 70 varieties of apples, 40 of pears, 15 of peaches, as many of plums, 20 of cherries, several quinces, besides nectarines, apricots, almonds, currants, gooseberries, and the walnut and hickory nut.[26]

During the winter of 1850-51 about 20,000 grafts were made at the Lewelling nursery, a part of which were those Seth Lewelling took, in March 1851, to California. Of this transaction Seth Lewelling wrote to E. J. Wickson: 'I believe I have the honor of being the first to distribute grafted fruit in California.' [27] These grafts sold at the nursery to Californians, Oregonians, or Washingtonians for $5 each.

In the 1850's a boom in fruit growing in the Northwest occurred. The Lewellings, Meek, and Ladd, as leaders, had set examples that every settler in Oregon and Washington seemed anxious to follow. A writer in *The Horticulturist* [28] believed that more attention was being paid to fruit growing in Oregon than in any other state in the Union. There was a long list of subscrib-

---

[26] *The Horticulturist*, IX: 98, 99.   [28] *The Horticulturist*, IX: 98.
[27] Wickson, *Calif. Fruits*, p. 75.

ers for *The Horticulturist* in the new state, of which there were
30 in the little hamlet of Oregon City. Fruit trees bore earlier,
more regularly, and made a greater annual growth than in the
East, and there were fewer pests. Good markets were near at hand
in the gold mines of the fabulous West, mines having been opened
in Idaho, then a part of Oregon, and in Oregon, as well as California.

In several early Roman Catholic missions in what is now Washington, agriculture in all its branches was practiced. The wife of
General Stevens, the first governor of the state, in 1889 wrote a
pleasing description of one of these missions, that of St. Joseph
d'Olympia, near Olympia, the old town that has always been the
capital of the state. The mission was, she tells us, 'a large dark
house or monastery, surrounded by cultivated land, a fine garden
in front filled with flowers bordered on one side, next the water,
with immense bushes of wall flowers in bloom; the fragrance resembling the sweet English violet, filling the air with its delicious
odor. Their fruit was a rarity, as there was but one more orchard
in the whole country.'

The Hudson's Bay Company had a flourishing farm at old Fort
Nisqually, near Tacoma, established in 1833, on which a little
later there was built a substantial white house, barns, granaries,
and where there were gardens and orchards. The first American
settlers in this part of Washington, then Oregon, found venerable,
hoary, moss-draped apple trees that the trappers must have planted
soon after coming to Nisqually Flats.

An item of interest in the horticultural history of Washington
pertains to a Black Tartarian cherry tree of enormous size that
stands four miles from Olympia. The legend is that this venerable
tree was propagated in Salem, Iowa, in 1845, and that it came
across the continent in Henderson Lewelling's traveling nursery.
The tree is said to have borne as many as 40 bushels of cherries
in a season—a worthy forerunner of the splendid cherry trees that
grow in this part of Washington.[29]

On the grounds about Vancouver Barracks, Vancouver, Washington, is an old apple tree, in front of which is a sign saying:

[29] Pellet, p. 12.

'The oldest apple tree in the Northwest grown from seeds brought from London, England, planted in 1825 by the Hudson's Bay Co.'

A brief history of the tree was written in 1836 by Mrs. Mary Whitman, wife of Marcus Whitman, missionary martyr of Walla Walla, Washington. Mrs. Whitman records that a gardener of the Hudson's Bay Company planted apple seeds from which came several trees, long pointed out as the oldest apple trees in the Northwest.

Bancroft gives this account of the tree:

At a lunch party in London, about 1825, given in honor of some young gentlemen who were about to embark for Fort Vancouver in the employ of the Hudson's Bay Company, seeds of the fruit eaten were slyly slipped by some young ladies into the waistcoat pockets of the young men. Upon their arrival at their destination, the young men, in overhauling their wardrobes, found the seeds and gave them to Bruce, the gardener at the Fort.

Cabeza de Vaca and Coronado in 1539 found a flourishing agriculture in New Mexico carried on by the Indians. In a nook in the hills near where Santa Fé now stands was a populous town of aborigines, in which corn, beans, and pumpkins were being grown in orderly gardens. In 1605 a colony of Spaniards from Mexico founded Santa Fé and planted European crops. The earliest continuous gardens in America may have been there.

In 1806 General Zebulon M. Pike, American soldier and explorer, led a band of Yankees to Santa Fé, which had been slumbering with little change, except a normal increase in population, for two centuries. What Pike saw in the way of gardens there must have existed in many smaller settlements in what is now Texas, New Mexico, Arizona, and possibly southern California, for not a few generations.

The towns Pike found in the Southwest were of one-story adobe houses, standing flush with the narrow streets, hardly showing signs of occupancy. A look through open hallways gave pictures of greenery in square gardens of trees, shrubs, or vines. In the middle of these inner courts, in what passed as palaces, there might sometimes be seen pools or fountains or, in lesser establishments, picturesque wells. Outside the towns were ranchos on which cattle and steers were raised. For the most part the fruits, flowers, and vegetables, if any, were in the courtyards of the low, rectangular houses. This picture, as painted by Pike, probably makes the gardens better than they were—or, at least, better than Spanish gardens of later years.

We get a very good account of the agriculture of New Mexico and the northern part of Mexico just before the Mexican War from Josiah Gregg's excellent *Commerce of the Prairies,* a classic in the history of this region. Gregg has been mentioned as one of the notable botanic explorers in the Southwest in the second quarter of the nineteenth century.

When Gregg reached New Mexico in 1831, there were about 70,000 people in the territory, most of whom were engaged in primitive agriculture. Their only tools were hoes, spades, and wooden plows, in which there was not a scrap of iron, not even a nail. All cultivated land was under irrigation. Corn was the staff of life, with some wheat, while in the gardens beans, squashes, and green and red peppers were grown by the Mexicans. In the fertile valleys in New Mexico, Gregg tells us, the settlements were thickly interspersed with vineyards, orchards, and cornfields. The orchards were planted with apples, peaches, and apricots, all seedlings and all wretchedly poor, though the grapes from Spain were delicious. We may assume that ornamental plants were not conspicuous, since Gregg, having the eye of a botanist, would undoubtedly have mentioned them if they had been.

Arizona has the reputation of being the driest state in the Union and for the most part irrigation is possible only in the southern part, where water may be had. Probably, the earliest Spanish settlers planted orchards and gardens sparingly near rivers where they could be irrigated, soon after they settled in New Mexico and as soon as or sooner than in California. The crops were the same as in New Mexico. It is doubtful if there was any horticulture in the state worthy of the name until after the period of this history. The first settlers had to learn that the growing season for some crops was reversed: cauliflower, radishes, peas, and others thrive better in winter. In the early period of gold mining, before the Civil War, gardening and fruit growing were largely in the hands of Chinese, who, with high culture and contending with heat and droughts rather better than Whites would do, grew a succession of fine crops. Such also was the gardening in Nevada, if any, about the first mining towns, until long after the period of this history.

It is doubtful whether any agricultural crops were planted in Utah or Nevada before 1847, when Brigham Young led his band of pioneers from Illinois westward to found Salt Lake City. It does not appear that the Spaniards made settlements in either of these states, though no doubt they made explorations. Until 1824 the Great Salt Lake was unknown to Whites; in that year James Bridger, a trapper, discovered the lake, after which the area was frequently visited by Whites, but without settlements until the Church of Jesus Christ or Latter-day Saints came. Nevada remained uninhabited by Whites until settlements in Utah had already been flourishing for some years.

The newcomers in Utah found little opportunity during the first few years to plant fruits and vegetables, so scarce were seeds and trees, and so terrible was the struggle for existence in combating drought, locusts, and preparing the land for the plow. One may say that horticulture began in Utah in 1850, or a year or two later, after which gardening and orcharding progressed by leaps and bounds. By 1860, pome and drupe fruits were being grown in the temperate valleys of the whole state, as were all the hardy vegetables. In Washington County in the southwestern corner of the state, the climate is so mild that European grapes, figs, and pomegranates were grown by the early settlers, and the making of wine was an early industry.

Far-seeing Brigham Young encouraged horticulture in Utah from the very beginning. It is doubtful that in any other state in the Union the growing of fruits, vegetables, and flowers made so rapid progress in so short a time. The author spent two years, 1897 to 1899, teaching botany and horticulture in the College of Agriculture at Logan, Utah, and was astonished to find how many and how splendid the orchards and gardens were in that state. Many of the orchards had been planted before 1860. They were to be found in every valley from the northern to the southern boundary. When it is remembered that the land was a desert, scourged with locusts, in which the earth yielded nothing without artificial help, one must pay tribute to Brigham Young and those who helped him settle Utah, as notable horticultural pioneers.

The following excerpt taken from an autobiographic manuscript of C. H. Oliphant, Salt Lake City, Utah, is an account of the beginning of horticulture in Utah: [30]

Soon after my arrival in Salt Lake City, the spirit was upon me to labor for the introduction of fruit into Utah. I sent East for scions to engraft on seedlings trees which had been produced in the country. This proved a failure. The mail that winter was left along the route at way stations. The next season it was gathered up by ox teams and my scions arrived several months after the season had passed when they could be used. The spring after my arrival, in 1854 . . . I went into the business of raising trees and introducing good varieties of fruit as fast as my circumstances would permit. For stocks to work, I paid 50 cents per piece for young peach trees. L. D. Young had one cherry tree, around the roots of this many sprouts come up; they were worthless only for stocks. For some of these to bud into I paid 2 dollars each. At that time there was no grafted or budded fruit in Utah. Previous to this, Lorenzo Dow Young, having been back to the States, had made an effort to bring a number of choice varieties of fruit across the Plains in a growing condition in a wagon. . . We succeeded in getting several varieties through, but lost all but one, and that proved to be the Rawles Jannet. This was the first introduction of this choice variety of apples into Utah. . . In about 1850 or '51, a person, name now lost, brought from the East, a lot of choice seeds. These were planted on what is now known as the old Carrington Place. A large portion of them were washed away. When what were left come into bearing, there developed some fine varieties. From these I propagated, named, listed them. From these have spread some of the finest varieties of peaches in Utah. Among them, the famous Carrington's Superb, Carrington's early, and several others. . .

In the fall of 1854, I sent to Ellwanger and Barry of Rochester, N. Y. for cuttings and small trees. They put me up about 40 dollars worth. There was then an express across the Plains; by this I directed it to be sent. By a strange fatality the parcel went by way of California. I traced it to San Francisco and there I lost all track of it. I made great efforts through friends, traveling Elders to get anything that would assist in growing into Utah.

In the fall of 1855 I worked and paid for all the peach pits I could

[30] Kindly furnished by Dr. John A. Widtsoe, Salt Lake City, one of the Council of the Twelve, of the Church of Jesus Christ of Latter-day Saints.

get at one cent a piece. I finished a house for Loran Farr and took my pay in peach pits. I also built a fence for Dr. Sprague for this pay. I now began to succeed in developing the nursery business. In the spring of 1856, I received by mail many seeds and cuttings. . .

I think it was in the fall of 1855 I went to President Young and obtained the use of the Social Hall for the purpose of calling a meeting in the interests of Horticulture. . . This was the first meeting in the interests of horticulture in Utah. A second meeting was held soon after. This same autumn, I did the initiatory labor, backed up by President Young and all the leading men of the Church, of getting up the meeting for the organization of the Deseret Horticultural Society. . . This was the initiatory step for the incorporating of the Deseret Agricultural and Manufacturing Society by the Utah Legislature.

I had by this time my nursery business well under way and it furnished me abundant labor. In 1856 I propagated mostly from the best Utah varieties of fruit. In the budding season of 1857 I had a very good assortment of imported varieties from which to bud. Many of these varieties were distributed by budding into stocks grown by my neighbors.

Some time in the Spring of 1856; President Young put his hands on my head and set me apart to make my calling the growing of trees, shrubs and the introduction of everything of this kind that is good among the saints in Utah, and to this end he blessed me.

The Far West, both near the coast and in the dry lands of the interior, furnished many esculents and ornamentals, some of which have been mentioned in earlier pages as having been introduced in the eastern states and Europe. Not a few of these were useful in the regions in which they grew wild, both for the first settlers and now, for food and in landscape plantings, especially the latter.

The most notable of the trees from the Pacific Coast is the California Big Tree, *Sequoia gigantea,* titan evergreen, often reaching a height of more than 300 feet. It is found in several groves on the western slopes of the Sierra Nevada Mountains. The tale of the introduction of this tree to the gardens of the East and of Europe is charmingly told in a little book by W. D. Ellwanger, son of the senior member of Ellwanger & Barry.

Sometime in the early 'fifties, according to Mr. Ellwanger,[31]

31 Ellwanger, pp. 1-8.

G. H. Woodruff, a New Yorker, went to California to seek his fortune in the gold fields. After a year or two of disappointments, he found himself in a grove of giant sequoias. Forlorn and disconsolate, he threw himself on the ground and gazed into the treetops. Squirrels were busy nibbling the cones of the big trees, and seeds were dropping all about him. He gathered a handful of seeds, put them in a snuffbox and sent them to Ellwanger & Barry. At a cost of $25, the box came by pony express across the continent from California to Rochester.

The seeds of the first shipment were sown in a greenhouse in 1855, those of a second, out of doors in 1856. In due course, the nursery obtained about 4000 trees, 400 of which were sent to England. Ellwanger & Barry offered the trees in their catalogue of 1857 with the following description:

> Washingtonia Gigantea, the Celebrated Big Tree of California; Wellingtonia of the English and Sequoia of the French; one of the most majestic trees in the world. Specimens have been measured up to 300 feet in height and thirty-two feet in diameter three feet from the ground. We think it will prove hardy here, as several specimens stood out unprotected last winter. Mr. Reid of New Jersey has found it hardy with him. One dollar to two dollars.

As descriptions of things from California read in the boom days of the 1850's, this advertisement was so modest that it had little sale appeal to Americans. But Europeans wanted all the trees they could buy. An English nurseryman, William Skirving, bought 2350 of them. The celebrated nurseries of Thomas Rivers and of Veitch bought large orders. Trees went to nurseries in France and Germany as well. In England the small trees sold at from one to two guineas each and at this price several lots of a hundred each were sold. Every collector of trees wanted them. Botanic gardens in large cities in Europe had specimens or avenues of sequoias. In 1865 Ellwanger & Barry paid Mr. Woodruff $1030.60 as his share of the profits from a snuffbox of seeds.

Mr. Ellwanger says that his father's firm had many records of where the sequoias were planted in Europe: whether on the grounds of this Duke or that; of avenues of them here and there; how they thrived in one or another botanic garden; but no record is more interesting than one in the memoirs of Alfred Lord Tennyson, written by his son. 'The great event of the year 1864,' the son says, 'was the visit of Garibaldi to the Tennysons, an incident of which was the planting of a Wellingtonia by the great Italian and ceremonies connected with it.'

Of the trees that grew from Mr. Woodruff's snuffbox of seeds, the writer knew a fine group of seven on the grounds of the Ellwanger & Barry nursery; a beautiful specimen near the village of Union Springs, Cayuga County, New York; and three specimens in Boston, said to have come from the first lot of seeds. In the winters of 1918 and 1921 all these trees succumbed to the cold, or more likely to drying out of foliage from winter winds. Seed of the sequoias is now easily obtainable and most nurseries of ornamental evergreens offer trees at very moderate prices.

PART III

15

BOTANIC EXPLORERS AND BOTANIC GARDENS

1800-1860

G ARDENING has been benefited so greatly in recent years by
plants brought from all parts of the world that we are likely
to forget the men who, a century ago, enriched American horticulture with species from our then unexplored western lands and foreign countries as well. In earlier chapters we have written of the
work of John Bartram, Humphrey Marshall, André Michaux,
and several lesser collectors before 1800. The period, however,
in which most work was done in collecting and domesticating
American plants was from 1800 to 1860. This was a period, too,
when not a few plants were brought to this country from foreign
lands. Also, the number of public and private botanic gardens
was greatly increased in these years.

It would be hard to find a more thrilling chapter in the annals
of any science than the story of the exploration, could it be written in full, of the American continent in search of plant material
to further the advancement of botany and the enrichment of gardens. During these years American and foreign botanists and
gardeners took their lives in hand to serve the sciences and arts
dependent on plants. Their work took them into the wilderness,
over mountains, through swamps, and exposed them to the dangers of wild animal life, the tortures of vermin, pillage by Indians,
vagaries of climate, and malevolent diseases. Not a few early plant
explorers died, some by violent death, in the prosecution of their
work.

François André Michaux (1770-1855) had traveled with his father in America in the 1790's (see pages 191-4) but had later returned to France. In 1801 he came again to America to explore what was then the 'Western States.' In June of 1802 he crossed the Alleghenies of Pennsylvania into West Virginia; went down the Ohio; crossed Kentucky in a southwesterly direction; then on into Tennessee to Nashville, thence to Knoxville, and on to his old home in Charleston. The year, with the explorations he had made with his father, having yielded him material for much writing, he returned to France to publish two notable books.

The first, *L'Ouest des Monts Alleghanys,* was published in Paris in 1804. It is a rich source of material on both wild and cultivated plants in the states through which Michaux traveled. The work, however, for which the younger Michaux is chiefly remembered is *L'Histoire des arbres forestiers de l'Amerique septentrionale.* An English translation was published in Philadelphia in 1859 under the title *North American Sylva,* in three volumes with 145 plates. This book long remained the standard treatise on the trees of the eastern United States—an indispensable work for all landscape gardeners.

At the beginning of the century, a man by the name of Matthias Kin, an eccentric German, was a contemporary of the elder Michaux. Little is known about him except that he collected southern azaleas for the Landreth Nurseries, and is said to have traveled much of the region east of the great plain with an inquisitive eye for whatever was rare or beautiful. He brought to the Landreths many valuable species. Kin was sent to America by a group of German plant-lovers to collect the species of the country. The financial agent of these Germans was a Philadelphia banker by the name of Meng, to whom Kin gave many new plants.

Meng planted many of the plants Kin sent him on the grounds about his home at Germantown. The grounds, some twelve acres in extent, passed into the hands of the Wistars; then became the home of Thomas Meehan; and is now Vernon Park, one of the most beautiful small parks of Philadelphia. It would be hard to find a park in all America that has been more carefully planned and planted, and one that has had more loving care during the past hundred and more years. Among the rare trees introduced by Kin there stood, until a few years ago, a very large *Magnolia macrophylla,* the large-leaved cucumber tree, believed to be the first of its species ever planted by man.[1]

It is to be regretted that so little is known of Kin, and that no botanist has seen fit to commemorate his name in some species. The occasional mention of him in early accounts indicates that he was an industrious and enthusiastic collector of southern and western plants east of the Mississippi.

Much as the botanic explorers of the eighteenth century may have wanted to cross the Mississippi, or even the Alleghenies, none dared to venture far from the guarded communities of the Atlantic Coast. It remained for the Lewis and Clark expedition to the Pacific to open the way for nineteenth-century explorers for new plant material, all made envious by the reports of this famous expedition in 1804-6. Mention has been made in early chapters of some of their contributions to the nurseries of Prince and Landreth. Space does not permit a detailed account of the plants brought from the West, but those most valuable to gardeners must be named.

From the seeds brought from the West by Lewis and Clark, M'Mahon and Landreth grew, besides those already mentioned earlier, the golden currant, *Ribes aureum,* grown for its showy, fragrant yellow flowers and somewhat for its large purple fruit; the western snowberry bush, *Symphoricarpos albus;* and among vegetable seeds were obtained from the Indians several sorts of corn, beans, and a wild pea. A good deal was learned about the agriculture of the western tribes of Indians; and, even though the vegetable products were not important for the East, the fact was determined that the western plains were not arid deserts, but were capable of supporting a varied and abundant agriculture.

One of the trees that first appears in literature in the history of this famous expedition was the western shadbush or service-berry, *Amelanchier alnifolia.* The plant is a low shrub, beautiful in leaf, flower, and fruit. The fruit is sweet and delicious, as many travelers who have had to eke out a scanty diet, as did Lewis and Clark, testify. It has long been an inmate of ornamental gardens

[1] *Garden and Forest,* VI: 248.

at home and abroad, but still awaits the hand of some plant breeder who could make out of this handsome ornamental a valuable fruit, both for the regions where the plant grows wild and all regions where fruits of exceptional hardiness are needed. Although this estimable plant was made known to botanists by Lewis and Clark, it was David Douglas who sent seeds of it to the London Horticultural Society in 1826, after which it became well known in European and American gardens.

The men of this expedition first took notice of the western elder, *Sambucus caerulea,* grown in the Pacific states for its fruits and as an ornamental, and of the yellow or bull pine, *Pinus ponderosa;* though first described by Nuttall in 1834, the western larch or tamarack, *Larix occidentalis,* was first seen by Lewis and Clark in the Bitter Root Mountains in 1806.[2] The western hemlock, *Tsuga heterophylla,* was first described in 1814 in the journal of the Lewis and Clark expedition.[3] So, also, was the splendid Douglas spruce, though it had been seen earlier by Archibald Menzies and was not introduced in gardens until 1827, when David Douglas sent it to England; *Abies grandis,* the western white fir, has a history almost identical to that of the Douglas spruce.[4]

The mahonia, *Mahonia Aquifolium,* was brought to the East by Lewis and Clark from what is now Oregon. Since its introduction in gardens, it has been one of the prized broad-leaved evergreens in regions where the peach is grown. The genus was named after Bernard M'Mahon by his friend Thomas Nuttall.

It was Lewis and Clark who first found, in 1805, in the Bitter Root Mountains, the beautiful blue-flowered camass, *quamash* of the Indians, so common in the Pacific Northwest, then and long after a common food plant of the Indians, and one for early Whites. Much later, Watson gave it the name *Camassia Cusickii,* and still later it became, as did two or three closely related species, a very desirable inhabitant of flower gardens. The bulb is much like the onion in appearance; and, boiled in a soup, eaten boiled like a potato, or made into a cake, it could in time of need be a very desirable garden esculent.

---

[2] Sargent, *Silva of North America,* XII: 12.
[3] Ibid. p. 75.   [4] Ibid. p. 91.

To single out the few plants named in this brief discussion does not do justice to the botanic discoveries made by the men of this expedition, the first white men to cross the Rocky Mountains within the present territory of the United States. Besides the few mentioned as having been brought back, the seeds of a great number of coniferous plants, in particular, and of many deciduous shrubs and trees were turned over to skilled propagaters, who, within a few years, were ready to distribute in quantity young plants or seeds to gardeners and foresters. The several journals of the expedition added much to the knowledge of the plants growing west of the Mississippi, and stimulated botanic explorers to make conquests in the plant world of this region.

Another botanist early in the nineteenth century who deserves brief mention was Gotthilf H. E. Muhlenburg (1753-1815), eminent in botany, but scarcely as a gardener or plant explorer. He was a Lutheran clergyman, living at Lancaster, Pennsylvania, the author of *Flora of Lancaster,* an admirable local floral. In 1813 he published a catalogue of the plants of North America in which about 3000 species were listed.

A fellow worker in botany, born a neighbor of Muhlenburg's in Lancaster, was Benjamin Smith Barton (1766-1815), who became a member of the group in Philadelphia that did so much for science, botany especially. His was a great name a century ago, but it does not appear that he contributed much to gardening, or as a plant explorer, other than to train men for the field and to describe the species they collected.

One of the early plant explorers on the Pacific Coast was Iwan Iwanowitsch Eschscholtz (1793-1831), a Russian naturalist who visited the west coast of North America, 1815 to 1818, where he discovered a number of plants that he described in the *Memoirs of the Academy of St. Petersburg.* He would be passed by, in this work at least, as one of the many plant explorers of lesser note, were it not that his name has been given to the California poppy, *Eschscholtzia californica,* California's state flower. Among other of Eschscholtz's discoveries in 1816 was the California lilac or blue myrtle, *Ceanothus thyrsiflorus,* a beautiful shrub, garden varieties of which are much grown, especially in European gardens.

To Frederick Traugott Pursh (1774-1820), a botanist, horticulturist, explorer, and author, all American gardeners are indebted for much aid in the fields of his activities. Although he was in the United States less than 20 years, one comes across his name at almost every turn in the botany and horticulture of the first half of the nineteenth century. Prominent as he became in American plant lore during the few years of his work in this country, it seems almost impossible to get a precise account of his life.

Pursh was born in Germany, where he trained in botany and horticulture before he came to America in 1799 to take charge of a botanic garden in Baltimore. His work in botany and horticulture became of note in 1802 when he took charge of the gardens at Woodlands, Philadelphia, the beautiful estate of William Hamilton, then considered the finest example of landscape gardening in America. In 1805 Pursh left Philadelphia for two years of botanic exploration in the northern states, after which, in 1807, he went to New York to Hosack's Elgin Botanical Garden.

While in Philadelphia, Pursh was associated with the several botanists and horticulturists who long made that city the most distinguished botanic center in the New World. He was a disciple, in particular, of Benjamin Smith Barton, who not only taught him, but provided him with funds for two extensive explorations in eastern America, which gave him first-hand knowledge and enabled him to begin assembling plants from all parts of America.

In 1812, Pursh went to England to avail himself of the help of English botanists and their collections of American plants, those growing as well as those in herbariums. In 1814 he published *Flora Americae Septentrionalis,* the second flora of North America north of Mexico. A feature of this flora was that it contained all the plants described by several botanists, of whom Pursh was one, from the Lewis and Clark expedition. Pursh's only other book, published in 1869, long after his death, was *A Journal of a Botanical Excursion in the Northeastern Parts of Pennsylvania and New York,* one of the most delightful accounts of a naturalist's explorations written in America. The journey was taken in 1806 and 1807.

When Pursh returned from England he settled in Montreal, with the intention of gathering material for a flora of Canada. His notes were burned and the flora he contemplated was never published, notwithstanding which he did much for the botany of Canada. His crowded life of 45 years came to a close in Montreal in 1820.

It was Pursh who first made known the beautiful azalea, *Rhododendron arborescens*. John Bartram had been its discoverer many years before in the mountains of Pennsylvania, but it was Pursh who first published a description. Two years later it was introduced in English gardens. It was Pursh, also, who gave the name to the common madrona of the Pacific Coast, *Arbutus Menziesii*, named after an early botanic explorer in this region, Menzies.

While in charge of Hamilton's Woodlands gardens in their palmiest days, Pursh had an associate of whom we know little and would like to know more. The man was John Lyon, a Scotchman, an excellent gardener, and a very good botanist. As was the case with many other good European gardeners in America, he would have escaped notice had he not joined Pursh on his plant-hunting expeditions and thereby brought himself to the notice of a famous American writer. The writer was Captain Mayne Reid, novelist and writer of books for boys. Reid writes that Lyon became a 'practical plant hunter and in that pursuit he made extensive journeys, preserving his accumulated gatherings at my father's nursery [near Philadelphia] until they amounted to a sufficiency to authorize a trip; thus he made alternate journeys of collection and voyages across the Atlantic.' And again: 'Mr. Editor, you will remember the *Magnolias, Halesias, Stuartias, Virgilias, Gordonias, Pinckneyas,* and other then rare native trees and shrubs, which decorated the old place—they were mainly the contribution of Mr. Lyon.' [5] On a tour of exploration in Tennessee, Lyon died of a fever, sometime between 1814 and 1818.

One of the commonest names found after American species of plants, especially those of the Pacific Coast, is that of Thomas

5 Reid, XIII: 256.

Nuttall (1786-1859), an Englishman, who came to Philadelphia in 1808 and also became a student of Benjamin Smith Barton. Nuttall was a naturalist and explorer by instinct. He made discoveries wherever his unwearied feet took him in geology and ornithology as well as botany. He managed to discover many plants of economic value, especially ornamental flowers, shrubs, and trees.

His first collections were made around Philadelphia, but soon he was searching the fields and woods of Delaware, Maryland, Virginia, the Carolinas, Georgia, Florida, and on and on to the Mississippi. In 1809-11, accompanied by John Bradbury, a Scotch naturalist, he explored the banks of the Missouri River beyond the villages of the Mandan Indians, the most skilled gardeners of all the western Indian tribes, and brought home an account of their agriculture. Beginning in 1819, he made collections along the Arkansas and Red Rivers in Louisiana, Arkansas, and Indian territory, with rich rewards in new species. But his most productive exploring venture was as a member of the Wyeth expedition to the mouth of the Columbia River, in 1834, where Wyeth was to found a fur-trading post. Here, on the Pacific Coast, Nuttall did his best work in botany, markedly so if considered from a horticulturist's point of view. From the mouth of the Columbia, Nuttall traveled down to California, thence to Hawaii, then home via Cape Horn.

Nuttall gave us the name *Wisteria* for the most beautiful of all hardy climbers. The word was coined, in 1818, for *Wisteria frutescens,* an American plant that had been in cultivation in England since 1724 as *Glycine frutescens.* The plant was named by Nuttall in honor of his friend Dr. Caspar Wistar. The American species, however, is not the plant of common cultivation. In 1818 John Reeves, an officer in the East India Company, sent to England from Canton, China, a vine that the English called *Glycine sinensis.* In 1825, De Candolle, the French botanist, referred the plant to Nuttall's *Wisteria.* This and the slightly hardier Japanese wisteria, *Wisteria floribunda,* are the climbers that adorn so many American and European homes.

It is said that Nuttall visited nearly every state in the Union, and that he made more discoveries than any other explorer-botanist in North America. Nearly all his plants came home as herbarium specimens, but he did bring back a considerable number for the garden and much valuable information about those first found by others. Nuttall's reputation as a botanist rests chiefly on his *Genra of North American Plants,* in two volumes, published in 1818. For a few years, beginning in 1822, Nuttall was a professor of botany and curator of the Botanic Garden at Harvard. In 1842-54 he published *North American Silva,* in three volumes, indispensable to those who would have first-hand knowledge of the trees of the Far West, none of which were in Michaux's earlier work. He also published *A Journal of Travels into the Arkansas Territory during the Year* 1819, a delightful book of American travel. It was printed in Philadelphia in 1821.

Nuttall was an ornithologist and geologist and wrote much on these subjects as well as on botany.

It was Nuttall who discovered the rather pretty prairie rose of the Southwest, *Rosa foliolosa,* a plant that ranges from Arkansas to Texas. The species was collected in the visit to Arkansas in 1818-20, but it did not reach gardens until collected by several other plant explorers, and a description had been published by Torrey and Gray in their *Flora of North America.*

We are indebted to Nuttall, also, for at least three species of *Coreopsis,* which he found in central and southern United States. The several species were introduced in the 1830's. Among western evergreens named by Nuttall is *Larix occidentalis,* an esteemed ornamental on the Pacific Coast. He also named the western mistletoe, *Phoradendron flavescens,* though earlier botanists must have seen it; also *Clematis ligusticifolia,* the western clematis; the beautiful California laurel, *Umbellularia californica;* the California horse chestnut, *Aesculus californica,* and the Oregon ash, *Fraxinus oregona.* The handsome small tree, *Ceanothus arboreus,* was discovered on Santa Catalina Island by Nuttall in 1835. The same year he first described the noble California sycamore, *Platanus racemosa,* which he found near Santa Barbara.

Another of the many physicians and botanists of Philadelphia whose names are commemorated in botany was William Gambel, who was graduated from the Medical School of the University of Pennsylvania in 1848. Instead of practicing medicine he traveled for some years as a botanist in the southern Rocky Mountains for the Academy of Natural Sciences of Philadelphia, making notable additions to the knowledge of botany in the Southwest. A western oak, *Quercus Gambelii,* was named in his honor by Thomas Nuttall in 1850. Nuttall, by the way, described most of the plants collected by Dr. Gambel.

Few other plant explorers in the first half of the nineteenth century traveled more widely, collected more plants, and met more men in the several sciences than Constantine Samuel Rafinesque (1783-1840). Rafinesque's father was a Frenchman, his mother a German, but the son had lived in Sicily for some years before he came to America in 1815 to spend the remainder of his life. From 1815 to 1818 he lived in New York and Pennsylvania, making the acquaintance of the leading naturalists in the New World.

His real work in science, especially in botany, began in 1818 when he became professor of botany and natural history in Transylvania College, a position he held for eight years. From this college, located in Lexington, Kentucky, he made many long, arduous trips through the Middle West, collecting, speaking, and writing. Much of what he wrote was not published, and of the large amount that was printed a good deal might better not have been. For example, in his *Neogenyton,* a pamphlet of 4 pages published in 1824, he described 66 new genera. His characterizations of plants were scant, vague, and often inaccurate.

In spite of all his shortcomings, after a century of disregard, Rafinesque is now being looked upon as a brilliant, if not wholly sane, genius to whom botany and horticulture owe a great deal. It was he who gave the generic name to the beautiful ornamental tree, *Cladrastis tinctoria,* which the elder Michaux had discovered in 1796.

The best-known botanist in the southern states in this period was Stephen Elliott (1771-1830), a descendant in the sixth generation from William Elliott, who came from England to Charles Town in 1670. The name is preserved in Charleston in Elliott Street. Elliott is remembered by botanists for his admirable *Sketch of the Botany of South Carolina and Georgia,* published in two volumes in 1821 and 1824. Elliott's book, by the way, contained 180 genera and 1000 species that Walter's earlier *Flora*

Caroliniana did not describe. As a botanist, he ever had the desire to make his knowledge useful and did much to popularize native plants for southern gardens. He discovered in the first years of the last century on the Savannah River in Georgia a beautiful shrub of the Heath family, now multiplied in gardens, *Elliottia racemosa*.

Elliott's name is associated with the Cherokee rose, beloved in all the South. Michaux had found it so thoroughly naturalized in the South at the beginning of the nineteenth century that he published it, under the name *Rosa laevigata*, as a native species. Elliott accepted it as such and said in his botany that it had been 'cultivated in the gardens of Georgia for upwards of 40 years' under the name of Cherokee Rose. Later it was found that it was a common wild rose in eastern Asia. Who brought it to America, when, and how it escaped to the woods of the Cherokee Indians, we do not know.

Besides being a botanist, for which he is now best known, Elliott was a banker, statesman, editor, planter, and was once elected president of a college, though he did not serve. It was he who published the first account of the American sloe, *Prunus umbellata*, an orchard plant, in his *Sketch of the Botany of South Carolina and Georgia*.

One of the many physicians who made substantial additions to American botany and horticulture as a plant explorer was William Baldwin (1779-1819). His death at the age of 40, while on an exploring trip up the Missouri, cut short a life full of promise for both medicine and botany. Even so he accomplished enough to bring forth one of the best of botanical biographies, *Reliquiæ Baldwiniannæ*, published in 1843, by his friend, neighbor, and fellow botanist, Dr. William Darlington.

Baldwin was a native of Chester County, Pennsylvania, home of so many botanists, and was, as were nearly all his fellow botanists from that region, a Quaker. Botanical study, excursions, and correspondence with the scientists about him and in Philadelphia made him an enthusiastic botanist even while a medical student; in the midst of his studies he became ship's surgeon on a vessel sailing to China, where he hoped to have time for botany. Returning from China in 1806, after a stay of two years, he took his medical degree in 1807 and began practice in Wilmington, Delaware, employing his leisure in studying the local flora.

His real work as a botanical explorer began in 1811 when he made a journey by boat in Georgia. He served as a surgeon in the War of 1812, and then settled down in St. Mary's, Georgia, as a professional plant hunter. Then followed a trip as surgeon-botanist on a ship to Buenos Aires, the chief object being to investigate 'vegetable products.'

His next and last botanical trip began in 1819 as surgeon-botanist, with Major Stephen H. Long, on that officer's famous expedition up the Missouri. In this party there were several other scientists of note, and all promised well for much good work. The project was thwarted, however, by Baldwin's death at Franklin, Missouri, on the banks of the Missouri River, when their work had scarcely begun.

Dr. Baldwin's work belongs to botany rather than to horticulture; but he did bring to gardening some new material and much new knowledge of plants introduced by others. Moreover, had he not done work in botany, William Darlington's charming biography, with much information for all who work with plants, would not have been written.

Dr. Edwin James (1797-1861), a botanist of whom one hears too little, deserves recognition in particular as a plant explorer. He was a native of Vermont and was educated at Middlebury College, from which he was graduated in 1816. The next three years he spent in Albany studying botany under Dr. John Torrey and Professor Amos Eaton, then the leading botanists in America, and medicine with his brother, Dr. John James. In 1819 he became botanist, geologist, and surgeon of the expedition commanded by Major Long, sent by the government to explore the region between the Mississippi and the Rocky Mountains. After Dr. Baldwin's untimely death, James took his place in charge of the botanic work. Scientific exploration in Texas seems to have begun with this expedition. On 14 July 1820, James and two companions reached the summit of Pikes Peak, the first white men to do so. The mountain was named James Peak by Major Long, supplanted later by the name in honor of General Pike, an earlier discoverer.

James's reputation as a botanist and plant explorer was largely established by the account of Long's expedition, which he wrote under the title *Account of an Expedition from Pittsburg to the Rocky Mountains in the Years* 1819 *and* '20, published in 1822-3. In it, among many other scientific matters, is a report on the flora of the Rocky Mountains, especially in Colorado. Horticulture is indebted to Dr. James for his descriptions of the conifers of this region, several of which are among the choicest narrow-leaved evergreens planted in the landscapes of the country.

The earliest botanical account of the very common mesquite of the Southwest, *Prosopis glandulosa Juliflora,* was given by James. It was he, who, in 1820, discovered the western scrub oak, *Quercus undulata.* The narrow-leaved cottonwood, *Populus angustifolia,* often planted in the Rocky Mountain states as a shade tree, was first described by James; in 1820, he found near the base of Pikes Peak the Colorado white pine, *Pinus flexilis.*

A notable event in the horticultural and botanical history of the Pacific Coast took place before the region was settled by Whites. In 1825 David Douglas (1798-1834) came to Oregon and spent two years in botanical explorations. Douglas was a Scotch gardener sent to Oregon to collect trees and plants for the Horticultural Society of London. In 1830 he again visited the Pacific Coast on a collecting expedition.

Although the noble Douglas fir had been seen by other Whites before Douglas found it on the Columbia River, it was he who took it to British landscapes in 1825. He, too, it was who discovered the important and handsome lumber and ornamental tree, the western larch or tamarack, *Larix occidentalis,* near one of the Hudson's Bay posts on the upper Columbia River in 1847, though it was not until 1849 that Nuttall described it, and not until 30 years later that it was brought East to the Arnold Arboretum.[6]

One of the best of the broad-leaved evergreens found on the Pacific Coast is the Islay, *Prunus ilicifolia,* sometimes called Spanish wild cherry, a native of southern California. It was David Douglas who brought it to the attention of horticulturists, having found it near Monterey, although the Mission Fathers had long

[6] *Garden and Forest,* IX: 491.

before planted it about their establishments. It was much used by the first English-speaking settlers in California as an ornamental shrub.

It was David Douglas who, in 1825-6, discovered the western dogwood, *Cornus Nuttallii*, one of the most beautiful plants of the Pacific Coast, certainly so when in flower. The plant was later named in honor of Thomas Nuttall by John James Audubon. Eventually botanists found it growing from British Columbia to southern California and, though one plant explorer after another introduced it into the gardens of Europe and the Atlantic states, it was found that it could almost never be grown out of its native soil. Douglas it was who sent the western shad-tree, *Amelanchier alnifolia*, to England in 1826, where, and in this country, it became a common ornamental. And in 1833 he first described the Oregon crab apple, *Pyrus fusca*, now an ornamental, the apples of which were long used by the Indians and white pioneers as a fall and winter fruit.

Rubus macropetalus, parent of several dewberries and one of the parents of two or three hybrids, all of great pomological importance, was first described by David Douglas. He found it in the valley of the Columbia River in 1832. It was Douglas who found the Pacific Coast gooseberry, *Ribes divaricatum*.

In 1825 Douglas discovered the Oregon wild cherry, *Prunus emarginata*, grown as a street and lawn tree in the Pacific Northwest. The same year he found on the banks of the lower Columbia the Oregon ash, *Fraxinus oregona*, a tree often planted for its shade in the Pacific Northwest. Of the several beautiful ornamental trees Douglas brought to the attention of gardeners, none is more noteworthy than the blue oak of California, *Quercus Douglasii*. He was the first gardener to call attention to several conifers of value in ornamental plantings: as the West Coast yew, *Taxus brevifolia*, in 1825; the western white pine, *Pinus monticola*, in 1831; the magnificent sugar pine, *P. Lambertiana*, in 1831; the yellow or bull pine, *P. ponderosa*, next in size and beauty to the sugar pine among pines; the digger pine, *P. Sabiniana;* the Monterey pine, *P. radiata*, in 1833, now much planted. *Abies amabilis*, one of the white firs, discovered in 1825, was another plant introduced in English gardens by Douglas; on the same day he discovered and later sent to England the red fir, *A. nobilis.*[7]

Douglas sent to England the seeds of baby blue-eyes, *Nemophila Menziesii,* and other members of the genus; farewell-to-spring, *Godetia amoena,* and other godetias, related to the evening primroses; two or three Collinsias; the blazing star, *Mentzelia Lindleyi;* the exquisite yellow globe tulip, *Calochortos pulchellus;* and several of the California poppies. While most of these are weeds or wildlings in California, all are pampered favorites in European flower gardens.

One cannot discuss the work of David Douglas without associating his name with that of Archibald Menzies (1754-1842), another Scotch botanist, in whose tracks Douglas almost literally stepped, a generation after. Menzies was on the Pacific Coast some years before the period under discussion, but this seems the best place to speak of his work.

Menzies was a Scotch surgeon in the British naval service and first visited the Northwest Coast in 1786, where he did some collecting. But it was as a member of Vancouver's famous expedition to explore the coasts of the two continents in the New World (1791-5) that most of Menzies' botanical work was done. On this trip he visited Monterey, San Francisco, and many points between the two and Vancouver Island to the north.

It was Menzies who first described one of the world's most beautiful broad-leaved evergreens, the madrona, *Arbutus Menziesii,* which he found near the mouth of the Columbia River. The tree, an inhabitant of the moist region of the Pacific Coast, did not become a garden plant until David Douglas collected seeds in Oregon and sent them to England. It was Menzies, also, who first discovered, among other notable western trees and shrubs, the Douglas fir, *Pseudotsuga taxifolia.*

The California laurel, *Umbellularia californica,* another of the beautiful broad-leaved evergreens of this continent, was discovered by Menzies on the shores of the Bay of San Francisco in 1792. The Pacific Coast white oak, *Quercus Garryana,* was discovered by him on the shores of Puget Sound on this memorable voyage,

[7] Sargent, *Silva of North America,* XII: 135.

but was later named by Douglas. *Chamaecyparis nootkatensis* was discovered by Menzies on the shores of Nootka Sound. *Thuya plicata,* which Sargent considers the 'noblest of its race,'[8] was discovered by Menzies in 1796. Menzies first saw the magnificent redwood of the Pacific Coast, *Sequoia sempervirens* (not to be confused with *Sequoiadendron giganteum* previously mentioned), in 1796, but it remained for David Douglas to rediscover it while Karl Theodor Hartweg introduced it in English gardens in 1846. *Picea sitchensis,* greatest of all spruces, was discovered by Menzies in 1792 and was introduced in English gardens by David Douglas in 1831.

Thomas Drummond first appears as a plant explorer in America as a member of the second expedition of Franklin, the famous English arctic explorer. He left the English party at Cumberland House, a Hudson's Bay Company post, to explore the Rocky Mountains in Canada. In 1831 he collected in the Alleghenies, then on to the regions about St. Louis, and New Orleans, thence in due course to Texas. Before coming to the New World, Drummond had been curator of the Belfast Botanic Garden and had an eye out for garden plants as well as herbarium specimens. The only other botanist of note to explore Texas before Drummond was Jean Louis Berlandier, so the Scotch gardener found nearly a virgin field. Of the plants Drummond sent to Scotland for garden culture, *Phlox Drummondii,* now grown in all temperate regions, is best known. The Texas fuchsia, *Malaniscus Drummondii,* and *Clematis Drummondii* are two other garden plants bearing his name. Drummond did some botanizing about Apalachicola, Florida, late in 1832; early in 1833 he went to Havana, where he died in March. No doubt Drummond's collections became of added value to gardening and botany because they passed through the hands of Sir Joseph Hooker, Keeper of the Royal Botanic Garden at Kew, under whose patronage the Scotch gardener worked in the New World.

The work of botanical explorers in the vast territory of Texas who added to the knowledge of botanic and gardening lore of the

[8] Ibid. x: 130.

Southwest in the period under consideration has been described earlier (see pages 361 ff.). Others were Charles Wright, who came to Texas in 1837 and collected there until 1852, and Ferdinand Lendheimer, who came in 1836. Possibly the most notable was Wright, who discovered the rather pretty *Acacia Greggii* of the Southwest in 1851, and named it after Josiah Gregg, botanist and author of *The Commerce of the Prairies* (see p. 390). The Mexican elder, a botanical variety of *Sambucus canadensis,* grown in the Southwest for its fruit and as an ornamental, was first seen by Wright in 1852. The noble and beautiful Arizona sycamore, *Platanus Wrightii,* he discovered in southern Arizona in 1851.

One of the botanists on the Mexican Boundary Survey whose work is of particular note was Dr. J. M. Bigelow, who found a great number of new plants of which several have become choice ornamentals. Of these, the Spanish dagger and the Joshua tree, members of the genus *yucca,* are best known. He also first described the fan palm, *Washingtonia filamentosa,* one of the common garden and street trees in southern California.

Few of these botanists who worked in Texas before the Mexican War went farther west into New Mexico on their scientific expeditions. This Far Western region was unsafe because of Indians and the difficulties of traveling in a country where there was little water. The one exception was Josiah Gregg. Gregg was a botanist, a physician, and a trader, as well as an author. Asa Gray and John Beglow described his plants and helped him prepare the botanic notes in his book. Gray dedicated a genus of Cruciferous herbs, *Greggia,* to him. An ash, *Fraxinus Greggii,* a native of southwestern Texas and Mexico, was discovered by Gregg in 1847 and further commemorates his name.

William Darlington (1782-1863) was one of several botanists who helped to make Chester County, Pennsylvania, famous for its botanic gardens. Darlington was by vocation a physician, his avocation, botany; his direct aid to gardening was not great, but he was one of the botanists in or near Philadelphia who sent seeds and plants to Europe and received similar items in exchange. Probably even more helpful were several botanical treatises that furnished knowledge of plants; and best of all were two books about fellow botanists: *Reliquiæ Baldwinianæ,* 1843, and *The*

Memorials of John Bartram and Humphry Marshall, 1849, which are among the most charming works to be found in garden libraries. Still another volume of value to gardeners was his *Agricultural Botany,* 1847, long the standard book on this subject. In this book, the first botany written for the tiller of the soil, cultivated plants and common weeds were described in plain, simple words. Darlington's *Flora Cestrica,* 1826, a description of the plants growing in Chester County, Pennsylvania, is one of the best local floras written in America, a model for all that have followed. Darlington enjoyed the friendship of the best botanists at home and abroad, from whom he obtained and distributed much botanical knowledge of benefit to all who work with plants.

Darlington's name was given by John Torrey to the curious insectivorous California pitcher plant, *Darlingtonia californica,* a native of California and Oregon. The plant is sometimes grown in wild- and water-gardens as a curiosity.

Some forty-odd learned societies elected Darlington to membership. If his correspondence with fellow botanists in these societies could be collected, both botanical and horticultural literature would be greatly enriched, as is shown by an occasional letter in this or that publication.

Colonel John C. Frémont rendered a most important service to botany and horticulture in four hazardous journeys made to the Far West in 1842, 1843-4, and 1845-7, and 1848. His first expedition was across the plains to the Rocky Mountains; the second expedition covered the same ground and went on to Oregon and California; the third expedition covered the general region of the second. The fourth journey to California in 1848 was of great importance to botanists and gardeners. Dr. John Torrey described the plants collected in the last two expeditions and published them in 1850 in *Smithsonian Contributions* as *Plantæ Frémontianæ.*

This flower-loving soldier's name is commemorated by the genus *Fremontia,* in which is a single species, *Fremontia californica,* the flannel bush, a rather handsome shrub that bears yellow flowers in great profusion. It was discovered by the great explorer in southern California in 1846 on his third transcontinental journey. His name is further commemorated in *Populus Fremontia,* a cottonwood much planted in the American Southwest. It was Frémont who discovered the incense cedar, *Libocedrus decurrens,* on the upper Sacramento River in 1846, several forms of which are cultivated; another conifer that he first saw was one of the nut or piñon pines, *Pinus monophylla,* in southern California in 1844. In 1845, Frémont discovered *Abies magnifica,* a red fir that Sargent says is the noblest of all its race.[9]

The plants Frémont and the collectors with him brought home were studied by John Torrey, Asa Gray, and William Darlington. Seeds and plants were turned over to various nurseries and soon horticulture was being enriched by nearly as many ornamentals as were brought back by Lewis and Clark. Among them were sunflowers, gaillardias, rudbeckias, verbenas, yuccas, lupines, asters, penstemons, gentians, goldenrods, silenes, phloxes, aquilegias, and larkspurs, herbaceous plants known to all gardeners. There were, as well, several shrubs; as, one of the *Shepherdias,* four *Ribes,* at least one *Vaccinium,* and numerous other shrubs that earlier explorers had described or brought home; several conifers, chiefly pines, from both the Rocky Mountains and the Pacific Coast.

A great number of trees, shrubs, and flowers were discovered and named by Charles Christopher Parry (1823-90), most of whose work, however, was done later than this period of history. Parry was born in England, educated in America, and in 1846 settled in Davenport, Iowa, to practice medicine. It would take a volume to recount Parry's services to botany and horticulture in the Middle West, the Rocky Mountains, Mexico, and the Pacific Coast, from 1846 to 1890. Parry's *Lilium Parryi* is well known to all gardeners. It was he who discovered *Picea Engelmanni; Pinus Torreyana, P. aristata;* the dwarf horse chestnut, *Aesculus Parryi; Ribes Viburnifolium;* the Mexican Rose, *Rosa minutifolia;* and the garden flowers *Zizyphus Parryi, Phacelia Parryi,* and *Frasera Parryi.*

Parry gave name also to the handsome and common manzanita, *Arctostaphylos Manzanita,* a magnificent evergreen, broad-leaved shrub, without which Pacific Coast gardens and woodlands would suffer greatly. No doubt earlier botanical explorers saw this com-

9 Ibid. XI: 139.

mon evergreen, admired and possibly described it before Parry
gave it the name now in use.

The most valuable services Parry gave as a plant explorer, in
the time of this history at any rate, began in 1850, when he joined
the scientific staff of the Mexican Boundary Survey and crossed
the California desert from San Diego to the mouth of the Gila
River, and on subsequent trips extending through two or three
years with the Survey, in which he traveled from the Pacific Ocean
to the Gulf of Mexico discovering many riches in botany, some of
value to horticulture. A record of his work is to be found in the
Report of the Mexican Boundary Survey, published in 1852. Perhaps, however, his examination of the flora of the central Rocky
Mountains, begun in 1861 at his own expense, yielded more in the
way of flowers, trees, and shrubs of interest to gardeners.

To Parry must be given credit for introducing to the East the
California walnut, *Juglans californica.* In 1850 he discovered one
of the piñon pines, *Pinus cembroides Parryana,* which is sometimes cultivated in California. Best known by gardeners of all
Parry's discoveries is the Colorado blue spruce, *Picea pungens,*
which he first saw on Pikes Peak in 1862.

The work of one of Parry's associates in the Mexican Boundary
Survey must also receive brief mention. Dr. George Thurber
(1821-90), quartermaster and commissary, was a naturalist of conspicuous ability, and for five years, beginning in 1850, he collected
plants between the Gulf of Mexico and the Pacific Ocean. He discovered many new plants, some of them of interest to cultivators,
described by Asa Gray in 1854 in a treatise entitled *Plantæ Thur-
bianæ.* Thurber added greatly to his services to horticulture when
in 1859 he became a professor of horticulture in a new institution,
the Michigan Agricultural College, the first man to hold such a
professorship in the United States. Later, in 1863, he became editor of *The American Agriculturist,* and for 22 years was one of
the most forceful horticultural writers America has produced.

During the years 1838-42, a United States Naval exploring expedition was on the Pacific Coast, with Charles Pickering as botanist. Several thousand specimens were collected, of which the
phanerogamous plants were described by Dr. John Torrey. Most

of the plants conspicuous enough to be of value to gardening had been found before Pickering saw them, but no doubt his large collection and notes helped in distribution.

In scientific works dealing with the botany of California, *Plantæ Hartwegianæ,* published by G. Bentham (1839-48), the English botanist, is often quoted. The publication takes its name from the collections of Karl Theodor Hartweg, a German gardener sent by the Horticultural Society of London to collect plants in Mexico and California. During the years 1838 and 1839 Hartweg was collecting in Alta, California, then a part of Mexico. According to Sargent, the most commonly cultivated coniferous tree in California is the Monterey cypress, *Cupressus macrocarpa,* which was first made known to botanists by Hartweg in 1847.[10]

One of the last British expeditions to discover plants of horticultural value in the United States was that of the Oregon Association sent out by a body of Scotchmen in 1852 to collect plants on the Pacific Coast. The expedition was led by John Jeffrey, a Scotch gardener. At this late date the forests of the Pacific Coast had been well explored; nevertheless, Jeffrey succeeded in taking back to Scotland a number of most remarkable plants, among them some of the best western ornamental evergreens. The following, to name but a few of Jeffrey's discoveries, are notable additions to ornamental plantations of trees: *Pinus Jeffreyi,* found near Mount Shasta; *P. Balfouriana,* from the same region; *P. Murrayana,* and *P. albicaulis,* from different parts of California; and *Tsuga Mertensiana,* formerly known as Patton's hemlock, near Mount Baker in northern Washington.

John Strong Newberry (1822-92) added to our knowledge of American botany, even though he came too late to take a hand in naming or introducing many plants of horticultural value. He was, in early life, a physician in Cleveland, Ohio; in later life, a professor of geology in Columbia University. But he was always much interested in botany, and for a few years before the Civil War was an able and diligent plant explorer in the Far West. In 1855 Newberry was appointed Acting Assistant Surgeon in the United States Army and accompanied an expedition under Lieutenant R. S. Williamson, which explored the region between San

10 Ibid. x: 104.

Francisco and the Columbia River. While Dr. Newberry made other explorations, usually as a geologist, it was on this Pacific Coast exploration that he made his most important contributions to the knowledge of plants. He reported on the plants collected on the Williamson expedition in the sixth volume of the *Pacific Railroad Reports,* in which he described the forest trees of northern California and of Oregon so fully and accurately that it was long one of the best sources of information about the trees of this region. He discovered in the Cascade Mountains of Oregon a leafless Ericaceous plant, out of which Torrey made a genus that he dedicated to Newberry under the name *Newberrya.* In 1860 Dr. Newberry published a catalogue of the trees and ferns of Ohio.

Dr. George Engelmann (1809-84), a physician in St. Louis, much too busy in his profession to do much exploring, was of great help to many collectors of plants, and put all gardeners in his debt by his contributions to the knowledge of American species of conifers, cacti, oaks, grapes, yuccas, and euphorbias. He was a German, born in Frankfort-on-Main in February 1809, and came to Missouri in 1832, to St. Louis in 1835. During the latter part of his life, mostly after the period of this history, he did some botanical exploring in Colorado, the Pacific Coast, North Carolina, Tennessee, and about Lake Superior. Grape growers of America and Europe are indebted to him for several papers on American vines, and gardeners generally for the papers entitled *The Yucca, The Agave, The Coniferae,* and *The American Oaks.*

Engelmann's name is commemorated best, perhaps, in a handsome evergreen oak, *Quercus Engelmanni,* found in southern California; though of almost equal importance is a spruce, *Picea Engelmanni,* discovered by Dr. C. C. Parry in the Rocky Mountains in 1862. To Engelmann belongs the honor of making known in 1873 the characters of the white fir, *Abies concolor,*[11] the handsomest of all firs planted as ornamentals, though several other plant explorers had seen it earlier.

The last of the plant explorers to come within the survey of this history is Dr. George R. Hall (1820-99), who was the fortunate introducer of several plants from China and Japan that are

[11] Ibid. xii: 123.

about as valuable as any to be found in American gardens. Dr. Hall graduated from the Harvard Medical School in 1846, and shortly began to practice medicine in Shanghai, China. In the years that followed, until at least as late as 1861, Hall sent, one after another, beautiful plants long cultivated in the Orient. Among these are several Retinosporas and Thujas, now notable in any collection of conifers.

Best known of Hall's evergreens is the Japanese yew, *Taxus cuspidata,* a relative of the English yew which cannot be grown very well in the northeastern part of the United States. This yew is probably Japan's greatest gift among evergreens to America. It was introduced by Parsons and Company, Flushing, Long Island. Hall's honeysuckle, *Lonicera japonica Halliana,* is even better known than the Japanese yew. One of the hardiest and most popular magnolias is *Magnolia stellata,* sent to America by Dr. Hall. Another of his beautiful trees is the Parkman crab apple, *Malus Halliana,* the 'Pink Pearl of the Orient,' sent with other plants to Francis Parkman in 1861. The Japanese wisteria, *Wisteria floribunda,* slightly hardier than its relative, the Chinese wisteria, was introduced by Dr. Hall in 1862 by seeds sent to Samuel Parsons. Dr. Hall, after many years in the Orient, returned to live at Bristol, Rhode Island, where he grew a notable collection of Asiatic evergreens.

These pages cannot include even brief sketches of botanists other than plant explorers, but a few botanists who worked the first half of the nineteenth century, to the enrichment of horticulture, have been mentioned elsewhere. Without their knowledge, especially as set forth in books, and without the encouragement they gave to horticulturists, gardening could never have made the progress it did in this period. Credit must be given five outstanding botanists: Benjamin Smith Barton (1766-1816); Amos Eaton (1776-1842); Jacob Bigelow (1787-1879); John Torrey (1796-1873); Asa Gray (1810-88).

The work of plant hunters in all parts of the world would have done gardening little good, other than to furnish the necessary descriptions of garden material, had it not been for botanic gardens where new plants might be tested. America was particularly fortunate in having established throughout the eighteenth and nineteenth centuries a number of public botanic gardens, supplemented by many more maintained by dealers in plants, owners of ornamental landscapes and greenhouses, and medical men who wanted herbs for professional use. Many of these have been mentioned earlier.

In or near Philadelphia are several notable botanic gardens. The oldest is Bartram's Garden (see pages 85-90), some trees and shrubs of which still remain. At Marshallton, near West Chester, is the Marshall Arboretum, where are many trees planted by Humphry Marshall in 1773. At Kennett Square is 'Longwood,' now owned by Longwood, Inc., founded by the Pierce family about 1800. There is also a garden at Haverford College, established in 1833.

In 1811, Bernard M'Mahon founded a botanic garden three miles north of the boundary of Philadelphia at that time. He called the garden 'Upsal,' and established it to grow native plants to exchange abroad.

Interest in botany and gardening at the beginning of the new century was recognized by Harvard College, which up until this time had had little to do with any of the sciences. In 1801 the Massachusetts Society for Promoting Agriculture, an organization incorporated in 1792, appropriated $500 for the establishment of the Massachusetts Professorship of Natural History at Harvard College. Work did not get under way until 1804. The Society made annual contributions and more funds were raised by subscription. In 1807 the grounds of the Cambridge Botanic Garden, consisting of seven acres, were laid out at the corner of Linnaean and Garden Streets, with William Dandridge Peck in charge, a position he held until his death in 1822.

This garden, at its start at least, seems to have been more concerned with agriculture and gardening than any other that had preceded it in this country. Among other objects specified in its charter was the 'sale and distribution of the seeds and roots of useful plants.' In 1813, the general court gave $1000, of which $600 was for the use of the Botanic Garden, '1st, to introduce into cultivation as many native plants as possible; 2nd, to devote an acre of land to raising seeds of culinary vegetables for distribution.'

Thomas Nuttall succeeded Peck in 1822, and was Curator until 1834, when the garden was taken in hand by William Carter, the original working gardener. He held this position until 1842, when Asa Gray became its director for the next 30 years. It is to be feared that under Nuttall and Gray the main interest was botany, the name of the garden becoming in due course 'The Botanic Garden of Harvard University.' It is true, however, that founders and members of the Massachusetts Horticultural Society, especially John Lowell and his son John Amory Lowell, gave the Garden strong financial backing in its first 50 years.

One of the distinguished patrons of gardening in the early part of the nineteenth century was Dr. David Hosack, a physician, who took his degree in medicine at the College of Philadelphia, in 1791. The next year he went to England and on to Scotland to continue his medical studies. In the course of his travels he met up with botanists and gardeners, and, falling in love with their subjects, became a student of both. In 1794 he returned to America with a fine collection of plants from the herbarium of the great Linnaeus. In 1795 he was made Professor of Botany and Materia Medica at Columbia College. At once he began making plans for a botanic garden to be maintained out of his own funds.

In 1801 Hosack purchased 20 acres of land from the Corporation of the City of New York 'between Bloomingdale and Kingsbridge,' distant from the city almost three miles and a half. The site is now not far from the heart of the city, Rockefeller Center being on a part of the land once covered by the garden. He named his new acquisition 'The Elgin Botanic Garden.' According to Dr. Hosack 'the primary object of attention [is] to collect and cultivate in this establishment the native plants of this country, especially such as are possessed of medicinal properties, or are otherwise useful. Such gardeners as were practically acquainted with our indigenous productions, have been employed.'

For these purposes the grounds seem to have been divided into a number of compartments, as far as possible according to 'the principles of botanic arrangements.' The garden was surrounded by a belt of forest trees and shrubs, both native and exotic, and these in turn 'were enclosed by a stone wall, two and a half feet in thickness, and seven feet high.'

Frederick Pursh was in charge of the Elgin Botanic Garden from 1807 to 1810, to its very great advantage. The names of such well-known botanists and gardeners as Bernard M'Mahon, William Prince, John Le Conte, William Darlington, and Stephen Elliott are mentioned as early advisers and contributors.

In 1805 the garden contained 1500 species of American plants; in 1811, 2200. From its catalogue, one learns that there was on the grounds 'an extensive conservatory, for the more hardy greenhouse plants, and two species of hothouses, for the preservation of those which require a greater degree of heat, the whole exhibiting a front of one hundred and eighty feet.' [12]

The Elgin Botanic Garden was transferred to the State of New York by virtue of an act passed 12 March 1810, and became the Botanic Garden of the State of New York under control of the College of Physicians and Surgeons. When this college became a part of Columbia University, in 1814, the management was taken over by the University. For half a century the garden was neglected, but eventually, as the city moved northward, it became a large source of income. About 1900 much of what had been the Elgin Botanic Garden was sold for $3,000,000, the purchase price less than a century before having been $74,265.75.

It remains to be said that in 1810 when Pursh gave up its management, Michael Dennison took it in charge until 1815, when it was rented by a Mr. Gentle, a seedsman; in 1823, by J. B. Driver, after which it sank into gradual neglect.

Another botanic garden, so notable that it was described by David Ramsay, the historian, was established in Charleston, South Carolina, in the year 1805. It was known as the Charleston Botanic Society and Garden. A piece of land was given by a Mrs. Savage, upon which the garden was laid out. The Medical Society of Charleston gave $300 to support it, and members of the Botanic Society paid dues of from $4 to $10. The sum of $1176 was thus raised, sufficient to pay for the services of a botanist-gardener, with several laborers under him. Ramsay wrote in 1808: 'From the proceeds of a lottery now pending, hopes are entertained that

---

[12] In 1806, Hosack published a catalogue, *Hortus Elginensis*, of which there was a second edition in March 1811, from which the statements given above have been taken.

the Society will be enabled to enlarge their plans to make their garden the repository of everything useful, new and curious in the world.' [13]

The Garden seems to have flourished amazingly at first— 'beyond the most sanguine expectations of its friends.' In it were indigenous and exotic plants, 'arranged according to the Linnaean system.' Plants were brought in by American botanists and were sent in by collectors in foreign countries. Notwithstanding the value of the Garden, and the pleasure it afforded, and though it was well supported, it soon began to run down. An attempt was made to revive it by selling the original lot and improvements and by purchasing more and better land, but it continued to languish, and finally was given up. For a time, M. Noisette, a famous gardener of French descent, was in charge. It was several times visited by William Baldwin, who spoke well of it.

Another botanic garden near Charleston was established by William Williamson, which, toward the end of the eighteenth century, passed into the hands of John Champney. This garden, located in St. Paul's district, consisted of 26 acres, 6 of which were fish ponds; 10 acres in pleasure grounds; the remainder in orchards and gardens. The pleasure grounds were planted with every variety of trees, shrubs, and flowers from Europe and America that could be grown, especially pears and pecans.[14]

A religious-communistic colony known as the Rappists, Harmonists, or Economists, founded a colony in Butler County, Pennsylvania, in 1804, to which they gave the name Harmony. The society had been organized in Wittenberg, Germany, in 1787, by George Rapp. Possessions were held in common; they believed in the second coming of Christ; and celibacy was the rule of the organization. This Society was interested in agriculture, horticulture, botany, and to a lesser extent in other natural sciences. These interests, by the way, like those of the Shakers and several other religious organizations of this period, were fostered by the food habits of the members; all were vegetarians.

John Melish, an Englishman, visited Harmony in 1811, and in his *Travels in the United States of America* gives an account of how the Harmonists were then living. In particular he de-

[13] Ramsay, II: 107, 108.   [14] Ibid. II: 230.

scribes the gardens, speaking of the labyrinth as a 'most elegant flower-garden, with various hedge rows disposed in such a manner as to puzzle people in getting into the temple, emblematical of Harmony.' The botanic garden he found 'well stored with plants and herbs.' There was, also, 'an elegant collection of plants, all natives of Harmony, carefully arranged according to the Linnaean system.'

In 1814 the colony moved to New Harmony, Posey County, Indiana, where work with gardening and botany was continued, but the Rappists remained in charge only ten years. The property was then sold to Robert Owen, and the original colony returned to Pennsylvania, where they remained in the settlement of Economy, near Pittsburgh, until late in the century. Here, too, they were interested in botany and horticulture. The Rappists imported to their settlement in Indiana many European plants, especially fruits, and, after the early French, planted the first orchard in the Middle West. In particular they experimented with European grapes, which, as in all other such ventures, failed.

Robert Owen, the Englishman who bought the New Harmony property, was a man of wealth, bent on revolutionizing religion, science, education, and agriculture. His colony consisted of some thousand or more people, most of whom had had rather exceptional opportunities for education. They seem to have been much interested as a group in the natural sciences, as well as agriculture; and in their college had several men at different times with considerable knowledge of botany. New Harmony became a center of horticultural and botanical knowledge and gave the people in this frontier a strong leaning to these divisions of plant interests.

Rafinesque, the eccentric French naturalist, was a frequent visitor and lecturer at New Harmony. No doubt he brought some of the treasures that he collected in the wilds of the Middle West, or from the botanical garden he founded in Lexington, to his friends in Indiana.

Rafinesque's garden in Lexington started off with a great flourish. The Legislature of the state of Kentucky chartered it 'for the purpose of establishing a botanical, agricultural and medical garden, in Lexington, as an auxiliary branch of Transylvania University.' It took the name of Transylvania University Botanical Garden, and was founded in 1824. The President and directors of the garden had great hopes for it as expressed in the prospectus. They said:

We hope you will hear with pleasure that a botanical garden has been established in the centre of North America, and that you will feel inclined to patronize this new institution which will become instrumental in collecting and spreading the beautiful and useful vegetable products of this region, particularly since they are all suitable to be cultivated in the open air in the Atlantic and Southern States, Mexico, Europe. . .

This, with other material, appeared in the *First Catalogue and Circular of the Botanical Garden of Transylvania University at Lexington, Kentucky,* for the year 1824. The authors were W. W. Richardson, President of the Board of Managers, and C. S. Rafinesque, Ph.D., Secretary. The pamphlet is one of 24 pages, printed alternately in French and English. It is, in the main, an appeal for plants and contains a list of plants that the garden could furnish other collectors. This garden lived only a year or two at most, during which time were published several catalogues and lists of now rare Americana.[15]

There was in this period of American gardening a botanic garden near Philadelphia of which one hears little because the owner neither spoke nor wrote much for the public. Nevertheless, it rivaled in importance the gardens of John Bartram and Humphry Marshall, after both of which it was modeled. It was founded about 1828 by John Evans, Radnor Township, Delaware County, a county split off from Chester County, Pennsylvania, in which both Bartram and Marshall had earlier established their gardens.

Evans, aided by a kinsman, Alan W. Corson, seems at first to have planted for pleasure, collecting all that could be had from American sources, and then turned his attention to Europe. Here he was able to take advantage of a rare opportunity. Sir William J. Hooker was then Director of Kew Gardens, and with him Evans corresponded and exchanged plants. While part of this

15 *Garden and Forest,* IX: 362.

correspondence was going on, Dr. Joseph Hooker, son of Sir William, was collecting in the Himalaya Mountains, and seeds and plants from that unexplored region of Asia were forwarded to Evans. Thus, there came many species of Himalayan flowers, shrubs, and trees to enrich American gardens. In particular many rhododendrons and rock-loving plants from the fringe of the eternal snows of the Himalayas were introduced.

The Evans garden, in its day, had several remarkable features. On a wooded hillside, along a mill-race, were rhododendrons and mountain plants from the Himalayas and from the several great American mountain systems. There was also a unique 'sand garden,' containing the plants Evans had collected in New Jersey and neighboring sandy regions. The rocky hills on the place were covered with conifers. A damp, shaded ravine had its canebrake. In an artificial pond were waterlilies and other aquatics; 'and every border and corner was occupied with appropriate specimens brought together from remote parts of the earth.' On the place were a great number of specimen trees, shrubs, vines, and collections of herbaceous plants.[16]

The Massachusetts Horticultural Society established an experiment garden in 1833, the first in America to be supported by a horticultural society. By the public the garden was considered a part of Mount Auburn Cemetery, also founded by the Society, but to the members of the organization, with the exception of Jacob Bigelow, who apparently used the Horticultural Society to further his dream of founding a garden cemetery, the garden came first. It covered 32 acres and in it were trees, flowers, fruits, and some vegetables. Plants were exchanged with other botanic gardens all over the world.[17] The garden, according to the agricultural papers of the time, was a great stimulus to horticultural pursuits.

Columbia, South Carolina, had a botanic garden in the middle of the period under discussion. In 1830 Robert E. Russel planted a garden of botanic rarities in what is now a part of the State House grounds in Columbia, giving it the name 'Russel Botanical Garden.' Russel sold plants, and for a time the garden prospered,

16 Garden and Forest, x: 182.   17 Manning, Robert, Jr., pp. 96-103.

but in 1837 he was driven to the wall through lack of money. The General Assembly of South Carolina purchased the property and leased it to its former owner. The old garden is perpetuated in part by some of the ornamental trees around the present State House. In a near-by churchyard there is said to be a slab marking the grave of one of Russel's children, 'Camellia Japonica Russel.'

In the South more than in the North, physicians planted physic gardens in which many standard medicinal herbs were grown for decoctions or oils. The poppy, in particular, was much grown for its use in the making of opium. During the Civil War, women in the South were asked by the surgeon-general, Samuel Preston Moore, to raise poppies for opium, that they 'may render the Confederacy essential service.' They were told that 'Purveyors will furnish the ladies with the seeds of the poppy if on hand or procurable'; and that 'the juice exuding from the punctured capsules, when sufficiently hardened, should be carefully put up and forwarded to the nearest purveying depot.'

Of the several early physic gardens in Georgia, that of Dr. Lindsey Durham, established about 1810 at Maxey, was best known. From it Dr. Durham, famous in the state, obtained a large part of his medical supplies, not only for his own practice but for other physicians. He seems to have established in this way a rather important industry.

Virginia was not so fortunate as South Carolina, Pennsylvania, and New York in having botanic gardens. In the period under discussion there was none, if we except the United States Botanic Garden, established in the District of Columbia in 1820. At first this garden covered an area of 5 acres, increased to 12.5 acres in 1824. The Federal Government had assigned the property to the Columbian Institute for a garden. Thomas Jefferson, John Adams, James Madison, and LaFayette were members of the Columbian Institute and were active in promoting the botanic garden. In spite of the high standing of its sponsors, the garden seems to have done little, and after lingering 20 years was discontinued.

The reasons for its discontinuance are shown by a report on its work in the House of Representatives in 1834: its activities were mainly in the purchase, care, and distribution of growing

plants; and, comparatively speaking, propagation, experimentation, and kindred activities were limited. The committee making
the report objected to giving away growing plants and cut flowers
to members of Congress and friends. They concluded that its
activities as an educational institution, as a scientific institution,
and as a botanic garden were wholly negligible. In May 1850, by
Act of Congress, the Botanic Garden was re-established on the
Mall; and, curiously enough, its administration, in 1856, was
put in the hands of the Joint Committee on the Library. The
site (about 12 acres) was between Maryland Avenue on the west,
Pennsylvania Avenue on the east, and the Capitol Grounds and
Third Street, S.W. Early in this century the Garden was located
south of Maryland Avenue.

Through the efforts of the Cincinnati Horticultural Society, a
public experiment station and botanic garden was established
in Cincinnati in 1848, at a time when no similar institution
existed in this great region. The new garden had been the country
residence of a Mr. Hoffner, about four miles from the city, and
consisted of 15 acres well stocked, at the time the Society purchased it, with trees, shrubs, flower and vegetable gardens, and
provided with a greenhouse and other buildings. It became a
testing place for native and foreign fruits and plants.

There was a Farmer's College in Cincinnati founded in 1856,
whose faculty edited an agricultural journal called *Cincinnatus,*
and which maintained a botanic garden at College Hill, Ohio.
The paper also served as the official organ of the Cincinnati Horticultural Society. Just what was accomplished by the garden does
not appear, but the publication, in the years 1856 and 1859,
printed a number of papers on natural history and gardening,
some by prominent horticulturists in Ohio, which must have contributed much to gardening. This publication, as well as the college and botanic garden, seems to have been neglected by writers
on these subjects.[18]

[18] Meisel, pp. 260-62.

16

THE DAWN OF PLANT BREEDING

NOT since men began to till the soil was there so great an opportunity to domesticate wild plants and improve those from the Old World as when Europeans came to America. For two hundred years the opportunity was almost wholly neglected; but, in the nineteenth century, men took readily and efficiently to the task.

The Whites found in the Americas a multiplicity of wild fruits, vegetables, flowers, shrubs, and trees worth domesticating; and a great diversity of soils and climates to which Old World esculents had to be adapted if they were to be grown. The fact that Indians had long carried on an American agriculture with many crops Europeans had never known was finally an incentive to try to domesticate wild relatives of European cultivated species, and to cultivate those the Indians were growing as well.

No fewer than 200 species of American tree, bush, vine, and small fruits bear edible products. There are now under cultivation 11 species of native plums, of which there are 433 purebred and 155 hybrid varieties; 15 species of American grapes, with 404 pure and 790 hybrid varieties; 4 species of raspberries, with 280 varieties; 6 species of blackberries, with 23 varieties; and 2 species of cranberries, with 60 varieties. Perhaps a score of minor native plants furnish vegetables, while the number of ornamental trees, shrubs, and flowers from American wild species sold by nurserymen, florists, and seedsmen would be hard to compute. Nearly all these plants, excepting a few the Indians grew, have come under cultivation in the last 150 years.

Although Cotton Mather in 1716 had reported the first hybrid in cultivation,[1] the first planned attempt in America to improve

[1] See Zirkle, C., *The Beginnings of Plant Hybridization*, pp. 103-7.

a fruit on a large scale began in the Prince Nursery in 1790, when the pits of 25 quarts of Green Gage plums were planted by William Prince, the second proprietor. The Princes named from the seedlings of these pits the White Gage, the Red Gage, Prince's Gage, and Washington, four varieties that were for many years standards and of which Washington is still grown. Long before the Princes began their work, however, there had been introductions of varieties of fruits that had originated from the almost universal practice of growing seedling trees, with the result that an occasional tree bore fruit so superior to its neighbors that its kind was perpetuated by budding or grafting.

The first experiments in hybridizing made in America were the work of William Bartram, who wrote to Colonel William Byrd of Virginia in 1739 that he was making observations 'upon the male and female parts in vegetables.' Sex in plants was under discussion in books by Camerarius and Linnaeus, and Bartram was at once eager to make experiments. To Byrd, he further wrote: 'I have made several successful experiments of joining several species of the same genus, whereby I have obtained curious colors in flowers, never known before; but this requires an accurate observation and judgment to know the exact time.' [2]

The first man in America to undertake as his life's work the breeding of plants was Joseph Cooper, Cooper's Point, Gloucester County, New Jersey, although it was his father who began the work. In the *Memoirs of the Philadelphia Society for Promoting Agriculture* is a short letter by Joseph Cooper, written in 1799, which shows that the writer and his father understood the art and necessity of selection in improving plants.

The Coopers experimented in the improvement by selection with peas, lettuce, squashes, asparagus, potatoes, and radishes. Seeds of some of these were sown as early as 1746, and an importation of peas for further work was made from England in 1752. Cooper could say in 1799 that he had selected potato, pea, and lettuce seed; had bred a special strain of corn as early as 1772; had advanced the ripening date of watermelons by a five-year selection; and had improved winter wheat by selection. Cooper introduced several new fruits, best of which was the Cooper plum, not

2 Darlington, p. 315.

often grown in America, but well known in France as La Dé-
licieuse, corrupted in England to Lady Lucy.

But even before Cooper and Bartram, men in America had
begun to think about the intermixture of plants, which must have
suggested to them that a species might be improved by selections
from a mixed population. In a paper in the *Philosophical Transactions,* Paul Dudley (1675-1751), Chief Justice of Massachusetts,
wrote that the intermixture of corn had been noticed by the
aborigines, who attributed such mixtures 'to the Roots and small
Fibres reaching to and communicating with one another.' Dudley, however, was 'of Opinion that the *Stamina,* or Principles of
this wonderful Copulation or mixing of Colours, are carried by
the Wind; and that the Season of it is, when the corn is in the
Earing, and while the Milk is in the Grain, for at that Time the
Corn is in a Sort of Estuation and emits a strong Scent.' [3]

Another early investigator in the physiology of plants and of
the fructification of maize was James Logan (see page 93), who
carried on many experiments and published a series of papers on
'Experiments concerning the Impregnation of the Seeds of Plants.'

Of all horticultural plants, more work has been done in the
United States in breeding the grape than any other; or at least
this is true of the period covered by this history. In grape breeding, until recent years, only native species and only two or three of
these received attention. The history of grape breeding in America can only be told as a part of the establishment of viticulture
in this country and must include also the early literature of the
grape.

The honor of setting forth the possibility of establishing viticulture in the United States on a foundation of varieties of native
species belongs to Dr. James Mease, one of the editors of the *Domestic Encyclopedia.* In this work he published an article on the
vine, in which he embodied a short paper on the same subject by
William Bartram. Mease wrote in 1804; Bartram in 1802.

In his article, Mease condemns the attempt to grow the Old
World grape in the New World and recommends the planting of
native grapes. He wrote:

[3] *Philosophical Transactions,* VI: 379, 380; see also pp. 54-5.

From the experience, however, of the editor and his friends who have found such difficulty in naturalizing foreign vines, he recommends the cultivation of the native grapes of the United States, particularly the *Vitis aestivalis* (*Vitis sylvestris*), or small blue or bunch grape; Bland's, Tasker's, or Alexander, and the Bull grape of Carolina and Georgia.

Another early book to devote some space to the grape was *Johnson's Rural Economy,* by S. W. Johnson, published in New Brunswick, New Jersey, in 1806. In it there are 42 pages on this fruit, with an excellent picture of training the grape. The method used is that of Europe, in which the vine is tied to a stake, as no one had yet tried to train the grapes on wires. Cultural methods are taken wholly from European books. Johnson mentions three American varieties: the Bull or Bullet grape, Bland's grape, and the Alexander's or Tasker's grape. He does not recommend the cultivation of these or of other native sorts and is almost wholly concerned with European varieties.

To John Adlum (1759-1836), a native of Pennsylvania, but long a resident of Georgetown, District of Columbia, belongs the credit of discovering a grape so superior that success in viticulture was certain in widely separated areas of the United States. After more than 200 years of vain effort to grow a foreign grape in the New World, Adlum crowned with success a venture to grow a native grape. The vines of this new grape were vigorous, healthy, productive, and bore fruits with beautiful bunches and berries, delicious to eat out of hand, and from which very good sweet and dry wines could be made.

The grape that was to make grape growing and wine making profitable in America is the Catawba. At 'The Vineyard,' near Georgetown, Adlum started an experimental vineyard early in the nineteenth century, and in 1819 added Catawba to his list of native and foreign varieties. At once it proved a better grape than any other in his plantation and he began its distribution, in which Prince of New York and Longworth of Ohio soon joined. For many years Catawba was the leading grape for table use and wine press, and is today one of the half-dozen most commonly grown grapes in eastern America. The Catawba had passed through several hands before it came to Adlum. Its place of origin is not known, but it probably came from the Catawba River region, Buncombe County, North Carolina.

In 1823 Adlum's *The Cultivation of the Vine* appeared, the purpose of which, the author says in his preface, was that 'of disposing some practical and useful information throughout the country on the best method of cultivating the native grape and of making wine.' In the book are descriptions of 24 varieties of grapes, so poorly described, however, that one can only guess whether they are native or foreign varieties; probably half of them are foreign. In this first edition, the Catawba is described as the 'Tokay,' but the name is changed to 'Catawba' in the second edition in 1828. Most of the book is devoted to wine making. The cultural directions are taken from European books.

While the Catawba was the first American grape to be generally cultivated in the United States, several others had been grown locally. One of these, the Alexander, deserves historical record as one of the first native grapes to be domesticated. The variety was found by John Alexander, gardener to Governor John Penn, in whose garden he introduced it a few years before the Revolution. It was distributed far and wide under several names, but as the Alexander it was probably the first native grape to receive a name. It was a coarse grape, with so much foxiness in flavor that it was not liked by those accustomed to European grapes. However, it made good wine, so good that Thomas Jefferson pronounced it 'worthy of the best vineyards of France.' The manner of its introduction has been given on pages 341 ff.

The Alexander is of particular interest to grape breeders because, almost without doubt, it was a hybrid between *V. Labrusca,* an American species, and *V. vinifera,* the European grape. It has the oval shape of the European grape, whereas American sorts have round berries; and its late season and thin, tender leaves bespeak Vinifera blood. Its place of origin was near a vineyard of European varieties, and hybridization might easily have taken place. The early descriptions strongly suggest some of the hybrids between *V. Labrusca* and *V. vinifera* made by E. S. Rogers.

Peter Legaux, the introducer of the Alexander, was an early American writer on grapes. In *The True American,* 24 March 1800, he published an article of 2000 words telling of his experience in growing grapes in America. The main part of the article is 'A Statement of the Expense and Income of a Vineyard, Made on Four Acres of Land, situated in Pennsylvania, in the 40th

Degree of Latitude.' The article is of little value and adds nothing to his reputation, concerning which his contemporaries did not agree. Johnson, one of them, speaks of him as a philanthropist; M'Mahon calls him a 'gentleman of Worth and Science'; while Rafinesque accuses him of fraud and deception. At any rate he was the first disseminator of an American grape of value.

In 1806 M'Mahon in his *American Gardener's Calendar* devotes a chapter to the vineyard, in which he describes in full 55 varieties of European grapes and mentions the following four species of native grapes:

1st. The *Vitis sylvestris,* or common bunch grape.

2nd. The *Vitis Vulpina* of Bartram; *V. Labrusca* of Lin. or Fox-grape.

3rd. The *Vitis taurina* of Bartram, or *Vitis Vulpina* of Lin. commonly called the Bull or Bullet-grape.

4th. The *Vitis serotina* or winter-grape, by some called the Bermudian grape.

Then follows a statement that is all important if M'Mahon knew what he was talking about and was not merely guessing. He says: 'There are several varieties produced by the intermixtures of the above, with one another, or with the varieties of the *Vitis vinifera* which are called hybrids or mules; the most noted is, 1. Alexander's or Tasker's grape; 2. Bland's grape; that called the Racoon grape.'

This is the first time hybridization as a means of improvement of grapes has been mentioned. We choose to think that M'Mahon was the first American to advocate hybridizing grapes, which a generation later was to become a means of breeding many good varieties. Most important, it enabled eastern grape growers to have in their vineyards many varieties with desirable characteristics of the European grape.

In this same discussion M'Mahon was first, it would seem, to advocate the growing of European grapes on native stocks. He wrote: 'I would suggest the idea of grafting some of the best European kinds, on our most vigorous vines, which, no doubt, would answer a very good purpose.' A hundred years later this was a common procedure at home and abroad.

The most notable plant breeder New England has produced was E. S. Rogers (1826-99), Salem, Massachusetts. Rogers worked with the grape only, and from crossings made in 1851 between Carter, an American grape, as the female parent, and Black Hamburg and White Chasselas, European grapes, as the male parents, produced a number of seedlings, of which 45 were meritorious enough to be introduced. Collectively these were known as 'Rogers' Hybrids.' Of the 45, 13 became well known in the vineyards of the whole country. These were: Goethe, Massasoit, Wilder, Lindley, Gaertner, Agawam, Merrimac, Requa, Aminia, Essex, Barry, Herbert, and Salem, several of which are still favorites in home vineyards.

In the history of plant breeding, no other man has had such good luck from one batch of seedlings. The same crosses made later by Rogers and others did not produce a single grape worth introducing. Perhaps better than the grapes Rogers produced was the stimulus he gave to grape breeding. Soon a hundred or more men in every part of the country were crossing grapes, with the result that before the end of the century 2000 new grapes had been introduced in America.

Possibly the most valuable variety of any fruit introduced in the nineteenth century was the Concord grape. The originator was Ephriam W. Bull (1805-95), Concord, Massachusetts. The Concord was a seedling from a chance seedling, which bore its first bunch of grapes in 1843. Bull planted seed from this bunch and in 1849 a promising vine bore fruit, which had so many good qualities that it was named. The new variety at once became popular after having been exhibited at an exhibition of the Massachusetts Horticultural Society in 1853. For the last 75 years more Concord grapes have been marketed in the United States than all other native sorts combined. Several other grapes came from Bull's vineyard, but no other of any considerable note.

About this time, another event of outstanding importance took place in American viticulture. At a meeting of the American Horticultural Society in 1852, Dr. William W. Valk, of Flushing, showed several bunches of grapes he had grown from seeds of Black Hamburg, produced from blossoms fertilized by Isabella. A. J. Downing had examined the grape a year earlier and had written: 'There can be no doubt that this is the first genuine cross between the foreign grapes and our natives.' [4] The name of this first hybrid grape is Ada. The cross was made and the seed was sown in 1845. Valk's Ada was the first cross of grapes in America by the hand of man.

The Ada was an insignificant fruit and hybridization was by this time common in garden plants, so that Valk's hybrid would not have been of note had he not had followers in the hybridization of grapes. John Fisk Allen, of Salem, Massachusetts, hybridized Golden Chasselas and Isabella, producing Allen's Hybrid, a really good grape. The imaginations of grape growers were fired and a score or more began at once to hybridize varieties of the Old World grape with those of our native species, hoping to get a bunch of *Vitis vinifera* on the vine of some native. Two men in particular had good luck: E. S. Rogers and his near rival in the race to grow hybrids, James H. Ricketts of Newburgh, New York. Ricketts also grew hundreds of seedlings, of which he named perhaps a score or more quite different from those of Rogers, because he used as parents several species, while Rogers used, for the most part, but two.

At no other time in America has interest in grape growing been quite so keen as in the years during the introduction of the grapes introduced by Rogers and Ricketts. Every fruit grower planted grapes. Greenhouses were built in which to hasten their propagation. Grape regions boomed in New York, Pennsylvania, Ohio, Michigan, Missouri, and in a lesser degree in other states. Propagators of grapes made fortunes. One old nurseryman told the author that he had carried over a thousand dollars' worth of rooted grape cuttings on his back in one load from the nursery to the express office.

Other men who hybridized grapes, inspired by the work of Rogers and Ricketts, were Caywood, Rommel, Stayman, and a little later Munson and Moore. Probably as many as 1000 hybrid grapes had been introduced before this enthusiasm for hybrids began to wane at the close of the century.

The introduction of the Delaware grape, brought to notice by Abram Thompson, editor of the *Delaware Gazette* (Delaware, Ohio), was another step forward. He first saw the fruit on one of

[4] *The Horticulturist,* VI: 245.

the neighborhood farms in 1849, and found that it had been grown on several farms for at least 20 years, having been brought from New Jersey. It was traced back to Paul H. Provost, a Swiss, of New Jersey. Where he got the variety, what was its origin, when it originated, and even its botanical status are all uncertain. Downing named it. For nearly a century it has been one of the half-dozen best native grapes, either for the table or the wine press. To most palates it is unsurpassed in flavor by any other native grape.

To grow thousands of seedling grapes, a dozen of which were good enough to be named and distributed, is an achievement sufficient to give a man a line in history. The man in this case is George W. Campbell (1817-98), who, in 1849, moved to Delaware, Ohio, and began ventures in several divisions of horticulture for a livelihood. Eventually he turned to breeding grapes, hybridizing several species for the many seedlings he grew. Of the dozen sorts he named, three—Triumph, Lady, and Campbell Early—became well known and may still be found in some collections. Of these three, Triumph was long notable as the variety of native grapes producing the largest bunches.

The strawberry grows wild, in one species or another, in every part of the globe, in temperate and even in sub-tropic climates. Yet, as a cultivated plant, it is a relatively new inhabitant of gardens. One reason is that cultivation does not improve the flavor, as it does with most other fruits, and wild strawberries, where they may be had, are preferred to those from a garden. The Greeks and Romans did not plant strawberries; they have been grown rather less than four centuries in French and English gardens. In America, some strawberries were grown in the colonies, but even a hundred years ago there were only three or four varieties worth planting. Strawberries could seldom be bought in the markets until the middle of the nineteenth century, and the varieties were much inferior in every way to those now in gardens.

Yet, new as the strawberry is, botanists do not agree what the wild parent or parents were. Almost certainly, American varieties are hybrids derived mainly from species native to North and South America. Though the botany of this fruit is a matter of argument, the main events in its history in America, the persons concerned, dates, and places are well known and can all be put down in brief space.

William Prince in 1771 offered four varieties for sale: Large Hautboy, a European sort derived from *Fragaria moschata;* the Chili, from Europe, but belonging to *F. chiloensis* from the Pacific Coast of North and South America; Redwood from Europe, a member of the *F. vesca* family; and the Wood, one of our American wild strawberries, *F. virginiana*. In 1791, the Prince catalogue contained a new variety, the Hudson, so much better than any of the other four that it may be said to be the first American variety of importance. By 1800 there were two other good varieties, Hudson's Bay and Early Scarlet. From these several varieties in the early years of the nineteenth century, strawberry culture in America was started.

The next event of importance in the history of the strawberry in America was the introduction of the Pine in 1804. The Pine is noteworthy as one of the ancestors of nearly all the hundreds of varieties that have since come and gone or are now grown in America. It belongs to *Fragaria chiloensis* and was common in England and France by the middle of the eighteenth century, but seems not to have reached America until after 1800. By 1825 there were perhaps some 30 or more named varieties of strawberries under cultivation, none of great value and all to be replaced in 1838 by the Hovey, which was the first really good strawberry in American gardens.

The cross from which Hovey came was made by Charles Mason Hovey on his grounds at Cambridge, Massachusetts, in 1834. It was not introduced until 1838, its fruits having been exhibited that year at a meeting of the Massachusetts Horticultural Society. The fruits were larger, better colored, firmer in flesh, and the plants more productive than those of any other variety that had yet been grown in America. The judges at the exhibition called it a 'perfect strawberry.' Plants of Hovey sold in 1840 at $5 a dozen, and the berries sold at 50 cents a quart in the Boston market—twice the price of any other variety. It was soon being grown in all parts of the country, and as late as 1880 was a standard variety. It was the first cultivated variety in America to originate from a cross in which man had a hand.

It was soon found that the Hovey bore large crops only when

another variety was planted near it. Strawberry growers did not then know, and for a long time would not believe, that some varieties were self-sterile, others with perfect flowers fertile, and that the sterile varieties should have fertile sorts planted near them if they were to be fruitful. A French botanist, Antoine Nicholas Duchesne, had discovered that there were fertile and sterile blossoms in strawberries in 1766, but the knowledge was slow in filtering down to gardeners as a matter of practical importance. In America, Nicholas Longworth advocated mixed planting (see page 312); soon his trenchant pen convinced all. By the middle of the century the terms 'perfect and imperfect,' 'fertile and infertile,' 'male and female,' 'hermaphrodite and unisexual' were well understood by strawberry growers.

The next strawberry of note was the Wilson, introduced in 1854 by James Wilson, Albany, New York. This berry has had the longest run of any American strawberry; it is possible that specimens of the Wilson might be found in some eastern garden today.

From an insignificant start in 1800, or thereabouts, the strawberry became a major garden plant by 1860. When the writer published *The Small Fruits of New York,* in 1925, he described 1362 named varieties of strawberries, nearly all of which originated in the United States. After the grape, the strawberry has received more attention from plant breeders than any other fruit in America.

There seems to have been no mention of red raspberries as a garden fruit until 1771, when, in a list of fruits offered for sale by William Prince, three red raspberries are listed: the White, English Red, and American Red. It turned out later that the English Red was an American berry, and its name was changed to Common Red; it was long under cultivation. This, the first variety of our native species, seems to have been English Red, or Common Red, whose origin is unknown, but which antedated 1771. This for many years was the best-known and most widely cultivated red raspberry in America. Plants of the European red raspberry had been grown from Virginia to New England in occasional gardens from early colonial times.

M'Mahon, in his *American Gardener's Calendar* of 1806, says there are many varieties of the European red raspberry, and mentions four, one of which, the Common Red, turned out to be a native berry. Another of the three is the Double Bearing, which 'produces one crop of fruit in June, and another in October.' Thus the autumn-bearing red raspberry goes back to 1806; no doubt Indians had always picked wild red raspberries in the fall. This berry, so often hailed as a rare curiosity in modern gardens, probably came into being as a mutant, just as yellow and cream-colored red raspberries occasionally appear among both wild and cultivated plants.

In 1832 William Robert Prince, in his *Pomological Manual,* published descriptions of 12 varieties, and named 6 more that 'merit culture.' The best of the 12, Prince says, was the Common Red. This berry is of interest because one sees from the description that it is a purple-berried sort, and is, therefore, a hybrid of a red and a black species. Whether it originated in the wild or in a garden, and who first grew it in a garden, we shall never know. We do know that it is the first such hybrid on record. Long after, headed by the Shaffer and the Columbian, these purple-fruited, purple-stemmed varieties took a position in American gardens superior to the blacks and nearly equal to the reds.

As with grapes, pomologists liked the Old World red raspberry better than derivatives of the New World species. One of the prominent breeders of varieties of the European red raspberry was Dr. William Brinklé (1799-1863), Philadelphia, a physician who chose fruit growing as an avocation. He grew hundreds of red raspberries from seed, out of which he selected many new varieties. One of these, the Orange, became a leading market variety, and several others were more or less grown in gardens.

The domestication of the black raspberry began a little later than that of the red. The first-named black variety was the Ohio Everbearing, brought in from the wild by Nicholas Longworth in 1832.[5] It was a freak variety that bore two crops in a season, the best one in October.

Improvement of the black raspberry really began in 1850, after the discovery of a better method of propagation than had hitherto

[5] See p. 313.

been known. The red raspberry, long cultivated in gardens, is propagated by taking suckers from mother plants. The black raspberry produces few suckers and is propagated by division, slowly and with difficulty. An observing farmer, H. H. Doolittle, Oaks Corners, New York, found that in nature the tips of black raspberries droop over to take root in the autumn. In imitation of nature, he bent canes over and buried the tips in the soil. Doolittle went to the woods in 1850 and selected the best wild black cap he could find, named it Doolittle's Improved Black Cap, and began to propagate it.

Doolittle found his black caps in fence rows and fields—whatever came to hand—tipped them and sold the young plants. In 1860 the American Pomological Society formally bestowed the name 'Doolittle Raspberry' on one of the best of the many sorts sent out by the originator, and as such it was grown for at least 50 years. The black caps were most cultivated from 1850 to 1900 when they were grown in large quantities—especially in Western New York—for drying, to supply lumber camps, Hudson's Bay Company establishments, and ships at sea. For this purpose they had no competition from either the reds or the purple-canes. While still grown in a small way for drying, the dried product is being rapidly displaced by canned berries.

The American red and the American black raspberries are species so distinct that neither botanist nor gardener could possibly mistake them, but there is a third group of varieties, the 'purple-canes,' which long confused everybody. Both botanists and growers thought that these varieties belonged to a distinct botanical species. In recent years it has been found that the purple-canes are hybrids of the blacks and the reds. No named purple-canes, known to be hybrids, were introduced within the range of this history. Within the last hundred years, at least a thousand varieties of reds, blacks, and purple-canes have been introduced by American plant breeders, of which many more than half are reds. A few purple-canes, Common Red being best known, all chance hybrids, were to be found in early gardens.

Blackberries and dewberries, cultivated in no other part of the world, becoming yearly more important in American gardens, were not domesticated from native plants until the second quarter of the nineteenth century. To pioneers in America, all the members of the blackberry family, whether in the Atlantic or Pacific states, were pestiferous weeds, mentioned only in discussions for the best means of keeping them down. The fruits were used only to make blackberry wine, highly esteemed as a cordial and a medicine. Either blackberries or dewberries grew abundantly in all the colonies, in the Gulf states, and on the Pacific Coast—no one needed to grow them in a garden. M'Mahon, the two Princes, and Coxe published books on fruits without mentioning the blackberry. William Kenrick, in *The New American Orchardist,* in 1822, was the first pomologist to recommend its cultivation, and he damned it with faint praise as a garden plant.

Kenrick was not only lacking in enthusiasm about planting blackberries, but was doubtful about the uses of the fruit. Under 'Uses' he writes: 'The blackberry is considered a pleasant and wholesome fruit if used in moderation. . . A jelly is made of the blackberry of considerable medicinal efficacy in nephritic disorders.' Neither statement is a very strong recommendation of a fruit for garden culture.

Almost before *The New American Orchardist* came off the press, three men were cultivating blackberries to which they had given names. Captain Joseph Lovett, Beverly, Massachusetts, in 1835 began the cultivation of plants brought in from the woods. Eventually he would grow only the Dorchester, which had been introduced about 1840 by Eliphalet Thayer, Dorchester, Massachusetts, as the Improved Highbush Blackberry, but which soon took the name of its place of origin. In 1834 Lewis A. Seaver, New Rochelle, New York, transplanted to his garden a plant from the wild, which bore berries of large size and fine flavor. William Lawton, a neighbor, began to distribute this berry under the name New Rochelle, and in 1854 gave an interesting account of it, and of blackberries and dewberries in general, before the Farmer's Club of the American Institute.[6] In 1856 the American Pomological Society voted that Lawton's 'New Rochelle' be called 'Lawton.'

In 1854 a blackberry was brought under cultivation at Burlington, New Jersey, under the name Wilson, which ripened just after the red raspberry, filling a space of time almost unoccupied by a hardy fruit. In 1865 the Kittatinny, from the mountains of

[6] *Genesee Farmer,* xv: 157.

the same name in New Jersey, was introduced. This berry was remarkable for its hardiness, resistance to disease, and vigor of plant. With Dorchester, Lawton, Wilson, and Kittatinny, the blackberry was off to a fine start, but in the years that have elapsed, plant breeders have done little with this splendid fruit, and the newer varieties are scarcely better than the first four.

Few who buy berries distinguish between dewberries and blackberries, and, in truth, it is not always easy for the botanist and gardener to tell where one begins and the other leaves off in the many species and varieties. The fact that some species of the two fruits hybridize rather easily does not help in classification. Still, in general, blackberries are tall and straight in growth; dewberries are low-growing and have trailing vines (some blackberries are trailers). The fruits of the dewberry are larger, more sprightly, juicier, and ripen earlier. Yet, despite the superiority of the fruits of the dewberry, no one undertook its domestication until after the blackberry was well established.

It would, by the way, be hard to say how many wild blackberries and dewberries there are in the world. Conservative botanists would admit at least 60 species; some would say there are several times that many. Most of this great number are in North America.

The task of domesticating the dewberry seems to have been begun by Dr. Miner, Honeoye Falls, New York, in 1854. Dr. Miner in that year planted seeds of a wild dewberry. From a great number of seedlings, two were saved that were long grown as 'Miner's Seedlings.' Joseph Harris, one of the best agricultural writers of that time, gave an admirable account of these two dewberries, the method of culture, and an estimate of the place in pomology of the dewberry. He thus gave the new fruit a standing in gardens.[7] Growers of bramble fruits in all parts of the country added 'Miner's Seedlings' to their list of plants.

The second dewberry to receive a name was the Bartel, brought to notice by Dr. Bartel, Huey, Illinois, who found in an old cornfield a wild plant with fruits 'of mammoth size.' Dr. Bartel named the new berry 'Bartel's Mammoth' (in a lithograph before me

[7] Ibid. XXII: 351.

ample justice is done to the word 'mammoth'). The Bartel was
not put on the market until the 1870's. It was distributed by *The
Fruit Recorder,* Palmyra, New York, as a subscription prize, under
the name Bartel, and the second American dewberry began to
find its way into gardens. The Bartel belongs to the North, and
eventually southern and western dewberries from species widely
different in plant and fruit came under cultivation to make this
fruit next most promient after the red raspberry among the
bramble fruits. As every horticulturist knows, a number of remarkable hybrids are now under cultivation in Texas and on the
Pacific Coast.

Another wild fruit to be domesticated in this period of gardening in America was one of the American gooseberries, *Ribes hir-
tellum.* Many European gooseberries had been imported in the
colonies; but, like the grapes brought over, they could not endure
the hot summers and cold winters, or resist fungi. In 1833 Abel
Houghton, Lynn, Massachusetts, planted seeds of a wild gooseberry and produced a seedling with well-flavored fruits. The new
variety was named Houghton. Two years later Charles Downing
planted seeds of Houghton, and out of many seedlings named the
best one Downing. Although in the years that have passed many
pure-bred and hybrid gooseberries have been grown in the country, these two are still standard sorts. The plants are among the
hardiest cultivated esculents.

Perhaps it should be said that the gooseberry, so beloved by
the British, has never found great favor in America. In England
gardeners have a thousand or more varieties; in America, perhaps,
a score are grown. In Great Britain, the gooseberry is a choice
dessert fruit; in the United States, it is used almost wholly for
culinary purposes. The fruits of the American varieties are not
nearly so large and handsome as those of the English sorts, but
they are just as palatable to eat out of hand or in kitchen preparations. Like the blackberry, the gooseberry awaits a genius in
plant breeding to make it as popular on this side of the Atlantic
as on the other. Meanwhile, it is less and less grown.

The Old World currant, close relative to the gooseberry, came
overseas with the Puritans, and thrives everywhere from New

England to Minnesota, south to Virginia and Kentucky, and from Oregon through Washington and British Columbia into Alaska. In fact, the American climate suits the currant so well that in the regions named it is an occasional escape from cultivation, growing as happily in the wild as any of the native species. In the period covered by this history, all the varieties of worth came from Europe, but in the years since 1860 several American breeders have originated sorts that have almost wholly taken the place of the Old World varieties.

The golden currant, *Ribes aureum,* and the buffalo currant, *R. odoratum,* found wild in the Central and Northwestern states, are much more commonly cultivated than the American black currant. They were much used by the Indians of this great region and were planted by the first white settlers at least as ornamentals. In the early days in Utah, the buffalo currant was commonly grown for table use, the berries varying from yellow through blue to black. Crandall is a cultivated variety of the golden currant, and Golden Prolific of the buffalo currant, both sorts having been long under cultivation. The golden currant was one of the species brought to the East by the Lewis and Clark expedition. It is much admired for its fragrant yellow blossoms.

Missouri is the home of a cultivated variety of the American wild black currant, *Ribes americanum.* The variety under cultivation, or once under cultivation, is the Sweet Fruited Missouri, a slight improvement on the wild currant that grows in most parts of North America east of the Rocky Mountains and north of the Gulf states. This currant is more often grown as an ornamental than for its fruit. The single variety once cultivated for its fruits was planted in gardens by the early settlers in Missouri when other currants were not to be had.

It did not take settlers long to discover that the cranberries growing in the swamps of the North Atlantic coast were good to eat. Mahlon Stacy, writing in 1780 from West Jersey to his brother in Yorkshire, England, reported that from 'May till Michaelmas we have great store of wild fruit, as strawberries and hurtelberries, which are like our bilberries in England' and then pays a special tribute to cranberries; 'the cranberries are like cherries for color and bigness, and may be kept until fruits come in again. An excellent sauce is made of them for venison, turkeys, and other great fowl. They are better to make tarts than either gooseberries or cherries. We have them brought to our house in great plenty by the Indians.' [8]

There is no record of cranberry culture until Kenrick's *New American Orchardist* appeared in 1833, in which the statement is made that Captain Henry Hull of Barnstable (Cape Cod) 'has cultivated the Cranberry twenty years.' This puts the beginning of cranberry culture at about 1802. And, again, Kenrick says: 'Mr. F. A. Hayden, of Lincoln, Mass., is stated to have gathered from his farm in 1830, 400 bushels of Cranberries, which brought him in Boston Market $6.00. Little by little, cranberry culture gained in importance. Until 1845 cultivated bogs were to be found only on Cape Cod, but in that year plantations were set out in New Jersey; a little later on Long Island; and still later a huge trade in this fruit was developed in Wisconsin and the Pacific Northwest.

Cranberry growing, the most unusual type of gardening in America, has been a lodestone to hundreds of adventurous souls looking for a new business. Cranberry bogs have been planted in nearly every northern state, but the industry is now confined to the few regions just named. From the '400 bushels' that F. A. Hayden grew in 1830, a hundred years later more than 1,000,000 bushels were harvested annually. In recent years, plant breeders have developed several new varieties, most of those before 1860 having been selected wild plants.

From European and native species of plums, 15 all told, more than 2000 varieties have been grown in America, nearly all of which have originated in the United States. Plums furnish a great diversity of varieties, differing in sizes, colors, shapes, flavors, aromas, textures, and in trees and foliage. Because of these variations and of the ease of hybridization, the plum has been a favorite fruit for plant breeders in America, where there are 12 wild species possessing characters that fit the fruits for table use, or make the trees handsome ornamentals.

The first variety of a native species to be planted in orchards was the Miner. This plum has been grown under several names

8 Smith, Samuel, pp. 111-12.

for each of which there are accounts of origin. Briefly, its history follows: In 1813, William Dodd, an officer under General Jackson, found a native plum growing in an Indian plantation in Alabama. The fruits were so handsome in color and size, and so good in flavor, that Dodd saved and planted pits at his home in Knox County, Kentucky. Soon this plum was being grown in half a dozen states under different names, but eventually it emerged in Wisconsin as the Miner, a name under which it was widely distributed and the one finally accepted by the American Pomological Society.

The second and the most notable of the several hundred named native plums is the Wild Goose. In 1820, M. S. McCance shot a wild goose on his farm near Nashville, Tennessee. In its craw, he found a plum pit, which he planted. Both tree and fruit had merit, and he gave the seedling the name 'Wild Goose.'

Most of the credit for the introduction of Wild Goose, however, belongs to John S. Downer, who, in 1820, began its propagation from his nursery at Elkton, Kentucky. Stimulated by the large sales of Wild Goose, Downer bred several other varieties of plums, the best of which was Downer's Prolific, introduced in 1854, which remained popular among native plums until the end of the century. Downer was a patron of every field of horticulture in Kentucky, being especially active in the distribution of new varieties of strawberries.

H. A. Terry was another active breeder of native plums in the middle of the nineteenth century. Terry was a native of New York, where he learned nursery work and fruit growing. He became a nursery journeyman, settling first in Michigan, next in Illinois, and finally in Crescent, Iowa. Here, beginning in 1857, he lived for more than 50 years, specializing in breeding plums and peonies. Probably no other man bred so many plums from American species, of which the best are Gold, Hammer, Hawkeye, Downing, and Milton. Of his peonies, more than a hundred were sent out as named varieties.

Since 1860 a score or more men and a dozen experiment stations have bred and introduced as many as a hundred varieties of the twelve species from which it is worth while to breed.

Henry Gore of Montreal was a Canadian whose work in breeding plums has almost escaped the notice of American pomologists.

Beginning at least as early as 1820, he grew thousands of seedlings with the hope that he could produce varieties of European plums more suitable for his northern climate. By 1840 he had introduced Dictator, Victoria, Colonel Wetherell, and Notre Bena, all distributed in Canada at the time, though none is probably to be found now.

These were the years when Belgian, French, and English pomologists were seeking to improve new varieties of fruits, giving most of their attention to pears. Of the many men in Europe devoting their lives to this work, Van Mons (see page 235) was most successful. He had by 1835 named and introduced several hundred varieties. Coxe, Kenrick, and Robert Manning were all keenly interested in the new pears Van Mons introduced, and, as soon as he offered the fruit for sale, they were brought to America. Among those importations were such splendid sorts as Bosc, Diel, Colmar, and Manning's Elizabeth.

Copying the methods of Van Mons in Belgium, a number of American fruit growers began breeding pears. One of the most successful of these was Governor Henry Waggoman Edwards of Connecticut, whose experiments were described in *The Magazine of Horticulture* in 1847: 'In the fall of 1817, and in the following spring, Governor Edwards planted the seeds of pears with the design of obtaining new and superior varieties of this fruit. In doing so, he selected the seeds of the best that could be procured, including many sorts, but the number was then very limited compared with our day.' Out of the selections of Governor Edwards, eleven pears were named, all of which had some renown a century ago, but none of which is now grown.

Governor Edwards, by the way, was one of the distinguished men in horticulture in New England in the first half of the nineteenth century. He was a grandson of Jonathan Edwards, and was born in 1779 in New Haven. After graduating from Princeton in 1797, he almost immediately became famous in the political life of the state and nation. He was always interested in pomology and is in the front ranks of the men who have contributed to it in America. Not the least of his good works was the inspiration he gave Manning, Wilder, Dana, Clapp, and a score of other amateur fruit growers to breed pears. Dana alone grew about

6000 seedling pears, following the methods of Van Mons and Edwards, one of which is Dana's Hovey, about the most delectable of all pears, introduced in 1854.

No doubt the first hybrid fruit grown in America was Prince's St. Germain pear, which Prince is said to have raised about 1806 from the old St. Germain pollinated from the flowers of White Doyenne. Not many pears, however, have been produced in this country from artificially produced hybrids—at least, not until recent years. The Kieffer, Garber, and Le Conte are hybrids of the European pear and the Chinese sand pear, all accidental seedlings.

Peter Gideon (1818-99) was the only man in America to pay attention to apple breeding before 1860. For years he had an ideal in mind for his work; and, happily, he obtained the apple he wanted. From boyhood, Gideon had been growing seedling fruits and finally narrowed his endeavors to obtaining a hardy apple for Minnesota, the state in which he lived. With this object in mind he crossed the Siberian crab with the common apple, and out of thousands of seedlings several fruits of promise were obtained. The best of them is Wealthy, from seed planted in Excelsior, Minnesota, in 1860, the cross having been made the year before. The Wealthy is one of the best varieties in the apple flora of the country, and is the only really good variety that can be grown in the northern part of the central states.

American apple growers are much indebted to several Canadians for good varieties. Perhaps most credit for a new apple is due the McIntosh family of Dundas County, Ontario, near the St. Lawrence River. Here, John McIntosh was born in 1777 and died in 1843. It was his good fortune to find growing wild in 1796 a number of seedling apple trees. He planted several of them in the orchard about his home, one of which he named McIntosh Red. The apple was almost certainly a seedling of Fameuse, so popular along the St. Lawrence. John McIntosh's son, Allan, born in 1815, began as a youth to propagate and distribute fruit trees, among which was McIntosh Red, which he first offered for sale in 1835. Although the tree was found in 1796, so long does it take to introduce new fruits that this splendid apple, now about the most popular one in America, was not largely grown until a hundred years after John McIntosh planted it in his home orchard.

Another Canadian horticulturist, Charles Rammage Prescott, is credited with having been the introducer of commercial apple growing in Nova Scotia. There had been some fruits grown in this province from the earliest French settlement, chiefly apples and pears, but there were few named varieties and no commerce in tree fruits until Prescott, in 1812, moved from Halifax to Wolfville, in the Annapolis Valley, and planted orchards and gardens. He it was who brought from the United States such standard sorts as Baldwin, Rhode Island Greening, and Northern Spy; and from England, Gravenstein, Blenheim, and Ribston, varieties that were the foundation of the important apple industry of Nova Scotia. From his trees the three English apples were distributed in New England.

Francis Peabody Sharp did for New Brunswick what Prescott had done for Nova Scotia as an introducer of fruits from older regions. Sharp moved to Upper Woodstock, New Brunswick, in 1844 and immediately began to grow fruit and nursery stock, bringing to his nursery all varieties of hardy fruits from England and the United States. Sharp's work is especially notable in that he became the first breeder of hardy fruits in Canada. At one time he had as many as 2000 seedlings. His best varieties are New Brunswick and Crimson Beauty apples; the latter is an especially valuable variety for cold regions.

Most noted of the Canadians who bred fruits and vegetables was Charles Arnold (1818-83), a native of England. In 1833 he came to Paris, Ontario, and in 1853 founded the Paris Nurseries. He became at once a breeder of fruits and vegetables, of which, out of thousands of seedlings, he introduced at least one noteworthy apple, Ontario, a cross between Northern Spy and Wagener. Of several named varieties of grapes, Othello, Brant, and Canada survive in collections. Canada is a good wine grape in northern regions. Arnold also bred red raspberries, but none of his varieties is now grown.

It is of interest to see what fruits the regions and states have contributed to horticulture, as would be, were the information available, similar data in regard to what parts of the country vegetables, flowers, and horticultural trees and shrubs come from. The data for fruits has been taken from the fruit books published by the State of New York. As will be seen, few of the fruits listed are from the work of plant breeders—nearly all are from chance seedlings, the breeders' art having been applied only in selection. Tree fruits and grapes only are listed, small fruits in these early years being few and very short-lived.

No part of the country has produced so many good apples as New England. One thinks at once of Baldwin and Rhode Island Greening, whose histories have been given on other pages. Besides these, there were Blue Pearmain, described by Kenrick in 1833; Bottle Greening, from Vermont; Fall Pippin, grown since the Revolution; Hubbardston, from Hubbardston, Massachusetts; Mother, from Worcester County, Massachusetts, in 1848; Peck Pleasant, from Rhode Island about 1800; Porter, Sherburne, Massachusetts, 1800; Pumpkin Sweet, Manchester, Connecticut, 1800; Canada Red, New England, a hundred or more years ago; Roxbury Russet, best of all russet apples, Roxbury, Massachusetts, 300 years ago; Sutton, from Sutton, Massachusetts, about a hundred years ago; Sweet Bough, from New England before 1817; Westfield, from the town of that name in Massachusetts, about 1760; and Williams, Roxbury, Massachusetts, about 1750.

Most of the pears that have originated in America are from New England. Among these are: Buffum from the farm of David Buffum, Warren, Rhode Island; Clapp Favorite, Dorchester, Massachusetts, on the farm of Thaddeus Clapp, first mentioned in 1860; Dana's Hovey, from the orchard of Francis Dana, Roxbury, Massachusetts, about 1854; Dearborn, once a favorite, from Roxbury, Massachusetts, found near the home of General H. A. S. Dearborn, in 1818; Mount Vernon, beautiful and delectable, from the garden of Samuel Walker, Roxbury, Massachusetts, about 1847; and Vermont Beauty, Grand Isle, Vermont, in the nursery of Benjamin Macomber, about 1860.

It would hardly be expected that many stone fruits would originate as far north as New England, yet there are several. The best of these is the Coe sweet cherry, grown by Curtis Coe, Middletown, Connecticut, from a pit of Ox Heart, about 1800. Another good sweet cherry from New England is Downer, from Samuel Downer, Dorchester, Massachusetts, about 1832.

Among plums, Bradshaw, long one of the most popular American plums, is from New England, but from what part is not known; it was being grown as early as 1846. Another plum from New England, the hardiest of Domesticas, originated at Bangor, Maine, on the farm of James McLaughlin, in 1840, and was given his surname.

No apricots were brought into being before 1860 in America, and but one nectarine, the Boston. This good nectarine was raised from a peach pit—hence is a seed sport, the first to be noted in American horticulture—by T. Lewis, Boston, Massachusetts, sometime before 1830. It is still a favorite in greenhouses in the East, and until recently was of commercial importance in orchard culture in California. The Foster peach, very like the excellent Late Crawford, originated about 1857 with J. C. Foster, Medford, Massachusetts. Probably about the first peach named in the United States was Heath Cling, until recently very popular; it is supposed to have originated in Massachusetts, possibly as a sister plant to Heath Free, which is known to have originated on the farm of General Heath, Roxbury, Massachusetts, about 1800.

Concord, best known of all American grapes, as has been said, originated in New England at Concord, Massachusetts, in the garden of Ephraim W. Bull, from a seed planted in 1843. E. S. Rogers of Salem, Massachusetts, originated thirteen notable grapes, most of which are still grown in American gardens (see page 437). Several other good grapes came from Massachusetts at an early date, the best of which is Diana, from Mrs. Diana Crehore, Milton, in 1834; Winchell, long the earliest and one of the hardiest of all American grapes, originated in Stamford, Vermont, about 1850.

New York has been prolific in notable varieties of fruits. Among apples there are: Chenango, from Chenango, 1854; Esopus, from Esopus in the Hudson River Valley, previous to 1800; Green Newtown, on Long Island before 1759; Jonathan, Ulster County, about 1800; Primate, long a standard autumn apple, originated on the farm of Calvin D. Bingham, Camillus, about 1840; Swaar, for two centuries a favorite apple with the Dutch along the Hudson in the valley, where it originated before 1700; Bailey Sweet, long a standard sweet apple, Perry; Early Strawberry, New York City, before 1800; Hawley, New Canaan, 1750; Twenty Ounce, probably Cayuga County, before 1845; and Wagener, Penn Yan, from seed planted in 1791.

In one orchard in Ontario County, New York, that of Henry Chapin, East Bloomfield, three well-known apples originated from seeds planted about 1800—Early Joe, Melon, and Northern Spy. It would be difficult to find another man whom chance had so favored in producing from one planting of apple seeds three choice varieties, one of which, Northern Spy, has for a hundred years been a leading fruit both in home and commercial orchards. Why the name 'Northern Spy' no one now knows, but certainly it has no connection with a spy in the Civil War, as one so often hears. It was relatively little known other than in western New York until the middle of the century; a few years later it had become a standard commercial variety in all the northern states.

Of the few pears that have originated in America, New York may be credited with Bloodgood, Flushing, about 1835; Lawrence, Flushing, introduced in 1843; Lawson, from the farm of a Mr. Lawson, Ulster County, about 1800; Reeder, nearly 'blight proof,' raised by Dr. Henry Reeder, Varick, about 1855; and Sheldon, from the farm of Major Sheldon, Huron, about 1815.

Many European plums of merit have originated in New York. Among valuable varieties long grown are: Duane, from the garden of James Duane, Duanesburg, about 1820; Gueii, Lanisburg, about 1830; Hudson, from the Hudson River Valley, about a century ago; Imperial Gage, from the Prince Nurseries, about 1790; Jefferson, from Judge Buel, Albany, about 1825; Lombard, most widely known of all plums in this country, raised by Judge Platt, Whitesboro, about 1830; Middlebury, Schoharie County, about 1850; Peters, first described by Prince of Flushing in 1828; Quackenboss, Schenectady, about 1828; Smith Orleans, Gowanus, Long Island, about 1825; Washington, Prince Nursery, Flushing, 1790; and Yellow Gage, also from the Princes, 1783.

Beginning with Yellow Gage in 1783, in no other part of the world have so many really good plums originated as in New York; yet, curiously enough, since 1860 no good plum came from the state until in recent years several good varieties were introduced by the Geneva Experiment Station.

Chili, or Hill's Chili, long one of the best commercial peaches in western New York, originated in the orchard of Pitman Wilcox, Chili, New York, early in the nineteenth century. One of the ancients in the peach orchards of the nineteenth century was Morris White, from Flushing, Long Island, soon after the Revolution. Red Cheek Melocoton is one of the earliest bud sports known in American pomology; it came from a bud of Lemon Cling, Flushing, Long Island, about 1800.

Clinton, one of the best wine grapes in eastern America, came from Clinton, about 1840; and Isabella, the most popular grape in America before Concord, was sent out by the Princes of Flushing in 1816; it was named after Isabella Gibbs of Brooklyn.

Among apples, New Jersey has given fruit growers Tompkins King, brought from Warren County to Tompkins County, New York, where it was given its name; another variety, for a century a leading commercial apple, is Yellow Bellflower, the original tree of which was standing when Coxe wrote in 1817.

New Jersey has been the home of some of America's best peaches, several of which originated before 1860. Two of these, Early Crawford and Late Crawford, are as good as any peaches ever grown in the United States, and during the nineteenth century were standard commercial varieties. Both originated with William Crawford, Middletown, New Jersey, soon after 1800. A peach never surpassed in quality by any other is Mountain Rose, which originated on the farm of a Dr. Marvin, Morristown, about 1850; Reeves, about 1840, from the orchard of Samuel Reeves of Salem; Smock from Middletown about 1850; Stevens from Middletown in 1858. Two other peaches, which were commercial varieties in the last century originating in New Jersey, are Stump and Troth.

New Jersey's most notable contribution to American horticulture in the way of a fruit was the Delaware grape, from the garden of Paul H. Provost.

Of the fruits that originated in Pennsylvania previous to 1860 there are, among apples: Maiden Blush, near Philadelphia, previous to 1817; Cooper Market, long a standard variety, 1804; Doctor, Germantown, 1800; Fallwater, Bucks County; Fanny, long a favorite, Lancaster, before 1800; Pennock, half a century ago a leading apple, originated on the farm of Joseph Pennock, Delaware County, about 1800; Smokehouse, once much grown, from the farm of William Gibbons, Lancaster County, before 1848; and, most noted of all, York Imperial from York, about 1790.

Several good pears have originated in Pennsylvania: Brandywine, on the banks of the Brandywine River, before 1844; Le Conte, near Philadelphia, about 1850; Seckel, the best known and most excellent of all American pears, originated near Philadelphia soon after the Revolution; another splendid pear from the state, Tyson, best of all early pears, originated on the land of Jonathan Tyson, Jenkintown, just after the Revolution.

Oldmixon Cling, one of the oldest peaches, together with Oldmixon Free, a variant, is said to have originated with Sir John Oldmixon, an early official in Pennsylvania, about 1730. The Hand Plum, named after General Hand of Revolutionary fame, originated in Lancaster about 1790 and was a favorite variety for a hundred years thereafter.

Curiously, considering the great number of seedling orchards in Maryland, no variety of a tree fruit of conspicuous merit originated in that state before 1860. From Maryland, however, came the Catawba grape, from a Mrs. Scholl, Clarksburg, Montgomery County, in 1819, although it is probable that it had earlier been brought from the Catawba River, North Carolina.

Of well-known fruits that originated in Virginia and West Virginia before 1860, there are, among apples: Grimes Golden, in West Virginia about 1800; Ralls, long a standard winter apple in the South, brought to the notice of fruit growers on the farm of Caleb Ralls, Amherst County, about 1800; Winesap, probably in Virginia in the colonial period; Buckingham, one of the oldest American apples; and Gilpin, or Red Romanite, before the Revolution.

Several noteworthy fruits have originated in the Carolinas, during the period covered by this history. Among apples may be named Nickajack, Macon County, North Carolina, before 1853; Red June, from North Carolina, about 1800. Although it originated long after the period of this history, opportunity is taken to mention a single pear, Lucy—most excellent in fruit and nearly blight proof—which originated on the farm of Mrs. Lucy Drake, Beaufort County, North Carolina, in 1880. The De Caradeuc, the only cultivated plum of its species, *Prunus cerasifera,* originated with A. De Caradeuc, Aiken, South Carolina, about 1850.

Possibly South Carolina's most notable contribution to the fruit list of America was the Herbemont grape, a variety that long held in the South the rank that Concord holds in the North; it came into the hands of Nicholas Herbemont, Columbia, South Carolina, early in the nineteenth century and was given his name; Lenoir, another grape popular in the South, cultivated as early as 1800, was named after a man named Lenoir who lived in Statesbury, South Carolina; Mish, one of the few Rotundifolia grapes under cultivation, was found about 1846 near Washington, North Carolina; and James, another Rotundifolia, came from North Carolina, but when and from what part is not known.

The most valuable apple to originate in Ohio is the Rome Beauty, introduced by H. N. Gillett, Lawrence County, in 1848; Willow Twig, origin unknown, came to new life in Ohio in 1848. In the great state of Ohio, early devoted to horticulture, no other apples, and no pears, peaches, plums, or grapes originated before 1860, though, as has been noted, Dr. Jared P. Kirkland, Cleveland, introduced seven varieties of sweet cherries, of which Wood is still grown.

Of the fruits that have originated in Kentucky and Tennessee, one may name, among apples, Ben Davis, sometime before 1800— just where is not known. Paragon, hardly to be distinguished from the better-known Winesap, originated on the farm of Major Toole, Fayetteville, Tennessee, from seed planted about 1830. As early as 1800, Captain William Chambers introduced the Early Harvest pear, Middletown, Kentucky. Another pear, the Pound, not fit to eat, but the largest and most nearly seedless of all pears, originated in Lincoln County about 1830. It is said, erroneously, to be 'blight proof.' Dyehouse, a very good sour cherry, originated in Lincoln County, Kentucky, about 1860. Probably the most widely grown native plum is the Wild Goose, which was grown from a pit taken from the crop of a wild goose by M. E. McCrance, Nashville, Tennessee, in 1820.

Alabama, in the years covered by this history, was the home of but one new fruit, the Miner plum, one of the first plums of a native species to come under cultivation; it was found on the Tallapoosa River by William Dodd, in 1813.

Indiana is credited with but one notable apple, Winter Banana, said to have been produced in Cass County about the middle of the nineteenth century. The only other tree fruit to originate in this state before 1860 was the Robinson plum, long one of the most popular native plums in the Middle West; it was found by a Mr. Pickett, Putnam County, about 1835.

Of worthy fruits originating in Michigan before 1860, there are among apples, Detroit Red, near Detroit more than two centuries ago, similar in color and flavor to Fameuse, but larger; and Shiawassee, another apple of the Fameuse group. Several peaches first came under cultivation in the famous Michigan peach belt, of which one of the oldest was Gold Drop, but where and when it originated is not known.

Few fruits originated in Wisconsin before 1860, but among these was the De Soto plum, chief representative of *Prunus americana,* near De Soto, by a Mr. Tupper, in 1853; Janesville, the hardiest of all grapes, came from the garden of F. W. Loudon, Janesville, 1858.

A good apple originating in Illinois was the Akin, still grown in the Middle West, on the farm of W. J. Akin, Lawrenceville. Another variety, once highly esteemed, is Babbit, from the farm of C. W. Babbit, Woodford County, about 1845; and, first for the state, was Walbridge, from the orchard of Joseph Curtis, in 1818. Sudduth, long a standard pear in the Mississippi River region, came from Sangamon County in 1820.

Iowa's contribution to new fruits before 1860 was chiefly in native plums. Among those of merit, still grown in the prairie states, are Forest Garden, Cedar Rapids, about 1860; and Wolf, Wapello County, about 1852.

Missouri can be credited with only one notable fruit before 1860, the Missouri Pippin apple, now little grown, from Kingsville, about 1840.

Arkansas has been the birthplace of two notable fruits that come within the range of this history: an apple, Arkansas or Mammoth Black Twig, came from Rhea Millis, in 1833. The Cynthiana grape, one of the best American varieties for red wines, almost identical with the well-known Norton, was sent from Arkansas to the Prince Nurseries, Flushing, Long Island, in 1850.

Although the variety originated after the period of this history, Kansas must be given credit for Stayman, an apple from the experimental orchard of Dr. J. Stayman in 1866.

It is only within the lifetime of men still living that Americans have done much in breeding vegetables, excepting, of course, the species that belong to the New World. Perhaps more attention has been given to breeding tomatoes than any other vegetable grown on this side of the Atlantic.

The tomato is mentioned in Virginia in 1781 by Jefferson,[9] and Washington grew it at Mount Vernon. It is doubtful whether either of the two men considered it an addition to the vegetable garden, although, almost without doubt, the scientific curiosity of both led them to taste so alluring a product. In 1802 an Italian painter introduced tomatoes in Salem, Massachusetts, but could not persuade anyone to eat the fruits. M'Mahon in his *American Gardener's Calendar,* 1806, speaks of tomatoes as being grown but mentions no varieties. As late as 1834, D. J. Brown,[10] a writer in the *United States Patent Office Report,* says the tomato was almost wholly unknown in this country as an esculent. On the other hand, a writer in *The Maine Farmer,* 21 August 1835, says the tomato, or Jerusalem apple, is found as a food in abundance in western markets. In any case, enough has been said to show that the tomato, the love-apple, or Jerusalem apple, of our grand-parents, with its dozen or more forms and thousand or more varieties, has been a commonly grown vegetable for rather less than a hundred years. In total yield, the country over—no vegetable is quite so cosmopolitan—the tomato must rank well toward the highest.

A landmark in the breeding of tomatoes was the introduction of the Trophy, a little after the middle of the century. It was a product of Dr. Hand, Baltimore County, Maryland, who began breeding tomatoes about 1850. In his work he crossed the small, smooth love-apple, commonly grown in gardens as an orna-mental, with the several larger garden varieties then being grown. These garden tomatoes all bore much convoluted fruit with the skin running deeply in the convolutions. The Trophy was a solid mass of flesh and juice, with small seeds, and the smooth skin of the love-apple. Trophy long remained a standard sort, and be-came the parent of the several races and hundreds of varieties we now grow.

9 Jefferson, p. 55.   10 *U. S. Pat. Office Rpt.,* 1854, p. 384.

After the tomato, sweet corn, among vegetables, was most improved in the nineteenth century. It will be recalled from a previous page that sweet corn was brought to the notice of American gardeners by an officer of Sullivan's army in 1779 when he brought to Plymouth, Massachusetts, a few ears from an Indian plantation on the banks of the Susquehanna. Sweet corn is not mentioned by Jefferson in his *Notes on Virginia,* 1801; or by M'Mahon, 1806; or by Gardiner and Hepburn, 1818; or by Fessenden, 1828. It seems to have first appeared in a seed catalogue, that of Thorburn, in 1828; and next in one by Bridgeman four years later.

In 1848 a premium of $300 was offered by the New York State Agricultural Society for the best essay on maize. The award was won by J. H. Salisbury, who says of sweet corn: [11] 'There are several sub-varieties as the Small Early Sweet, the Rhode Island Sweet, the Hematite Sweet, and a new variety made by crossing the Sweet with the Early Canada.' None of these varieties was very widely grown by gardeners. Early Canada was a flinty yellow corn and the resulting hybrid, though seldom mentioned, must have been the earliest yellow sweet corn; but yellow sweet corns were of small esteem until Golden Bantam appeared in 1902.

The improvement of sweet corn by hybridization seems to have been started in the 1820's by Dr. Gideon B. Smith, who named one of the hybrids Early White. In a letter in *The Albany Cultivator,* 1838, Dr. Smith wrote that Early White was a hybrid of two Indian corns, Tuscarora and the Sioux, from crosses made ten or twelve years earlier. It is evident from Dr. Smith's letter that the hybridization of corn was well understood by him, as no doubt it was by others. Yet so unimportant was sweet corn, there seems to have been no other hybridizer who put his work on record after Dr. Smith, until 1850, when the Reverend A. R. Pope, Somerville, Massachusetts, gave an account of breeding corn in *The Magazine of Horticulture,* December 1850. His first hybrids were made in 1845, and sometime between that date and 1850 he named one of his crosses Old Colony, the first variety of this vegetable to receive general recognition by seedsmen and gardeners; it was a favorite for forty years.

[11] New York State Ag. Soc., Trans. Salisbury, J. H., *Maize or Indian Corn,* 1848, pp. 678-845.

With the introduction of Stowell's Evergreen about 1850, sweet corn began to take its place in gardens as a well-liked vegetable. According to an account in *The Magazine of Horticulture,* in 1851, this variety originated with Nathan Stowell, Burlington, New Jersey, as a cross between Menomony, a soft field corn, and the Northern Sugar corn. At first the new corn was called Stowell's Sweet Corn but shortly took the name Stowell's Evergreen. Today, as ninety years ago, this variety is a favorite in gardens; and, meanwhile, has become one of the commonest varieties for canners and truckers.

After the Civil War, varieties of sweet corn multiplied apace. Down to the present, however, farmers still pluck ears of field corn for 'roasting ears,' as all did a century ago when sweet corn in the garden was a novelty.

One would expect that much would have been done with the improvement of beans, which the Indians were cultivating when the Whites came to North America. However, for four centuries, following the discovery of America, though beans of one kind or another were being cultivated wherever they are now grown in the New World, no one undertook to improve them. All the kinds of beans grown in gardens in these four hundred years were chance hybrids or sports selected from various local sources. Few of those who made selections of these chance seedlings are known, so that the horticultural history of the bean, down to 1880, when several men began to hybridize and select, seems not to have been recorded.

Lima beans are sharply divided in large whites and small whites in the catalogues of the last hundred years. Probably this division goes back to the wild limas of ages ago. There are also speckled limas, red limas, black limas, none of them now commonly cultivated, which probably go back to the wild species. The potato lima is another rather distinct group, in which the seeds are large, white, nearly circular, rather dry, with plants having longer and more pointed leaflets. These go back to Indian plantations. Another division may be made into pole limas and bush limas. It does not appear that the bush limas, now so popular, were known until 1875, when a dwarf lima was found along a Virginia roadside and was introduced a few years later.

Nearly all lima beans are introductions of the last hundred years, though Lawson, in *The History of Carolina,* 1718, describes beans that must have been limas. Probably these came from the West Indies. All the varieties of limas now grown came from several introductions from South America, the first of which was made by Captain John Harris, U.S.N.; who, in 1824, brought seeds from Lima, Peru, and grew them in his garden at Chester, New York, giving them a name from the city whence they came. In the years since then, few vegetables have had more attention than this one.

The common string bean, the 'snaps' of colonial gardeners, are of many types, of which the most usual division is that of pole beans and bush beans. The Indians grew only pole beans, which bore green pods with variously colored seeds, of several sizes and shapes. Most of the string beans grown during the years of this history were these climbing beans, popular now only in the South. Wax-podded or golden-podded beans, of which there are now a score or more varieties, are late comers in the bean family, having been introduced in Europe in the 1830's, thence to the United States in 1852.

As was the case with the dwarf limas, dwarf string beans are a product of the nineteenth century. One of the first named varieties was Refugee, listed in 1822 by Thorburn. It is still a favorite for late snap pods. Refugee was brought from France to England by refugee Huguenots, whence the name. Wax-podded dwarf string beans, of which there are perhaps a hundred varieties, have all been bred later than 1860, at which time, or a little later, varieties began to appear. Stringless snap beans date from the 1890's.

Scarlet runners were listed in Miller's *Dictionary* as grown in England in 1724, and probably they have been known much longer. They were common in the United States as early as 1800.

Until nearly the end of the nineteenth century, of the hundred or more varieties of peas listed in American seedsmen's catalogues, all but half a dozen or thereabouts came from England. Some of the most brilliant pages to be written in plant breeding are of work done with peas. Thomas Andrew Knight, John Goss, Dr. McLean, and Thomas Laxton are great names in horticultural literature, and all were Englishmen who did much to improve peas. Gregor Mendel, using peas, made discoveries that are now of great help in plant breeding. All these men were working between 1780 and 1860, and one would think might have stimulated some American to try to improve this valuable esculent. Yet, none did until toward the end of the nineteenth century, if we except the little done in selection by Joseph Cooper, and a variety introduced by the Landreth Seed Company in 1823, called Landreth's Extra Early; the manner of its origin is not known. Since 1860, many admirable varieties of peas have originated in the United States and Canada.

The three species and several races of pumpkins and squashes were long grown simply as pumpkins and squashes. There were few well-recognized varieties until after 1850. No one gave attention to improving the species and groups that came from the Indians. Several varieties were brought from South America by sea captains. Acorn, listed by Russel in 1827, and Valparaiso, listed by Thorburn in 1828, probably came from Chile. James J. H. Gregory, as we have seen, introduced the Hubbard in 1842. There is a suspicion that several other winter squashes introduced between 1800 and 1860, reputed to have come from South American Indians, originated in South America.

The muskmelon, early brought to America from the Old World, soon evolved into several types in the New World, but until long after 1860 our cultivated varieties mostly came from Europe. In M'Mahon's list of vegetables in 1806, there were thirteen varieties of muskmelons, all of which came from the Old World. Few vegetables have so many variations as muskmelons; they vary greatly in season, size, color of skin, color of flesh, smoothness of skin, flavor, aroma, and thickness of flesh; yet growers and seedsmen were not interested in making crosses, or fixing chance variations until after 1880. Perhaps two improvements in muskmelons may be noted between 1840 and 1860; one was the introduction of Jenny Lind, a green-fleshed melon, the other, Nutmeg, with heavily netted skin. Both were standard early melons for many years.

Nor was much done with cucumbers and watermelons until recent years. Cucumbers were early brought from the Old World, and early settlers found them as far south as Haiti and north to Montreal; but nothing is said about varieties, although they were mentioned in several eighteenth-century advertisements, until 1806, when M'Mahon, in his *Gardener's Calendar,* named eight, all from the Old World. Modern cucumbers gradually evolved from these and other European varieties without planned hybridization, or much selection, until 1872, when Tailby's Hybrid was exhibited. After that, especially from 1880 to the present, much interest has been shown in breeding this vegetable. Most of the kinds now grown by gardeners and truckers have originated since 1900. Modern cucumbers are little like those listed by M'Mahon in 1806.

The watermelon grows especially well in the warmer parts of America and has ever been a favorite vegetable in the New World, to which it was brought by early Spaniard settlers. It is one of the oldest cultivated plants. The Hebrews pined for it in the wilderness after having been accustomed to it in Egypt. It is mentioned in America by the earliest writers from Massachusetts to Florida; yet, until recent years, few attempts have been made to obtain new varieties, though it is easily improved by selection.

Watermelons vary in size from a few pounds to over a hundred; in shape, from round, oval, elliptical to oblong; the color may be light green to almost black, striped or marbled with greenish white; the flesh is white, cream, honey-yellow, pale red, red, or scarlet; the seeds vary from white through brown to black and are sculptured and engraved with spots or colored margins and tips. All of these characters are noted by early herbalists, and it would seem that modern culture has brought no new ones.

Yet within the range of this history, gardeners knew them only by the color of the skin and flesh and the shape. The early seed catalogues listed them as long or short, red-fleshed or yellow-fleshed, or some similar name in accordance with shape or color. During the last eighty years, hundreds of new varieties have been introduced, of which a few are grown for the market, and a few more in home gardens.

There are, to be sure, a score of other vegetables, the improvement of which is not mentioned in these pages. Chiefly, these are crops of the Old World, from where America has had, until recent years, nearly all the new varieties. A study of records would show that only an occasional cabbage, onion, lettuce, turnip, cauliflower, parsnip, or carrot was originated in this country before 1860. In the years since those covered by this history, improvements in almost every species grown in the vegetable garden have been greater than in all the years before.

At a guess, for there are few records available, much more was done in breeding flowers than vegetables between 1806, when M'Mahon listed species and varieties, and 1860 when this survey ends. By far the best account of new flowers in the United States for this period is to be found in the records of the Massachusetts Horticultural Society, a society that has held exhibitions of flowers as well as of fruits and vegetables from 1829 to the present time. From these records, we find that the herbaceous and shrubby flowers receiving most attention were the rose, geranium, camellia, dahlia, calceolaria, pink, pansy, phlox, petunia, fuchsia, verbena, aster, lily, water lily, peony, rhododendron, and azalea. Of this rather small list the most popular flowers, and those to which gardeners indoors and out devoted most of their attention, were the camellia, dahlia, geranium, phlox, verbena, rhododendron, and azalea, species greatly improved by the members of the Society in the first years of its existence.

17

HORTICULTURAL LITERATURE

1700-1860

COLONIAL gardeners had to rely almost wholly on English works, if, as is doubtful, many desired the printed word for guidance. Few of these early books separated horticulture from agriculture, unless, perhaps, some wealthy colonist brought over the magnificent herbals that English and Dutch gardeners were then using. Certainly none of these was reprinted in America, and though books in several fields of horticulture were printed in considerable numbers in England in the seventeenth and eighteenth centuries, only two on general agriculture containing horticultural material were reprinted in colonial America. The first of these was *The Husbandman's Guide,* published in Boston in 1710 by John Allen for Eleazar Phillips. The book contains, among other horticultural matters, 'Many Excellent Rules for Setting and Planting of Orchards, Gardens, and Woods, the times to Sow Corn, and all other sorts of Seeds.'

From present information it would seem that the second treatise on agriculture published in America was a reprint of another English work, John Smith's *Profit and Pleasure United, or the Husbandman's Magazene.* This book was printed in London in 1684 with a second edition in 1704. The full title of the American reprint in 1718 is:

The Husbandman's Magazene. Being a treatise of horses, mares, colts, oxen, cows, calves, sheep, swine, goats: with directions for their breeding & ordering. . . Together with plain rules for improving arable & pasture lands . . . sowing and harvesting: The management, improvement and preservation of fruit trees, plants & flowers . . . flax and hemp . . . bees. With cutts.

The only copy known of this early and rare work is in the library of the American Antiquarian Society, Worcester, Massachusetts.

One of the commonest books in colonial days was *The English Physician Enlarged,* by Nicholas Culpepper, a botanist of some repute and a physician notable for his advocacy of the Doctrine of Signatures, a theory that the external signs on plants indicated their value in medicine. Culpepper's book told at length what parts of the plants were of value, what diseases they would cure, when they should be gathered, and how they should be kept, with directions for their dosage in sickness. Every American physician and many householders owned the book, practiced its precepts, and grew or gathered herbs for medicinal uses.

Culpepper had a counterpart in America. John Tennent (1700-1760), a physician living in Virginia, in 1724 published *Every Man his Own Doctor,* 'a plain and easy Means for Persons to cure themselves by medicines grown in America'; or, again, a book for 'Those who can't afford to dye by the Hand of a Doctor.' The book was so popular that by 1736 Benjamin Franklin was publishing a fourth edition. In another treatise entitled *Essay on Pleurisy,* Tennent gave his experience with 'Snake-root,' the value of which he learned from the 'Senekka' Indians. Besides pleurisy, snakeroot cured gout, rheumatism, dropsy, and nervous disorders. The plant, *Polygala Senega,* has come down to us as Seneca Snakeroot, and in the two centuries since John Tennent wrote his essay, a thousand quacks have used it in patent medicines, and believers in simples still gather it.

Jared Eliot is given credit by students of agricultural literature for writing the first book on American agriculture, which was entitled *Essays upon Field Husbandry.* The six essays, which had appeared separately, were printed in one volume in Boston in 1760 with another edition in New York a little later. Eliot was a man of many parts: a minister, physician, botanist, investigator, author, and friend of Benjamin Franklin and every other notable American scholar of his day. Gardening and orcharding could not have been of much importance in Eliot's time, for they are scarcely mentioned. The sixth essay is devoted almost wholly to the mulberry and silkworms. But one of Eliot's correspondents, John Bartram, under date of 1 December 1762, makes suggestions in regard to cultivating native grapes, which, had they been heeded, would have put American grape growing ahead by more than a hundred years.[1] This letter contains, so far as now appears, the first recommendation to cultivate native grapes, or, for that matter, any native fruit.

Of the many accounts of fruit growing in colonial New York, no other quite equals Crèvecœur's *Thoughts of an American Farmer on Rural Subjects*.[2] Crèvecœur, born in Caen, France, in 1735, came to the English colonies in 1759 or 1760 from Canada. His was a family of distinction in France and he had been well educated. He traveled widely in America as a lieutenant in Montcalm's army in the French and Indian War, as a surveyor, and as an explorer in Michigan and Ohio, and in the French and English colonies along the Atlantic Coast. His wanderings were brought to an end in 1769, when he married an American girl, Mehitable Tippet, of Yonkers, after which his farm life began at Pine Hill, Orange County, New York.

In 1780 Crèvecœur went to France, where he wrote his three books: under the pen names 'An American Farmer,' 'A Farmer in Pennsylvania,' and 'Agricola.' Returning to America, he found his house burned by the Indians and his children scattered.

Crèvecœur is best remembered by his admirable book, *Letters from an American Farmer,* printed in England in 1782, which gives us by far the best account we have of American agriculture at the close of the Revolution. A second book, *Sketches of Eighteenth Century America, More Letters from an American Farmer,* contains scarcely less information and is even more pleasant reading, none the less interesting from the fact that the manuscripts were not published for nearly a century and a half after they were written.[3]

[1] Eliot, Reprint Edition, pp. 197-8, 200.
[2] *Sketches of Eighteenth Century America,* pp. 79-151.
[3] Reprinted in Everyman's Library, New York, 1916.

No one in the three colonies on the Delaware seems to have been inspired to write a book wholly devoted to any one phase of horticulture or agriculture. Perhaps an exception should be made in the case of Edward Antill's 'Essay on the Cultivation of the Vine,' which appeared in 1771 in *Transactions of the American Philosophical Society*.[4] This was the first printed treatise on any fruit published in the United States. Antill's home was in Shrewsbury, New Jersey, where he had a vineyard of European grapes, but what the acreage, the number of vines, or the kinds, the reader is not told. The essay is a rambling discussion of European grapes and European practices in growing them. Antill tells how to make wine and raisins. He quotes Columella, who wrote in the first century; ends his essay talking about figs; and throughout his pages discusses patriotism, religion, and various other matters. Nevertheless, until the publication of John Adlum's *Cultivation of the Vine* in 1823, Antill was America's chief authority on the grape.

American Husbandry was published anonymously in London in 1775. Of all our accounts of colonial agriculture, taking all the parts of North America that had then been settled, this book is the best as regards early practices, though it falls short in horticulture, possibly because there was little horticulture to write about.

The author of *American Husbandry* (his identity is still uncertain, though probably he was John Mitchell, the botanist) was familiar with every part of North America in which crops were then being grown, and knew the farming practices, the products, the markets, and the men most skilled in tilling the soil. From Canada and Nova Scotia, he follows the colonies, one by one, south to Florida and the West Indies. The agricultural possibilities of the valleys of the Ohio and Mississippi Rivers are discussed, with some mention of what French traders and trappers were doing in agriculture. The various fruits then being grown, including the grape, are frequently mentioned, with many accounts of vegetables and a few of flowers. The book was unknown or ignored in America until 1918, when Dr. Lyman Carrier called attention to it in the *Journal of the American Society of Agronomy*.

4 Vol. I: 117-98.

Happily, it is now available in an edition edited by Professor Harry J. Carman, published in 1939.

The Gardener's Kalendar by Mrs. Martha Logan was published in 1779 (see page 135). No copy of the book is now known, but it was long quoted as an authority on gardening matters. David Ramsey, writing in 1809, says: 'and to this day it regulates the practice of gardeners in and near Charleston.' Occasional writers refer to the book as Mrs. Logan's *Gardener's Cronicle,* but Ramsey no doubt used the correct title. The first almanac printed in South Carolina was Tooler's, for 1752. It contains a 'Gardener's Kalendar done by a lady of the Province and esteemed a very good one.' Possibly this work was also by Mrs. Logan. Certainly, succeeding numbers of *The Carolina and Georgia Almanac,* beginning in 1798, reproduced in six pages, are a part of Mrs. Logan's *Gardener's Kalendar.*

The second book on gardening printed on this side of the Atlantic also came from Charleston, in 1787. It was *The Gardener's Kalendar for South Carolina, Georgia and North Carolina* by Robert Squibb (see page 141). The book, according to an advertisement in the *Charleston Morning Post,* 5 February 1787, contained: 'an account of all work necessary to be done in the kitchens and fruit gardens every month of the year, with instructions for performing the same: also particular directions relative to soil and situation, adapted to the different kinds of plants and trees most proper for cultivation in these states.'

Much more in general use than agricultural books or farm journals during the first two hundred years of the printing press in America were the many almanacs published throughout the country. All contained calendars, without which no farmer could do his work; set forth the occupations appropriate for each month; gave a smattering of what then passed as science; and, most important of all, printed simple astronomical facts, particularly the phases of the moon, which enabled tillers of the soil to 'farm by the moon,' as most of them did long after farm books and journals were available. In a good many almanacs after post-colonial years there were useful memoranda of farm, orchard, and garden work, such as discussions of fertilizing, rotating crops, sowing seeds, harvesting, and similar farm practices.

The first American almanac was probably that of William Pierce, Cambridge, Massachusetts, published in 1639, although some ascribe the honor to Bradford's Press, in Philadelphia, in 1687. The most famous was, of course, *Poor Richard's Almanack,* launched in 1732 by Benjamin Franklin under the pseudonym of Richard Saunders, published in Philadelphia with a run of 25 years. Robert B. Thomas, of Boston, Massachusetts, published *The Farmer's Almanack* for 54 years, beginning in 1793; it has been continued by others down into the twentieth century, and was at all times a mine of information for farmers and gardeners. Probably no other of the many American almanacs enjoyed so great popularity, although, in its first issues at least, its imitation of *Poor Richard's Almanack* was patent.

The American Almanac and Repository of Useful Knowledge was another notable publication of the kind, printed in Boston from 1828 to 1861. It also catered to farmers, with much information on farm subjects.

From 1800 to the Civil War, nearly every town newspaper in America published an almanac. Country newspaper publishers in these years were more often than not reimbursed with firewood, maple sugar, hard cider, and other farm produce. Ready cash came mostly from job printing and advertisements, which the almanac shared with the paper. Thousands of copies were sold or given away.

The next book indigenous to the country after *American Husbandry* was Deane's *New England Farmer, or Georgical Dictionary,* in 1797 (see page 51). It was a cyclopedia of agriculture in which horticulture came in for full discussions in every field. The book was supposed to be the last word in scientific agriculture— but was very slippery science.

At the end of the century, and in the first years of the new, books began to come thick and fast on general agriculture, most of which contained more or less information on horticultural subjects; or, at least, information valuable to the fruit grower and gardener. Only brief mention can be made of these general works.

XXVa. Salt Lake City in 1853. *Courtesy of Dr. John A. Widtsoe, Salt Lake City.*

XXVb. Salt Lake City about 1863. *Courtesy of Dr. John A. Widtsoe, Salt Lake City.*

LETTERS

FROM AN

AMERICAN FARMER;

DESCRIBING

CERTAIN PROVINCIAL SITUATIONS,
MANNERS, AND CUSTOMS,

NOT GENERALLY KNOWN;

AND CONVEYING

SOME IDEA OF THE LATE AND PRESENT
INTERIOR CIRCUMSTANCES

OF THE

BRITISH COLONIES

IN

NORTH AMERICA.

WRITTEN FOR THE INFORMATION OF A FRIEND
IN ENGLAND,

By J. HECTOR ST. JOHN,
A FARMER IN PENNSYLVANIA.

LONDON,
PRINTED FOR THOMAS DAVIES IN RUSSEL STREET COVENT-
GARDEN, AND LOCKYER DAVIS IN HOLBORN.
M DCC LXXXII.

XXVI. Title page of J. Hector St. John de Crèvecoeur's *Letters from an American Farmer.*

ESSAYS

UPON

FIELD-HUSBANDRY

IN

New-England,

As it is or *may be* Ordered.

By JARED ELIOT, *M. A.*

Ecclef. v. 9.

¶ *Moreover, the profit of the Earth, is for all; the King himself is served by the Field.*

BOSTON:

Printed and Sold by *Edes* and *Gill*, in *Queen-Street*,

1 7 6 0.

XXVII. Title page of Jared Eliot's *Essays upon Field-Husbandry in New England.*

XXVIIIa. Hyde Park, near Poughkeepsie, New York. *From* Garden and Forest.

XXVIIIb. Shaker village at New Lebanon, New York. *Courtesy of the New York State Museum, Albany, New York.*

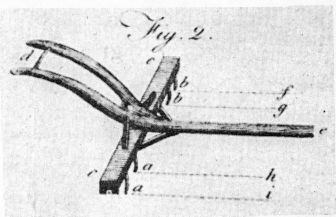

XXIXa. Wooden plows of the colonial period. *From Forsyth's* Principles of Agriculture, 1804.

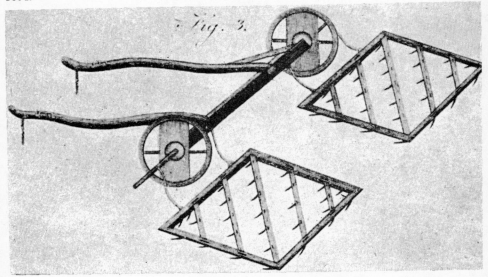

XXIXb. Harrow of the colonial period. *From Forsyth's* Principles of Agriculture, 1804.

XXXa. The grounds at Mt. Pleasant, country seat of James Beekman, at what is now First Avenue and 51 Street, New York; built in 1763-4; demolished in 1874. *From a painting by A. Hosier; courtesy of the New-York Historical Society.*

XXXb. John Bartram's house, west front. *From* Garden and Forest, IX, 1896.

HISTORY

OF

Agricultural Societies,

ON THE MODERN

BERKSHIRE SYSTEM.

From the year 1807, to the establishment of the
State Board of Agriculture in Albany,
January 10, 1820.

ALBANY :

PUBLISHED BY D. STEELE.

Packard & Van Benthuysen, Printers.

1820.

XXXI. Title page of Elkanah Watson's *History of Agricultural Societies.*

A NEW
VOYAGE
TO
CAROLINA;

CONTAINING THE

Exact Description and *Natural History*

OF THAT

COUNTRY:

Together with the *Present State* thereof.

AND

A JOURNAL

Of a Thousand Miles, Travel'd thro' several
Nations of *INDIANS*.

Giving a particular Account of their Customs,
Manners, &c.

By JOHN LAWSON, Gent. Surveyor-
General of *North-Carolina*.

LONDON:
Printed in the Year 1709.

Perhaps the most notable was John Beale Bordley's *Essays and Notes on Husbandry and Rural Affairs,* published in Philadelphia in 1799. Bordley was a lawyer and farmer, who lived near where the Wye River empties into Chesapeake Bay. Here, on a 1600-acre farm, he conducted an out and out experiment station. The book, largely a record of his experiments, struck the first note in scientific agriculture to be heard in America.

Out of George Washington's comprehensive diary could be taken excerpts in regard to his experiments sufficient to make a very good horticultural book. From his correspondence, still another volume might be published on all fields of agriculture, and this, in part, has been done. Two of the best English farm authors, Arthur Young and Sir John Sinclair, long corresponded with Washington in the years between the Revolution and his death. Washington's letters to and from these distinguished agriculturists were published in London in 1800 and 1801; in Alexandria, Virginia, in 1803; and in Washington in 1847. Many of the discussions relate to farm machinery, livestock, crop rotation, fertilizers, with not a few references to horticulture.

The first book devoted wholly to fruits to be published in America was William Forsyth's *A Treatise on the Culture and Management of Fruit Trees.* It was edited by William Cobbett, who supplied an introductory chapter and notes adapting the English book to American readers, and was published in New York in 1802, in Philadelphia in the same year, with a third edition in Albany in 1803. Still another edition came out in Philadelphia in 1803 under the title *An Epitome of Mr. Forsyth's Treatise on the Culture and Management of Fruit Trees,* edited 'By an American Farmer.'

Though the editor's attempts to adapt the teachings of an Englishman to Americans were not particularly successful, there were plain directions for planting, pruning, and harvesting fruits, with some consideration of the diseases of fruit trees—wide of the mark —with notes on gardening, on the planting and care of forest trees—(theses of small importance in a land still covered with forests)—and a number of pages on the building of farm habitations.

In 1804 a treatise was published in Washington, under the title *The American Gardener,* by John Gardiner and David Hepburn. While Gardiner's name appears first on the title page, the book was probably written by Hepburn; or, if not wholly written by him, was a result of his experience. Hepburn was a gardener who had had long service in England and America. The book follows the popular English style of practical suggestions for the months of the year. The first part is devoted to vegetables; the second, chiefly to fruit; and then follow pages on hothouses, greenhouses, and hops. A second edition appeared in 1818, and included *A Treatise on Gardening by a Gentleman of Virginia,* written by John Randolph.

A Treatise on Gardening by a Gentleman of Virginia has a curious history, as set forth by Marjorie Fleming Warner in the *Annual Report of the American Historical Society.*[5] The writer proves that the 'Gentleman of Virginia' was John Randolph, Jr. (1727-84), and says that his *Treatise* 'had been published at Richmond as early as 1793 or 1794, and that there apparently had been earlier printings.' If this surmise of 'earlier printings' is ever proved to be true, Randolph's *Treatise* may be the earliest American book on kitchen gardening. John Randolph, Jr., was, of course, a member of the great Randolph family of Virginia, and was the last King's attorney of Virginia, a loyalist who went to England at the outset of the Revolution and died there in 1784. In 1826 the *Treatise* was republished at Richmond, under the title *Randolph's Culinary Gardener.*

The first really serviceable book for all branches of horticulture published in America was Bernard M'Mahon's *American Gardener's Calendar,* Philadelphia, 1806, which has been mentioned and quoted many times in previous pages (see pp. 197-203). Asked to name the first real American landscape gardener, one would have to say, and then with some qualifications, Bernard M'Mahon. In his *American Gardener's Calendar* M'Mahon devoted 18 pages to 'Ornamental Designs and Planting.' The ideas on these pages were patently taken from Repton, the great English authority, but the material was digested and presented for American conditions.

5 Vol. i: 433-42. 1919.

M'Mahon was a convert to the new English school of naturalistic gardening and he urged gardeners to 'consult the rural disposition in imitation of nature'; advised them to abolish 'long straight walks'; recommended 'rural open spaces of grass-ground'; and suggested 'winding walks, all bounded with plantations of trees, shrubs, and flowers in various clumps.' To M'Mahon must be given credit for first putting in print in America any considerable advice on landscape gardening and for having had the good taste to enunciate satisfactorily the principles of naturalistic gardening which Parmentier and Downing were to expound so well some years later.

A curious little booklet on hedges was printed in Washington in 1807 under the title *Directions for the Transplantation and Management of Young Thorn or other Hedge Plants, Preparative to their Being Set in Hedges.* The author was Thomas Main, probably the nurseryman whom Jefferson mentions in his diary as the source of some of his plants.

The catalogues and advertisements of Grant Thorburn's seed and nursery establishments contributed greatly to the formation of a taste for gardening. Thorburn (see page 204) wrote continuously for the current press during his long life, under the *nom de plume* Laurie Todd, sometimes on horticulture, sometimes on the questions of the day. His life in America, enlivened by the author's imagination, formed the substance of a popular book by John Galt, published in London in 1830, entitled *Laurie Todd, or Settlers in the Woods.* His single horticultural book was *The Gentleman's and Gardener's Kalendar for the Middle States of North America,* published in 1812. There were also an admirable autobiography, published in 1852, and several books of fiction.

William Coxe has the distinction of being the first man in America to write on pomology. The descriptions of tree fruits in his book, *A View of the Cultivation of Fruit Trees,* published in Philadelphia in 1817, were so full, so painstakingly written, and the work was so well done that it remained the standard manual of tree fruits until Manning's *Book of Fruits* appeared in 1838. It is well described in its title page, which gives some idea of the fruit growing of the time:

A VIEW of the CULTIVATION of FRUIT TREES, and the Management of Orchards and Cider; with Accurate Descriptions of the Most Estimable

Varieties of NATIVE AND FOREIGN APPLES, PEARS, PEACHES, PLUMS, AND CHERRIES, Cultivated in the Middle States of America; Illustrated by Cuts of two hundred kinds of Fruits of the natural size; Intended to Explain Some of the errors which exist relative to the origin, popular names, and character of many of our fruits; to identify them by accurate descriptions of their properties and correct delineations of the full size and natural formation of each variety; and to exhibit a system of practice adapted to our climate, in the Successive States of A NURSERY, ORCHARD, AND CIDER ESTABLISHMENT.

Closely following Coxe's book came James Thacher's *The American Orchardist,* published in Boston in 1822 and improved in a second edition published in Plymouth in 1825. Thacher's book is the least good of the fruit books written in the first half of the nineteenth century, its only value, if any, lying in its discussions of fruit-tree diseases, though the descriptions of these and the remedies for them are nearly worthless. Thacher also wrote, among other works, one on *The Management of Bees.*

Thacher (1754-1854) was one of the geniuses of New England in the years immediately following the Revolution. He was a physician of note through the war, one of the leading patriots in the conduct of it, and a man of high standing. Besides the books on orchards and bees, he wrote a very good history of the Revolution. Perhaps he rated less high as a horticulturist than in his other fields of endeavor.

The first separate treatise to be wholly devoted to the grape was John Adlum's *Memoir on the Cultivation of the Vine in America and the Best Mode of Making Wine.* The book, only 142 pages, was published in Washington in 1823, with a second edition in 1828 (see page 435). Adlum did much for agriculture and horticulture in other ways. He had known Joseph Priestley, the great chemist, and with him had endeavored to aid agriculture through science. He became an intimate of Thomas Jefferson and tried through him, without success, to have a piece of land in Washington set aside for the purpose of 'cultivating an experimental farm.' He finally established an experimental vineyard in the District of Columbia and maintained it from his own funds. It is more for his experiments in cultivating native grapes, his urgent advocacy of their culture, inspired no doubt by Jefferson, and his introduction to cultivation throughout the land of the

Catawba, than for his book, that Adlum should be remembered in horticulture. Rafinesque named an attractive genus in the Fumitory family, *Adlumia,* after him.

Three years after Adlum's book on grapes, in 1826, John James Dufour's *The American Vine Dresser's Guide,* a notable book, appeared. The sub-title sets forth the author's aim: 'a treatise on the cultivation of the vine, and the process of wine making, adapted to the soil and climate of the United States.' The book was much larger than that of Adlum, and is much better, since Dufour gives an account, which Adlum did not, of what other grape growers in the country were attempting to do, with reasons for their failures. He speaks at some length of 'indigenous' grapes, and of their value in wine making. As did all the other foreigners who attempted to grow grapes in America, he shows strong prejudices against native vines, and where there was partial success in growing them, prefers to believe they were of European blood. The book is of particular interest in the parts setting forth Dufour's experiences in trying to found colonies in Kentucky and Indiana to grow grapes.

In 1827 another work on the grape appeared under the same title Dufour had chosen: *The American Vine Dresser's Guide,* by Alphonse Loubat (see page 225). The author was a Frenchman, and the book, of 138 pages, was alternately in French and English. As with Adlum, Loubat's work with grapes was of much more value to American vine dressers than his book; nevertheless, his *Vine Dresser's Guide* was considered valuable enough for a second edition in 1872, long after several other good books on grapes were to be had.

The publication in 1828 of *A Short Treatise on Horticulture* by William Prince of the famous Linnaean Botanic Garden marked the beginning of a new era in horticultural books in America. This was the first book of the kind in America that broke away from the English custom of treating horticulture in calendar style. The book was at once popular. Curiously enough, it was printed in but one edition, but this single edition must have been large, for the book is one of the commonest in rare book stores of the horticultural works printed before the Civil War. In it were described a great number of fruit and ornamental trees, shrubs, grapes, flowers, and greenhouse plants, with directions for their culture.

In 1830 William Robert Prince, aided by his father, wrote *A Treatise on the Vine* in which were: a history of the vine from the earliest times; descriptions of more than 200 foreign varieties and 80 native sorts; with directions for establishing and maintaining a vineyard. The description of varieties and the cultural directions were taken from the experience of the Prince Nurseries. This book was not only the largest volume on grapes yet published in America but was far and away the best up until then and for several decades after.

The Pomological Manual, written by William Robert Prince, aided by his father, was published in two volumes in 1831, with a second edition in 1832, in which the two parts were bound together. It contained full and accurate descriptions of the known varieties of all hardy tree fruits, excepting the apple. A good many of the descriptions, it is to be feared, were more or less padded with help taken from European fruit books; though, to be sure, most of the fruits had been grown on the author's grounds. This book is hardly equal in importance to the other books by the Princes.

William Robert Prince's *Manual of Roses* was published in 1846. This manual was the first good book printed in America on the rose, and one that remains to this day one of the best. It contains a good history of the rose, a discussion of the several classes then recognized by rosarians, and descriptions of all the varieties then known in Europe and America. The instructions on propagation and culture were particularly full and must have been valuable in a country where collections of roses, out of doors and indoors, were becoming popular.

Thomas Green Fessenden's *New American Gardener,* 1828, and *The American Kitchen Garden,* 1855, were the most popular garden books in America in the first half of the nineteenth century. Both contained practical directions for cultivating vegetables and garden fruits. They were of a cyclopedic nature and about as interesting reading as a dictionary; but they were typical of the times and were well liked by farmers and gardeners. By 1857 *The New American Gardener* had run into 30 editions; *The American*

Kitchen Garden seems to have been a rather poor condensation of the older work.

Fessenden (1771-1835) was an author and editor of note in his day. Besides his two garden books, he was the first editor of the old *New England Farmer,* and author of *The Complete Farmer and Rural Economist,* and of *The Silk Culturist,* and co-editor of the first two volumes of *The Horticultural Register and Gardener's Magazine* 1835-6. He was also a literary man of note—a satirical poet of sorts. He was an intimate friend of Hawthorne, who wrote a sketch of his life.

The first American book to be concerned wholly with flowers was written by Roland Green and published in Boston and New York in 1828. It was entitled *A Treatise on the Cultivation of Ornamental Flowers: Comprising Remarks on the Requisite Soil, Sowing, Transplanting, and General Management; with Directions for the General Treatment of Bulbous Flower Roots, Greenhouse Plants,* etc. It was chiefly general directions followed by a list of 88 out-of-doors flowers and 14 greenhouse plants. The out-of-doors list is curious in that it contains several trees, including the fir, a number of shrubs, the eggplant, and half a dozen plants that belong in the herb garden, plants that the author chose to call 'annual and biennial flowers.' The greenhouse plants are those 'which are commonly grown in rooms.' Grant Thorburn thought well enough of it to give it publication and push its sale in his New York store. Who Green was and what were his qualifications for writing the book do not appear in the reviews in the papers of the time.

The agricultural writings of William Cobbett seem never to have been appreciated in America. Cobbett published in this country three books on horticulture, and, though they were adaptations from English authors, his notes in each make them fairly satisfactory for American conditions. Besides these three there was *A Year's Residence in the United States of America* published in London in 1819, to which we have referred several times.

Of Cobbett's three American horticultural works, the first was *The American Gardener,* 'A treatise on the situation, soil, fencing and laying-out of gardens; on the making and managing of hot-beds and greenhouses, and on the cultivation of the several sorts of vegetables, herbs, fruits and flowers.' It was published in Baltimore in 1823, with five later editions, the last in New York in 1856. Though supposedly indigenous to America it is patently from a European point of view. In 1853, an abridgment of *The American Gardener* appeared under the title *Garden Flowers,* in which the older title was used as a running head.

In 1824 Cobbett's *American Orchardist and Cottage Economy* was published. It is a curious mixture of information about domestic economy and orcharding, as the following statement of its contents shows: 'containing information relative to the brewing of beer, making bread, keeping of cows, pigs, bees, ewes, goats, poultry, and rabbits, and relative to other matters deemed useful to the conducting of the affairs of a laborers family; to which are added instructions relative to the selecting, the cutting and the bleaching of the plants of English grass and grain, for the purpose of making hats and bonnets.' The American edition was bound with the second edition of Thacher's *American Orchardist,* as *The American Orchardist and Cottage Economy.*

The first half of the nineteenth century was a period in which a great number of seedsmen, large and small, began business in America. Several of the best known came from England and no sooner were their seed houses established than they undertook to write books on how to grow gardens. The two most notable were M'Mahon and Thorburn, whose books have been discussed, but a third writer of equal rank was Thomas Bridgeman (see page 250). Almost at once he began to publish horticultural books, and before his death in 1850 had given American horticulturists four treatises covering every phase of gardening.

The first of Bridgeman's books was *The Young Gardener's Assistant,* printed in Brooklyn in 1829. According to its expanded title, it was 'a catalogue of garden and flower seeds, with practical directions under each head, for the cultivation of culinary vegetables and flowers; also directions for cultivating fruit trees, the grape vine, etc., with a calendar showing the work to be done each month in the year.' Eventually this book ran through 13 editions, the last in 1865. It was the most popular of Bridgeman's four books. A revised edition, under the title *The American Gardener's Assistant,* appeared in 1867 and again in 1872.

Bridgeman's second book was *The Florist's Guide,* 'containing practical directions for the cultivation of annual, biennial, and perennial flowering plants, of different classes, herbaceous, shrubby, fibrous, bulbous, and tuberous-rooted; including the double dahlia, greenhouse plants, etc.' The book was published in New York in 1835 and ran into five editions, the last in 1847. Just as *The Young Gardener's Assistant* was for many years a standard work on vegetables, so was *The Florist's Guide* on flowers.

In 1836 Bridgeman published in New York *The Kitchen Gardener's Instructor,* a variation of *The Young Gardener's Assistant,* differing chiefly in containing fuller directions for growing vegetables. Under this title the book ran through five editions, the last in 1864. Much the same material appeared in a work published in Philadelphia under the title *Kitchen-Gardening.*

The last of Bridgeman's books was *The Fruit Cultivator's Manual,* printed in New York in 1844. Its contents were rather curious, since besides the usual hardy tree fruits, some attention was given to grapes, figs, and cranberries. As in most of these early books there was a calendar showing what work was to be done each month.

An early formal treatise on the strawberry to appear in America was printed in Albany in 1832. It was by W. Thorburn and consisted of 20 pages, published in *The New York Farmer and Horticultural Repository,* under the title 'The Fragaria: or Description of the most improved varieties of strawberries and raspberries cultivated in Great Britain and the United States: with directions for their culture.'

The first book on flowers to be serviceable to gardeners was *The American Flower Garden Directory,* under the joint authorship of Hibbert and Buist (see page 248), which was published in Philadelphia in 1832. It contained, as the authors tell us, 'practical directions for the culture of plants in the hothouse, gardenhouse, flower garden, and rooms or parlors for every month in the year; with a description of the plants most desirable . . . instruction for erecting a hothouse, greenhouse, laying out a flower garden . . . with lists of annuals, biennials, and ornamental shrubs.'

It was a rather sumptuous book, with a frontispiece of *Camellia japonica fimbriata,* then very popular. For some reason the book did not at once become popular, though later, in 1839, when revised by Buist, it ran through several editions and was long the recognized authority on flower growing. Looking at it now, one marvels that the times could have produced so good a volume, both in content and in printing and illustration.

Buist was probably the most prolific horticultural writer in America in the first half of the nineteenth century. His *Rose Manual* was published in Philadelphia in 1844, the first special book on the rose in America from the gardener's point of view; an earlier book, a sentimental effusion under the title *Queen of Flowers,* had appeared in 1841. The *Rose Manual,* which went through four editions in ten years, contained descriptions of the varieties of roses grown in America; accounts of the several species, illustrated with rather poor engravings; and instructions on propagation and care, of which the 'destruction of insects' makes it differ widely from a modern treatise on the rose. Prince's *Manual of Roses,* in 1846, was a much better work, but never got beyond the first edition, probably because Buist wrote in a simpler style.

The last and possibly the least popular of Buist's books was *The Family Kitchen Gardener,* published in 1852, which ran into direct competition with Bridgeman's earlier and better *The Kitchen Gardener's Instructor.* Buist's book contained the usual descriptions of species and varieties, cultural directions, and a discussion of garden implements. Besides its pages on vegetables, considerable space was given to fruits for gardens, and to kitchen and medicinal herbs. An innovation was the inclusion of botanical names as well as French and German names of the plants discussed.

One of the most valuable fruit books in the third decade of the nineteenth century was William Kenrick's *The New American Orchardist* (see page 210), published in 1833. The book was particularly valuable because of its accurate descriptions of varieties adapted to the Atlantic seaboard from Canada to Florida. As could be expected coming from this experienced grower, the discussions of culture and management are well done. Not so much can be said for the treatment of 'maladies' and 'noxious insects,' but at the time little was known of orchard pests. Kenrick, one of the original silk-culture enthusiasts, in 1835 published *The American Silk-Growers Guide*.

In 1836 the Watervliet Shakers (see pp. 205-7) published a combined catalogue and gardener's manual for their customers, which sold for six cents; for this small sum buyers of seeds got very good instructions on the raising of vegetables. Although the descriptions of varieties fall a little short, they are as complete as could be had at that time. In 1843 a larger manual was published under the title *Plain Instructions for the Selection, Propagation and Management of a Kitchen Garden*. The editor of both publications was Charles F. Crusman. In a way, they were the forerunners of the catalogues of the seedsmen who have followed, in which cultural instructions as well as lists and prices of seeds are given.

In 1838 Robert Manning (see p. 212) published his *Book of Fruits*. The work, as the author tells us, was 'a descriptive catalogue of the most valuable varieties of the pear, apple, peach and cherry for New England culture.' It contained besides the tree fruits some grapes, bush fruits, and ornamental trees and shrubs, with a number of very good plates. Manning was the first pomologist, European or American, who made all of his descriptions at first-hand and described no fruit 'not actually identified beyond a reasonable doubt of its genuineness.' The book is especially notable for its correct naming of varieties and its systematic pomology, fields that until then had been neglected. It at once superseded Coxe's, and, until Downing's great work came out in 1845, was the accepted authority. Manning intended this work to be the first of a series, but the volumes to follow never appeared.

The book was enlarged and published under the name *The New England Fruit Book* in 1844 by John M. Ives; and a third edition was edited by Ives and published as *The New England Book of Fruits* in 1847. Ives' illustrations were the best that had yet appeared in any American pomological work.

Henry A. S. Dearborn (1783-1851) was, in the first half of the nineteenth century, one of the most ardent American amateur horticulturists. He was a lawyer, politician, diplomat, general, man of wealth, and the author of several books besides the one on horticulture. His experience in horticulture before writing was in his own gardens and greenhouses; he was a moving spirit in organizing the Massachusetts Horticultural Society, of which he was the first president, and was instrumental in establishing an experimental garden and Mount Auburn Cemetery.

General Dearborn's book, *Monography of the Genus Camellia,* was a discussion of the most popular flower in the gardens of the South and in the greenhouses of the North. Besides giving a botanical classification of the genus, the author described and gave the histories of 270 varieties and directions for the culture of the members of the genus. The little book would hardly be worth noticing were it not that it was the first monograph of an ornamental plant published in America, and that General Dearborn and the camellia were well known in America wherever gardens were established.

Louisiana could boast, in these early years, of a book on gardening written in French, the language of most of its people. It was J. F. Lelièvre's *Nouveau Jardinier de la Louisiane;* although a small book, it covered the whole field of horticulture, with directions for growing fruits, vegetables, and flowers. It was published in New Orleans in 1838, and long continued to be the authority on growing vegetables, fruits, and flowers in the great regions that had been the Louisiana of the French.

The second really good book on flowers was *The American Flower Garden Companion,* by Edward Sayers, published in 1838. It was for the time and the subject a fairly large book, containing 179 pages and a preface of 12 pages. It was sponsored by two of the leading seed houses of the time, those of G. C. Thorburn and Joseph Breck & Co. A second edition appeared in 1839, and a larger, revised edition in 1846.

In 1839 Sayers published in Boston *A Treatise on the Culture of the Dahlia and Cactus.* The book was chiefly concerned with the dahlia, which was then becoming the most popular flower, and was the first book written wholly by an American on a special flower.

Sayers, by the way, seems to have been at home in several fields of horticulture, having published in 1837 *A Manual on the Culture of the Grape,* which holds but a small place among the many works on this fruit.

Sayers was the author also of *The American Fruit Gardener's Companion,* published in 1839. The author sets forth in a lengthy preface the aim of the book as 'a practical treatise on the propagation and culture of fruit; adapted to the Northern and Middle States.' It did not become popular, and is not comparable to several other books of the times on fruits.

Perhaps a book of as great value for American gardeners as any from European writers was by John Lindley, the English horticulturist, whose *Theory of Horticulture* marked the beginning of a new style. Lindley attempted to explain the fundamental operations of horticulture on physiological principles. The book was an immediate success in England, and American horticulturists were eager for an edition adapted to the soil and climate of the New World. In 1841 the first American edition was published in Boston. It could not have had better American sponsors. A. J. Downing was just beginning a notable career as a horticulturist, and Asa Gray was at the start of his life's work. These two men supplied notes for the American edition, which insured it popularity in this country. With the publication of a second edition, Lindley became the authority of all American horticulturists who had a leaning toward science.

If asked to name the author who, during this period, most influenced American horticulture by his pen, few would deny that honor to A. J. Downing. His first book, published in 1841 and by far his greatest, was *A Treatise on the Theory and Practice of Landscape Gardening.* The book, the author tells us in a lengthy sub-title, is adapted to North America with a view to the improvement of country residences. Comprising historical notices and general principles of the art, directions for laying out grounds and arranging plantations; the description and cultivation of hardy trees; decorative accompaniments to the house and grounds; the formation of pieces of artificial water; flower gardens, etc. With remarks on rural architecture. It was illustrated with many engravings.

During his lifetime, Downing published five editions of this book, making many changes and additions. The last was published posthumously in 1853. After his death in 1852, Henry Winthrop

Sargent re-edited his work, with further changes, adding a portrait of its famous author. Sargent's edition, in turn, went through five editions, the first in 1859, the last in 1875. In 1921 Frank A. Waugh edited an admirable new edition, bringing this work of a great master up to date. Landscape gardeners generally agree that it is without rival in any period or in any language in this field.

Downing's book on landscape gardening was published when the author was but 26 years old. Three years later, in 1844, his *Cottage Residences* appeared. In it were a series of designs for rural cottages and cottage villas. In comparison with his first one, this work is unimportant.

Quite as vital to pomology as the first book was to landscape gardening, however, was the third book of this gifted author. It appeared in 1845 under the title *The Fruits and Fruit Trees of America*. At once it became the standard American pomological authority, a place it long held, though often revised by Charles Downing. It was a treatise on the propagation of fruit trees and management of orchards, with descriptions of the varieties of fruits, native or foreign, cultivated on this side of the Atlantic. The book went through some twenty editions, the last in 1900; was several times enlarged and revised, and color plates were added. From 1857 on, the name of its editor, Charles Downing, appeared on the title page.

Much credit for the success of *The Fruits and Fruit Trees of America* should be given to Charles Downing. The two brothers had been associated in the Downing Nursery at Newburgh when the book first appeared, but Charles withdrew from the firm in 1850 to devote his life to testing varieties of fruits in a large experimental orchard. That his descriptions might be accurate, he planted and brought to fruitage more than 3000 varieties of fruits. He maintained this orchard until 1870, when the growing city of Newburgh encroached upon his property.

A. J. Downing founded *The Horticulturist* in 1846 and was its editor until his death. Then the editorials in *The Horticulturist* and others of his writings were brought together by his friend George William Curtis, and published in 1853 under the title *Rural Essays*. The book contained 'A Letter to his Friends' by the Swedish novelist Fredrika Bremer, who, on a visit to America, had come to know Downing and his work. The memoir by George

William Curtis and the letter by Fredrika Bremer constitute the best accounts we have of Downing's life and work.

The Natural History of the State of New York was a most valuable contribution to the agricultural literature of the country, and was by far the most elaborate that had yet appeared in this country having to do with natural history and agriculture. It consisted of 30 quarto volumes, each with many maps, plates, views, color plates, and splendid examples of the engraver's art in black and white. The State of New York expended more than a million dollars on the surveys and in printing and editing the report. The first volume was published in 1842, the last in 1896. Those in charge of the survey and the report were Dr. James Hall and Professors DeKay, Emmons, Beck, and Vanuxem, with a large corps of assistants.

Five volumes were of particular interest to agriculture and horticulture. Two discussed botany, two geology and soils, and the fifth was on agriculture, including farm crops, fruits, insects, and fungi. The latter was Volume III in the set, edited by Ebenezer Emmons, and appeared in 1851. There were 81 handsome color plates, many of which were of varieties of fruits. The discussions of insects and fungi of fruit crops were the fullest and most accurate that had yet been published in America. The other volumes contained a wealth of information of interest to agriculturists and horticulturists. Though published by the State of New York, much of the information applied equally well to other northeastern states.

The Flower Garden; or Breck's Book of Flowers appeared in 1851, a notable book from a famous seedsman, Joseph Breck. Breck's *The Young Florist; or, Conversations on the Culture of Flowers, and on Natural History* had been published in 1833. This earlier book was so small and contained so little on cultivated plants that it hardly deserves to rank as a horticultural work. It was as the author of *The Flower Garden* that Breck became best known. Besides instructions on cultivating flowers and very good descriptions of the leading species and their best varieties— annuals, biennials, and perennials—it gave full information on many ornamental shrubs and evergreens. It ran through five editions, each enlarged and improved, the last in 1866 under the title *New Book of Flowers,* revised when the author was seventy.

The rose came in for its full share of books in America in the first 50 years of the nineteenth century. One of the best of this period was written in 1847 by Samuel Parsons, entitled *The Rose: Its History, Poetry, Culture, and Classification* (see p. 270). Parsons was one of America's first writers on landscape gardening in the horticultural papers and magazines of the times, a charter member of the American Pomological Society, and long an honorary member of the Massachusetts Horticultural Society. His book ran through four editions, each revised and enlarged, the last appearing in 1883. It then reappeared in 1896 under the name *Parsons on the Rose,* which in turn was revised and reprinted in 1910. For over sixty years these books were among the best on the subject.

John Fisk Allen (see p. 266), whose avocation was the growing of water lilies, published three books that contributed much to American horticulture. The first of Allen's books was entitled *The Culture of the Grape* and was printed in Boston in 1847. The next year a much larger work on the grape was published under the lengthy title *A Practical Treatise on the Culture and Treatment of the Grape Vine.* As the sub-title explains, the book covers the history of the grape, directions for its treatment in the United States in the open air and under glass. An enlargement of the first work was widely read, having come out when grape growing out of doors and in glass houses was popular with both amateur and professional vintners. A second edition came out in 1853, enlarged and revised.

Allen's third book was on a much smaller scale, hardly being worth notice were it not that it was on a subject wholly new to American horticulturists and ushered in a mild fad, that of growing water lilies. It was entitled *Victoria Regia: or the Great Water Lily of America,* and was published in Boston in 1854. It contained an account of the discovery of this plant in the Amazon region, its introduction in the United States, and methods in cultivation, with illustrations of the plants as grown in Salem, Massachusetts.

From the time of its first printing in 1846 down to 1900, the fruit book in America most used by fruit growers, nurserymen, and later in colleges and schools was John Jacobs Thomas's *The American Fruit Culturist* (see p. 213). Probably no other horticultural work in America has been revised so often or published in such large editions. Why its popularity was so great is a little hard to understand, since its descriptions of varieties were largely compiled, often inaccurate, and not particularly well written. Downing's *The Fruits and Fruit Trees of America* was a much better book.

The first edition of the book was a small paper-covered volume, with the short title of *The Fruit Culturist,* published in New York, with 30 woodcuts. It was immediately popular, and by the end of 1847 four editions had appeared. It then became a best seller, and in 1849 came out under the longer title, the text increased, with 300 woodcuts. From then on *The American Fruit Culturist* came out every few years, until in 1903 the twenty-first edition was published with 758 pages and nearly 800 woodcuts.

A book that served fruit growers in northern New York and New England out of all proportion to its merits and circulation was published by Chauncey Goodrich in 1849. It was *The Northern Fruit Culturist; or the Farmer's Guide to the Orchard and Fruit Garden.* In 1850 a second edition, revised and enlarged, appeared, showing that the work was appreciated in the region for which it was intended; no doubt its sale was aided by the fact that the author was by vocation a bookseller and publisher. As an avocation he grew fruits and vegetables and maintained a nursery to supply his northern neighbors with plants. His place was a miniature experiment station that furnished much data for his book.

Another New England author who grew plants and seeds for sale and contributed not a little to the horticulture of the Northeast was Samuel W. Cole, of Maine. Cole seems to have been a man of various parts in his writings; he began his career in the 1830's by publishing the *Columbian Spelling Book;* then a book of poems under the title *The Muse;* and in 1835 turned to agriculture and printed *The Yankee Farmer.* Late in life (he died in 1851) he wrote *The American Fruit Book,* a comprehensive treatise containing information on 'propagating and managing fruit-trees, shrubs and plants; with a description of the best varieties of fruit, including new and valuable kinds.' It contained a great number of engravings of fruits, trees, insects, and methods of grafting, budding, and training, and ran into three editions of several thousands each.

One of the half-dozen outstanding American horticulturists of the nineteenth century who also wrote books was Patrick Barry (see p. 244). As a writer Barry became well known as the editor of *The Genesee Farmer,* from 1844 to 1852, and of *The Horticulturist,* after Downing's death in 1852, until 1855. Barry's chief contribution to horticultural literature, however, was *The Fruit Garden,* published in New York in 1851. It ran through three editions under its original title and two under the name *Barry's Fruit Garden,* given it in 1883, the work having been greatly enlarged and revised.

Barry's book struck a new note in American horticultural literature in that the author followed Lindley in attempting to explain and illustrate the physiology of fruit trees in all the various operations of orcharding. It had much to say about dwarfing trees and training them in the formal shapes, long popular in Europe. The fashion for these dwarf trees, the espaliers, the pyramids, and other forms common in the last half of the century, was fostered by this book. Still another feature was a rather better discussion of treating fungus diseases and insect pests than had appeared before.

The book of books in horticulture so far as size, color plates, and fine printing go, in the period of this history, was Charles Mason Hovey's *The Fruits of America.* Hovey was well known to all his generation as a nurseryman, a breeder of strawberries and camellias, and as the founder and editor of *The Magazine of Horticulture,* which, from 1835 to 1868, was the most popular periodical of its kind in America. *The Fruits of America, Containing a Selection of All the Choicest Varieties Cultivated in the United States* was issued in 28 quarto parts from 1852 to 1856. Volume III was never completed. A sub-title describes the book as 'containing richly colored figures and full descriptions of all the choicest varieties cultivated in the United States.' The parts completed contained 110 colored lithographs by William Sharp, a pioneer in color lithography, with portraits of Hovey and Sharp. The volumes are now collectors' items in both horticulture and lithography.

The earliest book on greenhouses published in America was Robert B. Leuchars' *A Practical Treatise on the Construction, Heating and Ventilation of Hot-Houses*. It was published (without date) about 1850 in New York, republished in Boston in 1851 and in San Francisco in 1860. The text contains, as the sub-title tells us, discussions of 'conservatories, greenhouses, graperies, and other kinds of horticultural structures; with practical directions for their management, in regard to light, heat, and air.' It was well written and illustrated with numerous engravings, and gives good idea of the progress of greenhouse building in the country.

One of the most successful authors from the point of view of book sales was R. G. Pardee, Palmyra, New York. His subject was small fruits, which were just coming into great popularity in all parts of the country. Pardee's book, published in 1854, was entitled *A Complete Manual for the Cultivation of the Strawberry*, 'with a description of the best varieties; also notices of the raspberry, blackberry, cranberry, currant, gooseberry, and grape.' This was one of the first works to discuss the blackberry, cranberry, and black raspberry, and since there were descriptions of varieties and directions for cultivating these new fruits, as well as the older ones, the book was in demand at once. It was published in New York in 1854 and by 1865 had run through eight editions.

The cranberry had hardly been mentioned in the book of literature of horticulture until Pardee gave it a little space. Two years later, 1856, it was to have a small volume devoted to it, and, all things considered, a very good one—a book still in use: B. Eastwood's *A Complete Manual for the Cultivation of the Cranberry*. It contained a description of the varieties then known, full cultural directions, and some remarks on cranberry regions and marketing.

Gardening for the South, written by William Nathaniel White, Athens, Georgia, in 1856, is said to have transformed gardening in the South. White was a Northerner who went to Georgia in 1847 and almost immediately became interested in southern horticulture. He was a writer for agricultural papers in the North and South, for Patent Office Reports, and at various times was an editorial writer for southern farm papers. Besides his various admirable writings, White carried on a well-conducted experiment station to test fruits, vegetables, flowers, and the tea plant. He is said to have been the first person in America to practice the protection of fruit trees from frost by smoke from slow-burning fires. The book ran through three editions, each revised and enlarged. It discussed vegetables, fruits and ornamentals 'for the states south of Pennsylvania; with gardening calendars for the same.'

In the 1850's the grape was receiving more attention from amateur fruit growers and plant breeders than any other fruit. Several authors wrote on this fruit, and grape catalogues were really books. By far the most popular was William Chorlton's *American Grape-Grower's Guide,* published in 1856, not of much interest now but then of immense popularity because it contained full information on growing grapes under glass, then one of the commonest horticultural industries. One gets the idea of the kinds of graperies under glass from the sub-title, in which we are told that, besides out-of-door culture of grapes, there are in the book discussions 'of the grape-vine in each department of hothouse, cold grapery, and retarding house.' The book went to four editions, the last three revised by Dr. George Thurber.

Robert Buchanan's *Culture of the Grape and Wine Making; with directions for the cultivation of the strawberry by N. Longworth,* published in Cincinnati in 1852, was better, but not much. Even so, Buchanan's inconspicuous treatise quickly ran through eight editions, the last in 1861.

Another Ohioan, Franklin Reuben Elliott, published a far larger and better fruit book in this decade. Elliott lived in Cleveland, then a friendly rival of Cincinnati in horticulture. In his *Fruit Book,* published in 1854, he attempted a history and an account of the methods of propagation and the management of fruit trees and shrubs, 'with descriptions of nearly all the varieties cultivated in this country; note of their adaptations to localities and soils in this country, and also a complete list of fruits worthy of cultivation.' This was comprehensive—a complete guide to orcharding in the whole country and the largest horticultural work yet published for the West. It passed through three editions and then in 1859 came out, enlarged and revised, in a fourth as Elliott's *Fruit Book;* then in another, undated but probably the same year, as *The Western Fruit Book.* Still later, in 1876, a much condensed book, 128 pages, was published in Rochester, New York, under Elliott's name, with the title *Hand-Book for Fruit-Growers,* popular enough to go through two editions in one year.

One of the Cincinnati horticultural circle, which just before the Civil War included probably the most enthusiastic horticulturists in America, .was E. J. Hooper, who in 1857 published *Hooper's Western Fruit Book,* 'a compendious collection of facts, from the notes and experience of successful fruit culturists, arranged for practical use in the orchard and garden.' It was published in Cincinnati and was considered not only an authoritative treatise, but a fine illustration of the printer's art, since it had color plates as well as black and white illustrations. A second edition came out in 1858. In all parts of the West, in the middle of the nineteenth century, what was written in *Hooper* was the final word.

Another of this Cincinnati group who made valuable contributions to horticultural literature was Dr. John Ashton Warder (see pages 313-14), the ablest and by far the best known of the horticulturists in southern Ohio, whose *Hedges and Evergreens* was published in 1858. It was well illustrated with engravings and was widely sold at this time when hedges and evergreens were being planted in the West. It was followed in 1867 with his more notable work, *American Pomology—Apples.*

In the 1850's, when so many fruit books were being published in Ohio, Indiana and Illinois could boast of but one each and Michigan of none. The book from Indiana was Henry Ward Beecher's *Plain and Pleasant Talks about Fruits, Flowers and Farming* (see page 317).

The first book from Illinois was C. Thurston Chase's *The Prairie Fruit Culturist: or What to plant and how to cultivate it in the West, a reliable treatise on fruits,* published in 1859. It was a small book and probably had no great influence.

The pear, always a favorite fruit, received little attention from writers. The only book of note in the years of this history was printed in 1859 by Thomas W. Field: *Pear culture. A Manual for the propagation, planting, cultivation, and management of the*

*pear tree; with descriptions and illustrations of the most produc-
tive of the finer varieties, and selections of kinds most profitably
grown for market.* This was about the best book of the times devoted to a single fruit, although L. E. Berckmans' booklet of 13
pages entitled *Pear Culture for the South,* published in 1859, was
very good as far as it went.

The report of the 1860 census states that 'forty papers and magazines, devoted almost exclusively to topics pertinent to farming
and gardening, are published in the country.' Probably as many
more, if Canada be included, had been founded and failed between the years 1800 and 1860. There had also been various
scientific reviews and repositories that had published articles on
horticulture.

For example, *The Medical Repository* began publication in
1797 in New York City. The founders of this publication proposed to give

accounts of insects—whether any uncommon dearth or numbers of
them; whether troublesome to man, beasts or vegetables; with as
accurate and minute notices as may be of their derivation, mode of
propagation, nature and extent of ravages, or other evils, as they may
occasion; of their appearance and disappearance, and of the means,
if any, of guarding against or destroying them.

The papers that followed in this magazine for the next twenty-
five years constitute the beginning of entomology, as applied to
agriculture, in America, few and unimportant though they may
now seem to be.

Another objective proposed by this journal was to publish
'Histories and progress and condition of vegetation, with regard
to growth, vigor and disease, independent of the ravages of insects—but marking the influence of manures and the local situation, both as to elevation and soil.'

For many years *The Medical Repository* published articles on
natural history; then, with the appearance of other publications
dealing with botany, entomology, and horticulture, essays on the
subjects grew fewer and fewer until in 1824 its printing ceased.
No doubt its strong leaning to botanical subjects was greatly stimulated by Samuel Latham Mitchell, one of America's first great

scientists, long one of the editors of the *Repository*. Perhaps the article of most interest to horticulturalists was John Bartram's paper, 'Account of the species, hybrids, and other vines of North America,' written in 1802, with notes by James Mease added in 1803. In 1811 a William Smith published an article on 'Observations on the decay of fruit trees, and on lean and shrivelled fruit. . .' In April 1806, April 1809, January 1810, July 1811, there were articles describing Hosack's famous Elgin Botanic Garden, the last two articles enriched with engravings.

The first agricultural paper published in America to pay particular attention to horticulture was the *New England Farmer,* which appeared in Boston in 1822 and continued until 1846. The editor until 1837, Thomas G. Fessenden, gave as much space to horticulture as to agriculture. One of his chief services to horticulture through his paper was to encourage the foundation of the Massachusetts Horticultural Society, an event brought to pass in 1829.

On 1 January 1828, publication of the *New York Farmer and Horticultural Repository* was begun in New York City and continued for several years. It was devoted to practical husbandry, gardening, and the sciences intimately connected with rural pursuits. The *Repository* was a monthly published under the patronage of the New York Horticultural Society, and deserves particular mention because it was one of the first agricultural magazines to be well illustrated. Articles appearing in it were over the names of the most noted agriculturists, horticulturists, and scientists of the day.

Another agricultural paper to devote much space to horticulture was the *Genesee Farmer,* founded in Rochester, New York, in 1831. It was published by Luther Tucker, an experienced journalist and a lover of horticulture, as was evident in his paper from the first to the last issue in 1839.

A second *Genesee Farmer* made its appearance under the name the *New Genesee Farmer and Gardener's Journal* in January 1840. It was edited by John J. Thomas and M. B. Bateham, two notable men in New York's galaxy of horticultural writers. Bateham was a partner in the first nursery planted in western New York, and was long proprietor of a well-known seed store in Rochester. His connection with the *Genesee Farmer* was of short duration, Thomas, the leading spirit from the first, soon taking full charge. But Bateham was not through with his horticultural endeavors. He went from Rochester to Columbus, Ohio, in 1843, where he started a nursery and in 1845 founded the *Ohio Cultivator*, which he edited until 1850. In 1847 he helped to organize the Ohio Pomological Society, which, in time, became the Ohio Horticultural Society, of which he was secretary until 1860.

The David Landreths, father and son, in 1832 began the publication of *The Floral Magazine and Botanical Repository*, which was published a few years and failed, probably because it was far in advance of its readers. It was not a large magazine, but had many color plates and descriptions of tropical ornamental plants.

The Horticultural Register and Gardener's Magazine was founded in 1835 and published until 1838. The first volume, published by George A. Barrett, was edited by Fessenden and J. E. Tischmacher; the second, edited by Fessenden and Breck, and the third and fourth by Breck alone, were published by Joseph Breck and Co.

A real horticultural magazine now appeared, *The American Gardener's Magazine, and Register of Useful Arts,* conducted by C. M. Hovey and P. M. Hovey, Jr. The first issue came out in Boston in January 1835. Two volumes appeared under this title and then the name was changed to *The Magazine of Horticulture, Botany, and all Useful Discoveries and Improvements in Rural Affairs.* Under the latter title, the magazine ran from January 1837 to 1868.

The next horticultural publication of real worth to appear was scarcely less notable, *The Horticulturist and Journal of Rural Art and Rural Taste,* by A. J. Downing and others. The first issue came out in July 1846, in Albany. Until his death in 1852 Downing did his editorial work at his home in Newburgh. The magazine went through many changes for thirty-odd years, the editors during the period of this history being Patrick Barry, for two years; then Barry and J. J. Smith, for one year; and for the next four, to 1860, J. J. Smith. From 1846 to 1860, this magazine was a friendly rival of Hovey's *The Magazine of Horticulture,* never surpassing the latter, unless in the matter of Downing's editorials and imaginative writings. Under Barry it was noted for its hand-colored plates of fruits and flowers, and handsome covers, paper, printing, and text.

Meanwhile, several lesser horticultural publications had their day. There was a *Gardener's Magazine* published in Boston in May 1854, edited and published by William S. King who boasted that his lack of connection with any commercial horticultural enterprise made it possible for him to serve his readers more objectively. This was a thrust at C. M. Hovey, who was both editor and nurseryman, as were numerous other horticultural editors of the time. This particular *Gardener's Magazine* seems to have failed to last out the year.

A Magazine of Gardening and Botany was published in Baltimore in 1834, another weakling that did not last long. In Ohio, Hooper and Elliott published *The Western Farmer and Gardener* in Cincinnati from 1839 to 1845, an attractive and valuable monthly with plates colored by hand. A little later, another noted horticulturist in Cincinnati, John A. Warder, published *The Western Horticultural Review,* from 1850 to 1853, which was continued for some months after as *The Western Horticultural Review and Botanical Magazine. The Philadelphia Florist* was published in 1852-3, and then or three years was known as *The Florist and Horticultural Journal.* During its brief existence it was noted for its color plates as well as its admirable text. Still later, Thomas Meehan published in Philadelphia *The Gardener's Monthly and Horticultural Advertiser,* a delightful magazine, from January 1859 to January 1888 with changes of title.

Deserving special notice as the first journal devoted wholly to pomology was *Hoffy's Orchardist's Companion,* a quarterly established and edited by William D. Brinckle, an amateur pomologist and a busy physician of Philadelphia. The quarterly was established in 1841, a beautiful quarto magazine with color plates, of which but one volume appeared. In 1860 Dr. Brinckle edited *Hoffy's North American Pomologist.*

In the Far West, three agricultural journals, all of which devoted much space to horticulture, were in existence before 1860. The earliest was *The California Farmer,* established in 1854; the second, *The California Culturist,* which appeared in 1859. Neither paper lasted for more than a few years, but both are mines of horticultural information to the historian, with their accounts of all the horticultural affairs in the primitive gardening world of the Pacific Coast. The third of these Far Western papers was *The Oregon Farmer,* published by W. B. Taylor in Portland from 1858 to 1861, which also gave much attention to horticultural matters.

18

HORTICULTURAL SOCIETIES

1790-1860

IN 1837 A. J. Downing said in Hovey's *Magazine of Horticulture*,[1] 'There are ten horticultural societies in the United States, whereas in 1818 there had been but one.' Although he believed that horticulture was making great progress in the country, he deplored the fact that neither the societies nor any individual city had a public experimental garden, such as those of the Royal Horticultural Society in London and the Jardin des Plantes in Paris. Fifteen years later in an editorial in *The Horticulturist* for July, he could say, 'There are now about forty.'

The first scientific group in this country to discuss matters of prime interest to gardeners was not a horticultural society but the American Philosophical Society (see page 82), organized in Philadelphia, 1769, to 'promote useful knowledge.' Benjamin Franklin was its chief sponsor and the first president. Of the long list of famous men who succeeded him in office, Thomas Jefferson (1797-1815) took the most interest in botany and gardening. However, it was during Franklin's presidency that a botanic garden was established. Caspar Wistar was another president who took great interest in plants, wild or cultivated.

In June 1784, a botanic garden was ordered planted, and a committee of two, Hopkinson and Rittenhouse, were to find a gardener. The garden was 'to be planted on 200 feet of the Arch St. lot next to the Observatory.' This garden does not appear to have been of great aid to either botanists or gardeners in the years that followed, but it shows, at least, that the society was interested

[1] III: 9.

in the two subjects. With the founding of the Academy of Natural Sciences at Philadelphia in 1812, the American Philosophical Society ceased to give much attention to botany and its allied arts.

Of much more importance than the botanic garden were the papers read by the botanists, several of which were of great importance to gardeners.

The paper of John Ellis, distinguished English botanist and Fellow of the Royal Society, published in 1769,[2] was an extract from a pamphlet entitled 'Catalogue of such foreign plants as are worthy of being encouraged in our American colonies for the purpose of medicine, agriculture and commerce.' There were subjoined 'directions for bringing over seeds and plants from distant countries in a state of vegetation.' This was at a time when exchanges of plants and seeds between Europe and America were at their peak, a time when such directions were much needed.

The same year, 1769, John Jones read a paper giving 'an account of a species of grape vine different from all others he had ever seen.'[3]

In 1771, Joseph Cooper (see page 432) wrote a letter to a Mr. Clifford, 'On the nature of the worms so prejudicial to the peach trees for some years past, and a method of preventing damage in the future.' The information was so valuable that the letter was read before the Society and published in the *Pennsylvania Gazette and Journal*.[4]

In November 1802, William Bartram read a paper entitled 'First attempt to describe our native grapes.' This paper contained a hint that American grapes might be hybridized.[5]

In this same year two other important papers appeared. John Ellis gave an 'Account of a method of preventing the premature decay of peach trees.'[6] This is probably an early reference to peach yellows. And Thomas Coulter gave a 'Description of a method of cultivating peach trees with a view to protect their premature decay; confirmed by the experiments of forty-five years, in Delaware state and the western part of the state of Pennsylvania.'[7]

Besides the essays pertaining to gardening, there were a great number on botanic subjects of prime interest to planters of native

[2] *Transactions*. I, Sec. 2. 255-71.
[3] Ibid. I, Sec. 4. 339-40.
[4] Ibid. XXII, Appx. 65.

[5] Ibid. XXII, Appx. No. 1. 325.
[6] Ibid. Appx. No. 2. 327-8.
[7] Ibid. 326.

ornamental plants; for example, a manuscript of the expedition of Lewis and Clark to the Pacific Coast in 1804 and one of the Dunbar Expedition to the new territory of Louisiana in 1804. The extant portions of André Michaux's manuscript diary of his travels in America were presented to the society by the younger Michaux in 1824.

The Charleston Museum was founded in South Carolina in 1773 and continues to the present time. In its aims, as set forth in the *South Carolina Gazette and Country Journal,*[8] there is this to say of the work to be done in the vegetable world:

Of Vegetables, they will thankfully receive every kind, from the loftiest Tree in the Forest, to the smallest plant in the field. . . At the same time the Society beg to be furnished with the best Accounts that can be given of the Uses and Virtues, either in Agriculture, Commerce, or Medicine, of which such tree or plant is possessed—the soil in which it most commonly grows . . . the Season in which it flowers, and when it bears the Fruit.[9]

The author has not been able to examine the publications of the Charleston Museum, but if it followed at all closely its original objects and aims, there must have been in its long history many papers of interest to gardeners.

The American Academy of Arts and Sciences, Boston, founded in 1780, published in its first years several papers of much interest to gardeners, and in the years that have followed, many papers containing information on botany, entomology, soils, and other subjects of indirect concern to cultivators of plants. In 1780, Benjamin Lincoln read 'A letter . . . relating to the ingrafting of fruit trees and the growth of vegetables; including the observations of his friend, on the growth of trees downward after the first year.' [10] In 1782, Peter Whitney read 'An account of a singular apple-tree producing fruit of different qualities; a part of the same apple being frequently sour and the other sweet.' [11] In 1790, Noah Webster, Jr., read a paper 'On the theory of vegetation.' [12]

8 30 March and 6 April 1773.   11 Ibid. Art. 22: 386-7.
9 Meisel, II: 36.   12 Ibid. Art. 26: 178-85.
10 *Memoirs*, I, pt. 2. Art. 23: 388-95.

To name there three papers does not do the Academy justice in its work for gardening and agriculture. Most of the botanists and the men interested in forestry, gardening, and agriculture in New England and New York were members and at one time or another read papers.

The University of the State of New York was established in May 1784, and reorganized three years later into much its present form. Beginning in 1831 and continuing through the 1850's, there were many papers on botany and several on cultivated plants that were of interest to horticulturists. The horticultural papers were chiefly botanic calendars showing the leafing and fruiting times of fruits and flowers, which, incidentally, give the names of the plants cultivated in gardens and their varieties.

The South Carolina Society for Promoting and Improving Agriculture and other Rural Concerns was organized in 1785 and ten years later became the Agricultural Society of South Carolina. It is still in existence and is, therefore, the oldest of the agricultural societies in the country to have had continuous life. It had in its early years an especially distinguished list of members and officers, including several governors, senators, and members of Congress. Throughout its long life there have been many notable men in the several fields of gardening, and many papers on horticulture that make a splendid contribution to the horticultural literature of the South.

Another early agriculture society to contribute much to gardening was founded by Charles Vaughan, of Hallowell, Maine (then a part of Massachusetts), in 1787, becoming the Kennebec Agricultural Society in 1807. This organization conducted an experiment station: in addition to meetings, it maintained gardens, nurseries, and orchards, from which were distributed seeds, plants, and cions, and from its farm sent out farm seeds and stock. It was radically different from other early organizations of its kind in that it made a special attempt to carry on correspondence with farmers. Vaughan, an Englishman, was one of the notable agriculturists of his time.

In chronological order, the next of these early scientific societies to include the cultivation of plants as a subject to be discussed was the Society for the Promotion of Agriculture, Arts, and Manufactures, founded in New York City in 1791, its headquarters being transferred to Albany in 1798. In 1804 it was reorganized with its name changed to the Society for the Promotion of Useful Arts. Its constitution stated: 'The objects of investigation for the Society shall be agriculture, manufactures, and arts, with such subjects of inquiry as may tend to explain and elucidate their principles.' Its first president was Robert R. Livingston, than whom no man in America was more interested in cultivated plants. Livingston presided over this organization 22 years, during which time agriculture and horticulture received much attention.

The Society for the Promotion of Useful Arts continued as sponsor of agriculture until the State Board of Agriculture was established in 1819. In 1824 the old organization merged with the Albany Lyceum of Natural History to form the Albany Institute. During its life of 15 years, the Society for the Promotion of Useful Arts published three volumes of *Transactions,* which contained discussions of the tree fruits and native grapes of which cultivated varieties were being introduced. Wine-making and cider-making were subjects taken up in several papers. Insects and fungous diseases received attention; and though, in the light of present knowledge, the remedies suggested were wholly useless, it was something to be aware of the pests and to try to control them.

The Board of Agriculture, successor to the Society for the Promotion of Useful Arts in 1819, in 1832 turned over its work to the New York State Agricultural Society. This splendid organization is still functioning, and for more than a hundred years has given much attention to every field of horticulture.

The Academy of Natural Sciences of Philadelphia, founded in 1812; the Linnaean Society of New England, established in 1814; the Literary and Philosophical Society of New York, begun in 1814; the Columbian Institute of Arts and Sciences, 1816; the Lyceum of Natural History of New York, 1817; the Troy Lyceum of Natural History, 1818; the Albany Institute, 1824; the Botanical Club of Washington, 1825; the Chester County Cabinet of Natural History, West Chester, Pennsylvania, 1826, founded by William Darlington, who was its president until his death in 1862; the Boston Society of Natural History, 1830; these are, perhaps, the leading societies of the period having to do with natural history that published in their reports articles and discussions of interest to botanists and horticulturists.

A notable event in this period of gardening history in Virginia was the organization of the Agricultural Society of Albemarle in 1817. Thomas Jefferson, then 74 years old, and Joseph C. Cabell were leaders in the new society. They had, however, as their associates, another ex-president, James Madison; two ex-governors of Virginia; a United States senator; an ambassador to the Court of St. James's; a Justice of the Supreme Court of the United States; a president of the University of Virginia; and a number of distinguished lawyers and planters. James Madison was the first president of the society. The 'Objects for the Attention and Enquiry of the Society,' as drawn up by Jefferson, were chiefly agricultural, but he does mention the grape, and at a fair, a year later, ten dollars was paid as a premium for 'the best domestic wine.'

That the Society was interested in horticulture is further shown by its action of 3 November 1817, when it was resolved: 'It is expedient forthwith to procure the establishment of a well supplied and well conducted nursery, from which the citizens of the surrounding country may be furnished with all the varieties of the most approved fruits.' The next year, Reuben Maury started a nursery, which seemed to satisfy its sponsors. This was the first nursery in the western part of Virginia and was a great stimulus to orchard planting, as it was also to the planting of fruit trees in Kentucky and Tennessee.

The several agricultural societies named are but the most prominent ones in the post-Revolutionary period. Though there were county and regional organizations in every Atlantic state, which gave more or less attention to horticulture, the chief interest in these years was in general agriculture, and fruits, vegetables, and flowers received comparatively little attention. There were, perhaps, half a dozen of these smaller agricultural societies each in New Jersey, New York, Pennsylvania, Virginia, and South Carolina. Some of these organizations maintained nurseries and libraries or distributed seed and plants. All held meetings more or less frequently.

These societies had a stimulating effect on every phase of agriculture in America. In a country then almost wholly agricultural, it was politically advantageous to belong to agricultural societies;

and, as in England then and now, it was socially correct to show interest and to be an officer or a speaker in one.

The first horticultural society to be organized in America was the New York Horticultural Society, founded 30 September 1818, at the home of Thomas H. Kennedy, Greenwich Street, New York City, with Thomas Storm as its president. The society was not incorporated until 22 March 1822, however, when its charter was approved by the state legislature. Its founders and members not only were the leading horticulturists in the state, but also numbered among its members the most prominent botanists of the times. Among these were Dr. David Hosack, for several years its president, Grant Thorburn, Michael Floy, Thomas Hogg, William Prince, André Parmentier, and Dr. John Torrey, who was its president in 1837 when the society ceased to exist.

It is a matter of regret that this organization did not continue throughout the century, as did its friendly rivals the Pennsylvania Horticultural Society and the Massachusetts Horticultural Society. Its intention was, at the start, to have a garden of 10 to 20 acres devoted to horticulture and botany. There was also to be a hall for public lectures, a library, a botanical cabinet, and a professor of botany and horticulture. For some time these plans were prosecuted vigorously; but, after 10 or 12 years, interest declined and the society died in 1833, having had a life of 15 years.

The Pennsylvania Horticultural Society was the second of these state organizations. It was founded on 20 November 1827, but did not receive its charter until 4 March 1831. Meanwhile its meetings had begun and its first annual exhibition was held in the autumn of 1830. It had much the same comprehensive plans as the earlier New York organization and the later Massachusetts society. More fortunate than the former, and growing and improving like the latter, it has continued to live and is now the oldest horticultural society in the country, having exercised a beneficial influence on horticulture for more than a century.

The Domestic Horticultural Society, with members in the ten counties about the Finger Lakes, was organized at Geneva, New York, in 1828, and was the third horticultural society in the country. This society was the forerunner of the Western New York Horticultural Society, which was for 50 years one of the leading organizations of its kind in the nation. This Domestic Horticultural Society held its meetings and exhibitions alternately at Geneva, Canandaigua, and Lyons. It held an exhibition at Geneva in June 1835, and a show of fruits and flowers at Canandaigua in September of the same year, after which there is scant record of its activities.

The fourth horticultural organization in the country was the Albany Horticultural Society, founded in Albany, 15 January 1829. Jesse Buel, noted pomologist, horticultural writer, politician, and legal authority, was the first president. In his presidential address, Buel gives farmers the following advice:

Let a family have a box, in which they may place all their apple cores, cherry, plum and peach stones. In the fall these seeds may be planted in a bed, weeded the next season, and then, either in the fall or spring, set in a nursery. The second year they may be inoculated, with such kind of fruit as the cultivator may chuse. Thus in five or six years every farmer may be enabled, with trifling labor and expense, to stock his farm and borders of his garden with all the variety of choice fruit that our country produces.

The Albany society had an existence of only a few years, but, largely because of the prominence of its president, gave impetus to the planting of orchards and gardens in the Hudson Valley, whose horticultural possibilities were beginning to be recognized.

Asked to name the horticultural organization in North America that has had the greatest influence on horticulture, few would hesitate to name the Massachusetts Horticultural Society, founded in Boston on 17 March 1829, to which many references have been made in this volume. Its charter members were among the most distinguished men in Massachusetts. It has held meetings year after year down to the present time, in which papers by its members and distinguished horticulturists from other parts of the country have presented the best information extant on fruits, flowers, vegetables, and landscape gardening. Its exhibitions, always offering generous prizes, have presented to the American public horticultural products of the best that the country has known. In 1833 it established and afterward maintained for some years an experimental garden of some 30 acres, then the largest garden of the kind in the country. The library of the Society has long been one of the best, if not the best, on horticultural subjects in North America. And through its annual reports it has been an important means of distributing horticultural information the world over. The publications have been continuous since 1839, sometimes in two parts, or even three, a year, with a considerable number of special papers.

From its organization in 1850 until 1900, the American Pomological Society was the largest and most active organization of pomologists in the world. This society is a union of two older organizations. In September 1848, a national pomological congress was held in Buffalo, called the American Congress of Fruit-Growers; a little later in the same year the North American Pomological Convention held a meeting at Castle Garden in New York City. In the Buffalo meeting 14 states and Canada were represented by 80 delegates from 15 horticultural societies. Representation was quite as wide and as great in the New York City meeting. After much bickering for two years, these two societies consolidated under the name 'The American Pomological Congress,' which was changed to the American Pomological Society in 1852.

In its first years, and perhaps for half a century after, the American Pomological Society was a great clearing house in which members from all over the continent could compare fruits and arrive at conclusions in regard to their merits. It settled questions in respect to the identity of varieties; determined synonyms under which the same fruit is known in different localities; and passed rules of nomenclature recognized the country over by pomologists. It abridged the lists of fruits by dropping from its catalogue the names of poor or indifferent sorts. Almost from the beginning, it has given medals for the best new fruits. Perhaps, however, its greatest work, especially in early years, was its maintenance through its meetings of cordial intercourse among pomologists.

The first report of the American Pomological Society was published in 1851 for the year 1850, under the title *American Pomological Congress,* and, curiously enough, was issued by the Ohio State Board of Agriculture. In 1852 the title was *Proceedings of the American Pomological Congress.* The succeeding reports have had the name *Proceedings of the American Pomological Society*. Reports have been published every two years almost regularly, and there have been a few special papers on the different fruits and at least one special *Catalogue of Fruits*.

The phenomenal success of the American Pomological Society was due to a score of notable American horticulturists who put their hearts and souls in this organization. As worthy as any of these men was Marshall P. Wilder, a founder, who was president of the Society, with the exception of a single term, from 1850 until his death in 1886. Wilder (1788-1886) was also a prominent member of the Massachusetts Horticultural Society for fifty-six years, and its president from 1841 to 1846. He was a prosperous merchant with interests in many public enterprises, who always had time for his orchards and gardens. He tested no fewer than 1200 varieties of pears, introduced many new kinds, including the Anjou; and was the introducer and breeder of many camellias, roses, azaleas, lilies, gladioli, orchids, and other fruits and flowers.

In the horticultural magazines of the times there are occasional references to the Agricultural, Horticultural, and Botanical Society, Jefferson College, Mississippi. But beyond the date of its organization in 1839, and the fact that papers on natural history, including gardening, were read, there is nothing to show what its other activities, if any, were, or how long the organization was in existence.

The first permanent state horticultural society in the north-central states was the Ohio Pomological Society, organized in Columbus, Ohio, in 1847. The meeting was called by B. C. Bateham, editor of the *Ohio Cultivator*. Early members included fruit growers, nurserymen, and gardeners, most of whom were professionals; but there were many who had chosen horticulture as an avocation. At a meeting in Cincinnati in 1865, the grape growers of the state, feeling that the society was not broad enough to serve them well, founded a new organization. In 1867, at a meeting in Sandusky, the two societies held a conference and merged into the Ohio State Horticultural Society, under which name the organization still continues with 85 years of service to its credit. Its annual reports have been exceptionally well edited, and have been read with profit by horticulturists of other states as well as Ohio.

The Detroit Horticultural Society was the earliest such organization in Michigan. It was founded in 1841 and had annual meetings and exhibitions until 1853. From the glowing accounts of displays of fruits, flowers, and vegetables, one judges that horticulture was a profitable vocation and a pleasant avocation in this city. After two or three attempts in earlier years, which came to naught, the State Horticultural Society of Michigan was organized in Jackson in 1857. It has had continuous existence down to the present time, and must be rated among the best in the United States, with an array of members prominent in the whole country hardly to be surpassed.

Logan's *Annual Indianapolis City Directory* is authority for the statement that the Indiana Horticultural Society was founded in 1840, with Henry Ward Beecher and James Blake as the most prominent founders. This first society seems to have been short-lived, and in 1860 was organized the one that is in existence today, of which reports have been issued since 1866 under the title *Transactions of the Indiana Horticultural Society*.

Illinois had a permanent horticultural society before Indiana. The Illinois State Horticultural Society was organized in 1856; its report of *Transactions* was issued the same year, and continues to appear. This was not the first attempt to start a horticultural society in Illinois. There had been some half-dozen or more earlier ventures, the first of which deserves more than passing notice, since it had its inception at a date when few agricultural organizations had been formed in the older states to the east.[13]

In 1817 Morris Birbeck, noted English traveler and author, settled in Edwards County, Illinois. In 1819 Edward Coles reached Illinois from Virginia and settled on a farm near Edwardsville. Coles, as well as Birbeck, was educated, energetic, and interested in what then passed as 'scientific agriculture.' In October 1819, an invitation was printed in the *Edwardsville Spectator* asking farmers to meet in Edwardsville to organize an agricultural society. The invitation was signed 'A Farmer of Madison,' who is supposed to have been Coles. The same autumn a meeting was held in Edwardsville; Morris Birbeck was elected president; Edward Coles, vice-president. The organization was called the State Agri-

13 *Trans. Ill. State Hort. Soc.* Blair, J. C., LXIV: 212-13.

cultural Society. All branches of agriculture, including horticulture, were given attention. This seems to have been the first such society organized west of the Alleghenies, although it did not long survive.

In 1845 Edson Harkness, Peoria County, tried to organize a society of fruit growers and nurserymen in central Illinois, but failed. The next year he was joined by C. R. Overman and Samuel Edwards, and the three succeeded in calling together a fruit growers' meeting. The same year, the Chicago Horticultural Society was formed, with J. H. Kenzie as president. On 1 and 2 October 1851, the Northwest Fruit Growers' Association was organized at Princeton, Illinois, having held a preliminary meeting in December 1850. In 1851 the Alton Horticultural Society was founded, with E. S. Hall as one of its leaders. This society held a fair in 1856, and plans were made for forming the Illinois State Horticultural Society; it was formally organized 17 December of that year, with 31 members present.

Horticulture in Illinois is much indebted to John A. Kennicott, a physician, who came to Chicago when it was a village and the surrounding region a wilderness of grass. He at once began planting trees and ornamental plants about his home. In 1856 he became one of the founders of the Cook Country Agricultural Society, which, in 1851, held a very successful fair in what is now the heart of Chicago. Later, he was a founder and the first president of the Northwestern Fruit Growers' Association.

The first permanent horticultural organization west of the Mississippi was the Missouri Fruit Growers' Association, founded in 1859. In 1868 it became the Missouri State Horticultural Society. Its first president was Norman J. Coleman, a distinguished lawyer, agricultural writer, and the first Secretary of Agriculture. *Coleman's Rural World* was one of the pioneer agricultural papers in the Mississippi Valley.

There may have been county and local fairs in the states on the Pacific Coast, as there may have been in Utah and possibly in New Mexico, before the end of the period under consideration, but it does not appear that there were state organizations except in California. In 1853 the California State Agricultural Society was formed, the membership being 856; in 1858 the first report was published. This organization catered strongly to horticulture: in its first fair, held in San Francisco in 1853, besides all the hardy fruits, flowers, and vegetables shown in great array, there were olives, almonds, figs, walnuts, and other rarities, surprising to the eyes of the newly arrived Easterners.

Another gauge of advance in agriculture and all its divisions was the great increase in the number and popularity of state and county fairs in the agricultural regions of the country. The first county fair in America, as they now exist, for the exhibition of agricultural products, was held in Pittsfield, Massachusetts, in 1810. By the middle of the century there was a fair in nearly every state and agricultural county. The influence of these organizations with their exhibitions, premiums, addresses, and opportunities for farmers to discuss the affairs of farming, was of inestimable value to all tillers of the soil.

State and county agricultural fairs owe their origin to a friend and disciple of Benjamin Franklin, Elkanah Watson, a seer and promoter in the development of the domestic economy of America, scarcely less useful to his country in this respect than Franklin himself. Watson was the author of a notable book on agricultural fairs, published in 1820, and of several pamphlets on agricultural and economic subjects, all valuable contributions toward the development of the country. He was born in Plymouth, Massachusetts, 22 January 1758. During the Revolution, he was prominent in several capacities. One of his tasks was to deliver dispatches to Benjamin Franklin in Paris, which gave him an opportunity to see the agriculture of the Old World. Afterwards he was engaged in business that took him to several states, which enabled him to see American agriculture and meet many prominent men in this country. In 1789 he moved to Albany, where, for eighteen years, he was prominent in banking, canal building, education, and agriculture in the State of New York. In 1807 he went to Pittsfield and became the founder of agricultural societies and fairs. He died in Kent, New York, in 1842.

Watson went into farming in Pittsfield with the avowed purpose 'to show Americans how to farm.' To establish a flock of Merino sheep, he purchased a pair of imported animals from his friend, Chancellor Livingston. This pair of sheep, tied to an elm in the public square of Pittsfield, constituted the first American fair in which exhibits were the prime object.

Writing in his *History of the Berkshire Agricultural Society,* in 1800, he says he was induced:

. . . to notify an exhibition, under the lofty elm tree, on a public square, in Pittsfield, of these two sheep. Many farmers and even females, were attracted to this first novel and humble exhibition. From this lucky incident, I reasoned thus: If two animals are capable of exciting so much attention, what would be the effect of a display on a larger scale of different animals. The farmers present responded to my remarks with approbation. We thus became acquainted, and from that moment to the present hour, Agricultural Fairs and Cattle Shows, with all their connections, have predominated in my mind greatly to the prejudice of my private affairs.

Thereupon Watson founded the Berkshire County Agricultural Society in 1810. In the winter of that year a charter was obtained from the Legislature of Massachusetts and the preliminaries perfected for a fair to be held the following September.

The Berkshire County Fair made Watson and the 'Berkshire System' famous throughout the whole country. Within a few years such fairs were being held in every agricultural community in the Union from Maine to Georgia, from the Atlantic to the Mississippi. In the 130 years that have gone by, Watson's pattern for a fair has been followed with few changes. Growers of animals, grains, fruits, vegetables, flowers, and makers of farm products and farm machinery have been incited to competition; have had the spirit of emulation stirred, and their interest aroused.

One gets an idea of the rapid growth of fairs following Watson's Berkshire System from Robert B. Thomas's *Old Farmer's Almanack,* published in 1824, 13 years after the first fair in Berkshire County. The account is written as a burlesque; but, reading between the lines, it is apparent that the fair had become in a very few years a common and important feature of American agriculture:

This is the month for cattle shows, and other agricultural exhibitions—Premiums are offered by various societies for the greatest crops; the best stock, and the best domestic manufactures, and thousands are pulling for the prize, with all their might.

The great Bull of Farmer Lumpkins is a Nonsuch!

Peter Nibble has raised a monstrous field of white beans!

Joe Lucky's acre of corn has seven stout ears to the stalk!

Dolly Diligence has outstript all in the bonnet line!

Tabitha Twistem's hearth rug is up to all Market-street!

The Linsey-Woolsey Manufacturing Company have made the finest piece of satinet that ever mortals set eyes on!

There is the widow Clacket's heifer, she is to be driven!

And, O, if you could only see 'Squire Trulliber's great boar! They say it is as big as a full grown rhinoceros!

Huzza, huzza for the premiums! Here's to the girl that can best darn a stocking, and to the lad that shall raise the biggest pumpkin!

BIBLIOGRAPHY

Acrelius, Israel. *Description of the Farmer and Present Condition of New Sweden.* Stockholm, 1759. Translation published in *Memoirs of the Pennsylvania Historical Society.* Philadelphia, 1874

Adlum, John. *A Memoir on the Cultivation of the Vine in America.* 2nd ed. Washington, 1828

Agricultural History. Washington, 1918 to date

American Farmer. Baltimore, 1819-93

American Gardener's Magazine. Boston, 1835-6

American Husbandry (2 vols.) London, 1775

American Philosophical Society Proceedings. Vol. xxii. 1884

American Philosophical Society Transactions. Vols. i-vi. Philadelphia 1769-1809

Anburey, Thomas. *Travels through the Interior Parts of America* (2 vols.) London, 1789

Andrews, Edward. *The Community Industries of the Shakers.* Albany, 1893

Arbor, Edward (editor). *The First Three English Books in America.* Edinburgh, 1885

Armstrong, Margaret. *Fanny Kemble, a Passionate Victorian.* New York, 1938

Ashe, Thomas. *Carolina, or a Description of the Present State of that Country,* etc. London, 1682 (Reprinted in *Narratives of Early Carolina,* edited by Alexander S. Salley, Jr. New York, 1911)

——. *Travels in America performed in 1806,* etc. London, 1808

Bancroft, Hubert Howe. *History of California.* Vols. xiii-xix of *History of the Pacific States of North America.* San Francisco, 1882-90

Bartram, John. *Observations on the inhabitants, climate, soil, rivers, productions, animals,* etc. . . . *made in his travels from Pensilvania to Onondago, Oswego and the Lake Ontario, in Canada.* London, 1751

Bartram, William. *First attempt to describe our native vines.* Philadelphia, 1802

——. *Travels through North & South Carolina, Georgia, East and West Florida,* etc. Philadelphia, 1791

Beach, S. A. *Apples of New York.* Albany, 1905

Beecher, Henry Ward. *Plain and Pleasant Talk About Fruits, Flowers and Farming.* New York, 1859

Beverley, Robert. *History and Present State of Virginia.* London, 1705 (Reprint as *History of Virginia.* Richmond, 1855)

Bowers, Claude G. *The Young Jefferson.* Boston, 1945

Boynton, Henry Walcott. *James Fenimore Cooper.* New York, 1931

Brandau, Roberta Seawell (editor). *History of Homes and Gardens of Tennessee* (The Garden Study Club of Nashville) Nashville, 1936

Brooks, W. S. *The Agricultural Papers of George Washington.* Boston, 1919

Bruce, Philip Alexander. *The Economic History of Virginia in the Seventeenth Century* (2 vols.), New York and London, 1896

Bryant, Edwin. *What I Saw in California.* New York, 1848

Buchanan, Robert. *The Culture of the Grape and Wine Making,* etc. Cincinnati, 1852

Butterfield, H. M. *History of Deciduous Fruits in California.* Sacramento, 1938

California Fruit-Grower. San Francisco, 1888 to date

California State Agricultural Society Reports. Sacramento, 1852 to date

Champlain, Samuel de. *Voyages* (Prince Society II) Boston, 1878-82

Cobbett, William. *A Year's Residence in the United States of America.* 2nd ed. London, 1819

Coit, J. E. *Citrus Fruits.* New York, 1915

Colden, Cadwallader. *Plantae Coldenhamiae.* Upsala, 1742

Colton, Walter. *Three Years in California, 1846-1849.* New York, 1850

Connor, Jeannette Thurber (editor and translator). *Colonial Records of Spanish Florida* (2 vols.) Florida State Historical Society, *Publications,* No. 5. Deland, 1925 and 1930. (Vol. II edited by J. A. Robertson)

Conover, George S. *History of Kanadasaga and Geneva* (MS. in library of Hobart College, Geneva, New York)

Cooney, L. M. *Garden History of Georgia* 1733-1933. Atlanta, 1933

Cooper, Joseph. Letter to Clifford in 1771 'On the nature of the worms so prejudicial to the peach trees for some years past, and a method of preventing damage in the future.' *Amer. Phil. Soc. Trans.* XXII. 1884

Coulter, Thomas. 'Description of a Method of cultivating peach trees, with a view to prevent their premature decay.' *Amer. Phil. Soc. Trans.* (O.S.) 5 (1802)

Coxe, William. *A View of the Cultivation of Fruit Trees, and the Management of Orchards and Cider,* etc. Philadelphia, 1817

Crèvecœur, Michel Guillaume St. John de (Hector St. John de, pseud.). *Letters from an American Farmer,* etc. London, 1782 (Reprinted in Everyman's Library. New York, 1916)

———. *Sketches of Eighteenth Century America.* (Reprinted in New Haven, 1925)

Cronise, Titus Fey. *The Natural Wealth of California.* San Francisco, 1868

Crusman, Charles F. *Introduction for the Selection, Propagation and Management of a Kitchen Garden.* Albany, 1843

Cuming, Fortescue. *Sketches of a Tour to the Western Country through the States of Ohio and Kentucky,* etc. 1807-1809. Pittsburgh, 1810

Cummings, Richard Osborn. *The American and his Food.* Chicago, 1940

Cutler, W. P. and J. P. (editors). *Life, Journals and Correspondence of Rev. Manasseh Cutler* (2 vols.) Cincinnati, 1888

Danckaerts, Jacob, and Sluyter, Peter. *Journal of a Voyage to New York,* 1679-1680. Brooklyn, 1867 (In the Long Island Historical Society *Memoirs,* I: 1-428)

Darlington, William. *Memorials of John Bartram and Humphry Marshall.* Philadelphia, 1849

Davis, John. *Travels in the United States of America.* London, 1803

Deane, Samuel. *Journal* (edited by William Willis). Portland, Ore., 1849

———. *The New England Farmer or Georgical Dictionary,* etc. 2nd ed. Worcester, Mass., 1797 .

Denton, Daniel. *A Brief Description of New York,* etc., 1670. (Furman ed. New York, 1845)

Depew, Chauncey M. *One Hundred Years of American Commerce.* New York, 1895

De Vries, David Peterson. *Voyages from Holland to America.* Translated from the Dutch by Henry C. Murphy. New York, 1853

Dixon, William Hepworth. *New America.* Philadelphia, 1867

Dow, G. F. *Arts and Crafts in New England,* 1704-1775. Topsfield, Mass., 1927

Downing, A. J. *The Fruits and Fruit Trees of America.* New York and London, 1845

———. *A Treatise on the Theory and Practice of Landscape Gardening,* etc. New York and London, 1841

Drayton, John. *A View of South Carolina.* Charleston, 1802

Dudley, Paul. *Observations on Some of the Plants in New England,* etc. Philosophical Transactions (abridged edition) VII. London, 1724

Dunbar, William. 'Exploration of the Red, the Black and the Washita Rivers.' *Documents Relating to the Purchasing and Exploration of Louisiana* (of Thomas Jefferson and William Dunbar). Boston, 1904

Dwight, Timothy. *Travels in New York and New England.* New Haven, 1821-2

Eddis, William. *Letters from America,* etc. London, 1792

Eliot, Jared. *Essays Upon Field Husbandry in New England,* 1748-1762. Edited by Harry J. Carman and Rexford G. Tugwell. New York, 1934

Ellis, John. 'Account of a method of preventing the premature decay of peach trees.' *Amer. Phil. Soc. Trans.* (O.S.) 5 (1802)

Ellwanger, W. D. *A Snuff-box full of Trees.* New York, 1909

Emmons, Ebenezer. *Natural History of New York* (Vol. III devoted to fruits) Albany, 1851

Essex Institute Historical Collections. Salem, Mass., 1859 to date

Fairbanks, George R. *The History and Antiquities of the City of St. Augustine, Florida.* New York, 1858

Faux, William. *Memorable Days in America.* London, 1823. (In Thwaite's *Early Western Travels.* Cleveland, 1905)

Fearon, H. B. *Sketches of America.* London, 1818

Fessenden, Thomas G. *New American Gardener.* Boston, 1828

Field, Thomas W. *Pear Culture.* New York, 1859

Fiske, John. *The Beginnings of New England,* etc. Boston and New York, 1889

———. *The Critical Period in American History,* 1783-1789. Boston, 1888

———. *Old Virginia and her Neighbors* (2 vols.) Boston and New York, 1900

Fitzpatrick, John C., *see* George Washington

Fletcher, S. W. 'A History of Fruit Growing in Virginia.' Reprinted from *Proceedings of the Thirty-seventh Annual Meeting of the Virginia Horticultural Society.* Staunton, Va., 1932

———. *A History of Fruit Growing in Pennsylvania.* I. *The Colonial Period* (1625-1827). II. *The Transition Period* (1827-1887). III. *The Fruit Growing of Our Times* (1887-1932) Reprinted from the *Proceedings of the Seventy-second and Seventy-third Annual Meetings of the State Horticultural Association of Pennsylvania,* 1931, 1932

———. *The Strawberry in North America.* New York, 1917

Force, Peter. *Tracts Relating to the Origin, Settlement, and Progress of the Colonies in North America,* etc. (4 vols.) Washington, 1836-46

Ford, P. L. *The Works of Thomas Jefferson* (12 vols.) New York, 1904

Frémont, John Charles. *Geographical Memoirs.* Cincinnati, 1856

Garden and Forest. A Journal of Horticulture, Landscape Art and Forestry. Conducted by Charles S. Sargent. New York, 1888-97

Gardener's Monthly and Horticulturist. Conducted by Thomas Meehan. Philadelphia, 1859-88

Gayarre, Charles. 'A Louisiana Sugar Plantation in the Old Regime.' *Harper's New Monthly Magazine,* March 1887

Geiser, Samuel W. *Naturalists of the Frontier.* Dallas, Texas, 1937

Genesee Farmer and Gardener's Journal. Conducted by Luther Tucker. Rochester, N. Y., 1831-9

Gerard, John. *Herball or Generall Historie of Plantes.* 2nd ed. enlarged by Thomas Johnson. London, 1633

Goode, G. Browne. *Beginnings of Natural History in America.* Washington, 1886

Gould, H. P. 'Observations on Peach Growing in Maryland.' *Maryland Experiment Station Bulletin* 72. College Park, 1901

Grant, Anne. *Memoirs of an American Lady* (2 vols.) London, 1808 (Reprinted by James Grant Wilson. Albany, 1876)

Gray, Asa, and Trumbull, J. H. 'Review of de Candolle's *Origin of Cultivated Plants.' American Journal of Science*. Series III. Vol. XXV. New Haven, 1883

Gregg, Josiah. *Commerce of the Prairies*. In Thwaites's *Early Western Travels*. Cleveland, 1905

Hakluyt, Richard. *Divers Voyages Touching the Discovery of America*. Edited by John Winter Jones. London, 1850

Harshberger, John W. *The Botanists of Philadelphia and their Work*. Philadelphia, 1899

Hedrick, U. P. *The Cherries of New York*. Albany, 1915

———. *The Grapes of New York*. Albany, 1908

———. *History of Agriculture in the State of New York*. Albany, 1933

———. *The Peaches of New York*. Albany, 1917

———. *The Pears of New York*. Albany, 1921

———. *The Plums of New York*. Albany, 1911

———. *The Small Fruits of New York*. Albany, 1925

Herrick, Francis Hobart. *Audubon, The Naturalist* (2 vols.) New York, 1917

Higginson, Francis. *New-England's Plantation*. London, 1630 (3rd ed. Boston, 1792)

Hilton, William. 'A Relation of Discovery Recently Made on the Coast of Florida.' In Force's *Tracts*. Vol. IV. Washington, 1846

Holland, James W. *Agricultural History XII.*

Hooper, E. J. *Hooper's Western Fruit Book*, etc. Cincinnati, 1857

Horticultural Register and Gardener's Magazine (4 vols.). I. Edited by Thomas G. Fessenden and J. E. Teschmacher. Boston, 1835. II. Edited by Thomas G. Fessenden and Joseph Breck. Boston, 1836. III. Edited by Joseph Breck. Boston, 1837. IV. Edited by Joseph Breck. Boston, 1838

The Horticulturist and Journal of Rural Art and Rural Taste. Albany, Philadelphia, and New York, 1846-75

Hosack, David. *Hortus Elginensis*. 2nd ed. New York, 1811

Hovey, C. M. *The Fruits of America*, etc. (2 vols.) Boston, 1852-6

Hume, H. H. *Camellias in America*. Harrisburg, 1946

Illinois Horticultural Society Transactions. Chicago, 1856 to date

Imlay, Gilbert. *A Topographical Description of the Western Territory of North America*, etc. London, 1792

Jefferson, Thomas. *Garden Book*, 1766-1824. Edited by Edwin Morris Betts. Philadelphia, 1944

———. *Notes on the State of Virginia*, etc. Philadelphia, 1801

Johnson, Edward. *Wonder Working Providence of Sion's Savior in New England*. London, 1654

Johnson, J. H. 'Old Maryland Manors,' etc. *Johns Hopkins Studies in Historical and Political Science*. Vol. I. No. 7. Baltimore, 1883

Jones, Hugh. *The Present State of Virginia.* London, 1724 (Sabin reprint, No. 5. New York, 1865)

Josselyn, John. *An Account of Two Voyages to New England,* etc. London, 1674 (Reprinted by Tuckerman. Boston, 1865)

———. *New-Englands Rarities Discovered,* etc. London, 1672 (several American reprints)

Kalm, Peter. *Travels into North America,* etc. Translated by J. R. Forster (2 vols.) London, 1770-71

Kemble, Frances Anne. *Journal of a Year's Residence on a Georgian Plantation in 1838-39.* New York, 1863

La Hontan, Armand Louis, Baron de. *Nouveaux Voyages.* 1703 (Translated by R. G. Thwaites as *New Voyage to North America.* Chicago, 1905)

Lascarbot, Marc. *Histoire de la Nouvelle-France,* etc. 2nd ed. Paris, 1611

Lawson, John. *A New Voyage to Carolina,* etc. London, 1709 (Reprinted as *The History of Carolina.* Raleigh, N. C., 1860)

Le Page du Pratz. *Histoire de la Louisiane,* etc. (3 vols.) Paris, 1758 (English ed. in 2 vols. London, 1763)

Lewis, Meriwether, and Clark, William. *Original Journals of Expedition,* 1804-1806. Edited by Reuben Gold Thwaites (7 vols.) New York, 1904-05

Lodge, Henry Cabot. *A Short History of the English Colonies in America.* New York, 1881

The Magazine of Horticulture. First published as the *American Gardener's Magazine,* 1835-6. Boston, 1837-68

Maine Pomological Society Report. 'History of Gardening in Maine.' 1873

Manning, Robert. *Book of Fruits.* Salem, Mass., 1838

Manning, Robert, Jr. *History of Massachusetts Horticultural Society,* 1829-1878. Boston, 1880

Marshall, Humphry. *Arbustum Americanum.* Philadelphia, 1785

Martineau, Harriet. *Retrospect of Western Travel.* London and New York, 1838

———. *Society in America* (2 vols.) London, 1837

Martyr, Peter, *see* Edward Arbor

Massachusetts Agricultural Repository and Journal. Boston, 1793-1832

Massachusetts Historical Society Collections. Boston, 1794 to date

M'Mahon, Bernard. *The American Gardener's Calendar.* Philadelphia, 1806

Meisel, Max. *A Bibliography of American Natural History* (3 vols.) Brooklyn, 1924-9

Michigan State Horticultural Society Reports. Lansing, 1870 to date

Morse, Jedidiah. *The American Universal Geography.* 5th ed. Boston, 1805

Myers, Albert Cook. *Narratives of Early Pennsylvania, West New Jersey, and Delaware, 1630-1707*. New York, 1912

New Genesee Farmer and Gardener's Journal. Edited by John J. Thomas and M. B. Bateman until 1843, when Thomas took full charge. Rochester, N. Y., 1840-44

New York Historical Society Collections. Series II. Vol. III. Part I.

New York State Agricultural Society Proceedings. Albany, 1842 to date

New York State Historical Association Proceedings. Albany, 1901-21

Northern Traveler and Northern Tour, etc. New York, 1826

Nuttall, Thomas. *A Journal of Travels into the Arkansas Territory, during the Year* 1819. Philadelphia, 1821

Oberholtzer, Ellis Paxson. *Robert Morris, Patriot and Financier*. New York, 1903

Olmsted, Frederick Law. *A Journey in the Back Country*. New York, 1860

———. *A Journey through Texas*. New York, 1857

O'Reilly, Henry. *The Greatest Nursery in the World: Ellwanger & Barry*. Reprint from *The Illustrated Register of Rural Affairs*. Rochester, 1859

Original Narratives of Early American History. Edited by J. Franklin Jameson. New York, 1906-17

Pacific Rural Press. San Francisco, 1871

Parker, Arthur C. *An Analytical History of the Seneca Indians*. Rochester, 1926

Parkman, Francis. *Pioneers of France in the New World*. 25th ed. Boston, 1894

Pellet, Kent. *Pioneers in Iowa Horticulture*. Des Moines, Iowa, 1941

Penn, William. 'Letter from William Penn to the Committee of the Free Society of Traders.' London, 1683

Pennsylvania Magazine of History and Biography. Philadelphia, 1877-1904

Peters, Richard. *Memoirs of the Philadelphia Society for the Promotion of Agriculture*. Vols. I-V. Philadelphia, 1808-26

Pierson, Hamilton W. *Jefferson at Monticello*. New York, 1862

Plymouth, Mass. *Records of the Town of Plymouth*. Plymouth, 1889-1903

Ramsay, David. *The History of South Carolina, from its First Settlement in* 1670 *to the Year* 1808 (2 vols.) Charleston, 1809

Ravenel, Harriott Horry (Mrs. St. Julien). *Charleston, the Place and the People*. 1st ed., 1906. New York, 1929

———. *Eliza Pinckney*. New York, 1896

Reid, Captain Mayne. 'The Plant Hunters in America.' *The Horticulturist*. Vol. XIII. 1858

Reynolds, Helen Wilkinson. *Year Book of the Dutchess County Historical Society*. Poughkeepsie, 1935

Rhode Island Historical Society Collections. Providence, 1827-1902

Robertson, J. A., *see* Jeannette Thurber Connor

Rochefoucauld Liancourt, Duc de la. *Travels through United States of North America, the Country of the Iroquois, and Upper Canada, in the years* 1795, 1796, *and* 1797, etc., *with an Authentic Account of Lower Canada* (4 vols.) London, 1800 (Translated by H. Neuman)

Sagard-Théodat, Gabriel. *Histoire du Canada.* Paris, 1636

Sale, Edith Tunis (editor). *Historic Gardens of Virginia.* Richmond, 1923

Salley, Alexander Samuel. *Narratives of Early Carolina,* 1650-1708. New York, 1911

Sargent, Charles Sprague. *Scientific Papers of Asa Gray* (2 vols.) Boston and New York, 1889

———. *Silva of North America* (14 vols.) Cambridge, Mass., 1891-1902

Shaffer, E. T. H. *Carolina Gardens.* New York, 1937

Shaw, W. H. *History of Essex and Hudson Counties in New Jersey.* Philadelphia, 1884

Slate, George L. *Lilies for American Gardens.* New York, 1939

Sluyter, Peter, *see* Jacob Danckaerts

Smith, Captain John. *Works of Captain John Smith,* 1608-1631. Edited by Edward Arbor. Birmingham, England, 1884

Smith, Samuel. *The History of the Colony of Nova-Cæsaria, or New Jersey.* Burlington, N. J., 1765

Smith, Rev. Thomas. *Journal.* Edited by William Willis. Portland, 1849

Strachey, W. *Historie of Travaile into Virginia Brittania,* etc. Hakluyt Society Publication, edited by R. H. Major. London, 1849

Sturtevant, Edward Lewis. *Notes on Edible Plants.* Edited by U. P. Hedrick. Albany, 1919

Talleyrand-Périgord, Dorothée duchesse de. *Memoirs* (3 vols.) 1831-1850. Edited by Princesse Radziwell

Taylor, John. *Being a Series of Agricultural Essays, Practical and Political.* 'By a citizen of Virginia.' Georgetown, 1813

Thacher, James. *The American Orchardist.* Boston, 1822

Thomas, David. *Travels through the Western Country in the Summer of* 1816, etc. Auburn, N. Y., 1819

Thomas, Elizabeth Patterson. *Old Kentucky Homes and Gardens.* Louisville, 1939

Thompson, Maurice. *Alice of Old Vincennes.* Indianapolis, 1900

Trollope, Frances (Mrs. T. A.). *The Domestic Manners of the Americans* (2 vols.) London (Reprinted in one volume. New York, 1832)

U. S. Patent Office Reports

Vallejo, Guadalupe. 'Ranch and Mission Days in Alta California.' *Century Magazine.* New Series XIX. 1891

Van der Donck, Adrian. 'Description of the New Netherlands.' *Old South Leaflets*. No. 69. Boston

Virginia Magazine of History and Biography. Richmond, 1893 to date (1915 vol. cited)

Volney, C. F. *A View of the Soil and Climate of the United States of America*. Philadelphia, 1804

Warner, Marjorie Fleming. *Annual Report of the American Historical Society*. Vol. I. 1919

Washington, George. *Diaries* (4 vols.) Edited by J. C. Fitzpatrick. Boston and New York, 1925

Watson, Elkanah. 'History of Agricultural Societies on the Modern Berkshire System.' In *History of the Rise, Progress, and existing conditions of the western Canals in the State of New York*. Albany, 1820

Watson, John Fanning. *Annals of Philadelphia and Pennsylvania* (2 vols.). Philadelphia, 1842

Welles, Edwin Stanley. *The Beginnings of Fruit Culture in Connecticut*. Hartford, 1936

Wickson, Edward J. *The California Fruits and How to Grow Them*. 2nd ed. San Francisco, 1891

———. *California Vegetables*. 5th ed. San Francisco, 1923

Will, George F., and Hyde, George E. *Corn among the Indians of the Upper Missouri Valley*. St. Louis, 1917

William and Mary College Quarterly, etc. Williamsburg, 1892 to date

Williams, Edward. *Virginia*. 1650 (Reprinted in Force Collection Tracts. No. 11. 1844)

Willich, A. F. M. *Domestic Encyclopedia*. 1st American edition by James Mease in 5 vols. Philadelphia, 1804

Willis, William (editor). *Journals of the Rev. Thomas Smith, and the Rev. Samuel Deane*. Portland, Ore., 1849

Wilson, Samuel. *An Account of the Province of Carolina*, etc. London, 1682 (Reprinted in Salley's *Narratives of Early Carolina*, 1650-1708. New York, 1911)

Wood, William. *New Englands Prospect*. London, 1635 (Reprinted in *Mass. Hist. Soc. Collections*. Series I. Vol. III. Also in publications of the Prince Society. Boston, 1865)

Woods, John. *Two Years Residence in the Settlement on the English Prairie in the Illinois Country, United States*, etc. London, 1822

Woodward, Carl Raymond. 'Agriculture in New Jersey.' Reprinted from *New Jersey—A History*, edited by Irving S. Kull. New York, 1930

Young, Alexander. *Chronicles of the First Planters of the Colony of Massachusetts Bay* (1630-1636) Boston, 1846

Zirkle, Conway. *The Beginnings of Plant Hybridization*. Philadelphia, 1935

INDEX